D1603325

THE BIOLOGY
OF GROUND-DWELLING
SQUIRRELS

The Biology
of Ground-Dwelling
Squirrels

Annual Cycles,
Behavioral Ecology,
and Sociality

Edited by

JAN O. MURIE AND GAIL R. MICHENER

UNIVERSITY OF NEBRASKA PRESS

Lincoln and London

Publication of this book
was aided by a grant from
the University of Alberta Central
Research Fund

The paper in this book meets the guidelines for permanence
and durability of the committee on Production Guidelines for
Book Longevity of the Council on Library Resources

Contents

Contents

Contents

Contents

Contents

Introduction

The ground-dwelling sciurids (*Cynomys, Marmota,* and *Spermophilus*) are prominent members of mammalian communities in much of central and western North America. Most species are obligate hibernators, and research on them has been dominated until recently by studies of hibernation and circannual cycles. Although a landmark monograph on the social organization of black-tailed prairie dogs was published by John A. King in 1955, additional studies of sociality were few until the 1970s. With the rise to prominence of the sociobiological perspective, resulting largely from the publication in 1975 of *Sociobiology: The New Synthesis* by E. O. Wilson, a renewed interest in the social systems of ground squirrels has emerged.

Ground-dwelling squirrels are unique among the smaller mammals of the Nearctic in that they are strictly diurnal, large enough to be readily visible, and often present in open habitats. These characteristics make ground squirrels, prairie dogs, and marmots eminently suitable for field studies of behavior. Results of studies during the past 10 years have been applied to hypotheses concerning parental investment, sex-ratio adjustment, avoidance of inbreeding, and nepotism. Additionally, the literature on aspects of social organization has become sufficiently rich that two syntheses concerning the evolution of sociality within the group have been published.

This volume arises from a symposium on sociality in ground squirrels, prairie dogs, and marmots held in Banff, Alberta, Canada, from 29 September to 3 October 1982. The symposium, the first such gathering of biologists working on these mammals, was organized to encourage an exchange of ideas and information, to provide an opportunity to evaluate existing knowledge of sociality of squirrels, and to suggest directions for future work. An understanding of social systems within any group depends on knowledge of many other aspects of their biology, including phylogeny, behavioral ontogeny, and characteristics of life history. Therefore people were invited to speak on those topics as well as on topics more central to an evaluation of sociality in ground squirrels, such as social interactions, use of space, mating systems, and kinship. We suggested themes to many speakers but allowed them wide latitude in choosing their subject matter. Of the 22 invited speakers, 20 prepared chapters for this symposium volume. Nine of the contributions are primarily review papers; the remainder are based on hitherto unpublished data. They represent a range of perspectives and a variety of emphases. Some are relevant mainly to ground squirrel biology, but most have broader implications either for other areas of mammalogy or for general principles of social behavior.

The first section comprises three papers with a comparative view encompassing sciurids other than ground dwellers. The summary of phylogeny of Nearctic sciurids by Hafner, although no doubt subject to modification as more extensive studies are done, provides an essential framework for evolutionary interpretations of social behavior within the group. Ferron's summary of his own and others' work on ontogeny of behavior in arboreal and ground squirrels stresses environmental influences and includes recommendations for extending comparative research in this area. Heaney presents a synthesis of the life-history tactics of tree squirrels in the New World and compares trends and environmental influences with similar data for ground squirrels. More integrated approaches, like these, of the behavioral biology of arboreal and terrestrial sciurids are long overdue.

The second section deals with annual cycles and hibernation. Michener reviews the timing of annual cycles and develops her views on the role of temporal overlap of age- and sex-classes in the evolution of sociality. Both Phillips and Joy examine intraspecific variation in phasing of annual cycles in animals from populations that experience different environmental regimes. Such studies represent a healthy trend toward evaluating variability within species, a departure from earlier, more "typological" views. Bintz extends the conventional wisdom that hibernation is an adaptation to avoid homeothermy in winter by developing a hypothesis for water stress as a selective factor promoting the evolution of hibernation.

Section 3 consists of two review chapters on communication. Owings and Hennessy outline a "management" view of communication that stresses the functional basis of observed variation in vocalizations of ground squirrels. Their approach to some degree rationalizes the conflict between ideas of communication as information transfer or manipulation. In the second chapter, Halpin provides an overview of the all-too-scanty information on the role of chemical communication in mediating social interactions. Ground squirrels may prove to be one of the best groups of mammals for experimental studies of scent communication in the field, and this chapter is a useful starting point for future endeavors.

The three chapters in section 4 consider aspects of mating systems. Dobson

Introduction

examines a number of hypotheses that could account for differences in the mating tactics of males; his analyses of interspecific variation point toward experimental intraspecific tests. Holmes describes a monogamous mating system in hoary marmots and evaluates the influence of environmental constraints by comparing it with polygynous populations of marmots. Finally, Schwagmeyer elaborates on the possible functional significance of multiple mating by female ground squirrels. Since multiple paternity may be a consequence of multiple mating, knowledge of paternity is critical to our interpretation of kin-differential behavior, a phenomenon increasingly documented among ground squirrels.

The next section considers several aspects of spatial relations and their influence on social relations. Holekamp reviews the literature on dispersal processes and evaluates the evidence for various hypotheses concerning proximate cause and ultimate function. Here, as is true for many other areas of the behavioral ecology of squirrels, the suggestion for experimental studies is timely. Although, as is pointed out in several chapters in this book, we still lack much descriptive information, the basis for a variety of experimental approaches exists. McLean surveys the methodological problems in assessing spacing behavior of female ground squirrels and includes a plea for consistency in analyzing use of space and in classifying interactions. The question of real versus methodological differences between studies is a persistent one. The remaining two chapters in this section are based mainly on original data. Balph summarizes the results of several years of work by him and his graduate students on the behavior and ecology of Uinta ground squirrels. He emphasizes the interrelation of the environmental regime with the annual cycle, use of space, and patterns of social interaction. Murie and Harris report on factors affecting recruitment in a population of Columbian ground squirrels and emphasize the desirability of investigating the extent to which familiarity, not just kinship, structures social relations.

In the final section on kinship and sociality, Armitage evaluates the influences of kinship on recruitment of females in several colonies of yellow-bellied marmots over 20 years. His study is an exemplar of the long-term research necessary to answer questions concerning selective processes. Vestal and McCarley examine the spatial relations of kin in two populations of thirteen-lined ground squirrels, a common species about which little is known. Their analysis points out the need for caution in drawing conclusions about sociality in species that occur in relatively low densities and for which sample sizes are often small. Davis extends our knowledge of the effects of kinship in social interactions among Richardson's ground squirrels with a detailed analysis of interactive behavior. His chapter illustrates the role multivariate statistical techniques can play in field studies of behavior.

Introduction

The final chapter by King is based on his keynote address at the symposium. In it he gives a retrospective view of the interpretation of function, using prairie dog burrows as an example, and suggests a new direction for future study of sociality in ground squirrels.

Written accounts frequently lack the air of excitement and inquiry evident when scientists are gathered at a conference where there is opportunity for immediate give-and-take. Nevertheless, we trust that readers of this book will find it rewarding and that some of the numerous directions for future research suggested either explicitly or implicitly in the papers will be pursued in the future.

Throughout, the generic name *Spermophilus* is used in preference to *Citellus*, *S. parryii* replaces *S. undulatus* for Arctic ground squirrels, and *S. elegans* is used in place of *S. richardsonii elegans* for the Wyoming ground squirrel.

We are grateful to the many people who facilitated the organization of the symposium and the production of this volume. First and foremost, the symposium could not have succeeded without the enthusiasm and goodwill of all who attended. The staff at the Banff Centre, particularly Catherine Hardy, ensured that the practical matters associated with the conference ran smoothly. The Natural Sciences and Engineering Research Council of Canada provided a generous grant to subsidize travel and lodging costs of speakers. The University of Lethbridge and the University of Alberta partially underwrote other costs of the symposium. The assistance of D. Michener and M. Harris, as members of the organizing committee, was indispensable. L. Davis, D. Hackett, W. King, D. Lickley, L. Maslen, D. Walsh, and J. Waterman cheerfully helped with the many tasks associated with the conference. The Central Research Fund of the University of Alberta provided a grant to partially support the costs of publication.

We thank the following people for taking the time to review one or more of the manuscripts for us: K. B. Armitage, R. J. Baker, E. B. Bakko, D. F. Balph, M. Bekoff, A. R. Blaustein, D. A. Boag, R. J. Brooks, N. Burley, J. A. Byers, D. Chitty, J. Craig, D. E. Davis, J. F. Downhower, C. Dunford, A. R. French, M. Garrett, M. A. Harris, D. F. Hennessy, R. S. Hoffmann, R. H. Horwich, J. W. Hudson, J. R. King, D. G. Kleiman, R. R. Koford, D. W. Leger, P. N. Lehner, G. F. McCracken, M. L. Morton, D. Muller-Schwarze, L. W. Oring, E. T. Pengelley, S. Pfeifer, N. A. Slade, C. C. Smith, G. E. Svendsen, R. H. Tamarin, L. C. H. Wang, J. F. Wittenberger, R. H. Yahner, and F. C. Zwickel.

The Contributors

KENNETH B. ARMITAGE is Professor and Chairman of the Department of Systematics and Ecology at the University of Kansas, Lawrence, Kansas.

DAVID F. BALPH is Professor and Chairman of the Department of Fisheries and Wildlife at Utah State University, Logan, Utah.

GARY L. BINTZ is Associate Professor of Biology at Eastern Montana College, Billings, Montana.

LLOYD S. DAVIS is a Research Biologist in the Ecology Division of the Department of Scientific and Industrial Research, Havelock North, New Zealand.

F. STEPHEN DOBSON is a NATO Postdoctoral Fellow in the Department of Zoology at the University of Alberta, Edmonton.

JEAN FERRON is Professeur in the Département des sciences pures at the Université du Québec at Rimouski.

DAVID J. HAFNER is Curator of Zoology at the New Mexico Museum of Natural History in Albuquerque, New Mexico.

ZULEYMA T. HALPIN is Associate Professor of Biology at the University of Missouri – St. Louis.

MARGARET A. HARRIS is a Research Associate in the Department of Zoology at the University of Alberta, Edmonton.

LAWRENCE R. HEANEY is Curator of Mammals at the Museum of Zoology, University of Michigan, Ann Arbor.

DAVID HENNESSY is a Visiting Scholar in the Department of Psychology at the University of California, Davis.

KAY E. HOLEKAMP is a Postdoctoral Fellow in the Department of Biology at the University of California, Santa Cruz.

WARREN J. HOLMES is Assistant Professor of Psychology at the University of Michigan, Ann Arbor.

JANET E. JOY is a Postdoctoral Fellow in the Department of Zoology at the University of Texas, Austin.

JOHN A. KING is Professor of Zoology at Michigan State University, East Lansing.

HOWARD MCCARLEY is Professor of Biology at Austin College, Sherman, Texas.

IAN G. MCLEAN is a Postdoctoral Fellow in the Department of Biological Sciences at the University of Lethbridge, Alberta.

GAIL R. MICHENER is an NSERC University Research Fellow in the Department of Biological Sciences at the University of Lethbridge, Alberta.

JAN O. MURIE is Professor in Zoology at the University of Alberta, Edmonton.

DONALD H. OWINGS is Professor of Psychology at the University of California, Davis.

JOHN A. PHILLIPS is a comparative physiologist in the Research Department of the Zoological Society of San Diego, California.

P. L. SCHWAGMEYER is Assistant Professor of Psychology at the University of Oklahoma, Norman.

BEDFORD M. VESTAL is Associate Professor of Zoology at the University of Oklahoma, Norman.

1. Comparative Aspects

DAVID J. HAFNER

University of New Mexico

Chapter 1

Evolutionary Relationships of the Nearctic Sciuridae

Abstract. Fossil, morphological, and biochemical data bearing on the evolutionary relationships of Nearctic Sciuridae genera are reviewed, and current areas of controversy and ignorance are identified. In contrast to the formerly hypothesized relationship of flying squirrels (*Glaucomys*) and Nearctic tree squirrels, *Glaucomys* is best considered a distantly related taxon, possibly originating from a paramyine ancestral stock apart from that of all other Nearctic sciurids. Marmots, formerly regarded as relics of the extinct Miocene *Protospermophilus* lineage, are instead closely allied with other Nearctic terrestrial sciurid genera, and together with *Ammospermophilus, Spermophilus,* and *Cynomys* they form a closely related phyletic line derived from the Miocene *Miospermophilus*. Prairie dogs (*Cynomys*) may be paraphyletically derived from within *Spermophilus,* which is apparently in the midst of a major phyletic radiation. The presumed evolutionary history of the Nearctic sciurids, characterized by long periods of relatively slow phyletic change punctuated by major evolutionary bursts, is outlined. The degree of sociality of Nearctic terrestrial sciurid taxa does not correlate with either phyletic position or broad ecological role but is better explained in terms of socioecological or energetic parameters.

Introduction

The Nearctic Sciuridae comprises a diverse assemblage of rodents of nine described genera, including flying squirrels (*Glaucomys),* tree squirrels (*Sciurus* and *Tamiasciurus*), chipmunks (*Tamias* and *Eutamias*), marmots (*Marmota*),

Comparative Aspects

prairie dogs (*Cynomys*), and ground squirrels (*Spermophilus* and *Ammosper-mophilus*). Elucidating the phyletic relationships of Nearctic sciurid taxa to one another and to Palearctic sciurids is critical not only for our understanding of their evolutionary and zoogeographic history, but also for interpreting the evolution of sociality within the family (e.g., Armitage, 1981; Barash, 1974; Clark, 1973; Downhower and Armitage, 1971; Hoogland, 1981; King, 1955; Michener, 1983). Interspecific variation in social systems of ground-dwelling species may be explainable via differences in behavioral ecology (Michener, 1983, this volume) or body-size energetics (Armitage, 1981), but possible genetic con-straints on the development of sociality due simply to common ancestry must also be considered. Relying upon erroneous phyletic reconstructions could lead to mistaken perceptions of social development within the family.

The family Sciuridae is essentially cosmopolitan; only the genera *Ammosper-mophilus* and *Cynomys* appear to be autochthonous to the Nearctic region (Black, 1963, 1972). However, only the Holarctic subgenus *Spermophilus* (including a Holarctic species, *S. parryii*) has been treated in comprehensive systematic studies (Gromov et al., 1965; Nadler et al., 1982). Until more extensive compa-rative studies of Holarctic taxa are available, phyletic relationships among Nearctic sciurids must be determined solely from comparisons of Nearctic taxa. Including Palearctic forms, while doubtlessly adding to the resultant evolution-ary picture, would probably not alter the phyletic arrangement of the Nearctic taxa themselves.

The latest comprehensive evaluation of evolutionary relationships within the Nearctic Sciuridae (Black, 1963) was based upon a detailed examination of Tertiary fossil material. The purposes of this study are to summarize current knowledge pertaining to species groups within the Nearctic Sciuridae, focusing on tribal and subtribal affinities, and to review the current understanding of phyletic relationships among those species groups. Considering all Nearctic spe-cies groups in a single comprehensive study not only allows resolution of major ambiguities in previous evolutionary studies, but also permits a broader view of general evolutionary stages within the Sciuridae as related to paleoecological environments and geological events. The intent of this review is not to propose the final word on Nearctic sciurid evolution but to compile available information on the subject and to delineate major areas of ignorance and debate.

Materials and Methods

To gain a perspective of the broad phenetic relationships of the Nearctic sciurids, 26 cranial and 14 postcranial measurements (Table 1.1) were taken from cleaned

4

skeletons of adult specimens of 26 species representing most Nearctic genera (see Appendix 1.1). Detailed descriptions of measurements may be obtained from the author. Additionally, three standard external measurements were read directly from the specimen tags. Owing to a dearth of complete adult skeletal material of many taxa, samples ranged from one to three individuals per species. A modification of the exemplar method was employed (for review, see Sneath and Sokal, 1973:183). The exemplar approach is best reserved for divergent taxa, since the difference between taxa is assumed to be greater than intrataxon variability (e.g., owing to sex or geographic variation). The results of these analyses must therefore be viewed only as general comparisons, with more confidence accorded those comparisons at higher taxonomic levels. Cluster analysis of intertaxon correlation matrices based on standardized variables was performed with the unweighted pair-group method using arithmetic averaging (UPGMA) of the NT-SYS program package (Rohlf et al., 1974) on the IBM 370 computer at the University of New Mexico (UNM). Standardized variables and the resultant character correlation matrix were treated in a principal components analysis (PCA) from the same program package at UNM.

Species Groups within the Living Nearctic Sciuridae

Initial identification and delineation of species groups (from the subfamilial to the subgeneric levels) within the Nearctic Sciuridae were based on morphological and ecological similarities (Ellerman, 1940; Howell, 1938; Major, 1893; Miller and Gidley, 1918; Pocock, 1923; Simpson, 1945), as were presumed evolutionary relationships among these groups. Both the phyletic validity of and presumed relationships among *some* of these groups have been supported via fossil studies (Black, 1963; Bryant, 1945) or more recent immunological, chromosomal, or electrophoretic studies (see Hafner, in review). Unfortunately, there has been a tendency among systematists to accept the validity and presumed phyletic placement of *other* groupings not so supported. Black (1963:126) stated, ''That the flying squirrels are descended from tree squirrels seems obvious and there is certainly nothing in their morphology that would argue against such a derivation,'' although the phyletic position of *Glaucomys* was then and remains very much debated. Nadler (1966a:579–580) accepted without question the phyletic positioning of *Marmota* outside the subtribe Spermophilina (which includes *Spermophilus, Cynomys,* and *Ammospermophilus*). However, fossil evidence (James, 1963) indicates that *Ammospermophilus* may have diverged from the *Spermophilus-Cynomys* lineage before *Marmota,* such that *Ammospermophilus* (not *Marmota*) may represent the outgroup to the sister

5

group including *Spermophilus, Cynomys,* and *Marmota.* While I agree with Nadler (1966*a*:579) that phenetically defined subgeneric and generic groups within the Sciuridae probably do represent phyletic units, I believe that elucidation of evolutionary relationships within and among these groups must be supported by other lines of evidence (e.g., paleontological study and genetic analyses). The following review of the taxonomic history of the Nearctic Sciuridae and phenetic relationships among living forms emphasizes the criteria upon which these species groups have been based; for a more detailed taxonomic history, see Moore (1959).

Taxonomic history. The current taxonomic arrangement of the Sciuridae dates from Pocock's (1923) analysis of the baculum and glans penis in the family. Howell (1938) revised the North American ground squirrels and presented a classification of the Nearctic Sciuridae based primarily on cranial morphology. Simpson (1945) in general followed Pocock's classification, except that he reduced Pocock's subfamilies to tribal rank and included the flying squirrels (formerly family Petauristidae) as a subfamily (Petauristinae) of the Sciuridae. Following Howell's (1938) inclusion of all ground squirrels into the genus *Citellus* (an invalid name credited to Oken; see Hershkovitz, 1949), Simpson (1945) reduced *Ammospermophilus* to subgeneric rank. However, Bryant (1945) recognized the generic validity of *Ammospermophilus* based on myological and skeletal characteristics of Recent forms. Bryant (1945) further disagreed with Simpson's (1945) retention of *Tamiasciurus* in a separate tribe of tree squirrels, a distinction based on its vestigial baculum (Pocock, 1923). Layne (1952) argued that the vestigial baculum is a specialization within *Tamiasciurus* and that it is not sufficient evidence to warrant placing *Tamiasciurus* and *Sciurus* in separate tribes. Black (1963) elevated the chipmunk genera *Tamias* and *Eutamias* to tribal rank (Tamiini), considering them intermediate between the tree squirrels (*Tamiasciurus* and *Sciurus,* reunited into the tribe Sciurini) and the ground squirrels and marmots (Marmotini). Both Black (1963) and James (1963) recognized *Ammospermophilus* as a valid genus based on fossil evidence. Pending further evidence, Black (1963) reluctantly retained the subfamily Petauristinae, which he felt was polyphyletically derived from different tribes of tree squirrels. Black also argued for replacement of the subordinal term Sciuromorpha by Protrogomorpha, although Wood (1980) preferred the older name. In light of the parallel development of sciuromorphy in lineages independently evolved from the Paramyinae (Black, 1963) and the retention of protrogomorphy in the earliest sciurid, *Protosciurus* (Emry and Thorington, 1982), I prefer to follow Black's (1963) use

6

of Protrogomorpha. The current taxonomic arrangement for the living Nearctic Sciuridae is as follows:

Suborder Protrogomorpha
  Family Sciuridae Gray, 1821
    Subfamily Sciurinae Baird, 1857
      Tribe Tamiini Black, 1963
        Tamias, Eutamias
      Tribe Sciurini Burmeister, 1854
        Sciurus, Tamiasciurus
      Tribe Marmotini Simpson, 1945
        Subtribe Marmotina Moore, 1959
          Marmota
        Subtribe Spermophilina Moore, 1959
          Spermophilus, Cynomys, Ammospermophilus
    Subfamily Petauristinae Simpson, 1945
      Glaucomys

Phenetic relationships. Historically, supraspecific groupings within the Nearctic Sciuridae have been based primarily on skeletal characteristics. I therefore consider here the interrelationships of these groups with respect to skeletal morphology. The projection of 26 species representing most Nearctic genera (except *Tamias*) onto the first two axes of a principal components analysis of 40 skeletal and three external measurements is shown in Figure 1.1. The first and second components explain 91% (82% and 9%, respectively) of the total variance in the data set; the third component accounts for only 2% of the total variance and has an associated eigenvalue of less than 1. Loadings of the characters on the two principal factors are provided in Table 1.1. These loadings and the high percentage of variance explained on the first component indicate that most of the variance along principal component I (PCI) is due to size, with the species arranged from smallest (*Eutamias*) to largest (*Marmota*). Although representatives of a particular taxon are in close proximity, overlap is evident between small-sized sciurids, even between divergent taxa. A UPGMA correlation phenogram (Figure 1.2; cophenetic correlation coefficient = 0.781) depicts the phenetic relationships of the same taxa based on shape, so that the obfuscating effects of size are somewhat reduced. With the exception of the clustering of *Spermophilus parryii* (a large, robust squirrel) with *Marmota,* all recognized genera and subgenera are separated in this analysis. That *S. parryii* is phyletically allied with the other members of the genus *Spermophilus* has been amply documented by Nadler (1966*a*) and

7

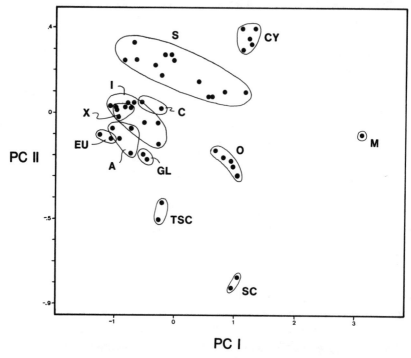

FIGURE 1.1. Depiction of Nearctic sciurid taxa projected onto the first two principal components (PC) of a PC analysis based on 40 skeletal and three external characters. (S = *S. [Spermophilus]*; C = *S. [Callospermophilus]*; I = *S. [Ictidomys]*; X = *S. [Xerospermophilus]*; O = *S. [Otospermophilus]*; CY = *Cynomys*; M = *Marmota*; A = *Ammospermophilus*; EU = *Eutamias*; GL = *Glaucomys*; TSC = *Tamiasciurus*; SC = *Sciurus*.)

others based on chromosomal and biochemical analyses (*S. franklinii* [subgenus *Poliocitellus*] was not included in the phenetic analysis, since no postcranial material was available). Recent biochemical and karyological studies have supported the validity of most of these phenetically identified species groups (Bolles, 1981; Cothran et al., 1977; Ellis and Maxson, 1979; Hafner, 1981; Hight et al., 1974; Hoffmann and Nadler, 1968; Mascarello and Bolles, 1980; Mascarello and Mazrimas, 1977; Nadler, 1966a, 1966b, 1968; Nadler et al., 1971a, 1973; Schindler et al., 1973; but see Birney and Genoways, 1973; Nadler et al., 1977). Interestingly, the phenogram clusters the taxa into groups that reflect different ecological or ecoethological units: (1) small-sized (*Ictidomys*), medium-sized (*Spermophilus* and *Cynomys*), and large burrowers (*S. parryii* and *Marmota*); and (2) climbing forms ranging from desert-adapted, relatively agile shrub

TABLE 1.1. Character loadings on principal components (PC) resulting from principal components analysis of the Nearctic Sciuridae

Character	PCI	PCII
Total length (L)	.937	−.286
Tail length (TL)	.520	−.784
Hind-foot length (HF)	.964	−.160
Condylobasal length (CBL)	.995	−.010
Condyloincisor length (CIL)	.996	.019
Zygomatic breadth (ZB)	.975	.181
Bullar breadth (BB)	.982	.030
Nasal length (NL)	.970	.100
Postorbital width (PO)	.505	−.653
Interorbital breadth (IO)	.839	−.450
Breadth at masseteric tubercles (MT)	.895	.353
Rostral breadth (RW)	.956	.068
Bullar length (BL)	.849	−.059
Interbullar width (IB)	.867	.092
Diameter of postsquamosal sinus opening (PS)	.423	.634
Width of foramen magnum (WFM)	.967	−.108
Height of foramen magnum (HFM)	.852	−.118
Occlusal length of upper tooth row (UTR)	.964	.135
Palatal width at M^3 (alveolar) (LWM)	.766	−.371
Palatal width at P^4 (alveolar) (LWP)	.947	.076
Width of incisors at tip (LWI)	.926	.147
Width M^1 (WUM)	.871	.353
Width right Pm^3 (WPR)	.746	.635
Width left Pm^3 (WPL)	.745	.634
Moment arm of *M. masseter* (MAM)	.991	.021
Length of articular process (LAP)	.989	.063
Length of coronoid process (CP)	.959	−.068
Width of angular process (WA)	.843	.474
Moment arm of *M. temporalis* (MAT)	.933	.188
Length of humerus (LH)	.977	−.092
Length of ulna (LU)	.948	−.096
Length of olecranon process (LO)	.977	.118
Length of metacarpal III (LMC)	.978	−.003
Length of scapula (LS)	.986	.047
Width of scapula (WS)	.942	.096
Height of scapular spine (HS)	.856	.077
Length of femur (LF)	.965	−.183
Length of tibia (LT)	.924	−.310
Length of metatarsal III (LMT)	.888	−.398
Length of calcaneus (LC)	.980	−.134
Length of astragalus (LA)	.980	−.103
Width (1) of astragalus (W1A)	.962	−.175
Width (2) of astragalus (W2A)	.984	−.068

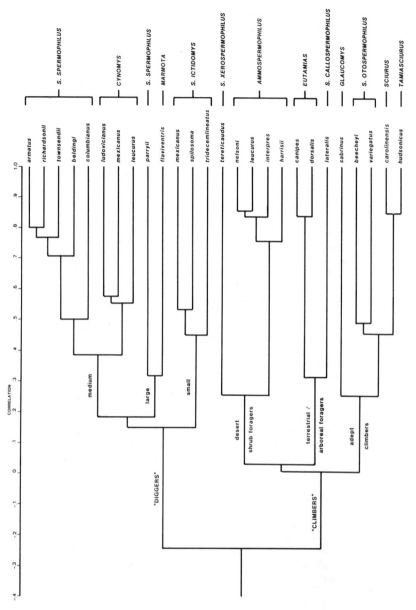

Figure 1.2. Phenetic clustering of Nearctic sciurid taxa in a UPGMA correlation phenogram based on cranial and postcranial skeletal morphology. Note that major clustering follows broad ecological lines (see text), although most genera and subgenera are well delineated.

climbers (*Ammospermophilus* and *Xerospermophilus;* Hafner, 1981; Zembal and Gall, 1980) and forms that forage in trees but burrow in the ground (*Eutamias* and *Callospermophilus*) to the more adept climbers (*Glaucomys, Sciurus, Tamiasciurus,* and *Otospermophilus*). This ecological segregation of the groups demonstrates the utility of phenetic analysis of morphometric data in recognizing ecological groups (also see Findley, 1973; Findley and Wilson, 1982; Smartt, 1978). However, caution must be used in inferring phylogeny from these sorts of analyses (e.g., Seaman, 1982), especially in a group such as the Sciuridae that may demonstrate a considerable degree of homoplasy (especially convergence and parallelism) and retention of primitive characters (Black, 1963:126; Emry and Thorington, 1982:33; Hight et al., 1974:12–13; James, 1963:90).

Evolutionary Relationships

Fossil history. The extensive Nearctic Tertiary fossil record for the Sciuridae (Black, 1963) provides an important reference point from which to evaluate phyletic relationships of the Recent forms. Subsequent to Black's (1963) study, several important fossil forms have been described that bear on those more conjectural aspects of Black's (1963:227–242) proposed phylogeny.

Black (1963:238) tentatively extended *Ammospermophilus* back to the early Clarendonian (early Pliocene) based on two mandibles referred to that genus, while noting the contrary opinion of Shotwell et al. (1963). James (1963) described *A. fossilis* from the early Clarendonian on the basis of material that included a nearly perfect skull. According to James (1963), *Ammospermophilus* probably diverged in the Miocene and had already attained nearly modern form by Clarendonian times. Gustafson (1978) has since named another fossil form (*A. hanfordi*) from the Blancan of south-central Washington that bridges the extensive temporal gap in the fossil record of *Ammospermophilus,* which had extended from Clarendonian to Holocene times (Kurten and Anderson, 1980).

Black (1963:129) noted that *Eutamias* and *Tamias* cannot be distinguished on the basis of the fragmentary fossil material available and stated that his assignment of all fossil chipmunks to *Tamias* was therefore purely arbitrary. Resolution of both the time of divergence of the two forms and attendant questions regarding the generic recognition of the taxa must therefore be based on analysis of Recent forms (reviewed in Hafner, in review). Because no fossil material referable to *Tamiasciurus* is yet known, elucidation of its evolutionary history and its relationship to *Sciurus* must also be based on comparative analysis of Recent forms.

The late Pliocene derivation of *Cynomys* from *Spermophilus* indicated by Black (1963) has been further supported by the description of a late Pliocene

11

ground squirrel (*S. kimballensis:* Kent, 1967) that was morphologically intermediate between the two genera. The supposed record of *Cynomys* from the late Miocene or early Pliocene (Green, 1960), questioned by Black (1963:226), has been referred instead to the late Pleistocene (Green, 1963). The extensive fossil record detailing the origin of *Cynomys* has been reviewed elsewhere (Clark et al., 1971).

Black's (1963) alignment of *Glaucomys* with tree squirrels (*Sciurus*) was apparently based on broad similarities of the two Recent taxa, since fossil material of *Glaucomys* is unknown. Such an alignment might represent a rather seductive, but totally unsubstantiated, dogma that would derive the arboreal gliding squirrels from the tree squirrels. However, studies of fossil forms (Engesser, 1979; James, 1963; Major, 1893; Mein, 1970) indicate that flying squirrels probably did not descend from tree squirrels and, moreover, that flying squirrels may not even possess a paramyine ancestor common to the other sciurids and may themselves be polyphyletic in origin. On the basis of fossil flying squirrels (assigned to *Sciuropterus*) from the late Miocene to middle Pliocene of North America (still the only petauristine fossils from the New World), James (1963) proposed several possible phyletic routes leading to *Glaucomys*. The common element in these proposed routes is the early divergence of *Glaucomys* relative to other Nearctic sciurids, well before the early Miocene divergence of the tree squirrel lineage (Black, 1963). Although flying squirrels (Petauristinae) may be polyphyletic in origin (James, 1963; Mein, 1970), additional fossil material and biochemical analysis of Recent forms are needed to resolve the phyletic confusion evident in this diverse assemblage.

In deriving *Marmota* from the Miocene–early Pliocene *Protospermophilus* lineage, Black (1963:163, 238–239) pointed out the loose association of the two and further stated that for *Marmota* "a derivation from the true ground squirrels cannot at present be ruled out." Unfortunately, fossil evidence bearing on this issue is as yet unavailable.

Biochemical analyses. Elsewhere (Hafner, in review) I have presented the results of an analysis of allozymic complements of representative species of Nearctic sciurid genera and reviewed the karyological, allozymic, and immunological studies pertaining to sciurid systematics. Although taxonomically piecemeal, these studies generally support the phyletic arrangement derived from a cladistic analysis of those allozymic data (Hafner, in review; Figure 1.3). This phyletic arrangement is, in turn, in general agreement with the phylogeny based on fossil criteria (Black, 1963), with two major exceptions. *Glaucomys,* speculatively aligned with *Sciurus* by Black (1963), is placed as an out-group to all other

12

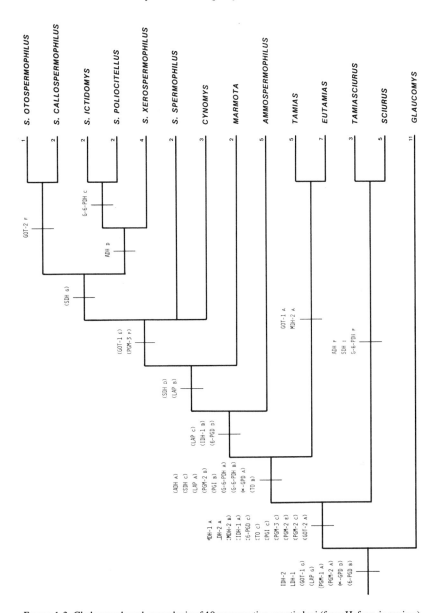

FIGURE 1.3. Cladogram based on analysis of 19 presumptive genetic loci (from Hafner, in review). Alleles not in parentheses are shared by all taxa in that clade. Numbers at branch termini indicate number of autapomorphous alleles, possibly indicative of relative time since divergence and/or relative rate of protein evolution in that lineage.

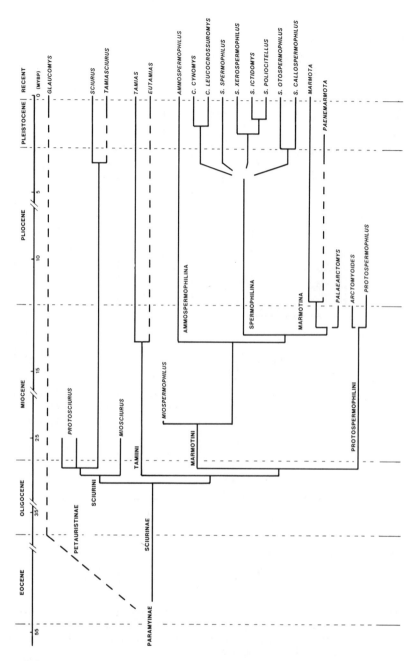

FIGURE 1.4. Summary phylogeny of the Nearctic Sciuridae (note time scale). Presumed relationships without fossil documentation are indicated by dashed lines.

14

Nearctic taxa by most biochemical analyses. *Marmota,* tentatively considered the sole survivor of the extinct *Protospermophilus* lineage by Black (1963), is clearly allied instead with the spermophile lineage, sharing a possibly closer relationship with *Spermophilus* and *Cynomys* than does the genus *Ammospermophilus.* The Recent Nearctic terrestrial squirrels, then, are a more closely related assemblage than was previously thought.

Conclusions

Evolution of Nearctic Sciuridae. The phylogeny of the Nearctic Sciuridae depicted in Figure 1.4 is based upon available fossil and biochemical evidence. Several aspects of this phylogeny remain especially provisional. A more confident assessment of the phyletic history of the flying squirrels, and of timing of divergent events within the tree squirrel and chipmunk lineages, awaits more conclusive fossil and/or biochemical evidence. In light of the agreement of fossil (James, 1963; Major, 1893; Mein, 1970) and biochemical (Ellis and Maxson, 1980; Hafner, in review; but see Hight et al., 1974) studies, I regard *Glaucomys* as a distantly related clade relative to the other Nearctic sciurids, although I do not imply that *Glaucomys* is necessarily representative of the possibly polyphyletic Petauristinae. The *Glaucomys* clade probably diverged before the initial radiation of the other Nearctic tribes, possibly originating from a different paramyine ancestor.

As is apparent in Figure 1.4 and as noted by Black (1963:240): ''The history of the Sciuridae in North America has been one of short evolutionary spurts and long periods of slow change.'' If the flying squirrels are indeed derived from a paramyine ancestor different from that of other sciurids, then the initial sciurid ''spurt'' occurred during the radiation of modern rodent families, from late Eocene to middle Oligocene times (Wilson, 1972). In fact, if sciurids are derived from multiple paramyine lineages, such a polyphyletic origin would best be reflected in reorganization at the family level. Certainly a major radiation in the Sciuridae occurred at the close of the Oligocene. From a semiarboreal (Black, 1963, 1972) or arboreal (Emry and Thorington, 1982), forest-dwelling, generalized squirrel there evolved specialized arboreal forms (*Sciurus* and *Miosciurus*), a ground-dwelling, arboreal-foraging form (chipmunks), and semifossorial forms (*Miospermophilus* and *Protospermophilus*). This radiation may have been triggered by the general drying trend beginning in the early Eocene (Axelrod, 1950, 1979) that led to the replacement, by late Miocene times, of large tracts of mesic forest by open plains and widespread grasslands in the Great Plains (MacGinitie, 1953). The drying trend itself resulted from the gradual uplift of the

Rocky Mountains, which produced a marked reduction in annual rainfall owing to rainshadow effects. At the close of the Miocene, the gradual uplift of the Sierra Nevada initiated similar drying effects, transforming the Mojave-Sonoran and Great Basin areas into incipient deserts and further fragmenting forest areas as the dry grasslands spread (Axelrod, 1950, 1979). At this time, perhaps in response to new ecological opportunity, there appeared several marmotlike forms: *Arctomyoides,* apparently derived from the *Protospermophilus* lineage, and the lineage including *Palaearctomys, Paenemarmota,* and *Marmota* (Black, 1963), which I have depicted as arising from the *Spermophilus-Cynomys* clade based on genic (Hafner, in review) and immunological analyses (Ellis and Maxson, 1980). Near the close of the Miocene, *Ammospermophilus* originated as an arid-adapted specialist. *Ammospermophilus* appears to have shared a long history of association with the North American deserts (Hafner, 1981). The fragmentation of eastern and western forests by the developing central plains may have resulted in a major dichotomy in the chipmunk lineage, producing eastern (*Tamias*) and western (*Eutamias*) forms (Ellis and Maxson, 1979). (Contrary to Nadler et al. [1969, 1977], Ellis and Maxson [1979] recommend retaining these taxa at the generic level.) As drying trends continued into the Pliocene, the apparently less-specialized *Protospermophilus* and their marmotlike descendent *Arctomyoides* both disappeared, as did *Palaearctomys.* Their disappearance may have resulted in part from overwhelming competition from the more specialized *Spermophilus* and *Marmota,* as well as from the reduction and fragmentation of preferred woodland habitat (Black, 1963). To this point, then, the history of the Nearctic Sciuridae appears to have been one of bursts of adaptive radiation associated with the opening of new ecological opportunities (as noted by Black, 1963), followed by periods of thinning out of morphological types via competition.

The next major phyletic diversification began in the late Pliocene, when the gradual orogeny of the western mountain ranges underwent a sudden acceleration (Wright and Frey, 1965). Whereas speciation in *Ammospermophilus* accompanied the gradual fragmentation of North American desert regions (Hafner, 1981), the spermophile lineage underwent a truly explosive phyletic radiation. This radiation resulted in a highly specialized terrestrial form (*Cynomys;* Nadler et al., 1971a) as well as forms within *Spermophilus* adapted to hot deserts (*Xerospermophilus*), cold deserts to cold grasslands and tundra (*Spermophilus*), tallgrass (*Poliocitellus*) and shortgrass (*Ictidomys*) prairies, xerophyllous scrub communities (*Otospermophilus*), and ponderosa-Jeffrey pine forests (*Callospermophilus*). The marked diversity in morphological types within *Spermophilus* suggests that the genus may still be in the midst of this pulse of tachytelic evolution. If the supposed close relationship of *Cynomys* and the subgenus

Spermophilus (Black, 1963; Nadler et al., 1971*a*, 1971*b*) is confirmed, *Spermophilus* would be a paraphyletic genus relative to *Cynomys* (sensu Farris, 1974; Platnick, 1977).

Taxonomic implications. Based on immunological and genic data (Hafner, in review), *Marmota* has been placed within the clade derived from *Miospermophilus* rather than that derived from *Protospermophilus*. Moreover, *Marmota* is somewhat more closely allied to the *Spermophilus-Cynomys* clade than is *Ammospermophilus*. As such, *Marmota* could either be included within the subtribe Spermophilina, eliminating the need for subtribe designation for the marmots, or retained as a separate subtribe, with *Ammospermophilus* recognized at the same taxonomic level. The latter arrangement best reflects both the early separation of the *Ammospermophilus, Spermophilus-Cynomys,* and *Marmota* clades and the close relationship of *Cynomys* and *Spermophilus*. Further, the segregation of the *Protospermophilus-Arctomyoides* lineage from the other Marmotini in the late Oligocene warrants recognition at the same taxonomic level (tribal) as the other derivatives of this sciurid radiation. Thus, from the Oligocene sciurid radiation we can recognize four tribes: Sciurini (tree squirrels), Tamiini (chipmunks), Marmotini (Recent terrestrial squirrels and allies), and the Protospermophilini (new form; extinct Tertiary terrestrial squirrels). Further, the late Miocene radiation of the Marmotini resulted in the subtribes Ammospermophilina (new form; antelope ground squirrels), Marmotina (Recent marmots and extinct allies), and Spermophilina (Recent ground squirrels and prairie dogs). Accordingly, the classification of Black (1963) is amended as follows:
Tribe Marmotini Simpson, 1945
 Subtribe Marmotina Moore, 1959
 Marmota, Palaearctomys, Paenemarmota
 Subtribe Spermophilina Moore, 1959
 Spermophilus, Cynomys, Miospermophilus
 Subtribe Ammospermophilina (new form)
 Ammospermophilus
Tribe Protospermophilini (new form)
 Protospermophilus, Arctomyoides

Sociality in Nearctic terrestrial sciurids. Armitage (1981:39) and Michener (1983:531–535) have independently proposed five grades of sociality observed in a variety of Nearctic sciurid species. Applying these grades to the phylogeny proposed herein reveals no compelling pattern of concordance between degree of sociality and phyletic position. For example, species in the genus *Marmota* span

17

the full range of social grades, from asocial species to those that live in multi-harem colonies (Armitage, 1981) or form egalitarian polygynous harems (Michener, 1983). Similarly, little concordance is seen between the species' grade of sociality and its broad ecological role as indicated by skeletal morphology (Figure 1.2). The lack of concordance between either a species' phyletic position or broad ecological role and its degree of sociality may provide indirect support for models proposed by Armitage (1981) and Michener (1983) to account for the evolution of sociality in these sciurids. Armitage (1981) concluded that degree of sociality is primarily determined by the interrelated effects of body-size energetics (which in turn determine specific reproductive effort), seasonality, and age at dispersal. Michener (1983, this volume) concluded that the timing of the annual cycle and causal environmental parameters have promoted the evolution of social structures based upon genetic relatedness of females and stressed the importance of intra- and interspecific predation and avoidance of inbreeding in this social structuring. Although such socioecological and energetic factors appear more promising as the primary determinants of sociality, ethological research should consider possible phyletic components. Behavioral patterns that may be more easily explained by common ancestry may represent vestigial behavioral traits originally molded by primitive environmental constraints that no longer exist.

Acknowledgments

Curators at the following institutions kindly made available to me specimens under their care: American Museum of Natural History (AMNH), Museum of Vertebrate Zoology, University of California, Berkeley (MVZ), Museum of Southwestern Biology, University of New Mexico (MSB), and National Museum of Natural History, Washington, D.C. (USNM). Mark S. Hafner, John C. Hafner, James L. Patton, and Robert S. Hoffmann provided valuable comments on an earlier draft of the manuscript. This study was supported in part by a grant from the Research Allocations Committee of the University of New Mexico.

Literature Cited

Armitage, K. B. 1981. Sociality as a life-history tactic of ground squirrels. Oecologia, 48:36–49.

Axelrod, D. I. 1950. The evolution of desert vegetation in western North America. Carnegie Inst. Washington Publ., 590:215–306.

———. 1979. Age and origin of Sonoran Desert vegetation. Occas. Papers California Acad. Sci., 132:1–74.

18

Baird, S. F. 1857. Mammals: general report upon the zoology of the several Pacific railroad routes. Repts., Explorations and Surveys for the railroad route from Mississippi River to Pacific Ocean. Washington, D.C., 8:1–757.

Barash, D. P. 1974. The evolution of marmot societies: a general theory. Science, 185:415–420.

Birney, E. C., and H. H. Genoways. 1973. Chromosomes of *Spermophilus adocetus* (Mammalia: Sciuridae), with comments on the subgeneric affinities of the species. Experientia, 29:228–229.

Black, C.C. 1963. A review of the North American Tertiary Sciuridae. Bull. Mus. Comp. Zool., Harvard, 130:109–248.

———. 1972. Holarctic evolution and dispersal of squirrels (Rodentia: Sciuridae). Evol. Biol., 6:305–322.

Bolles, K. 1981. Variation and alarm call evolution in antelope ground squirrels, *Ammospermophilus* (Rodentia: Sciuridae). Diss. Abst. Int., 41B:2857.

Bryant, M. D. 1945. Phylogeny of Nearctic Sciuridae. Amer. Midland Nat., 33: 257–390.

Burmeister, H. 1854. Systematische Uebericht der Thiere Brasiliens, welche wahrend einer Reise durch die Provinzen von Rio de Janeiro und Minas Geraes. gesammelt oder beobachtet. Erster Teil, Saugethiere (Mammalia). Berlin, Georg Reimer. 392 pp.

Clark, T. W. 1973. A field study of the ecology and ethology of the white-tailed prairie dog (*Cynomys leucurus*): with a model of *Cynomys* evolution. Unpubl. Ph.D. dissert., Univ. Wisconsin, Madison, 215 pp.

Clark, T. W., R. S. Hoffmann, and C. F. Nadler. 1971. *Cynomys leucurus.* Mamm. Species, 7:1–4.

Cothran, E. G., E. G. Zimmerman, and C. F. Nadler. 1977. Genic differentiation and evolution in the ground squirrel subgenus *Ictidomys* (genus *Spermophilus*). J. Mamm., 58:610–622.

Downhower, J. F., and K. B. Armitage. 1971. The yellow-bellied marmot and the evolution of polygamy. Amer. Nat., 105:355–370.

Ellerman, J. R. 1940. The families and genera of living rodents. British Mus. (Nat. Hist.), London, 1:1–689.

Ellis, L. S., and L. R. Maxson. 1979. Evolution of the chipmunk genera *Eutamias* and *Tamias.* J. Mamm., 60:331–334.

———. 1980. Albumin evolution within New World squirrels (Sciuridae). Amer. Midland Nat., 104:57–62.

Emry, R. J., and R. W. Thorington, Jr. 1982. Descriptive and comparative osteology of the oldest fossil squirrel, *Protosciurus* (Rodentia: Sciuridae). Smithsonian Contrib. Paleobiol., 47:1–35.

Engesser, B. 1979. Relationships of some insectivores and rodents from the Miocene of North America and Europe. Bull. Carnegie Mus. Nat. Hist., 14:1–68.

Farris, J. S. 1974. Formal definitions of paraphyly and polyphyly. Syst. Zool., 23: 548–554.

Findley, J. S. 1973. Phenetic packing as a measure of faunal diversity. Amer. Nat., 107:580–584.

Findley, J. S., and D. E. Wilson. 1982. Ecological significance of chiropteran morphology. Pp. 243–260, in Ecology of bats (T. H. Kunz, ed.). Plenum, New York, 425 pp.

Gray, J. E. 1821. On the natural arrangement of vertebrose animals. London Medical Repository, 15:296–310.

Green, M. 1960. A Tertiary Cynomys from South Dakota. J. Paleontol., 34:545–547.

———. 1963. Some late Pleistocene rodents from South Dakota. J. Paleontol., 37: 688–690.

Gromov, I. M., D. I. Bibikov, N. I. Kalabukhov, and M. N. Meier. 1965. Fauna SSSR. Mlekopit ayushchie. Vol. 3, no. 2. Nazemnye Belich'i (Marmotinae). Nauka, Moscow-Leningrad. 466 + ii pp.

Gustafson, E. P. 1978. The vertebrate faunas of the Pliocene Ringold Formation, south-central Washington. Bull. Mus. Nat. Hist., Univ. Oregon, Eugene, 23:1–62.

Hafner, D. J. 1981. Evolution and historical zoogeography of antelope ground squirrels, genus Ammospermophilus (Rodentia: Sciuridae). Unpubl. Ph.D. dissert., Univ. New Mexico, Albuquerque, 224 pp.

———. In review. Biochemical systematics of the Nearctic Sciuridae (Mammalia: Rodentia). Syst. Zool.

Hershkovitz, P. 1949. Status of names credited to Oken, 1816. J. Mamm., 30:289–301.

Hight, M. E., M. Goodman, and W. Prychodko. 1974. Immunological studies of the Sciuridae. Syst. Zool., 23:12–25.

Hoffmann, R. S., and C. F. Nadler. 1968. Chromosomes and systematics of some North American species of the genus Marmota (Rodentia: Sciuridae). Experientia, 24: 740–742.

Hoogland, J. L. 1981. The evolution of coloniality in white-tailed and black-tailed prairie dogs (Sciuridae: Cynomys leucurus and C. ludovicianus). Ecology, 62:252–272.

Howell, A. H. 1938. Revision of the North American ground squirrels, with a classification of the North American Sciuridae. N. Amer. Fauna, 56:1–256.

James, G. T. 1963. Paleontology and nonmarine stratigraphy of the Cuyama Valley Badlands, California. Part 1. Geology, faunal interpretations, and systematic descriptions of Chiroptera, Insectivora, and Rodentia. Univ. California Publ. Geol. Sci., 45: 1–154.

Kent, D. C. 1967. Citellus kimballensis, a new late Pliocene ground squirrel. Bull. Univ. Nebraska State Mus., 6:17–26.

King, J. A. 1955. Social behavior, social organization, and population dynamics in a black-tailed prairiedog town in the Black Hills of South Dakota. Contrib. Lab. Vert. Biol., Univ. Michigan, 67:1–123.

Kurten, B., and E. Anderson. 1980. Pleistocene mammals of North America. Columbia Univ. Press, New York. 442 pp.

Layne, J. N. 1952. The os genitale of the red squirrel, Tamiasciurus. J. Mamm., 33: 457–459.

Evolutionary Relationships of the Nearctic Sciuridae

MacGinitie, H. D. 1953. Fossil plants of the Florissant beds, Colorado. Carnegie Inst. Washington Publ., 599:1–198.

Major, F. 1893. On some Miocene squirrels with remarks on the dentition and classification of the Sciurinae. Proc. Zool. Soc. London, pp. 179–215.

Mascarello, J. T., and K. Bolles. 1980. C- and G-banded chromosomes of *Ammospermophilus insularis* (Rodentia: Sciuridae). J. Mamm., 61:714–716.

Mascarello, J. T., and J. A. Mazrimas. 1977. Chromosomes of antelope squirrels (genus *Ammospermophilus*): a systematic banding analysis of four species with unusual constitutive heterochromatin. Chromosoma, 64:207–217.

Mein, P. 1970. Les sciuropteres (Mammalia, Rodentia) neogenes d'Europe Occidentale. Geobios (Lyon), 3:7–77.

Michener, G. R. 1983. Kin identification, matriarchies, and the evolution of sociality in ground-dwelling sciurids. Pp. *in*, pp. 528–572, *in* Recent advances in the study of mammalian behavior (J. F. Eisenberg and D. G. Kleiman, eds.), Spec. Publ., Amer. Soc. Mammal., 7:1–753.

Miller, G. S., Jr., and J. W. Gidley. 1918. Synopsis of the suprageneric groups of rodents. J. Washington Acad. Sci., 8:431–448.

Moore, J. C. 1959. Relationships among the living squirrels of the Sciurinae. Bull. Amer. Mus. Nat. Hist., 118:155–206.

Nadler, C. F. 1966*a*. Chromosomes and systematics of American ground squirrels of the subgenus *Spermophilus*. J. Mamm., 47:579–596.

———. 1966*b*. Chromosomes of *Spermophilus franklinii* and taxonomy of the ground squirrel genus *Spermophilus*. Syst. Zool., 15:199–206.

———. 1968. The serum proteins and transferrins of the ground squirrel subgenus *Spermophilus*. Comp. Biochem. Physiol., 27:487–503.

Nadler, C. F., R. S. Hoffmann, and K. R. Greer. 1971*a*. Chromosomal divergence during evolution of ground squirrel populations (Rodentia: *Spermophilus*). Syst. Zool., 20:298–305.

Nadler, C. F., R. S. Hoffmann, and D. M. Lay. 1969. Chromosomes of the Asian chipmunk, *Eutamias sibericus* Laxmann (Rodentia: Sciuridae). Experientia, 25:868–869.

Nadler, C. F., R. S. Hoffmann, and J. J. Pizzimenti. 1971*b*. Chromosomes and serum proteins of prairie dogs and a model of *Cynomys* evolution. J. Mamm., 52:545–555.

Nadler, C. F., R. S. Hoffmann, J. H. Honacki, and D. Pozin. 1977. Chromosomal evolution in chipmunks, with special emphasis on A and B karyotypes in the subgenus *Neotamias*. Amer. Midland Nat., 98:343–353.

Nadler, C. F., L. W. Turner, R. S. Hoffman, and L. Deutsch. 1973. Chromosomes and giemsa-bands of the Idaho spotted ground squirrels, *Spermophilus brunneus* (Howell). Experientia, 29: 393–394.

Nadler, C. F., R. S. Hoffmann, N. N. Vorontsov, J. W. Koeppl, L. Deutsch, and R. I. Sukernik. 1982. Evolution in ground squirrels. II. Biochemical comparisons in Holarctic populations of *Spermophilus*. Z. Saugetierk., 47:198–214.

Comparative Aspects

Platnick, N. I. 1977. Paraphyletic and polyphyletic groups. Syst. Zool., 26:195–200.

Pocock, R. J. 1923. The classification of the Sciuridae. Pp. 209–246, in Proc. Zool. Soc. London, 1923:1–481.

Rohlf, F. J., J. Kishpaugh, and D. Kirk. 1974. Numerical taxonomy system of multivariate statistical programs (NT-SYS). State Univ. New York, Stony Brook, 239 pp.

Schindler, A., R. J. Low, and K. Benirschke. 1973. The chromosomes of the New World flying squirrels (*Glaucomys volans* and *Glaucomys sabrinus*) with special reference to autosomal heterochromatin. Cytologia, 38:137–146.

Seaman, R. N. 1982. Numerical taxonomic analysis of seven genera of Nearctic squirrels. 62nd Ann. Meet. Amer. Soc. Mamm., Abstr. no. 3.

Shotwell, J. A., R. G. Bowen, W. L. Gray, D. C. Gregory, D. E. Russell, and D. Taylor. 1963. The Juntura Basin: studies in earth history and paleoecology. Trans. Amer. Philos. Soc., N.S., 53, 1:1–77.

Simpson, G. G. 1945. The principles of classification and a classification of mammals. Bull. Amer. Mus. Nat. Hist., 85:1–350.

Smartt, R. A. 1978. A comparison of ecological and morphological overlap in a *Peromyscus* community. Ecology, 59:216–220.

Sneath, P. H. A., and R. R. Sokal. 1973. Numerical taxonomy. W. H. Freeman, San Francisco, 573 pp.

Wilson, R. W. 1972. Evolution and extinction in early Tertiary rodents. Proc. 24th Int. Geol. Cong., 1972, sec. 7:217–224.

Wood, A. E. 1980. The Oligocene rodents of North America. Trans. Amer. Philos. Soc., 70(5):1–68.

Wright, H. E., Jr., and D. G. Frey (eds.). 1965. The Quaternary of the United States. Princeton Univ. Press, Princeton, 922 pp.

Zembal, R., and C. Gall. 1980. Observations on Mohave ground squirrels, *Spermophilus mohavensis*, in Inyo County, California. J. Mamm., 61:347–350.

Appendix 1.1: Specimens Examined

Specimens examined from the indicated institutions (see Materials and Methods and Acknowledgments) are as follows: **Glaucomys**: *G. sabrinus:* IDAHO: Idaho Co.; Newsome Cr., 9 mi. above jct. Clearwater R. (MVZ 90957); Selway Divide, 3 mi. W Iron Mtns. (MVZ 90962); **Tamiasciurus**: *T. hudsonicus:* NORTH DAKOTA: Pembina Co.; R44W, T163N, sec. 31 (MSB 15480); **Sciurus**: *S. carolinensis:* MASSACHUSETTS: Plymouth Co.; Thomastown section Middleboro (MSB 12058); NEW YORK: Sullivan Co.; 3 mi. W Liberty (MSB 11530); **Eutamias**: *E. canipes:* NEW MEXICO: Otero Co.; Sacramento Mtns. (MSB 35040); *E dorsalis:* NEW MEXICO: Hidalgo Co.; Aspen Spring, Animas Mtns. (MSB 13039); **Ammospermophilus**: *A. harrisii, A. interpres, A. leucurus,* and *A. nelsoni:* mean values for adult specimens of each species (total n = 1,872) examined in Hafner, 1981; **Marmota**: *M. flaviventris:* COLORADO: Archuleta Co.; Gordon Cr., near jct. Piedra R. (MSB 10074); **Cynomys (Cynomys)**: *C. mexicanus:* MEXICO: Coahuila;

San Juan Neponuceno, 5 mi. N La Ventura (MVZ 91188, 91189); *C. ludovicianus:* MON-TANA: Rosebud Co.; 4 mi. NE Lee (MVZ 93212, 93213); KANSAS: Meade Co.; 15 mi. SW Meade, 2,500 ft. (AMNH 137326); *C. (Leucocrossuromys): C. leucurus:* WYOMING: Albany Co.; 18.5 mi. W jct. rts. 230 and 130 on Wyo. 230 (MSB 13087, 13088); *Spermophilus (Spermophilus): S. armatus:* WYOMING: Jackson (USNM 250743); IDAHO: Cassia Co.; Mt. Harrison (MVZ 72124); *S. beldingi:* OREGON: Lake Co.; 19.8 mi. W Lakeview (MSB 40713, 40715); *S. columbianus:* OREGON: Grant Co.; N fork Malheur R., 5,000 ft. (MVZ 83640); MONTANA: Lincoln Co.; head Pete Cr., 4,400 ft. (MVZ 134497); *S. parryii:* ALASKA: Aleutian Is., Unalaska, Unalaska Is. (MVZ 51168); 110 mi. SSE Barrow, East Oumalik (MVZ 116858); Pitmegea R., Cape Sabine (MVZ 123899); *S. richardsonii:* CANADA: Saskatchewan; 30 mi. S Swift Current (MVZ 54557, 54558); *S. townsendii:* UTAH: Millard Co.; Garrison (MVZ 78476); WASHINGTON: Benton Co.; S side Yakima R., 2 mi. SE Richland, 375 ft. (MVZ 93234, 93236); *S. (Callospermophilus): S. lateralis:* COLORADO: Archuleta Co.; Gordon Cr., near jct. Piedra R. (MSB 10060); Fremont Co.; 5 mi. S Victor (MSB 11945); *S. (Otospermophilus): S. beecheyi:* CALIFORNIA: Alameda Co.; Strawberry Canyon, Oakland (Berkeley) (MVZ 99445, 11450); *S. variegatus:* NEW MEXICO: Bernalillo Co.; Embudo Canyon (MSB 22241); Hell's Canyon, 17 mi. E Isleta Pueblo (MSB 22248); Sierra Co.; Caballo Dam (MSB 16766); *S. (Xerospermophilus): S. tereticaudus:* ARIZONA: Pima Co.; 12 mi. SE Tucson (MSB 14163, 14164); Tucson (MVZ 99830, 99832); CALIFORNIA: Imperial Co.; Pilot Knob, Colorado R. (MVZ 10722); *S. (Ictidomys): S. mexicanus:* TEXAS: Kerr Co.; Kerrville, 1,750 ft. (MVZ 99797, 99799); Val Verde Co.; ½ mi. NE Del Rio (MVZ 93789); *S. spilosoma:* NEW MEXICO: San Juan Co.; 14 mi. S, 6 mi. E Shiprock (MSB 12417); 12 mi. S Bloomfield (MSB 17194); McKinley Co.; 4 mi. N, 2 mi. W Estrella (MSB 12569); *S. tridecemlineatus:* TEXAS: Grayson Co.; 5 mi. S Dennison (MVZ 99786); KANSAS: Ellis Co.; Hays (MSB 17223); IOWA: Dickinson Co.; 3 mi. W Spirit Lake (MSB 7615).

JEAN FERRON

Université du Québec à Rimouski

Chapter 2

Behavioral Ontogeny Analysis of Sciurid Rodents, with Emphasis on the Social Behavior of Ground Squirrels

Abstract. The purposes of this chapter are to suggest a standardized method for data collection with regard to behavioral ontogeny, to promote interspecific comparisons as essential tools for understanding the adaptive "fine tuning" of developmental patterns, and to synthesize current knowledge of the ontogeny of social behavior in ground squirrels.

Behavioral development can be divided into two parts: emergence of behavior patterns during early ontogeny, and integration to adult life during later ontogeny.

Observations during early ontogeny are compiled in the following manner: for each behavior pattern, the earliest and latest ages of appearance of the behavior are given with a mean calculated for a series of young of each species. An analysis of the ontogeny of social behavior of two ground squirrels, *Spermophilus columbianus* and *Spermophilus lateralis,* is performed in this manner. The results are then compared with those obtained for two arboreal squirrels, *Tamiasciurus hudsonicus* and *Glaucomys sabrinus*. From this comparison and other data available on ground squirrels, it appears that gross interspecific differences in ontogenetic rates are controlled by factors such as predation pressure, hibernation, and complexity of locomotion. Interspecific differences in the development of agonistic, cohesive, and neutral behavior patterns in ground squirrels are probably linked to social organization within each species.

Data collection during later ontogeny should be concerned with the following parameters: social interactions with the different categories of kin and nonkin, dispersal, variation in home range, behavioral time budget, and activity cycles of juveniles. Some results concerning ground squirrels are presented, and their relation to adult social organization is discussed.

Recommendations on the orientation of further studies on behavioral ontogeny in ground squirrels complete this review.

Introduction

Although there is a considerable amount of literature concerning sciurid growth (see reviews by Hirshfield and Bradley, 1977; Koeppl and Hoffmann, 1981; Levenson, 1979), comparatively little is known about behavioral ontogeny in this group (see reviews by Ferron, 1981; Horwich, 1972; Michener, 1981). Furthermore, data collection on behavioral development varies from one author to another. Consequently, there have been few attempts to compare the behavioral ontogeny of different squirrel species. Horwich (1972), in his classic study on the ontogeny of social behavior in the gray squirrel (*Sciurus carolinensis*), is the first to have tried such an interspecific comparison, but his analysis was restricted by the lack of standardization in the collection of data on behavioral development. More recently, this problem was circumvented by applying the same method of study to several squirrel species (Ferron, 1981); some similarities and specific adaptations in the behavioral ontogeny of these species were established. My purposes here are to describe in detail this standardized method of data collection with regard to behavioral ontogeny and to extend it to the juvenile period that was not included in previous work (Ferron, 1981). Interspecific comparisons are promoted as being essential tools for understanding the adaptive "fine tuning" of developmental patterns. I conclude with an attempt to synthesize current knowledge on social behavior ontogeny in ground squirrels.

Following the classification developed by Williams and Scott (1953) in their ontogenetic study of the house mouse (*Mus musculus*), the development of rodents may generally be divided into four distinct periods: neonatal period, from birth to ear opening; transition period, ending with opening of the eyes; socialization period, ending with weaning; juvenile period, ending with sexual maturity. The emergence of behavioral patterns occurs during the first three periods (early ontogeny), and the integration to adult life is more intensive during the fourth period (later ontogeny). Since these two parts of behavioral development require different study methods, they will be treated separately.

25

TABLE 2.1. Age (in days) at which some physical and nonsocial behavior patterns develop in four sciurid species

Species	Ears open (hearing)	Eyes open	Olfactory exploration	Walking on all fours (regularly)	Out of nest (irregular)	Out of nest (at will)	Ingesting solid food	Upright alert posture
Ground squirrels								
S. columbianus	20–23[a] 22.3	18–23 20.1	15–18 15.9	14–17 15.1	17–22 20.9	23–26 25.5	21–26 23.8	24–26 25.5
S. lateralis	17–20 18.3	22–29 25.3	20–25 22.3	16–23 20.1	28–35 31.6	36–37 36.6	28–32 30.9	31–37 33.8
Arboreal squirrels								
T. hudsonicus	18–22 20.1	26–36 31.4	28–29 28.4	26–27 26.5	33–34 33.8	37–39 38.3	37–41 38.4	45–51 46.6
G. sabrinus	21–26 23.7	33–42 36.9	25–36 27.5	31–34 32.1	45–49 47.9	48–50 49.0	49–55 51.1	—

[a] The first number represents the earliest age of appearance of the behavior and the second one the latest age. The number with the bar above is the mean for 17 S. columbianus from five litters, 15 S. lateralis from four litters, 14 T. hudsonicus from three litters, and fourteen G. sabrinus from three litters.

Early Ontogeny

Standardized method for data collection. Instead of recording only the earliest age of emergence for each behavior pattern for the species under study, a practice commonly used by other authors (e.g., Broadbooks, 1958; Eibl-Eibesfeldt, 1951; Layne, 1954), I concur with Horwich (1972) that it is more informative to give the earliest and latest ages of emergence for each behavior pattern. Additionally, I include a mean calculated for young from several litters of each species (Ferron, 1981). Because of the inaccessibility of nests in the field and the likelihood that mothers will move the litter if disturbed, I recommend capturing gravid females and housing them in special "maternity cages," kept under field conditions to minimize perturbation of the female and to respect the influence that environment might have on the development of young squirrels. Maternity cages, whose size must be adapted to each species (e.g., 60 cm long and 30 cm by 30 cm in section for *Spermophilus* spp.), must be designed to allow direct observation in the nest through a transparent window. A special sliding door isolates the female outside her nest without handling; the nest can then be opened from the outside and the young can be easily manipulated. Surgical gloves are used to manipulate the young; each litter is handled with different gloves previously impregnated with the odor of the nest. Young are individually identified at birth by nail clipping. Later, fur dyeing or ear tagging can be used. Each day the young are observed in the nest and, when older, in the cage itself; checked for different reflexes and behavior patterns; and measured, weighed, and physically inspected.

Comparative early ontogeny of social behavior in two ground squirrels. The preceding method was applied to the study of social behavior development in two ground squirrels species, the Columbian ground squirrel *(Spermophilus columbianus)* and the golden-mantled ground squirrel *(S. lateralis)*, before weaning.

To achieve a better understanding of the timing of emergence of different patterns of social behavior, I present basic information on physical development and ontogeny of nonsocial behavior (Table 2.1).

Hearing, defined as the reactiveness of young to a sudden noise (e.g., hand clapping), becomes functional before the eyes open in *S. lateralis,* as in most sciurid species (Ferron, 1981). In *S. columbianus* the eyes begin to open shortly before the appearance of hearing, so Williams and Scott's (1953) classification of development into four distinct periods does not hold for this species. Nevertheless, the appearance of vision remains a key event in the early life of both species (Ferron, 1981).

27

TABLE 2.2. Age (in days) at which social behavior patterns develop

Species	Cohesive				Agonistic			
					Defense			
	Teat searching on sibling	Social grooming	Play fighting	Pseudocopulation	Undirected jump	Directed jump	Crouched posture	Turning on back
Ground squirrels								
S. columbianus	1	21–28[a]	24–28	24–31	4–9	19–24	15–25	10–16
	1	25.2	26.2	28.2	6.2	22.1	21.5	13.0
S. lateralis	1	30–38	31–39	31–41	2–4	25–28	15–29	8–15
	1	33.8	35.8	35.2	2.7	26.2	22.9	11.4
Arboreal squirrels								
T. hudsonicus	3	36–39	40–43	37–41	2–4	31–36	34	16
	3	37.6	40.4	39.3	3.7	32.6	34.0	16.0
G. sabrinus	5	34–54	47–53	50–54	12–15	35–42	38	15–17
	5	47.8	50.9	52.8	13.9	37.3	38.0	16.1

Olfaction is probably functional early in ontogeny, as in other rodents (Baker and Meester, 1977). Although exploration of the environment is necessarily linked with emergence from the nest, young taken out of the nest for laboratory manipulation were seen sniffing substratum and objects long before emergence; active olfactory exploration coincides approximately with the ability to walk regularly on all fours.

Columbian ground squirrels begin earlier than golden-mantled ground squirrels to wander out of the nest irregularly (retrieved by their mothers) and at will (without maternal interference). In both species, a series of other behavior patterns appears shortly before or after emergence from the nest (Ferron, 1981). For example, in both ground squirrel species upright alert postures and ingestion of solid food coincide with emergence from the nest. Sometimes young begin to nibble at food brought by the mother before they emerge from the nest.

Emergence from the nest appears to be a key event with regard to the appearance of many behavior patterns. Consequently, when comparing species, the

28

		Agonistic *continued*						Neutral	Other		
				Threat							
Biting	Foot stamping	First sign Anal gland Evagination	Fully developed Anal gland Evagination	Arching back	Tail piloerection	Tooth chattering	Interindividual smelling	Pulling food from sibling	Cheek rubbing	Back rubbing
17-	—	14-19	29-31	25-31	21-24	30-31	18-23	26-35	24-34	28-35
		17.0	29.3	29.2	22.6	30.5	20.3	29.9	28.8	31.5
26-28	—	17-22	25-26	25-31	25-28	23-27	30-40	30-36	32-42	41-42
27.0		19.3	25.5	28.1	26.8	24.7	34.0	33.9	36.6	41.6
32-51	35-41	—	—	—	—	32	36-44	45-	43-45	—
46.2	38.3					32.0	39.9		44.0	
41-51	47[a]	—	—	—	—	53[a]	34-48	53-	after	—
48.3							42.2		55	

NOTE: See Table 2.1 for explanation. When the earliest and the latest ages of emergence coincide only one number is given. No mean is given when a behavior pattern continues to emerge during the juvenile period or when noticed in only one animal.

[a] One observation.

rate of development should be considered not only in absolute value but with respect to emergence from the nest.

Social behavior can be divided into three categories: neutral (or recognitive), agonistic, and cohesive (Table 2.2); see Ferron (1979, 1980, 1981) and Sheppard and Yoshida (1971) for definitions of these categories of behavior.

The first social behavior pattern to emerge in both ground squirrel species is searching for teats on siblings. This cohesive behavior pattern occurs from the first few days after birth till opening of the eyes. The development of the other cohesive behavior patterns, social grooming, pseudocopulation, and play fighting, is delayed, because it is timed with emergence from the nest.

Neutral social behavior promotes recognition between conspecifics and usually consists of interindividual smelling. The development of this behavior also coincides with emergence from the nest and, consequently, with the possibility of encounters with conspecifics other than the mother or siblings. Some "passive" interindividual smelling probably occurs between littermates much earlier while they are tightly grouped in the nest or with their mother when they search for teats or are groomed by her.

The first agonistic behavior to appear is an undirected defensive jump exhibited during the neonatal period; it emerges earlier in the golden-mantled ground squirrel than in the Columbian ground squirrel. With the opening of the eyes, this defensive jump becomes oriented toward the stimulus. Also during the neonatal period, the young of both species turn on their backs when disturbed; *S. lateralis* is again faster in developing this behavior than *S. columbianus*. Another defensive pattern is the crouched posture that emerges shortly before the eyes open in the two ground squirrel species. Biting, which can be either defensive or offensive, is a rare behavior in young Columbian ground squirrels and therefore a mean age of emergence cannot be calculated; however, this species begins to bite earlier than the golden-mantled ground squirrel.

When threatening, ground squirrels of both species typically use an arched-back posture along with tail piloerection. During high-intensity threat, the anal glands are also evaginated. Some tooth chattering may also be performed during threat. All these signals appear before emergence from the nest in *S. lateralis,* whereas they show up shortly after (or during in the case of tail piloerection) that event in *S. columbianus*. Full anal gland evagination, arched-back posture, and tooth chattering appear at younger ages in *S. lateralis* than in *S. columbianus*. Species comparisons, both with respect to emergence from the nest and in absolute age, indicate that golden-mantled ground squirrels are more precocial than Columbian ground squirrels in the development of many agonistic patterns, whereas the latter are faster in developing cohesive and neutral patterns of social behavior. According to the classification of Michener (1983), *S. lateralis* is asocial (social grade 1) and *S. columbianus* has a harem social structure with male dominance (social grade 3). The relative timing of development of agonistic, cohesive, and neutral patterns of social behavior differs between these species in accordance with social organization. In the present case it would be important for the asocial species, *S. lateralis,* to possess its agonistic behavior signals before emergence from the nest, whereas this is not the case for the more social S. *columbianus*. The difference in time of appearance of social behaviors could also be interpreted as a delay in the development of agonistic patterns in relation to the harem social structure of the Columbian ground squirrel.

Pulling food away from siblings is another social behavior noticed in young of both ground squirrel species. In both this behavior occurs a few days after they

30

begin feeding on solid food; relative to emergence from the nest, it appears earlier for *S. lateralis* than for *S. columbianus,* though in absolute age the latter is more precocial.

Body rubbing, which is related to scent marking and consequently to social communication, is developed in the period surrounding emergence from the nest. Cheek rubbing appears at the same age as the ability to wander out of nest at will in *S. lateralis* and a few days after that event in *S. columbianus.* Cheek rubbing is followed a few days later by the emergence of body rubbing, which is a more elaborate behavior pattern involving also dorsal glands (see Ferron, 1977; Steiner, 1974, for descriptions).

Comparison with other sciurid rodents. The development of behavior in an arboreal sciurid, the red squirrel *(Tamiasciurus hudsonicus),* and a gliding sciurid, the northern flying squirrel *(Glaucomys sabrinus),* has been studied by the same method (Tables 2.1 and 2.2) (Ferron, 1981). At birth and in the first few days thereafter, the young of all species behave in almost the same manner. Their behavioral repertoire is simple and includes many reflexes. This is not surprising because young of all four species are altricial and are kept in a closed nest protected by the mother.

From the basic repertoire, definitive behavioral patterns gradually emerge in about the same sequence in all species, but the rate of development is closely correlated with emergence from the nest, which differs among species according to the difficulty of moving in the environment. The more complex is locomotion, the later is emergence from the nest. Consequently, the development of all behavior components related to emergence is also delayed. Habitat, and hence type of locomotion, might be a key factor in explaining the slower rate of behavioral ontogeny in *G. sabrinus,* a glider, compared with *T. hudsonicus,* a tree squirrel, which itself develops less rapidly than *S. lateralis,* a ground squirrel inhabiting rock slides, which in turn is surpassed by *S. columbianus,* a ground dweller of alpine and subalpine meadows. Complexity of locomotion thus seems directly related to speed of behavioral ontogeny.

Defense is similar in terrestrial and arboreal squirrels. The northern flying squirrel exhibits slightly slower development of defensive behavior patterns than the red squirrel, except for the undirected defensive jump, which appears much later in *G. sabrinus* than in *T. hudsonicus.* Threatening is performed differently by tree and gliding squirrels than by ground squirrels, so interspecific comparisons are difficult to make. The arboreal species are more vocal, and some of their postures are different. Nevertheless, as in ground dwellers, there is a link between emergence of social behavior patterns and adult social organization in

31

arboreal squirrels. In *T. hudsonicus* and *G. sabrinus,* cohesive behavior patterns appear about the time of emergence from the nest. In the northern flying squirrel, which is gregarious and not very aggressive, neutral social behavior (interindividual smelling) appears several days before emergence from the nest, whereas these two events are synchronous in the red squirrel, a territorial and solitary species. In addition, threatening behavior patterns such as foot stamping and tooth chattering hardly begin to emerge during the socialization period in *G. sabrinus,* whereas in *T. hudsonicus* the appearance tooth chattering is completed shortly before emergence from the nest and that of foot stamping at about the same time as emergence from the nest. In both species, cohesive behavior patterns show up concomitantly with emergence from the nest. Consequently, neutral behavior emerges proportionally earlier in the more social species, whereas threatening behavior patterns are more precocial in the less social species. This difference between arboreal species is comparable to the findings on ground squirrels, where the more social species has a proportionally slower development of threatening behavior than the less social species. Horwich (1972) pointed out that aggressive growling developed much later in *Sciurus carolinensis* than in *T. hudsonicus.* Growling is significantly associated with the territorial system of red squirrels; gray squirrels do not display territoriality. Thus the time of development of agonistic behaviors may be an important correlate of social organization. A larger sample is necessary to confirm the tendency among sciurid rodents for agonistic behaviors to develop relatively later in the more social species.

Broadening the comparison to other squirrel species reveals that there are many factors controlling behavioral development. According to Emmons (1979), some African rain-forest squirrels (e.g., *Aethosciurus poensis* and *Paraxerus cepapi*) are born in an advanced stage of development corresponding to that reached by temperate-zone squirrels at an age of 3 to 4 weeks. She further states that this difference in reproductive pattern is the result of a complex of environmental pressures. The immediate effect of such precocity is that young spend a shorter time in the nest. Since there are more potential nest predators in Africa than in temperate regions, early emergence from the nest may be an adaptation to reduce the chances of predation on young. Ewer (1966) reported that African ground squirrels (*Xerus erythropus*) open their eyes at 12 days of age, which indicates precocity in African ground-dwelling sciurids as well. Thus, the starting point of behavioral ontogeny is not uniform for all sciurid rodents; young of most species are altricial at birth, but in extreme ecological conditions a more advanced stage of development may be reached.

Size does not seem to be of primary importance in the timing of behavior development. For example, the Columbian ground squirrel is larger than the golden-mantled ground squirrel and develops faster, whereas the gray squirrel (Horwich, 1972) is larger than the red squirrel but develops more slowly.

Ground squirrels (*Spermophilus* and *Ammospermophilus* spp.) that hibernate have more rapid developmental rates than nonhibernating ground squirrels of the same size (Neal, 1965; Pengelley, 1966). Since there is a close relation between physical development and behavioral development, the relation between hibernation and physical development can probably be applied to behavioral development also. The faster behavioral development of *S. columbianus* and *S. lateralis*, species that hibernate, compared with red squirrels and northern flying squirrels, species that do not hibernate, supports this relation. However, the interpretation of the relation between growth rate and hibernation has recently been questioned (Koeppl and Hoffmann, 1981; Levenson, 1979), indicating that more information is needed to evaluate the role of hibernation in ontogeny.

Because behavioral development studies are still scarce on other ground squirrels and all sciurids in general, interspecific comparison must rely primarily on the age of appearance of two events that most influence behavioral ontogeny: opening of the eyes and emergence from the nest. Indeed, as Ferron (1981) mentioned, a period of intense behavioral development begins with the opening of the eyes and terminates with weaning and the ability of the young to wander out of the nest at will. Most of the repertoire of social behavior is developed during this period. Locomotory patterns are also improved during this period (e.g., bounding, jumping, sitting). Exploration and alertness emerge. Young gain more and more nutritive independence from their mother. Self-grooming improves, along with other comfort behavior patterns. Data on these two crucial events are available for many species (Table 2.3). Detailed studies on behavioral ontogeny (Ferron, 1981; Horwich, 1972) suggest that the two events have a comparable influence on the emergence of different individual and social behavior patterns in all sciurid species, but this hypothesis still needs to be tested.

There is great variability among ground squirrels in the ages at which they open their eyes and emerge from the nest. Although some ground dwellers open their eyes or emerge from the nest later than some tree squirrels and some flying squirrels, there is a general tendency for faster development in ground squirrels than in tree and flying squirrels. Rapid ontogeny appears to be a major difference between terrestrial and arboreal sciurids. The development of the brain should be studied closely to determine if the nervous system develops more slowly in arboreal and gliding species or if at least some parts of it continue to mature so as to achieve better coordination when a behavior pattern is put in place, thus increasing the chance of survival.

Behavioral development thus seems to be under the control of various factors,

Comparative Aspects

TABLE 2.3. Age (in days) at which some sciurids open the eyes and emerge from the nest

Species	Opening of the eyes	Out of nest (retrieved and/or precociously)	Out of nest (no maternal interference or not specified)	Source
North American ground squirrels				
Spermophilus beecheyi	34–37	—	56	Fitch, 1948*; Tomich, 1962; MacClintock, 1970
S. beldingi	18–20	—	24	Morton and Tung, 1971
S. columbianus	18–23	17–22	23–26	Present study*
	19–23	—	21–29	Shaw, 1925*
	17–20	—	27–28	Michener, 1977*a;* pers. comm.*
	—	—	24–32	Murie and Harris, 1982
S. elegans	21–24	—	32–42	Clark, 1970
S. franklinii	18–21	—	Shortly after eyes open	MacClintock, 1970; Turner et al., 1976
S. lateralis	22–29	26–36	33–42	Present study*
S. mohavensis	30–31	—	—	Pengelley, 1966
S. parryii	20–22	—	Shortly after eyes open	Banfield, 1974; Mayer and Roche, 1954
S. richardsonii	22–25	—	28–32	Michener, 1977*a,* 1977*b,* pers. comm.*
S. tereticaudus	27–34	—	—	Neal, 1965*; Pengelley, 1966
S. townsendii	19–22	—	Shortly after eyes open	Svihla, 1939
S. tridecemlineatus	21–23	—	26–28	Bridgewater, 1966*
	24–28	—	Shortly after eyes open	Johnson, 1931*
Ammospermophilus harrisii	25–27	—	—	Neal, 1965*
A. leucurus	34–36	—	—	Pengelley, 1966
Cynomys ludovicianus	33–37	—	35–42	Banfield, 1974; Johnson, 1927
C. mexicanus	35–40	38	39–40	Pizzimenti and McClenaghan, 1974*
Tamias striatus	33	—	35	Wolfe, 1966

continued

34

TABLE 2.3. *continued*

Species	Opening of the eyes	Out of nest (retrieved and/or precociously)	Out of nest (no maternal interference or not specified)	Source
North American ground squirrels *cont'd.*				
Eutamias amoenus	30–33	—	42	Broadbooks, 1958
E. minimus	29–31	—	—	Forbes, 1966
E. palmeri	25–26	—	±35	Hirshfield and Bradley, 1977
E. panamintinus	29–30	—	±35	Hirshfield and Bradley, 1977
Marmota monax	26–28	—	42–49	Banfield, 1974; Mac-Clintock, 1970
African ground squirrel				
Xerus erythropus	12	—	—	Ewer, 1966
African rain-forest squirrels				
Paraxerus cepapi	8	19	21	Viljoen, 1977*
Aethosciurus poensis	10	18	26	Emmons, 1979*
Tree squirrels				
Tamiasciurus hudsonicus	26–36	33–34	37–39	Ferron, 1981*
Sciurus aberti	±42	±49	±63	Nash and Seaman, 1977
S. carolinensis	28–30	29–46	54–58	Horwich, 1972*
S. vulgaris	31–32	36–42	45	Eibl-Eibesfeldt, 1951*
Flying squirrels				
Glaucomys sabrinus	33–42	45–49	48–50	Ferron, 1981*
G. volans	24–32	37–40	41–44	Muul, 1969; Linzey and Linzey, 1979; Ritter and Vallowe, 1978*

* Studies that have the most reliable data.

the most important probably being terrestrial versus arboreal way of life. The degree of sociality appears to influence the fine tuning of agonistic behavior development. Predation pressure may, under severe conditions, lengthen the gestation period and accordingly shorten the birth-to-weaning period (i.e., early ontogeny). Hibernation probably also affects behavioral development, but further investigation is needed to assess its relative importance in controlling the rate of development. Further research on a variety of terrestrial and arboreal squirrels species is needed to identify all the factors controlling behavioral ontogeny and to evaluate their respective influence in each species' developmental pattern.

Later Ontogeny

Standardized method for data collection. Once individual and social behavior patterns are functional, young squirrels must gradually become integrated into the adult social organization. The study of later ontogeny is mainly concerned with quantitative features related to the use of space and to social interactions. This analysis begins with emergence from the nest and continues until sexual maturity, which occurs the following spring in many species of *Spermophilus*. However, some squirrel species reach sexual maturity at the age of 2 (e.g., *S. columbianus, Marmota flaviventris*) or 3 years (e.g., *M. olympus*), lengthening the juvenile period accordingly (Barash, 1974).

As with early ontogeny, studies on the behavioral ontogeny of juveniles are rather variable with respect to data collection (see, for example, Dunford, 1977*a*, 1977*b*; Michener, 1981; Saunders, 1970, for ground dwellers; Ferron, 1974; Horwich, 1972, for tree squirrels), thus restricting interspecific comparisons, a tool essential to achieve a clear understanding of the mechanisms underlying behavioral ontogeny.

Standardization of data collection is more difficult for later ontogeny than for early ontogeny, since the former is much more complex (i.e., more variables to consider) and involves fieldwork in different habitats with different ease of observation.

Changes in nature, frequency, and duration of social interactions with age ought to be collected according to kinship, location, age, and sex of interactants.

Dispersal is an important parameter related to social life of juveniles and to the use of space. Age, sex, distance traveled, litter size, and population density must be taken into account. In conjunction with the study of dispersal, data on size and location of home range during juvenile period must be analyzed.

Another important aspect of later ontogeny is time sharing between different behavioral activities (e.g., feeding, grooming, locomotion, alertness, exploring, marking, aggression, cohesion) in terms of frequency as well as duration. The comparative study of annual and daily activity cycles of juveniles and adults is also of interest, since it can be used to examine frequency of social interactions in terms of probability of encounters.

Comparative later ontogeny. Since the preceding recommendations toward standardizing data collection with regard to ontogeny during the juvenile period have not yet been systematically applied, a synthesis explaining the mechanisms governing behavioral development during this period is not currently possible. However, certain trends can be detected from the existing literature.

Studies by Dunford (1977*b*) on *S. tereticaudus,* Michener (1981) on *S. richardsonii,* and Saunders (1970) on *S. armatus* concerning social interactions and dispersal of juvenile ground squirrels reveal that juveniles remain in sibling groups, use the natal burrow, sleep together, interact cohesively (''amicably''), and gradually increase their range of movement in the 2–4 weeks after emergence. Thereafter litters begin to break up as juveniles become independent, sleep alone, have their own core areas, and interact agonistically with nonkin. Probably all species exhibit an initial period in which juveniles are closely associated in sibling groups and with the mother, followed by a period of increasing independence from the family unit. Independence occurs at a young age (e.g., 10–12 weeks, Michener, 1981) in species that first breed as yearlings, and at older ages (e.g., yearling or 2-year-old, Barash, 1974) in species that first breed at 2–3 years old. The same general pattern of developing independence was noticed in a tree squirrel, *S. carolinensis,* by Horwich (1972), and I have some evidence that it is the same for another tree squirrel, *T. hudsonicus* (Ferron, 1974). Close association with mother and sibs and subsequent increasing independence from the family unit seem to be widespread among sciurid rodents.

However, there are some interspecific differences in later behavioral ontogeny related to the variety of social systems in sciurid rodents. The social structure of ground-dwelling sciurids is based upon genetic relatedness between females, and social interactions with kin differ from those involving nonkin in social species (see review in Michener, 1983). Since sharing of space is closely related to social structure, locations of interactions may also affect the social response of juveniles, as shown by Michener (1981).

Typically, dispersal is sex biased in ground squirrels (see review by Holekamp, this volume) and in some tree squirrels (e.g., *T. hudsonicus:* Smith, 1968) but apparently is not sex biased in another tree squirrel, *S. carolinensis* (Thompson, 1978). Since sex-biased dispersal is observed in species characterized by female kin groups as well as in asocial species, probably various factors influence

37

sex differences in dispersal. Dispersing juveniles differ in the distances males and females move, with males moving farther (Holekamp, this volume; Michener and Michener, 1973). Factors such as litter size (Dunford, 1977*a*; Pfeifer, 1982) and population density (Barash, 1973; Michener, 1981) may affect dispersal rate.

During the juvenile period there is a tendency for home-range size to increase and overlap of home ranges between littermates to decrease in ground and tree squirrels (Barash, 1973; Dunford, 1977*b;* Horwich, 1972; Michener, 1981). The extent of this process is necessarily linked to degree of sociality and space-sharing patterns of each species.

Studies on behavioral time budget variations during the juvenile period are still uncommon and are mainly concerned with the frequency of behavioral acts (Ferron, 1974; Michener, 1981). More studies must be conducted before general trends can be detected. The study by Michener (1981) showed that there is a decrease in frequency of social behavior during the juvenile period as well as an increase in feeding before hibernation. Studies of other social ground dwellers that do or do not hibernate are required to determine how hibernation influences behavioral strategy.

No one has yet examined in detail social interactions of juveniles in relation to daily and annual activity of adults to evaluate how the probability of encounters affects frequency of interactions between the different categories of kin and nonkin.

Juvenile behavioral development is closely linked to adult social organization, the nature of the habitat, population density, and the existence or absence of hibernation. The relative importance of each of these factors is still to be established for most species. In particular, we need data to elucidate the nature of the relation between juvenile development and the social grade of ground-dwelling sciurids, according to the classifications of Armitage (1981) and Michener (1983). A more comprehensive synthesis on sociality including all sciurids remains to be formulated; however, comparative studies are the key to a clear understanding of the mechanisms of integration of juveniles to the adult social organization.

Conclusion

Since research on the behavioral development of sciurids is highly variable with regard to data collection, it is urgent to standardize a study method if interspecific comparisons are to be used to achieve a clear understanding of the mechanisms controlling behavioral development. To reach a thorough comprehension of the factors regulating the ontogeny of ground dwellers, interspecific comparison must be extended to tree squirrels and flying squirrels. Various factors control the rate of development during early ontogeny, and their relative importance fluctuates from one species to the other. The most prominent factors already identified are the complexity of locomotion, the degree of sociality, predation pressure, and hibernation. Later ontogeny is mainly influenced by the social organization of adults. Nevertheless, other factors such as the nature of the habitat, population density, and the existence or absence of hibernation may also influence behavioral development of juveniles.

Further studies on the behavioral ontogeny of sciurid rodents are imperative to determine all the factors that control it and to evaluate their relative importance in each species. To attain this goal, it is necessary to investigate as many species as possible from a wide array of ecological niches. Only then will it be possible to formulate an extensive synthesis of the mechanisms governing the behavioral ontogeny of squirrels.

Acknowledgments

This study was supported by NRCC postgraduate scholarships awarded to me during my Ph.D. work along with an NRCC grant (A-0078) to Dr. Pirlot, by an NRCC postdoctorate fellowship, and later by an NRCC (NSERC) grant (A-0093). The Station de Biologie de l'Université de Montréal, the University of Alberta, and the Université du Québec à Rimouski have also provided funds, equipment, or both.

Special thanks are expressed to P. Pirlot and A. L. Steiner, who supervised part of this research. I am grateful to A. Strachan for helpful comments on the manuscript and to R. H. Horwich, G. R. Michener, and M. Bekoff for reading and thoughtfully criticizing the manuscript. I also thank R. Beauséjour, M. Roy, J. Prescott, and Y. Jean for their fieldwork and J. Jean and L. Sylvestre for their contribution to preparation of the manuscript.

Literature Cited

Armitage, K. B. 1981. Sociality as a life-history tactic of ground squirrels. Oecologia, 48:36–49.

Baker, C. M., and J. Meester. 1977. Postnatal physical and behavioural development of *Praomys (Mastomys) natalensis* (A. Smith, 1834). Z. Saugetierk., 43:295–306.

Banfield, A. W. F. 1974. Les mammifères du Canada. Les Presses de l'Université Laval, Quebec, 406 pp.

Barash, D. P. 1973. The social biology of the Olympic marmot. Anim. Behav. Monogr. 6:171–245.

Comparative Aspects

―――. 1974. The evolution of marmot societies: a general theory. Science, 185: 415–420.

Bridgewater, D. D. 1966. Laboratory breeding, early growth development and behavior of *Citellus tridecemlineatus* (Rodentia). Southwestern Nat., 11:325–337.

Broadbooks, H. E. 1958. Life history and ecology of the chipmunk, *Eutamias amoenus*, in eastern Washington. Misc. Publ. Mus. Zool., Univ. Michigan, 103:1–42.

Clark, T. W. 1970. Early growth, development, and behavior of the Richardson ground squirrel (*Spermophilus richardsoni elegans*) Amer. Midland Nat., 83:197–205.

Dunford, C. 1977a. Behavioral limitation of round-tailed ground squirrel density. Ecology, 58:1254–1268.

―――. 1977b. Social system of round-tailed ground squirrels. Anim. Behav. 25: 885–906.

Eibl-Eibesfeldt, I. 1951. Beobachtungen zur Fortpflanzungsbiologie und Jungendentwicklung des Eichhörnchens (*Sciurus vulgaris L.*). Z. Tierpsychol., 8:370–400.

Emmons, L. H. 1979. Observations on litter size and development of some African rainforest squirrels. Biotropica, 11:207–213.

Ewer, R. F. 1966. Juvenile behaviour in the African ground squirrel, *Xerus erythropus* (E. Geoff.). Z. Tierpsychol., 23:190–216.

Ferron, J. 1974. Etude éthologique de l'écureuil roux d'Amérique. Unpubl. Ph.D. dissert., Univ. Montréal, Montreal, Quebec, 311 pp.

―――. 1977. Le comportement de marquage chez le spermophile à mante dorée (*Spermophilus lateralis*). Nat. Canadien, 104:407–418.

―――. 1979. Le comportement agonistique de l'écureuil roux (*Tamiasciurus hudsonicus*). Biol. Behav., 4:269–285.

―――. 1980. Le comportement cohésif de l'écureuil roux (*Tamiasciurus hudsonicus*). Biol. Behav. 5:119–139.

―――. 1981. Comparative ontogeny of behaviour in four species of squirrels (Sciuridae). Z. Tierpsychol., 55:193–216.

Fitch, H. S. 1948. Ecology of the California ground squirrel on grazing lands. Amer. Midland Nat. 39:513–596.

Forbes, R. B. 1966. Notes on a litter of least chipmunks. J. Mamma. 47:159–161.

Hirshfeld, J. R., and W. G. Bradley. 1977. Growth and development of two species of chipmunks: *Eutamias panamintinus* and *E. palmeri*. J. Mamm., 58:44–52.

Horwich, R. H. 1972. The ontogeny of social behavior in the gray squirrel (*Sciurus carolinensis*). Advances in ethology (Beihefte zur Z. Tierpsychol.), 8:1–103.

Johnson, G. E. 1927. Observations on young prairie dogs (*Cynomys ludovicianus*) born in the laboratory. J. Mamm., 8:100–115.

―――. 1931. Early life of the thirteen-lined ground squirrel. Kansas Acad. Sci., 34:282–290.

Koeppl, J. W., and R. S. Hoffmann. 1981. Comparative postnatal growth of four ground squirrel species. *J. Mamm.*, 62:41–57.

Layne, J. N. 1954. The biology of the red squirrel, *Tamiasciurus hudsonicus loquax* (Bangs), in Central New York. Ecol. Monogr., 24:227–267.

Levenson, H. 1979. Sciurid growth rates: some corrections and additions. J. Mamm., 60:232–235.

Linzey, D. W., and A. V. Linzey. 1979. Growth and development of the southern flying squirrel (*Glaucomys volans volans*). J. Mamm., 60:615–620.

MacClintock, D. 1970. Squirrels of North America. Van Nostrand Reinhold, New York, 184 pp.

Mayer, W. V., and E. T. Roche. 1954. Developmental patterns in the Barrow ground squirrel, *Spermophilus undulatus barrowensis*. Growth, 18:53–69.

Michener, G. R. 1977a. Effect of climatic conditions on the annual activity and hibernation cycle of Richardson's ground squirrels and Columbian ground squirrels, Canadian J. Zool., 55:693–703.

———. 1977b. Gestation period and juvenile age at emergence in Richardson's ground squirrel. Canadian Field-Nat., 91:410–413.

———. 1981. Ontogeny of spatial relationships and social behaviour in juvenile Richardson's ground squirrels. Canadian J. Zool., 59:1666–1676.

———. 1983. Kin identification, matriarchies, and the evolution of sociality in ground-dwelling sciurids. Pp. 528–572, *in* Advances in the study of mammalian behavior (J. F. Eisenberg and D. G. Kleiman, eds.). Spec. Publ., Amer. Soc. Mamm., 7:1–753.

Michener, G. R., and D. R. Michener. 1973. Spatial distribution of yearlings in a Richardson's ground squirrel population. Ecology, 54:1138–1142.

Morton, M. L., and H. L. Tung. 1971. Growth and development in the Belding ground squirrel (*Spermophilus beldingi beldingi*). J. Mamm., 52:611–616.

Murie, J. O., and M. A. Harris. 1982. Annual variation of spring emergence and breeding in Columbian ground squirrels (*Spermophilus columbianus*). J. Mamm., 63:431–439.

Muul, I. 1969. Mating behavior, gestation period and development of *Glaucomys sabrinus*. J. Mamm., 50:121.

Nash, D. J., and R. N. Seaman. 1977. *Sciurus aberti*. Mamm. Species, 80:1–5.

Neal, B. J. 1965. Growth and development of the round-tailed and Harris antelope ground squirrels. Amer. Midland Nat., 73:479–489.

Pengelley, E. T. 1966. Differential developmental patterns and their adaptive value in various species of the genus *Citellus*. Growth, 30:137–142.

Pfeifer, S. L. R. 1982. Disappearance and dispersal of *Spermophilus elegans* juveniles in relation to behavior. Behav. Ecol. Sociobiol., 10:237–243.

Pizzimenti, J. J., and L. R. McClenaghan, Jr. 1974. Reproduction, growth and development, and behavior in the Mexican prairie dog, *Cynomys mexicanus* (Merriam). Amer. Midland Nat., 92:130–145.

Ritter, R. A., and H. H. Vallowe, 1978. Early behavioral ontogeny in the Southern flying squirrel, *Glaucomys volans volans*. Proc. Pennsylvania Acad. Sci., 52:169–175.

41

Saunders, D. A. 1970. The ontogeny of social behaviour of Uinta ground squirrels, Unpubl. M.S. thesis, Utah State University, Logan, 42 pp.

Shaw, W. T. 1925. Breeding and development of the Columbian ground squirrel. J. Mamm. 6:106–113.

Sheppard, D. H., and S. M. Yoshida. 1971. Social behavior of captive Richardson's ground squirrels. J. Mamm., 52:793–799.

Smith, C. C. 1968. The adaptive nature of social organization in the genus of tree squirrels *Tamiasciurus*. Ecol. Monogr., 38:31–63.

Steiner, A. L. 1974. Body-rubbing, marking, and other scent-related behavior in some ground squirrels (Sciuridae), a descriptive study. Canadian J. Zool., 52:889–906.

Svihla, A. 1939. Breeding habits of Townsend's ground squirrel. Murrelet, 20:6–10.

Thompson, D. C. 1978. Regulation of a northern grey squirrel (*Sciurus carolinensis*) population. Ecology, 59:708–715.

Tomich, P. Q. 1962. The annual cycle of the California ground squirrel, *Citellus beecheyi*. Univ. California Publ. Zool., 63:213–282.

Turner, B. N., S. L. Iverson, and K. L. Severson. 1976. Postnatal growth and development of captive Franklin's ground squirrels (*Spermophilus franklinii*). Amer. Midland Nat., 95:93–102.

Viljoen, S. 1977. Behaviour of the bush squirrel, *Paraxerus cepapi cepapi* (A. Smith, 1836). Mammalia, 41:119–166.

Williams, E., and J. P. Scott. 1953. The development of social behavior patterns in the mouse in relation to natural periods. Behaviour, 6:35–65.

Wolfe, J. L. 1966. A study of the behaviour of the eastern chipmunk *Tamias striatus*. Unpubl. Ph.D. dissert., Cornell University, 102 pp.

LAWRENCE R. HEANEY

University of Michigan

Chapter 3

Climatic Influences on Life-History
Tactics and Behavior of
North American Tree Squirrels

Abstract. Tree squirrels inhabit virtually all of the forested portions of North America, in habitats ranging from low-diversity coniferous forests to high-diversity rain forests. Body size is greatest in the middle latitudes and decreases toward the equatorial and boreal regions. Body size is correlated with both home range size and litter size. Litter size is positively correlated with latitude, but the number of litters per year is inversely correlated with latitude, so that average annual production of young shows little variation throughout the continent and is not correlated with climate. Length of breeding season is positively correlated with mean annual precipitation and percentage of the year that is frost-free; long breeding seasons occur in warm, moist forests where squirrels feed on many species of plants and where home ranges are small. Exclusive territoriality (and defense of food resources) is rare, occurring only in northern coniferous forests, where cones form a highly irregular food source. Males typically have home ranges larger than those of females, and males overlap extensively with females. Adult females often have nonoverlapping home ranges. Home ranges are large where squirrels are large, where density is low, where few species of food items are used, and where it is seasonally and annually dry. Differential use of food resources by males and females may be common. Tree squirrels differ significantly from ground squirrels in that tree squirrels are smaller, do not delay reproduction beyond the first year, do not show a correlation of body size with annual production of young, do not hibernate, and do not form colonies.

43

Introduction

North America is graced with sciurid rodents from sea to sea. Unlike most other continents where morphological types of squirrels grade gradually into one another, North America has four discrete types of squirrels that belong to four phylogenetic units. The ground squirrels, the primary subjects of this volume, are members of the tribe Marmotini; the marmotines may be characterized as primarily herbivorous, terrestrial dwellers of grasslands and semideserts. The chipmunks, tribe Tamiini, are primarily terrestrial granivores of midlatitude forested regions; they are sometimes grouped with the marmotines in the subfamily Marmotinae. The flying squirrels, subfamily Petauristinae, are arboreal granivores that are widespread in northern and midlatitude forests but are limited in diversity and usually in abundance. Finally, the tree squirrels, subfamily Sciurinae, are the predominant arboreal granivores of most forested portions of the continent (Bryant, 1945; Moore, 1959).

Tree squirrels and ground squirrels occupy mostly exclusive areas that together include virtually all of North America. The purpose of this chapter is to compare these two dominant sciurid groups through documentation of life-history, ecological, and behavioral traits. Comparison of these two sciurid guilds allows empirical establishment of trends of life-history traits and provides the basis for discussions of hypotheses regarding the evolution of social behavior in sciurids. I will first summarize major trends in life history and behavioral features of tree squirrels in relation to climatic variation. I will then contrast life-history traits of tree squirrels with those of ground squirrels, in the context of describing the influence of life-history tactics on social behavior.

Methods

A set of 22 variables was compiled for 20 populations of tree squirrels from Panama to central Alberta. Data come from relatively extensive studies that provide information on most of the variables considered here. Data from two geographically nearby studies of a given species were often combined; those from hunted, introduced, and urban populations were usually excluded. The 14 biological variables used were weight (for adult males and females), two measures of food use, five of demographic features, and five of reproductive effort (Table 3.1). Because most publications did not specify the source of litter size data (i.e., placental scars, corpora lutea, small embryos, etc.), I combined counts of nestlings and large embryos for estimates of litter size. The number of young produced per female per year was calculated by multiplying the number per litter by

44

the percentage of adult females that bred and summing over litters. For example, if 75% of the adult females had an average of one young in a spring litter and 50% had one young in a summer litter, the total number of young per female was calculated as 1.25. Densities were taken from what the authors described as ''good habitat'' when available. Most climatic parameters were estimated from mapped data in the 1967 Climatic Atlas of the United States (U.S. Department of Commerce, Environmental Data Services) and the National Atlas of Canada (Macmillan Company of Canada, Toronto) but were taken from original publications when possible.

Eight climatic parameters were chosen to estimate the environment of each tree squirrel population. The climate of a region was defined in terms of three major variables: temperature, precipitation, and solar insolation. Because temperature and precipitation vary greatly, some measure of variation was required. For this study I chose mean annual temperature, mean daily temperature of the warmest and coldest months, and the difference between the warmest and coldest months as measures of temperature. I used mean annual precipitation and the ratio of the lowest mean monthly precipitation to the highest mean monthly precipitation as measures of precipitation. The precipitation ratio, calculated as 1 − (driest/wettest month), yields an index with values from 0 (aseasonal) to 1 (highly seasonal). Percentage of the year that is frost-free is the portion of the year when free water is available and most plant growth occurs. Latitude was included as a measure of insolation, because the annual amount of energy received from the sun is a function of latitude. All data were analyzed using nonparametric bivariate correlation analysis and, where noted, least-squares linear regression.

Quantitative Trends in Life-History Tactics of North American Tree Squirrels

Four genera of tree squirrels occur in North America; two of these (*Microsciurus* and *Syntheosciurus*) are poorly known and are not discussed below. Of the two remaining genera, *Sciurus* contains 15 species that occur from Panama to southern Canada (as well as additional species in South America and Eurasia), and *Tamiasciurus* contains three species that occur in western and especially northern forests from Mexico to northern Canada (E. R. Hall, 1981; Lindsay, 1981). *Tamiasciurus* is usually placed in its own tribe, the Tamiasciurini. Although its phyletic relationships are in doubt (Callahan and Davis, 1982), *Tamiasciurus* and the other New World tree squirrels (members of the tribe Sciurini) probably are not closely related. Thus there is likely to be a phylogenetic component in any differences between *Sciurus* and *Tamiasciurus*.

45

North American tree squirrels may be characterized as living in four major forest types: tropical broadleaf rain forest; eastern deciduous broadleaf forest; western coniferous forest; and northern coniferous forest. A continuum exists between these extreme types, and we might expect a continuum of tree squirrel life-history characteristics. In an analysis that covers such a broad geographic area, samples that represent all climatic regimes are desirable, and each regime should be represented by a similar number of data points. However, this is not possible, given our ignorance of most squirrels south of the Mexican border and our spotty knowledge of squirrels in the United States and Canada. Fortunately, at least one species that is well known occurs in each of the major forest types, so that description of major trends is possible. The five best-known species are *Sciurus granatensis,* in tropical broadleaf rain forest (studied only in Panama); *Sciurus carolinensis* and *S. niger,* in eastern deciduous broadleaf forest in the eastern United States and Canada; *Sciurus aberti,* in western coniferous forest in the southwestern United States; and *Tamiasciurus hudsonicus,* in northern and western coniferous forest.

The primary parameters that allow definition of the life-history tactics and basic ecology of tree squirrels are body size, food use, rate of reproduction, longevity, and spatial distribution (Table 3.1). To put these data into the perspective of climatic variation, one must be able to test for correlations at least with temperature and precipitation and some measure of their seasonality. Accordingly, Table 3.2 includes eight descriptors of climate for each of the 20 populations (see Methods). Each of the primary life-history parameters is discussed below, in relation both to other life-history parameters and to the climatic variables. The approach I have taken is an empirical and descriptive one. Each of the correlations discussed below may be regarded as a hypothesis that should be tested using other populations and species, as should each of the discussions of causality.

Body size. Body size is one of the most important variables influencing both life-history tactics and social behavior of ground squirrels (Armitage, 1981), and other data suggest that this is true of most mammals (Millar, 1977, 1981; see also review by Eisenberg, 1981). The following discussion attempts to establish the general trends in North American *Sciurus* and *Tamiasciurus;* trends within a given species may or may not parallel the general trends.

Most ecological studies use weight as a measure of size, and most of the analyses presented here are based on weight. It is desirable to document broad-scale body-size variation, but for many populations, only body length is available. Within an ecological type (e.g., tree squirrels or ground squirrels) the two variables are very highly correlated (Roth and Thorington, 1982), and thus body

46

length is likely to provide an adequate measure of size within North American tree squirrels.

Within North American members of the genus *Sciurus*, body size increases substantially with latitude (Fig. 3.1, Table 3.3). Median size of *Sciurus* increases regularly with latitude to about 30°N and decreases somewhat from that point to 45°N, the northern limit for the genus. Body-size variation in *Tamiasciurus* is not concordant with the trends in *Sciurus;* they are consistently smaller than nearly all *Sciurus* and do not show any clear pattern in size variation that is correlated with latitude. However, if only eastern North American populations of *Tamiasciurus* are considered (Table 3.3), size increases from North Carolina to New York and subsequently drops to Labrador; it is the western populations that are unexpectedly large at low latitudes. At the midlatitudes (25°–40°) western *Sciurus* also tend to be larger than eastern *Sciurus* at the same latitude.

Where two species of *Sciurus* are sympatric, the larger tends to occur in the drier/more variable habitat. For example, *S. niger* and *S. carolinensis* in the eastern United States show this pattern (Packard, 1956), as do *S. variegatoides* and *S. granatensis* in Panama (Heaney, pers. obs.; W. E. Glanz, pers. comm.).

McNab (1971) suggested that body-size trends in North American tree squirrels are affected primarily by the size of the food particles they eat and by intrafamilial competition. The data on food size that he presented are not sufficient to allow statistical analysis, and the literature does not provide the necessary quantitative data. However, *S. granatensis* consumes nuts that are larger and harder than those eaten by *S. niger* or *S. carolinensis,* but the weight of *S. granatensis* is only half to a third that of the latter species. Thus I consider McNab's food-size hypothesis for tree squirrels to be weak and probably not rigorously testable given the available data. His competition hypothesis is not supported by studies of *S. niger* and *T. hudsonicus* in eastern deciduous forest (Pesce, 1982), but few data are available and the hypothesis deserves further investigation.

Because the correlation of weight with latitude is distinctly different for *Sciurus* and *Tamiasciurus,* subsequent analysis and discussion are based on two data sets, one including both genera and one including only *Sciurus* (Table 3.4).

Food use. All *Sciurus* and *Tamiasciurus* forage extensively on the ground and in trees; for example, *S. aberti* spends almost exactly half of daylight hours on the ground (J. G. Hall, 1981), and other species are similar. All species studied cache food items, and only in *S. aberti* is caching considered moderately rather than extremely important. All species feed primarily on large seeds, nuts, or cones (except *S. aberti,* which feeds on pine buds and bark) and often use fungi heavily. The total number of plant species known to be eaten ranges from 14 and 20 in

47

Comparative Aspects

TABLE 3.1. Population parameters for *Sciurus* and *Tamaisciurus* in North America. Values enclosed in parentheses are rough estimates that were not used in analyses. Climatic parameters associated with each population appear in Table 3.2

Species	(1) Adult male weight (g)	(2) Adult female weight (g)	(3) Number of plant species eaten	(4) Number of major foods	(5) Biomass (g/ha)	(6) "Good" density (no./ha)
S. aberti, Arizona	589	602	14	2	412	0.7
S. aberti, Utah	645	623	—	—	—	—
S. carolinensis, Virginia	—	—	—	—	—	15.9
S. carolinensis Maryland	593	593	—	—	8,065	13.6
S. carolinensis, Kansas	549	580	25	7+	450	0.82
S. carolinensis, Texas	—	—	30	11	—	3.5
S. carolinensis, Illinois	(535)	—	76	10	—	3.7
S. carolinensis, Ohio	526	533	52	—	1,015	1.93
S. carolinensis Minnesota	612	604	—	—	1,242	2.03
S. granatensis, Panama	464	440	61	7+	1,160	2.5
S. griseus, California	750	960	20	6	—	(4.3)
S. niger, Florida	—	1,078	(6+)	(2+)	431	0.4
S. niger, Kansas	690	680	39	6	1,449	2.1
S. niger, Illinois	771	766	76-	10	2,282	3.0
S. niger, Ohio	—	—	(5+)	(3+)	—	5.7
S. niger, Michigan	761	771	—	—	845	1.1
S. niger, Minnesota	743	753	—	—	281	0.38
T. hudsonicus New York	182	187	45	11	197	1.08
T. hudsonicus British Columbia	—	238	66	10	264	1.11
T. hudsonicus, Alberta	—	—	—	—	—	0.146

Data come from the following sources: *S. aberti*, Arizona: Farentinos, 1972a, 1979; J. G. Hall, 1981; Keith, 1965; Reynolds, 1966. *S. aberti*, Utah: Pederson et al., 1976. *S. carolinensis*, Virginia: Doebbl and McGinnes, 1974; Montgomery et al., 1975. *S. carolinensis*, Maryland: Flyger, 1960. *S. carolinensis*, Kansas: Packard, 1956. *S. carolinensis*, Texas: Goodrum, 1940. *S. carolinensis*, Illinois: Brown and Yeager, 1945. *S. carolinensis*, Illinois: Brown and Yeager, 1945. *S. carolinensis*, Ohio: Nixon and McClain, 1969, 1975; Nixon et al., 1968; Nixon et al., 1975. *S. carolinensis*, Minnesota: Longley, 1963. *S. granatensis*, Panama:

(7) Male home range size (ha)	(8) Female home range size (ha)	(9) Home range size ratio ($♂/♀$)	(10) Percentage of young in population	(11) Percentage of year breeding	(12) Litter size	(13) Litters per year	(14) Young per year per $♀$
18.2	9.3	1.97	—	33	3.4	1.0	3.4
6.3	(0.9)	(7.0)	37.8	—	—	—	—
0.53	0.40	1.3	38.2	—	—	—	—
0.77	0.49	1.2	—	—	—	—	—
—	—	—	41.7	75	2.40	(2 –)	—
—	—	—	(45.0)	(83)	2.7	—	—
—	—	—	(34.6)	83	2.68	1.42	3.8
—	—	—	54.5	83	2.87	1.16	3.33
1.42	—	—	(27)	75	2.86	1.2	3.43
4.0	1.2	3.3	42.0	83	1.9	1.9	3.6
3.3	1.4	2.3	—	50	2.6	1.0	2.6
—	—	—	—	92	2.38	(2−)	—
—	—	—	46.9	83	2.6	(1 +)	—
—	—	—	42.2	83	2.51	1.47	3.69
—	—	—	(65.5)	—	—	—	—
—	—	—	39.7	83	2.92	1.2	3.51
—	—	—	—	—	3.11	(1)	—
0.129	0.173	0.72	34.1	83	4.2	(2-)	—
1.07	0.90	1.18	—	75	3.7	0.83	3.1
—	—	—	—	50 +	3.85	0.77	3.0

ilanz et al., 1982; Heaney and Thorington, 1978. *S. griseus,* California: Ingles, 1947; Steinecker and Browning, 1970. *S. niger,* Florida: Moore, 1957. *S. niger,* Kansas: Packard, 1956. *S. niger,* Illinois: Brown nd Yeager, 1945. *S. niger,* Ohio: Nixon and McClain, 1975; Nixon et al., 1968. *S. niger,* Michigan: Allen, 942. *S. niger,* Minnesota: Longley, 1963; Thoma and Marshall, 1960. *T. hudsonicus,* New York: Hamilon, 1939; Hatt, 1929; Layne, 1954. *T. hudsonicus,* British Columbia: Smith, 1968. *T. hudsonicus,* Alberta: Kemp and Keith, 1970; Rusch and Reeder, 1978.

Comparative Aspects

TABLE 3.2. Climatic parameters for *Sciurus* and *Tamiasciurus* populations described in Table 3.1. Sites and species are listed in the same order as in Table 3.1

Species	(15) Mean annual precip. (cm)	(16) Mean annual temp. (°C)	(17) % of year frost-free	(18) Latitude (°N)	(19) Precip. ratio	(20) Temp. range (°C)	(21) Coldest month temp. (°C)	(22) Warmest month temp. (°C)
S. aberti, Arizona	58	6	43	35	.75	21	−1	20
S. aberti, Utah	46	7	49	38	.75	28	−7	21
S. carolinensis, Virginia	112	13	75	37	.25	19	2	21
S. carolinensis, Maryland	112	13	75	39	.25	22	2	24
S. carolinensis, Kansas	90	14	60	39	.80	28	−1	27
S. carolinensis, Texas	112	21	96	31	.45	18	10	28
S. carolinensis, Illinois	112	13	75	38	.25	25	02	27
S. carolinensis, Ohio	102	13	73	39	.25	22	02	24
S. carolinensis, Minnesota	76	06	56	44	.80	30	−9	21
S. granatensis, Panama	267	25	100	9	.89	3	24	27
S. griseus, California	70	15	92	39	.83	20	7	27
S. niger, Florida	135	19	97	29	.63	12	15	27
S. niger, Kansas	90	14	60	39	.80	28	−1	27
S. niger, Illinois	112	13	75	38	.25	25	2	27
S. niger, Ohio	102	13	73	39	.25	22	2	24
S. niger, Michigan	90	8.8	60	43	.50	25	−4	21
S. niger, Minnesota	76	6	56	44	.80	30	−9	21
T. hudsonicus, New York	81	10	60	43	.25	25	−4	21
T. hudsonicus, British Columbia	96	5	33	50	.75	27	−2	25
T. hudsonicus, Alberta	45	—	22	54	.75	33	−10	23

NOTE: Data come from the following sources: *S. aberti,* Arizona: Farentinos, 1972*a*, 1979; J. G. Hall, 1981; Keith, 1965; Reynolds, 1966. *S. aberti,* Utah: Pederson et al., 1976. *S. carolinensis,* Virginia: Doebbl and McGinnes, 1974; Montgomery et al., 1975. *S. carolinensis,* Maryland: Flyger, 1960. *S. carolinensis,* Kansas: Packard, 1956. *S. carolinensis,* Texas: Goodrum, 1940. *S. carolinensis,* Illinois: Brown and Yeager, 1945. *S. carolinensis,* Ohio: Nixon and McClain, 1969, 1975; Nixon et al., 1968; Nixon et al., 1975. *S. carolinensis,* Minnesota: Longley, 1963. *S. granatensis,* Panama: Glanz et al., 1982; Heaney and Thorington, 1978. *S. griseus,* California: Ingles, 1947; Steinecker and Browning, 1970. *S. niger,* Florida: Moore, 1957. *S. niger,* Kansas: Packard, 1956. *S. niger,* Illinois: Brown and Yeager, 1945. *S. niger,* Ohio: Nixon and McClain, 1975; Nixon et al., 1968. *S. niger,* Michigan: Allen, 1942. *S. niger,* Minnesota: Longley, 1963; Thoma and Marshall, 1960. *T. hudsonicus,* New York: Hamilton, 1939, Hatt, 1929; Layne, 1954. *T. hudsonicus,* British Columbia: Smith, 1968. *T. hudsonicus,* Alberta: Kemp and Keith, 1970; Rusch and Reeder, 1978.

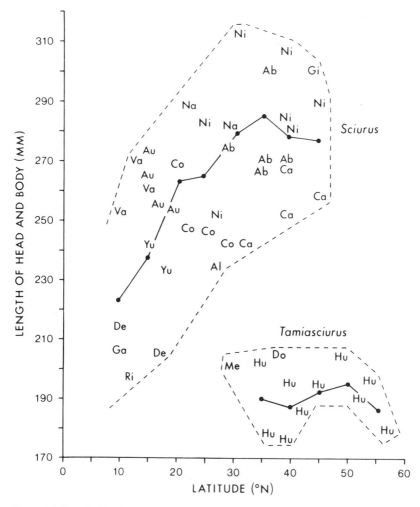

FIGURE 3.1. Length of head and body of North American tree squirrels plotted against latitude. Solid line indicates median body length for 5° intervals. Data and name codes from Table 3.3.

TABLE 3.3. Mean length (in mm) of head and body for North American tree squirrels. "Letter code" is the identifier for points in Fig. 3.1.

Species	Letter code	Length of head and body	Latitude (°N)	Location	Source
Sciurus aberti	Ab	274	29	Chihuahua	Anderson, 1972
S. aberti	Ab	267	35	Arizona (central)	Hoffmeister and Diersing, 1978
S. aberti	Ab	297	36	Arizona (northern)	Hoffmeister and Diersing, 1978
S. aberti	Ab	270	36	New Mexico (west-central)	Hoffmeister and Diersing, 1978
S. aberti	Ab	268	39	Colorado (central)	Hoffmeister and Diersing, 1978
S. alleni	Al	232	27	Coahuila	Baker, 1956
S. aureogaster	Au	265	15	Chiapas (coastal plain)	Musser, 1968
S. aureogaster	Au	273	15	Chiapas (highlands)	Musser, 1968
S. aureogaster	Au	255	17	Chiapas and Tabasco	Musser, 1968
S. aureogaster	Au	254	19	Colima	Musser, 1968
S. carolinensis	Ca	240	31	Louisiana	Lowery, 1974
S. carolinensis	Ca	252	39	Kansas	Cockrum, 1952
S. carolinensis	Ca	269	39	Maryland	Paradiso, 1969
S. carolinensis	Ca	258	45	Minnesota	Gunderson and Beer, 1953
S. colliaei	Co	269	20	Jalisco and Colima	Musser, 1968
S. colliaei	Co	247	22	Nayarit	Anderson, 1962
S. colliaei	Co	243	25	Sinaloa	Anderson, 1962
S. colliaei	Co	242	29	Chihuahua	Anderson, 1972
S. deppei	De	214	10	Costa Rica	Goodwin, 1946
S. deppei	De	205	17	Oaxaca	Goodwin, 1969
S. granatensis	Ga	206	10	Costa Rica	Goodwin, 1946
S. griseus	Gr	300	44	Oregon	Bailey, 1936
S. nayaritensis	Na	289	22	Zacatecas	Lee and Hoffmeister, 1963
S. nayaritensis	Na	283	25	Durango	Baker and Greer, 1962

TABLE 3.3. *continued*

Species	Letter code	Length of head and body	Latitude (°N)	Location	Source
S. nayaritensis	Na	282	29	Chihuahua	Anderson, 1972
S. niger	Ni	251	27	Coahuila	Baker, 1956
S. niger	Ni	312	31	Louisiana	Lowery, 1974
S. niger	Ni	284	39	Kansas	Cockrum, 1952
S. niger	Ni	306	39	Maryland	Paradiso, 1969
S. niger	Ni	280	40	Colorado	Armstrong, 1972
S. niger	Ni	289	45	Minnesota	Gunderson and Beer, 1953
S. richmondi	Ri	196	12	Nicaragua	Jones and Genoways, 1971
S. variegatoides	Va	253	10	Costa Rica	Goodwin, 1946
S. variegatoides	Va	271	13	El Salvador	Harris, 1937
S. variegatoides	Va	261	15	Chiapas (coastal plain)	Musser, 1968
S. yucatanensis	Yu	242	15	Chiapas and Guatemala	Musser, 1968
S. yucatanensis	Yu	233	18	Tabasco	Musser, 1968
T. douglasi	Do	204	38	California	Lindsay, 1981
T. hudsonicus	Hu	202	35	Arizona	Lindsay, 1981
T. hudsonicus	Hu	179	36	North Carolina	Komarek and Komarek, 1938
T. hudsonicus	Hu	177	39	Maryland	Paradiso, 1969
T. hudsonicus	Hu	195	40	Colorado	Armstrong, 1972
T. hudsonicus	Hu	186	42	New York	Layne, 1954
T. hudsonicus	Hu	192	42	Minnesota	Gunderson and Beer, 1953
T. hudsonicus	Hu	204	49	Alberta	Soper, 1973
T. hudsonicus	Hu	190	52	Manitoba	Soper, 1961
T. hudsonicus	Hu	196	54	Alberta	Soper, 1970
T. hudsonicus	Hu	180	57	Labrador	Harper, 1961
T. mearnsi	Me	201	30	Baja California	Lindsay, 1981

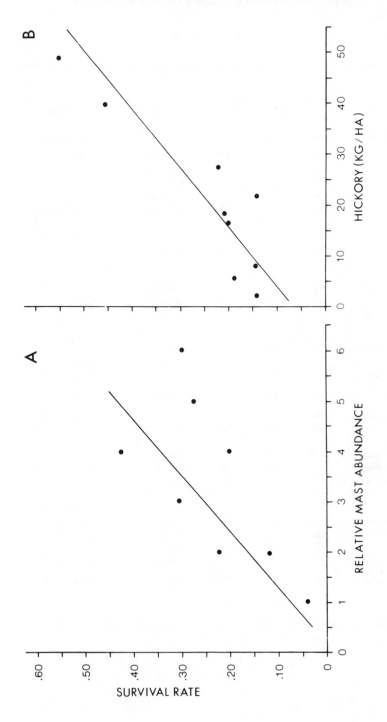

FIGURE 3.2. Survival rate of *Sciurus carolinensis* juveniles in North Carolina (A) and adults in Ohio (B) plotted against relative food abundance. A from Barkalow et al. (1970); surv. = 0.093 (mast) + 0.0119 (r = 0.66). B from Nixon et al. (1975); surv. = 0.0086 (hickory kg/ha) + 0.0666 (r = 0.89).

species in relatively arid regions (*S. aberti* and *S. griseus*) to 60 or 70 in many species (Table 3.1); most of these are incidental foods that are eaten rarely. The number of species used extensively is far smaller, ranging from two in *S. aberti* to 10 or 11 in many species. With few exceptions, heavily used items are cachable foods. For example, large nuts of four species provide 73% of the annual food of *S. granatensis,* and three of these are cached regularly (Glanz et al., 1983). Availability of mast is one of the major determinants of survivorship in many populations; in *S. carolinensis,* survivorship of adults and juveniles is highly correlated with the size of the mast crop (Fig. 3.2). Successful breeding in *S. carolinensis* is nearly absent in years of very poor or absent mast crop (Nixon and McClain, 1969; Nixon et al., 1975). A similar dependence on the mast crop has been demonstrated for *T. hudsonicus* (Kemp and Keith, 1970; Rusch and Reeder, 1978) and suggested for *T. douglasii* (Sullivan and Sullivan, 1982).

Animal foods (which range from insects to bird eggs and carrion) are of variable importance to tree squirrels: *S. granatensis* rarely eats animal foods (Glanz et al., 1982); only pregnant and lactating females of *T. hudsonicus* eat animal matter regularly (Smith, 1968), and *S. carolinensis* populations rely on animal matter variously for 2% (Nixon et al., 1968) to 11% (Packard, 1956) of their diet.

Reproductive output. Adult weight typically is inversely related to litter size among mammals (Eisenberg, 1981; Millar, 1977), and this is generally true of North American tree squirrels (see Comparative Life-History Tactics of Tree and Ground Squirrels, below). The significance of this correlation is based in large part on the two populations of *Tamiasciurus.* If these are deleted, the relation appears to be curvilinear, with the small tropical species and the large north temperate species all having relatively small litters; a rank correlation within *Sciurus* alone is not significant (Table 3.4). Apparently weight influences litter size, but the influence may be overridden by other factors.

Litter size of populations within a species is usually positively correlated with latitude (Millar, 1977). This is clearly true of North American tree squirrels of both genera (Fig. 3.3). However, tree squirrel populations in the midlatitudes produce more litters than those at high latitudes, and the one population in the tropics that has been studied produces the greatest number of litters. The number of litters per year (as well as litter size) is highly correlated with mean annual temperature (Table 3.4). The multiplicative result of litter size times number of litters, that is, total reproductive output, varies little across all populations. All populations produce about 3.4 young/year (Fig. 3.3), though there is a low-level ($0.10 > P > 0.05$) correlation with latitude if *Tamiasciurus* is included, but not

Table 3.4. Rank correlations (Kendall's tau-*b*) of variables for all *Sciurus* and *Tamiasciurus* (above diagonal) and *Sciurus* only (below the diagonal).

Variable	1	2	3	4	5	6	7	8	9
1. Male weight	—	.89**	—	—	—	—	—	—	—
2. Female weight	.88**	—	—	—	—	—	—	—	—
3. Number plants eaten	—	—	—	.49	—	.47	—	—	—
4. Number major plants	—	—	—	—	—	—	—	−.80	—
5. Biomass	—	—	.73	—	—	.68**	—	—	—
6. Density	—	—	.62	.75*	.88*	—	—	—	—
7. Male range	—	—	—	—	−1.00**	−.80	—	.90**	—
8. Female range	—	—	−1.00**	−1.00**	−1.00**	−1.00**	.80	—	—
9. ♂/♀ range ratio	—	—	—	—	—	—	—	—	—
10. % young	—	—	—	—	—	—	—	—	—
11. % year breeding	—	—	.82*	—	—	—	—	−1.00**	—
12. Litter size	—	—	—	—	—	—	—	—	−1.00**
13. Litters/year	—	—	—	—	—	—	—	—	—
14. Total young	—	—	—	—	—	.68	—	—	—
15. Mean precipitation	—	—	.72**	.65	—	.38	—	—	—
16. Mean temperature	—	—	—	—	—	—	—	—	—
17. % frost-free	—	—	—	—	—	.35	—	—	—
18. Latitude	—	—	—	—	—	—	—	—	—
19. Precipitation ratio	—	—	—	—	—	−.44*	—	—	—
20. Temperature difference	—	—	—	—	—	—	—	—	—
21. Coldest month	—	—	—	—	—	—	—	—	—
22. Hottest month	—	—	—	—	—	—	—	—	—

for *Sciurus* alone (Table 3.4). There is also a significant correlation with precipitation, but again this is not true for *Sciurus* alone (Table 3.4). Given the range in body sizes and in the habitats occupied by tree squirrels, this low level of variation in annual reproductive output is remarkable; I know of no other taxon in which a similar pattern has been found.

The length of the breeding season (measured as the percentage of the year when pregnant or lactating females are found) is correlated with the percentage of the year that is frost-free and with mean annual precipitation (Table 3.4); this correlation seems to reflect only the unsurprising tendency to have a longer breeding season where it is warm and where the forest is continuously productive and a shorter breeding season where the forest has seasonally shortened productivity owing to cool or dry weather. The length of the breeding season is also significantly longer where the squirrels feed on many species of plants (i.e., relatively warm, moist forest) and is shorter where they feed on few plant species (i.e., cool or dry forest). Within *Sciurus,* length of the breeding season is also negatively correlated with the home range size of the female. These correlations

10	11	12	13	14	15	16	17	18	19	20	21	22
—												
—	—	—	—	—	—	—	—	—	—	—	—	—
—	.58*	—	—	—	.59*	—	—	—	—	—	—	—
—	—	—	—	—	—	—	—	—	—	—	—	—
—	—	−.53*	.72	—	—	—	.40	—	—	—	—	—
—	—	—	.61	.66*	.41*	—	.38*	—	−.38*	—	—	—
—	—	—	—	—	—	—	—	−.47	.47	—	—	—
—	—	—	—	—	—	—	—	—	—	—	—	—
—	—	−.99**	—	—	—	—	—	−.68	.68	−.71*	.78*	—
—	—	—	—	—	—	—	—	—	—	—	—	.54
—	—	—	—	.54	.66**	—	.50*	—	—	—	—	—
—	—	—	−.73**	—	−.45*	−.67**	−.62**	.52**	—	—	−.54**	−.58**
—	—	−.65	—	—	—	.65**	—	—	—	—	—	—
—	—	—	—	—	.56*	—	—	−.50	—	—	—	—
—	.78**	−.56*	.90**	—	—	.29	.72**	−.50**	—	.55**	.68**	.43*
—	—	−.68**	—	—	.48*	—	.56**	−.34	—	−.34*	.53**	.57**
—	.47	−.62**	—	—	.79*	.70**	—	−.61**	—	−.67**	.81**	.51**
—	—	.43	—	—	−.49*	−.41*	−.50**	—	—	.65**	−.64**	—
—	—	—	—	—	—	—	—	—	—	—	—	—
—	—	−.52*	—	—	−.51**	−.52**	.66**	.65**	—	—	.77**	—
—	—	−.52*	—	—	.66**	.73**	.85**	−.59**	—	−.79*	—	.54**
—	—	−.63*	—	—	.46*	.80**	.63**	—	—	—	.56**	—

NOTE: Correlations significant at the 0.01 level are marked by two asterisks; those significant at the 0.05 level are marked by one asterisk; those not marked by asterisks are significant at the 0.10 level. Variable numbers are the same as in Tables 3.1 and 3.2.

emphasize the interplay among density, home range size, food abundance, and breeding strategy.

Population turnover. Reproductive output is one of two major factors that determine the potential rate of increase of a population; the other is the rate of turnover, which is defined by two closely related variables, longevity and mortality. Longevity has been studied only in *S. granatensis* (Glanz et al., 1982), *S. carolinensis* (Barkalow et al., 1970), and *Tamiasciurus hudsonicus* (Kemp and Keith, 1970; Rusch and Reeder, 1978). Both species of *Sciurus* exhibit annual and multiannual fluctuations in mortality, with mean annual survival of 55% to 60%. *T. hudsonicus* were much more variable; mean annual survival ranged from 61% in spruce to 7% in aspen, with substantial yearly variation. Adult survivorship is generally high; it is 75% annually in *S. granatensis* (Glanz et al., 1982), 52% in *S. carolinensis* (Barkalow et al., 1970), and 66–79% in *T. hudsonicus* (Kemp and Keith, 1970; Rusch and Reeder, 1978). Survivorship is higher

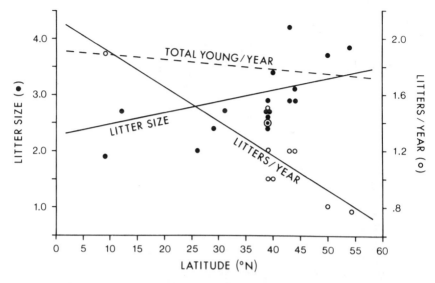

FIGURE 3.3 Mean litter size and number of litters per year for North American tree squirrels plotted against latitude. Closed circles = litter size; litter size = 0.0199 (latitude) + 2.20. Open circles = litters per year; litters/year = 0.0239 (latitude) + 2.126. Dotted line = total number of young/ ♀ /year = 0.0118 (latitude) + 3.807). Data from Tables 3.1 and 3.2.

in adult females than in adult males in *S. carolinensis* (Barkalow et al., 1970), but the reverse is true in *T. hudsonicus* (Rusch and Reeder, 1978). Equally detailed data on other species do not yet exist. However, mortality can be estimated from a commonly available population parameter. If a population has annually stable numbers and age distributions, then the mean annual percentage of juveniles in the population equals mean annual mortality rate. The accuracy of the mean annual percentage of young as an estimator of mortality depends on the degree to which the population approaches a stable state. In *S. granatensis* the method is remarkably accurate (Glanz et al., 1982), which I find sufficiently encouraging to accept it as a rough measure.

The mean annual percentage of young in populations of *Sciurus* varies from 38% to 55% ($\bar{X}$ = 42.9%, SD = 5.5) (Table 3.1). The lowest value is from *S. aberti* (which has unusually low reproductive output), and the highest is from a hunted population of *S. carolinensis* in Ohio. In two populations of *Tamiasciurus* it was 34% and 62%, the former an unhunted population in deciduous forest in New York, the latter a hunted population in coniferous forest in Alberta. The possible effect of hunting is indicated by data on *S. niger* in a heavily hunted population in Ohio, in which the percentage of young in the fall increased steadily from 65.5% to 78.3% as the population shrank and became extinct (Nixon et al., 1974).

Density and biomass. The preceding discussions define two dimensions of population dynamics, relative reproductive output and mortality. Population size is also defined by density and biomass. Home range size, which is defined by movements of individuals, also defines a dimension of density; it is discussed below.

Documented "good" densities of *Sciurus* range from about 0.4/ha (*S. niger* in Minnesota) to almost 16/ha (*S. carolinensis* in Virginia), with a mean of 3.82 (n = 15, SD = 4.68). Documented abundances of *T. hudsonicus* are usually lower, ranging from 0.15/ha in Alberta to 1.1/ha in British Columbia, but studies not included in Table 3.1 (e.g., Pesce, 1982) indicate densities as high as 5.1/ha, so the two genera do not differ greatly.

Density is significantly correlated with the total number of young produced each year (Table 3.4); this is primarily a reflection of the low density and reproductive output of *S. griseus* and the high density and output of *S. carolinensis*. Density is also correlated with the seasonality of precipitation and mean annual precipitation; this merely emphasizes once again the observations that densities are low in much of the western United States, where the squirrels inhabit pine forests in regions with generally low and highly seasonal precipitation.

Biomass is the multiplicative result of body size and density; because weight and density are poorly correlated, one may not assume that biomass follows the same trends they do. Biomass is significantly correlated with density, and among *Sciurus* is negatively correlated with home range size (Table 3.4). Biomass is negatively correlated with litter size (Table 3.4). These correlations again indicate that there are few squirrels where home ranges are large (especially in arid regions), but they also indicate that squirrels under low biomass conditions tend to have large litters.

Home range size. Home range size strongly influences the population dynamics of tree squirrels, in that it affects the number of squirrels with overlapping ranges and hence the potential to interact with other individuals and to compete for food, mates, nesting sites, and so on. Male home ranges average about twice the size of those of females, which implies that intersexual contact is maximized (Pesce, 1982). The sexual difference also implies that males have the opportunity to use a different set of food resources, because males would find more clumps of preferred food sources and might rely less on secondary food items than do females.

Data from *S. granatensis* show that males take advantage of the opportunity at times (Glanz et al., 1982; Heaney and Thorington, 1978).

Home range size for males, and also females, is positively correlated with weight and negatively correlated with density (Fig. 3.4) and negatively correlated with the total number of plant species used and the total number of young produced per year (Table 3.4, Fig. 3.4). For *Sciurus* taken alone, home range size is also negatively correlated with the length of the breeding season (Table 3.4). Among environmental variables, both precipitation and precipitation seasonality (Table 3.4, Fig. 3.4) and latitude are weakly correlated with home range. The correlations may be restated as follows: home ranges are large where squirrels are large, where density is low, where few species of plants are used, and where the climate is annually and seasonally dry.

The ratio of male to female home range sizes varies from 1.2 to 3.3 among species of *Sciurus* (Table 3.1), and from 0.8 to 1.3 among *Tamiasciurus hudsonicus* (Table 3.1; Pesce, 1982). The home-range ratio is negatively correlated with litter size and temperature seasonality and positively correlated with the temperature of the coldest month; it is also weakly correlated ($0.10 > P > 0.05$) with seasonality of precipitation (Fig. 3.5, Table 3.4). In other words, in areas where females produce many small litters (rather than a few large litters), which are areas where seasonality of rainfall is high but seasonality of temperature is relatively low (i.e., exclusive of the forests of the north), adult males have enlarged home ranges.

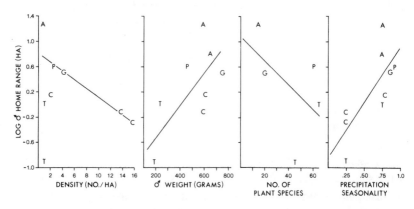

FIGURE 3.4. Correlations of home range size of adult males with density, weight, number of plant species eaten, and precipitation seasonality for North American tree squirrels. Letter codes are: A = *Sciurus aberti*, C = *S. carolinensis*, G = *S. griseus*, P = *S. granatensis*, T = *Tamiasciurus hudsonicus*. Regression equations: male home range size (HRS) = − 0.070 (density) + 0.81 (for *Sciurus* only); HRS = 0.002 (weight) − 0.78; HRS = − 0.016 (number of plant species) + 0.98; HRS = 1.732 (precipitation seasonality) − 0.83. Data from Tables 3.1 and 3.2.

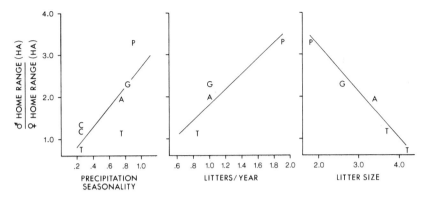

FIGURE 3.5. Ratio of male/female home range size plotted against precipitation seasonality, number of litters per year, and litter size. Letter codes as in Fig. 3.4. Regression equations: ♂ / ♀ home-range ratio (HRR) = 2.26 (precipitation ratio) + 0.43; HRR = 1.66 (litters/year) + 0.22; HRR = − 1.08 (litter size) + 5.30. Data from Tables 3.1 and 3.2.

Harestad and Bunnell (1979) asserted that intersexual differences in home-range size among mammals are due to sexual dimorphism in size. This is not true of tree squirrels, in which males and females are of similar size but male home ranges are much larger than those of females (Table 3.1). The ratio of home range sizes is not correlated with weight (Table 3.4).

Social and Breeding Behavior
of North American Tree Squirrels

The social interactions of tree squirrels may be divided into three classes: behaviors associated with mating, behaviors associated with home range defense, and amicable behaviors directed toward kin and neighbors. The following is a summary of the generally scarce data on these topics.

Mating behavior. Male tree squirrels (excluding those from territorial populations) often follow and approach nonestrous females and occasionally groom them (Heaney and Thorington, 1978; Koford, 1982; Thompson, 1977). In *S. carolinensis,* males follow females only during the 5 days before estrus and rely heavily on olfactory cues to locate females (Thompson, 1977, 1978a). Estrus lasts for a single day in all species, and all species exhibit similar ''mating bouts.'' In such bouts, four to 12 males gather near a female (or are dispersed in her home range for *T. douglasii:* Koford, 1982) and follow her across the ground and through the canopy, within her home range. Dominance between males

61

Comparative Aspects

during bouts, defined by proximity to the female and successful aggression against challengers, is more often exhibited by the male(s) whose home range includes the mating site in *T. douglasii* (Koford, 1982), *S. aberti* (Farentinos, 1972*b*), and probably *S. granatensis* (Heaney and Thorington, 1978), or by males who are old and high in the dominance hierarchy, as in *S. carolinensis* (Pack et al., 1967; Thompson, 1977, 1978*a*). Dominance changes often, and aggression between the male closest to the female and all others is high, but most copulations are performed by dominant males. Female *S. aberti, S. granatensis,* and *T. douglasii* are known to solicit copulation from young and subordinate males (Farentinos, 1980; Heaney and Thorington, 1978; Koford, 1982). *S. granatensis* and *S. carolinensis* typically mate only once or twice (Heaney and Thorington, 1978; Thompson, 1977), whereas *S. aberti* and *T. douglasii* mate two or more times, often with a different male each time (Farentinos, 1972*b*, 1980; Koford, 1982). Multiple matings probably occur in *T. hudsonicus* as well, but data are scanty (Smith, 1968).

Home range defense. Two types of territoriality exist among North American tree squirrels: female intrasexual territoriality and exclusive territoriality. Female intrasexual territoriality, in which adult females exclude other adult females but do not exclude males or, apparently, subadults, has been documented thoroughly only in *S. granatensis,* but it occurs during lactation in *S. griseus* and *S. aureogaster* (Brown and McGuire, 1975; Ingles, 1947) and some populations of *S. carolinensis* (Nixon et al., 1975). In *S. granatensis* this is associated with differential feeding habits by the sex and age classes; females cache food extensively, whereas males do not (Heaney, unpubl. data). This system of territoriality does not interfere with what is otherwise a typical *Sciurus* breeding system.

Exclusive territoriality among tree squirrels has been documented only in *Tamiasciurus hudsonicus* and *T. douglasii,* and only in some populations of those species. Under this system, all individuals maintain exclusive territories except females, who tolerate nursing and recently weaned young and potential mates on the day of estrus. The few documented cases of exclusive territoriality (Rusch and Reeder, 1978; Smith, 1968) involve squirrels in Canadian-zone or western coniferous forest. These populations are different from the patterns seen in *Sciurus* in that the male / female home range size ratio is near one, and they are also notable as cases in which females produce at most one litter per year. The *T. douglasii* studied by Koford (1982) did not defend the edges of their home ranges (ca. 25% of the range), and males had home ranges larger than those of females.

62

In the cases in which *T. hudsonicus* has been found to be nonterritorial (Layne, 1954; Pesce, 1982), males have home ranges much larger than those of females, and females generally have more than one litter per year.

Amicable behavior. Family units of tree squirrels sometimes remain together for more than a month after weaning (Farentinos, 1972*b*). These family units may be responsible for reports of several squirrels' sharing nests over winter (*S. aberti:* Keith, 1965; *S. carolinensis:* Bakken, 1959). Irregular sharing of nests by adults of both sexes has been noted in *S. aberti* (Farentinos, 1972*b*) and *T. hudsonicus* (Pesce, 1982). Allogrooming between adult females has been noted in *T. hudsonicus* (Ferron, 1980; Layne, 1954). Other potential cohesive behaviors noted in captive individuals are nonaggressive pursuit, pseudocopulation, and mock fighting (Ferron, 1980, 1981; Horwich, 1967).

Discussion. The social system of North American tree squirrels seems relatively simple. None of the species form colonies, nor do young usually remain associated with their mothers past weaning. In all species, females usually mate with old or familiar males that are high in the dominance hierarchy, although females of most species sometimes solicit copulation with young males. Male control of females during mating bouts is limited in success. Most variation occurs in the degree of territoriality and in relative home range size of males and females, that is, in the number of individuals who interact. This variation can be envisioned as occurring along a single axis that is correlated with, and perhaps determined by, several demographic and environmental factors. At the low end of the scale is *S. granatensis,* at the high end are territorial populations of *T. hudsonicus,* and in the middle are all other known species and nonterritorial populations of *T. hudsonicus.* Along this axis, which is primarily latitudinal, tree squirrels have female-exclusive territories, little territoriality, and complete territoriality in sequence and have much, some, and little male / female home range differential and overlap. Obvious demographic parallels are density (high, high to low, and low) and average litter production (two, more than one, and no more than one per year). The number of major and secondary foods varies from many to moderate to few along the axis as well, and caching seems to be of less than major importance only in some midaxis species (*S. aberti*). Although many climatic parameters appear to contribute, it appears that length of the season when little to no fresh food is available (owing to cold, drought, or heavy rains), which varies from short to moderate to long along the axis, is the major climatic component.

The data presented here suggest that tree squirrel social behavior is influenced primarily by food resources, which are themselves strongly influenced by climate. For example, *Tamiasciurus hudsonicus* is territorial where the long winters and sporadic production of a critical food resource, conifer cones, make defense of cone caches crucial and make it impossible to produce two litters in a year (Smith, 1968). The same species shows the midaxis social system (male/female overlap, female avoidance) where less severe winters and abundant moisture make cone production more regular, increase the supply of other foods early in the spring, allow higher densities, and allow production of two litters per year (Pesce, 1982). In *Sciurus* the degree of sexual dimorphism in home range size, and hence the number of male/female interactions, is associated with the number of plant species used and by home range size, which are influenced by mean annual temperature and precipitation and by the seasonality of those variables.

The implied correlation between numbers of litters and type of territoriality discussed above is tenuous because of small sample sizes and requires further investigation. However, the correlation suggests an alternative to previous hypotheses that attempt to explain nonterritoriality in some populations of *Tamiasciurus* through purported competition with other sciurids, or through lack of suitable food, both of which appear to be false (Pesce, 1982). I suggest that populations of *Tamiasciurus* that produce no more than one litter each year will be found to be territorial, and those populations that often produce more than one litter each year will not be territorial and will show substantial dimorphism in home range size. I believe the cause is related to male reproductive strategies, but I am unsure of the mechanism. An ideal place to test this prediction is southern Vancouver Island, where Millar (1970) found that *T. hudsonicus* produces two litters in some years; this is not true elsewhere in British Columbia. The intermediate type of territoriality described for a population of *T. douglasii* by Koford (1982) supports this hypothesis, since he found that multiple annual litters were unusual but did occur.

Comparative Life-History Tactics
of Tree and Ground Squirrels

The life-history tactics of ground squirrels (*Cynomys, Marmota,* and *Spermophilus*) recently were summarized by Armitage (1981), and my discussion draws heavily on his work. I will begin by comparing significant trends in the two groups and will then discuss the influence of life-history tactics on the behavior of the two groups.

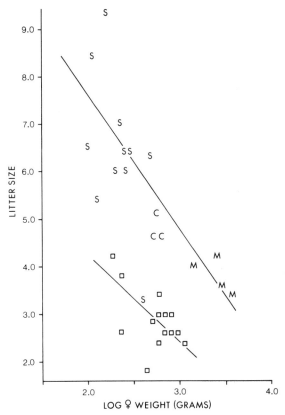

FIGURE 3.6. Log of female weight plotted against litter size for tree squirrels (open squares) and ground squirrels (C = *Cynomys*, M = *Marmota*, S = *Spermophilus*). For tree squirrels, litter size = 7.95 − 1.844 (log weight), $r = -0.65$; for ground squirrels, litter size = 13.25 − 2.834 (log weight), $r = -0.66$. Data from Tables 3.1 and 3.5.

Body size. Ground squirrels show a greater range of body sizes than do tree squirrels (Table 3.5, Fig. 3.6), with marmots far exceeding tree squirrels in the upper range. Unlike tree squirrels, ground squirrels show no correlation of body size with latitude (Fig. 3.7A). This lack of overall correlation may indicate a greater variety of ecological strategies within the ground squirrels or may merely reflect the greater topographic (and attendant climatic) diversity within their range.

Reproductive output. In a review of mammalian reproduction, Millar (1977) pointed out that sciurids as a whole do not show a correlation between body size

TABLE 3.5. Life-history data on North American ground squirrels. Weights and litter size are from Armitage (1981) unless noted by asterisks; other data are from the sources indicated. Values enclosed in parentheses are rough estimates that were not used in analyses.

Species	Adult male weight (spring; g)	Adult female weight (spring; g)	Biomass (g/ha)	Density (no./ha)	Litter size	Male home range size (ha)	Female home range size (ha)	Latitude (°N)	Source
Cynomys gunnisoni	720	600	—	—	4.6	—	—	38	—
C. leucurus	750	575	2,120	3.2	5.1*	0.9	—	41	Clark, 1977
C. ludovicianus	600	525	7,650	22.0	4.6	0.28	0.28	44	King, 1955
Marmota caligata	4,050*	3,600*	1,530	0.4	3.4*	13.8	13.8	62	Holmes, 1979, pers. comm.
M. flaviventris	3,600	2,560	—	—	4.2	0.92	0.67	39	Armitage, 1974
M. monax	3,100	2,800	—	—	3.6	—	—	40	—
M. olympus	1,900	1,400	—	—	4.0	—	—	48	—
Spermophilus armatus	333	266	6,890	23.0	6.0*	—	—	42	Slade and Balph, 1974
S. beecheyi	625	480	11,105	20.1	6.3	0.55	0.42	38	Owings et al., 1977
S. beldingi	284	243	11,570	43.9	6.4	—	—	38	Murie and Harris, 1978;
S. columbianus	490	406*	5,465	12.2	3.3*	0.42	—	50	Murie et al., 1980
S. elegans	266	203	—	—	6.0	—	—	41	Haggerty, 1968
S. franklinii	325*	275*	210	0.70	6.4*	(0.77)	(0.65)	47	
S. lateralis	155	130	—	—	5.3	—	—	40	
S. parryii	—	—	—	3.0	7.2*	1.83	—	68	Carl, 1971
S. richardsonii	260	225	5,700	23.5	7.0	0.23	0.18	50	Michener, 1979
S. tereticaudus	145	100	7,200	58.8	6.5	0.17	0.17	32	Dunford, 1977
S. townsendii	—	155	—	—	9.3	—	—	39	
S. tridecemlineatus	135	133	533	4.3	8.4	(0.10)	(0.10)	44	Silverman, 1981
S. tridecemlineatus	—	—	—	2.9	5.9	4.7	1.4	34	McCarley, 1966
S. variegatus	—	—	—	23.0	3.8*	(0.40)	0.15	30	Johnson, 1981

and litter size, and also that sciurids have relatively small young at birth and at weaning but have high growth rates and long lactation periods. As noted here, he found that marmotines have unusually large litters and also require unusually great increases in energy intake to support lactation (more than three times maintenance levels versus a mean of 1.65 times maintenance for all mammals). Data on tree squirrels are insufficient for quantitative comparison of these features with marmotines, except in litter size.

Tuomi (1980, Fig. 3) showed that the relation between litter size and maternal weight for all mammals is curvilinear rather than linear; small mammals (less than about 500 g) have a positive correlation between litter size and weight, whereas large mammals (greater than 500 g) show a negative correlation. Marmotines lie at the peak of this curve, that is, they have the largest litter sizes of any mammals he examined. North American *Sciurus* (data from Table 3.1) average larger in size but have smaller litters than the marmotine means used by Millar and Tuomi and so fall into Tuomi's "large mammal" group.

Adult weight is negatively correlated with litter size among temperate and boreal tree squirrels, and this is true for the ground squirrels as well (Fig. 3.6). Disregarding the tropical tree squirrels for the moment, the slope for the body size/litter size curve is approximately the same in the two groups, but ground squirrels produce much larger litters than do tree squirrels of the same size. However, tropical tree squirrels have smaller litters than expected on the basis of their size. Owing to the correlation of size with latitude, latitude and litter size of tree squirrels are strongly correlated (Fig. 3.7B), but they are not correlated in ground squirrels. With few exceptions, ground squirrels produce at most a single litter per year, whereas tree squirrels usually produce more than one.

As Armitage (1981) noted, there are probably conflicting selective pressures acting on litter size. Although this is likely to be true, data on tree squirrels do not support his hypothesis that litter size is most strongly influenced by body size. Tree squirrels have consistently smaller litters than do ground squirrels of the same size (Fig. 3.6). Moreover, in at least one case tree squirrels do not have larger neonates (Eisenberg, 1981). *Cynomys ludovicianus, Sciurus carolinensis,* and *S. niger* have similar maternal weights (525, 575, 750 g) and similar neonate weights (15, 16.5, 16 g), but the prairie dogs have litters about twice the size of those of tree squirrels (4.6, 2.7, and 2.6). Thus there does not appear to be a trade-off between number and size of young. However, a larger sample is clearly desirable.

Some large ground squirrels delay reproduction until they are 2 or 3 years of age and sometimes regularly skip litter production every other year (Armitage, 1981); no tree squirrel is known to do either.

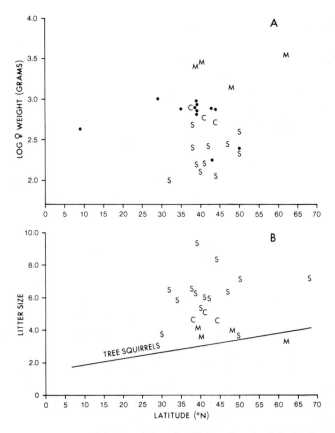

FIGURE 3.7. Log of female weight (A) and litter size (B) plotted against latitude. C = *Cynomys*, M = *Marmota*, S = *Spermophilus*, solid dots = tree squirrels. Data from Tables 3.1, 3.2, 3.5.

Population turnover. Survivorship appears to be higher among adult tree squirrels than among ground squirrels and is roughly equal to that among marmots. The very large *Marmota flaviventris* has mean annual adult survivorship of 74% (Armitage and Downhower, 1974), compared with 52%, 75%, and 76% in adult *Sciurus carolinensis, S. granatensis,* and *T. hudsonicus* and 42% in *Spermophilus armatus* (Slade and Balph, 1974). Survivorship of immatures during their first year is low (and highly variable) in all species: *Spermophilus lateralis,* 18% (14–60%: Bronson, 1979); *Marmota flaviventris,* 49% (7–77%: Armitage and Downhower, 1974); *Sciurus granatensis,* 18% (0–55%: Glanz et al., 1982); *S. carolinensis,* 26% (4–44%: Barkalow et al., 1970); and *Tamiasciurus hudsonicus,* 32% (0–66%: Rusch and Reeder, 1978).

68

Density and biomass. Tree squirrels have densities ranging from 0.4 to 16/ha, with a mean of 3.8. Ground squirrel densities are usually higher; they range from 0.4 (*M. caligata*) to 58.8/ha (*S. tereticaudus*), with a mean of 17.2 (n = 14, SD = 17.4). The highest densities typically occur in moist montane meadows at midlatitudes (*S. armatus* and *S. beldingi*), and the lowest in arid low-elevation grasslands (*C. leucurus* and *S. tridecemlineatus*) and arctic areas (*S. parryii* and *M. caligata*) (Table 3.5). Unlike tree squirrels, which show a significant correlation between density and number of young produced per year, ground squirrels, in spite of their greater variation in litter size, show a random pattern in this relationship (Table 3.5).

Biomass estimates for ground squirrels are greater on average than for tree squirrels, with means of 5,844 g/ha (SD = 3,953) and 1,392 g/ha (SD = 2,092) respectively. Ground squirrels show more variation within a given habitat type than do tree squirrels within any given habitat type; for example, *S. tridecemlineatus* and *C. ludovicianus* estimates are 533 and 7,650 g/ha, although they are . often syntopic.

Home range size. Tree squirrel home ranges average larger than those of ground squirrels. Among males, tree squirrel ranges (mean = 3.95 ha; 0.13–18.2) average twice as large as those of ground squirrels (mean = 2.38 ha; 0.10–13.8; Table 3.5), but there is substantial overlap. In most cases home ranges of male ground squirrels are no more than 1.3 times as large as those of females, whereas in *Sciurus*, male ranges average twice as large as those of females (Tables 3.1, 3.5).

Density and home range size are highly correlated in both tree and ground squirrels (Fig. 3.8). There is nearly complete overlap between the two groups along the regression line. Body size does not appear to play any role in the correlation, because species of any given size are scattered along the plot. As discussed below, species with various levels of social complexity are also scattered along the plot without any apparent pattern.

Sociality. Analysis of life-history parameters led Armitage (1981) to conclude that an index of sociality could be predicted on the basis of age at first reproduction and age at which adult weight is reached, using the formula:

Sociality = 0.619 + 2.314 (age of first reproduction)
− 0.843 (age adult weight reached).

Because nearly all tree squirrels first reproduce at 9–12 months (approximate average = 0.85 year) and reach adult weight at 1 year, his equation yields a sociality index of 1.74 for tree squirrels, on a scale of one to five. Species at his level 2 of sociality "aggregate in favorable habitat; all members of colony (= aggregate) live individually." Data that explicitly address this prediction for tree squirrels are not available, but the prediction seems consistent with descriptions of tree squirrel populations and the level of interaction of individuals. I suggest that tree squirrels do exhibit cohesive groupings, both between mother and offspring and, to a greater extent, between adult males and females. Males of nonterritorial populations shape their home ranges both to overlap large numbers of females and to avoid areas unoccupied by females, thus implying cohesive behavior (Koford, 1982; Pesce, 1982). I predict that young tree squirrels will, when they are able, establish home ranges adjacent to those of their mothers (see Smith, 1968) and show relatively more amicable behavior (such as nest sharing) toward kin than toward nonkin. Sociality often appears to develop out of existing kin-directed behavior (Armitage, 1981; Michener, 1983). Kin-directed behavior has been reported for tree squirrels in the form of nestsharing, as noted above, and might be expected in alarm calling, a common trait among social and nonsocial ground squirrels. I predict that female red squirrels with recently weaned young in the vicinity will chatter at predators more frequently than will males and that populations characterized by short-distance dispersal among

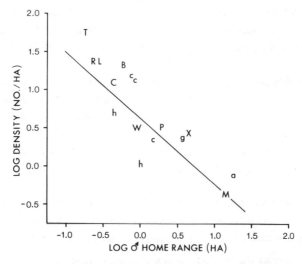

FIGURE 3.8. Log of density plotted against log of male home range size. B = *Spermophilus beecheyi*; C = *S. columbianus*; L = *Cynomys ludovicianus*; M = *Marmota caligata*; P = *S. parryii*; R = *S. richardsonii*; T = *S. tereticaudus*; W = *C. leucurus*; X = *S. tridecemlineatus*; a = *Sciurus aberti*; c = *S. carolinensis*; g = *S. granatensis*; h = *Tamiasciurus hudsonicus*. Regression equation: log of density = 1.66 – 1.89 (log of home range); $r = -0.88$ ($P < 0.01$).

70

young will show higher levels of chattering overall than will populations characterized by long-distance dispersal.

Squirrels and life-history tactics theory. Because all squirrels allocate at most 2% of their energy to reproduction (Armitage, 1981; see also Husband, 1967; Montgomery et al., 1975), they should be considered K-selected, on an $r-K$ continuum (Stearns, 1976). Armitage (1981) compared several life-history features of ground squirrels and concluded that for these species "the $r-K$-selection model is not useful and leads only to tedious comparisons of particular traits between species." He agreed with Western (1979) that life-history parameters that are closely correlated with size (e.g., gestation time, growth rates, life-span, litter weight) contribute the greatest amount of variation to a multispecies comparison among closely related mammals.

The data compiled here allow further testing of the appropriateness of the $r-K$ model. If we can describe ground squirrels as living in a more variable environment than tree squirrels, as seems reasonable, then ground squirrels should exhibit the following features relative to tree squirrels: 1, rapid development; 2, high r-max; 3, early reproduction; 4, high resource thresholds; 5, small body size; 6, semelparity; 7, shorter life; 8, larger litters; 9, smaller neonates; 10, less parental care; and 11, fewer litters per year (predictions from Stearns, 1976, Table 3). Of these predictions, six are probably true (1, 2, 4, 7, 8, 11), four are probably false (3, 5, 9, 10), and one is true for neither (6). This mixture of correct and incorrect predictions supports Armitage's conclusion that it is more useful to consider the selective costs and benefits of individual characteristics than to try to fit a species into an $r-K$ model, and that attempts at the latter are doomed to failure.

A second model of life-history tactics, which has not previously been applied to sciurids, is bet hedging (Stearns, 1976). This model focuses on the importance of variability of juvenile mortality as a selective agent. In particular, for species such as squirrels, in which both the amount and the variability of mortality in adults are lower than in juveniles, the model predicts that with increasing variability of juvenile mortality, there should be: 1, later maturity; 2, smaller reproductive effort; 3, longer life; 4, fewer young per litter; and 5, more litters per year. The data cited above suggest that juvenile *Marmota* experience somewhat lower mortality than tree squirrels or *Spermophilus*. However, annual variability in all species is very high (see discussion above), and the model makes the same predictions for all species. Thus, application of this model is inappropriate, although more precise data may eventually detect small but usable differences.

I conclude that neither generalized model of life-history tactics adequately deals with the life-history trends shown by North American squirrels, and that until a better model and a more detailed data set are developed, a character-by-character analysis of selective pressures will be most conducive to new insights.

Conclusion

There appear to be four fundamental ecological differences between ground squirrels and tree squirrels. First, with a few notable exceptions, ground squirrels feed primarily on grass and herbaceous vegetation that is extremely abundant for a short portion of the year but cannot be stored. Tree squirrels feed primarily on seeds, which are higher in energy but probably less abundant than foliage and often can be stored for long periods. Second, many species of ground squirrels hibernate, whereas tree squirrels do not. Third, ground squirrels produce larger litters and have lower survivorship than do tree squirrels. Fourth, because tree squirrels are arboreal, they live in a three-dimensional environment rather than the effectively two-dimensional environment of ground squirrels.

The effect these differences have on sociality might be viewed from two perspectives. First, the differences do not result in any substantial or consistent difference in density and home range size between the two groups. In both groups, density and home range size of all species are apparently affected by climatic variables, but all such variation is independent of degree of sociality.

Second, the differences do allow some ground squirrels to exist in places with short growing seasons for both the plants (which die or become dormant) and the squirrels (which hibernate). Species that live in the most extreme conditions, mountain-dwelling marmots, form one group of highly social species. Some prairie dogs, which constitute a second group of highly social species, occur in habitats similar to those inhabited by less social species, where growing seasons are long. Prairie dogs are not unique or extreme in any of the variables investigated here, so their development of sociality must be investigated by some other approach.

Are there fundamental differences in the social systems of tree and ground squirrels? The data presented above suggest that the differences are in degree only, but the data are incomplete and some crucial questions are unanswered. First, What are the spatial and social characteristics of forest-dwelling, seed-eating marmotines such as *Spermophilus lateralis,* and do they bridge the remaining gap between tree and ground squirrel social and mating systems? Second, What is the frequency of reproduction in marmotines, and does this remove the apparent difference in mean annual production of young? If not, does the difference in litter size indicate that predation is typically higher and exerts stronger selective pressure on ground squirrels? Third, Does the additional spatial component of arboreal tree squirrels alter their modes of interaction in a consistent and significant manner, relative to ground squirrels? And finally, Does hibernation impose restrictions on population dynamics that facilitate the development of a high degree of sociality, thus decreasing the likelihood of the evolution of highly social tree squirrels?

The preceding discussion establishes two major points. First, the behavior of North American squirrels has evolved in the context of diverse life-history adaptations and is likely to be understood only when viewed in that context. Second, one of the ultimate selective agents acting on both behavior and life-history traits is climate, and that too is a necessary part of our context.

Acknowledgments

During the long genesis of this chapter, I have benefited from spirited discussions with and editorial comments from K. Armitage, G. Barrowclough, S. Dobson, W. Glanz, G. Glass, R. Hoffmann, J. Honacki, R. Koford, H. Levenson, G. Michener, J. Murie, P. Myers, A. Pesce, S. F. Peters, N. Slade, S. Smith, R. Thorington, and R. Timm. I wish to thank S. Campbell and G. Lake for assistance with preparing the manuscript and M. Van Bolt for preparing the illustrations. Computer services were provided by the University of Michigan Academic Computer Center; other facilities and services were provided by the University of Kansas, University of Michigan, and the Smithsonian Institution. This paper was inspired by fieldwork sponsored by the Smithsonian Tropical Research Institute.

Literature Cited

Allen, D. L. 1942. Population and habits of the fox squirrel in Allegan County, Michigan. Amer. Midland Nat., 27:338–379.

Anderson, S. 1962. Tree squirrels (*Sciurus colliaei* group) of western Mexico. Amer. Mus. Novitates, 2093:1–13.

———. 1972. Mammals of Chihuahua: taxonomy and distribution. Bull. Amer. Mus. Nat. Hist., 148:149–410.

Armitage, K. B. 1974. Male behavior and territoriality in the yellow-bellied marmot. J. Zool. London, 172:233–265.

———. 1981. Sociality as a life-history tactic of ground squirrels. Oecologia, 48:36–49.

Armitage, K. B., and J. F. Downhower. 1974. Demography of yellow-bellied marmot populations. Ecology, 55:1233–1245.

Armstrong, D. M. 1972. Distribution of mammals in Colorado. Monogr. Mus. Nat. Hist., Univ. Kansas, 3:i–415.

Bailey, V. 1936. The mammals and life zones of Oregon. N. Amer. Fauna, 55:1–416.

Baker, R. H. 1956. Mammals of Coahuila, Mexico. Publ. Mus. Nat. Hist., Univ. Kansas, 9:125–335.

Baker, R. H., and J. K. Greer. 1962. Mammals of the Mexican state of Durango. Publ. Mus., Michigan State Univ. (Biol. Ser.), 2:25–154.

Bakken, A. 1959. Behavior of gray squirrels. Proc. Southeastern Assoc. Game and Fish Comm., 13:393–406.

Barkalow, F. S., R. B. Hamilton, and R. F. Soots. 1970. The vital statistics of an unexploited gray squirrel population. J. Wildl. Mgmt., 34:489–500.

Bronson, M. T. 1979. Altitudinal variation in the life history of the golden-mantled ground squirrel (*Spermophilus lateralis*). Ecology, 60:272–279.

Brown, L. G., and L. E. Yeager. 1945. Fox squirrels and gray squirrels in Illinois. Bull. Illinois State Nat. Hist. Surv., 23:449–536.

Brown, L. N., and R. J. McGuire. 1975. Field ecology of the exotic Mexican red-bellied squirrel in Florida. J. Mamm., 56:405–419.

Bryant, M. D. 1945. Phylogeny of Nearctic Sciuridae. Amer. Midland Nat., 33:257–390.

Callahan, J. R., and R. Davis. 1982. Reproductive tract and evolutionary relationships of the Chinese rock squirrel, *Sciurotamias davidianus*. J. Mamm., 63:42–47.

Carl, E. A. 1971. Population control in Arctic ground squirrels. Ecology, 52:395–413.

Clark, T. W. 1977. Ecology and ethology of the white-tailed prairie dog (*Cynomys leucurus*). Milwaukee Public Mus., Publs. Biol. Geol., 3:1–97.

Cockrum, E. L. 1952. Mammals of Kansas. Publ. Mus. Nat. Hist., Univ. Kansas, 7:1–303.

Doebbl, J. H., and B. S. McGinnes. 1974. Home range and activity of a gray squirrel population. J. Wildl. Mgmt., 38:860–867.

Dunford, C. 1977. Social systems of round-tailed ground squirrels. Anim. Behav., 25:885–906.

Eisenberg, J. F. 1981. The mammalian radiations: an analysis of trends in evolution, adaptation, and behavior. Univ. Chicago Press, Chicago, 610 pp.

Farentinos, R. C. 1972a. Observations on the ecology of the tassel-eared squirrel. J. Wildl. Mgmt., 36:1234–1239.

———. 1972b. Social dominance and mating activity in the tassel-eared squirrel (*Sciurus aberti ferreus*). Anim. Behav., 20:316–326.

———. 1979. Seasonal changes in home range size of tassel-eared squirrels (*Sciurus aberti*). Southwestern Nat., 24:49–62.

———. 1980. Sexual solicitation of subordinate males by female tassel-eared squirrels (*Sciurus aberti*). J. Mamm., 61:337–341.

Ferron, J. 1980. Le comportement cohesif de l'écureuil roux (*Tamiasciurus hudsonicus*). Biol. Behav., 5:119–138.

———. 1981. Comparative ontogeny of behaviour in four species of squirrels (Sciuridae). Z. Tierpsychol., 55:193–216.

Flyger, V. F. 1960. Movement and home range of the gray squirrel (*Sciurus carolinensis*) in two Maryland woodlots. Ecology, 41:365–369.

Glanz, W. E., R. W. Thorington, J. Madden, and L. R. Heaney. 1982. Seasonal food use and demographic trends in *Sciurus granatensis*. Pp. 239–252, *in* The ecology of a tropical forest: seasonal rhythms and long-term changes (E. Leigh, A. S. Rand, and D. M. Windsor, eds). Smithsonian Institution Press, Washington, D.C. 468 pp.

Goodrum, P. D. 1940. A population study of the gray squirrel in eastern Texas. Bull. Texas Agr. Exp. Sta., 591:1–34.

Goodwin, G. G. 1946. Mammals of Costa Rica. Bull. Amer. Mus. Nat. Hist., 87: 271–474.

———. 1969. Mammals from the Mexican state of Oaxaca, Mexico, in the American Museum of Natural History. Bull. Amer. Mus. Nat. Hist., 141:1–270.

Gunderson, H. L., and J. R. Beer. 1953. The mammals of Minnesota. Occas. Papers Mus. Nat. Hist., Univ. Minnesota, 6:i–190.

Haggerty, S. M. 1968. The ecology of the Franklin's ground squirrel (*Citellus franklinii*) at Itasca State Park, Minnesota. Unpubl. M.S. thesis, Univ. Minnesota, Minneapolis. 90 pp.

Hall, E. R. 1981. The mammals of North America. Vol. 1. John Wiley, New York, 600 + 90 pp.

Hall, J. G. 1981. A field study of the Kaibab squirrel in Grand Canyon National Park. Wildl. Monogr., 75:1–54.

Hamilton, W. J., Jr. 1939. Observations of the life history of the red squirrel in New York. Amer. Midland Nat., 22:732–735.

Harestad, A. S., and F. L. Bunnell. 1979. Home range and body weight—a reevaluation. Ecology, 60:389–402.

Harper, F. 1961. Land and fresh-water mammals of the Ungava Peninsula. Misc. Publ. Mus. Nat. Hist., Univ. Kansas, 27:1–178.

Harris, W. P., Jr. 1937. Revision of *Sciurus variegatoides,* a species of Central American squirrel. Misc. Publ. Mus. Zool., Univ. Michigan, 38:1–39.

Hatt, R. T. 1929. The red squirrel: its life history and habits, with special reference to the Adirondacks of New York and the Harvard Forest. Roosevelt Wildl. Ann., 2:4–146.

Heaney, L. R., and R. W. Thorington. 1978. Ecology of Neotropical red-tailed squirrels, *Sciurus granatensis,* in the Panama Canal Zone. J. Mamm., 59:846–851.

Hoffmeister, D. F., and V. E. Diersing. 1978. Review of the tassel-eared squirrels of the subgenus *Otosciurus.* J. Mamm., 59:402–413.

Holmes, W. G. 1979. Social behavior and foraging strategies of hoary marmots (*Marmota caligata*) in Alaska. Unpub. dissert., Univ. Washington, Seattle, 130 pp.

Horwich, R. H. 1967. The ontogeny of social behavior in the gray squirrel (*Sciurus carolinensis*). Adv. Ethol. (Berlin), 8:1–103.

Husband, T. P. 1967. Energy metabolism and body composition of the fox squirrel. J. Wildl. Mgmt., 40:255–263.

Comparative Aspects

Ingles, L. G. 1947. Ecology and life history of the California gray squirrel. California Fish and Game, 33:139–158.

Johnson, K. 1981. Social organization in a colony of rock squirrels (*Spermophilus variegatus,* Sciuridae). Southwestern Nat., 26:237–242.

Jones, J. K., Jr., and H. H. Genoways. 1971. Notes on the biology of the Central American squirrel, *Sciurus richmondi.* Amer. Midland Nat., 86:242–246.

Keith, J. O. 1965. The Abert squirrel and its dependence on ponderosa pine. Ecology, 46:150–163.

Kemp, G. A., and L. B. Keith. 1970. Dynamics and regulation of red squirrel (*Tamiasciurus hudsonicus*) populations. Ecology, 51:763–779.

King, J. A. 1955. Social behavior, social organization, and population dynamics in a black-tailed prairiedog town in the Black Hills of South Dakota. Contrib. Lab. Vert. Biol., Univ. Michigan, 67:1–123.

Koford, R. R. 1982. Mating system of a territorial tree squirrel (*Tamiasciurus douglasii*) in California. J. Mamm., 62:274–283.

Komarek, E. V., and R. Komarek. 1938. Mammals of the Great Smoky Mountains. Bull. Chicago Acad. Sci., 5:137–162.

Layne, J. N. 1954. The biology of the red squirrel, *Tamiasciurus hudsonicus loquax* (Bangs), in central New York. Ecol. Monogr., 24:227–267.

Lee, M. R., and D. F. Hoffmeister. 1963. Status of certain fox squirrels in Mexico and Arizona. Proc. Biol. Soc. Washington, 76:181–190.

Lindsay, S. L. 1981. Taxonomic and biogeographic relationships of Baja California chickarees (*Tamiasciurus*). J. Mamm., 62:673–682.

Longley, W. H. 1963. Minnesota gray and fox squirrels. Amer. Midland Nat., 69:82–98.

Lowery, G. H., Jr. 1974. The mammals of Louisiana and its adjacent waters. Louisiana State Univ. Press, Baton Rouge, 565 pp.

McCarley, H. 1966. Annual cycle, population dynamics and adaptive behavior of *Citellus tridecemlineatus.* J. Mamm., 47:294–316.

McNab, B. K. 1971. On the ecological significance of Bergmann's rule. Ecology, 52:845–854.

Michener, G. R. 1979. Spatial relationships and social organization of adult Richardson's ground squirrels. Canadian J. Zool., 57:125–139.

———. 1983. Kin identification, matriarchies, and the evolution of sociality in ground-dwelling sciurids. Pp. 528–572, *in* Recent advances in the study of mammalian behavior (J. F. Eisenberg and D. G. Kleiman, eds.). Spec. Publ., Amer. Soc. Mamm., 7:1–753.

Millar, J. S. 1970. The breeding season and reproductive cycle of the western red squirrel. Canadian J. Zool., 48:471–473.

———. 1977. Adaptive features of mammalian reproduction. Evolution, 31:370–386.

———. 1981. Pre-partum reproductive characteristics of eutherian mammals. Evolution, 35:1149–1163.

76

Montgomery, S. D., J. B. Whelan, and H. S. Mosby. 1975. Bioenergetics of a woodlot gray squirrel population. J. Wildl. Mgmt., 39:709–717.

Moore, J. C. 1957. The natural history of the fox squirrel, *Sciurus niger shermani*. Bull. Amer. Mus. Nat. Hist., 113:1–72.

———. 1959. Relationships among living squirrels of the Sciurinae. Bull. Amer. Mus. Nat. Hist., 118:153–206.

Murie, J. O., and M. A. Harris. 1978. Territoriality and dominance in male Columbian ground squirrels (*Spermophilus columbianus*). Canadian J. Zool., 56:2402–2412.

Murie, J. O., D. A. Boag, and V. K. Kivett. 1980. Litter size in Columbian ground squirrels (*Spermophilus columbianus*). J. Mamm., 61:237–244.

Musser, G. G. 1968. A systematic study of the Mexican and Guatemalan gray squirrel, *Sciurus aureogaster* F. Cuvier (Rodentia: Sciuridae) Misc. Publ. Mus. Zool., Univ. Michigan, 137:1–112.

Nixon, C. M., and M. W. McClain. 1969. Squirrel population decline following a late spring frost. J. Wildl. Mgmt., 33:353–357.

———. 1975. Breeding seasons and fecundity of female gray squirrels in Ohio. J. Wildl. Mgmt., 39:426–438.

Nixon, C. M., R. W. Donohoe, and T. Nash. 1974. Overharvest of fox squirrels from two woodlots in western Ohio. J. Wildl. Mgmt., 38:67–80.

Nixon, C. W., M. W. McClain, and R. W. Donohoe. 1975. Effects of hunting and mast crops on a squirrel population. J. Wildl. Mgmt., 39:1–25.

Nixon, C. M., D. M. Warley, and M. W. McClain. 1968. Food habits of squirrels in southeast Ohio. J. Wildl. Mgmt., 32:294–305.

Owings, D. H., M. Borchert, and R. Virginia. 1977. The behavior of California ground squirrels. Anim. Behav., 25:221–230.

Pack, J. C., H. S. Mosby, and P. B. Siegel. 1967. Influence of social hierarchy on gray squirrel behavior. J. Wildl. Mgmt., 31:720–728.

Packard, R. L. 1956. The tree squirrels of Kansas: ecology and economic importance. Misc. Publ. Mus. Nat. Hist., Univ. Kansas, 11:1–67.

Paradiso, J. L. 1969. Mammals of Maryland. N. Amer. Fauna, 66:i–193.

Pederson, J. C., R. N. Hasenyager, and A. W. Heggan. 1976. Habitat requirements of the Abert squirrel (*Sciurus aberti navajo*) on the Monticello District, Manti-Lasal National Forest of Utah. Utah State Div. Wildl. Res., Publ. 76 9:i–108.

Pesce, A. 1982. Dynamics of a non-territorial population of red squirrels (*Tamiasciurus*) in southeastern Michigan. Unpubl. M.S. thesis, Univ. Michigan, Ann Arbor, 58 pp.

Reynolds, H. G. 1966. Abert's squirrels feeding on pinyon pine. J. Mamm., 47:550–551.

Roth, V. L., and R. W. Thorington, Jr. 1982. Relative brain size among African squirrels. J. Mamm., 63:168–173.

Rusch, D. A., and W. G. Reeder. 1978. Population ecology of Alberta red squirrels. Ecology, 59:400–420.

Silverman, D. L. 1981. The behavioral ecology of the thirteen-lined ground squirrel

(*Spermophilus tridecemlineatus*). Unpubl. M.S. thesis, Univ. Michigan, Ann Arbor, 45 pp.

Slade, N. A., and D. F. Balph. 1974. Population ecology of Uinta ground squirrels. Ecology, 55:989–1003.

Smith, C. C. 1968. The adaptive nature of social organization in the genus of tree squirrels (*Tamiasciurus*). Ecol. Monogr., 38:31–63.

Soper, J. D. 1961. The mammals of Manitoba. Canadian Field-Nat., 75:171–219.

———. 1970. The mammals of Jasper National Park, Alberta. Canadian Wildl. Serv. Rep. Ser., 10:1–80.

———. 1973. The mammals of Waterton Lakes National Park, Alberta. Canadian Wildl. Serv. Rep. Ser., 23:1–55.

Stearns, S. C. 1976. Life history tactics: a review of the ideas. Quart. Rev. Biol., 51: 1–45.

Steinecker, W. E., and B. N. Browning. 1970. Food habits of the western gray squirrel. California Fish and Game, 56:36–48.

Sullivan, T. P., and D. S. Sullivan. 1982. Population dynamics and regulation of the Douglas squirrel (*Tamiasciurus douglasii*) with supplemental food. Oecologia, 53:264–270.

Thoma, B. L., and W. H. Marshall. 1960. Squirrel weights and populations in a Minnesota woodlot. J. Mamm., 41:272–273.

Thompson, D. C. 1977. Reproductive behavior of the grey squirrel. Canadian J. Zool., 55:1176–1184.

———. 1978a. The social system of the gray squirrel. Behaviour, 64:305–328.

———. 1978b. Regulation of a northern grey squirrel (*Sciurus carolinensis*) population. Ecology, 59:708–715.

Tuomi, J. 1980. Mammalian reproductive strategies: a generalized relation of litter size to body size. Oecologia, 45:39–44.

Western, D. 1979. Size, life history, and ecology in mammals. African J. Ecol., 17: 185–204.

2. Annual Cycles

GAIL R. MICHENER

University of Lethbridge

Chapter 4

Age, Sex, and Species Differences in the Annual Cycles of Ground-Dwelling Sciurids: Implications for Sociality

Abstract. Annual cycles of hibernating sciurids are composed of a predictable sequence of events: vernal emergence from hibernation, breeding, gestation, lactation, juvenile emergence, prehibernatory fattening, autumnal immergence, and hibernation until the subsequent spring. Typically adult males emerge in spring before adult females (to maximize their access to sexually receptive females), and adults emerge before subadults (to maximize the time available to breed and for young to grow).

Species at high elevations and northern latitudes usually have short active seasons terminated by the almost synchronous disappearance of all cohorts, whereas species at low elevations and southern latitudes tend to have long active seasons characterized by asynchronous immergence of cohorts. When immergence is asynchronous, the typical sequence of disappearance is adult males, adult females that did not wean young that summer, adult females that did wean young, subadult females, and finally subadult males. This sequence is determined by the competing needs of energy for either reproduction (adults) or growth (subadults) versus prehibernatory fat deposition.

The least social species tend to be those that mature as yearlings and in which asynchronous immergence results in juveniles' spending a significant proportion of their first summer of life out of contact with adults. The most social species tend to be those with extensive temporal overlap in the active seasons of adults and subadults and thus include species in which adults remain active as late as juveniles, species in which subadulthood is spread over several years, and species that do not hibernate. Greater knowledge about annual cycles of activity and seasonal variation in rates of social interactions is needed to determine the role that synchrony in the active seasons of cohorts may have played in the evolution of sociality in sciurids.

Introduction

Obligate seasonal hibernation is characteristic of most North American marmotine species whose ranges occur north of 30°N. For such species the annual cycle is partitioned into an inactive (hibernation) season and an active season. Terminal arousal from hibernation and resumption of activity in spring appear to be commitment points from which each annual cycle commences (Heller and Poulson, 1970; Michener, 1979). A predictable sequence of biological events follows vernal emergence: breeding, gestation, lactation, juvenile emergence, prehibernatory fattening, and immergence. Although all hibernating marmotines exhibit the same sequence of annual events, some species have short active seasons of about 4 months (e.g., *Spermophilus columbianus, Marmota flaviventris, M. olympus*), whereas others have long active seasons of 7–8 months (e.g., *S. richardsonii, Cynomys leucurus*). For facultative hibernators (e.g., *S. beecheyi*) and nonhibernators (e.g., *C. ludovicianus*) there is no period of total inactivity by all cohorts, but these species also exhibit an annual cycle of biological events similar to that of obligate hibernators.

The time and sequence of autumnal immergence vary among species such that there are species-specific differences in the extent of overlap of aboveground activity of different cohorts, particularly of adults and juveniles. For species with short active seasons, all cohorts immerge within a period of several weeks, whereas for species with long active seasons some cohorts enter hibernation 2–3 months in advance of other cohorts in the same population (e.g., Michener, 1977). Thus the ability for individuals of different age-sex groups to interact socially is constrained by the nature of each species' annual cycle.

The purposes of this article are (1) to characterize the types of annual cycles found in ground squirrels, prairie dogs, and marmots; (2) to propose types of data needed to augment our knowledge of annual cycles; and (3) to discuss interactions among species' size, age at first reproduction, length of active season, and sociality.

Time of Vernal Emergence

The time at which different species terminate hibernation and appear aboveground is partly dependent on latitude and altitude (Table 4.1). Southern species (e.g., *S. tereticaudus*) and low-elevation species (e.g., *S. richardsonii*) typically resume activity in January to March, whereas northern species (e.g., *S. parryii*) and high-elevation species (e.g., *S. beldingi*) emerge aboveground in April to May. Within a species, emergence tends to occur later at higher elevations (e.g., *S. columbianus, S. lateralis*), at more northerly latitudes (e.g., *M. monax*), and in more continental locations (e.g., *S. richardsonii*). Aspect also affects the time of vernal emergence within a population such that animals on southwest-facing slopes emerge earlier than those on northeast-facing areas (Shaw, 1925*a*). The common feature among species is that vernal emergence is cued to environmental factors associated with onset of vegetative growth. Because the date of resumption of activity differs from year to year (Table 4.1), annual variation in time of vernal emergence within a population can be compared with annual variation in climatic factors. Correlations have been noted between time of spring emergence and ambient conditions such as snow cover (Bronson, 1980; Phillips, this volume), snow depth (Morton and Sherman, 1978; Murie and Harris, 1982), air temperature (Knopf and Balph, 1977; Michener, 1977; Murie and Harris, 1982; Tileston and Lechleitner, 1966; Yahner and Svendsen, 1978), and soil temperature (Iverson and Turner, 1972; Michener, 1979; Wade, 1950). For northern and mountain-dwelling species, emergence typically occurs when snow is receding and/or shallow soil layers are thawing. Not only do animals resume aboveground activity later in cold or snowy years, but the total emergence period tends to be compressed, with all individuals appearing within a short period compared with warmer years (Balph, this volume; Knopf and Balph, 1977;[1] Michener, 1977, 1979).

Lability in emergence dates (Table 4.1) indicates that animals are not programmed to emerge at a precise time. However, there are limitations to the period over which individuals appear aboveground. Weather conditions prevailing at the time of vernal emergence sometimes also occur earlier in the year (Michener, 1977, 1979; Murie and Harris, 1982), yet early emergence rarely or never occurs, suggesting a temporal threshold in response to ambient conditions. Conversely, when winter weather persists beyond the usual time of spring emergence, animals eventually emerge despite continuing cold, snowy conditions (Michener, 1977). Thus there is a two-stage threshold: early in the year animals do not respond to warm ambient conditions that later are sufficient to initiate resumption of surface activity, and late in the year animals emerge despite cool ambient conditions that earlier were insufficient to cause emergence. Two selective factors probably constrain the time over which vernal emergence occurs.

1. In Table 1 of Knopf and Balph (1977) the mean emergence date for yearling males in 1967 should read 3 May (Balph, in litt.).

TABLE 4.1. Time of vernal emergence and annual variation in vernal emergence dates, based on studies that span at least three consecutive years

Species	Latitude °N	Altitude m	Location[a]	Years studied	Date of emergence[b] Earliest	Latest	Range (days)	Source
Spermophilus armatus	42	1,920	UT	7	20 March	16 April	27	Balph, this volume[c]
S. beldingi	38	3,000	CA	3	22 April	17 May	25	Morton and Sherman, 1978[c]
S. columbianus	47	775	WA	6	19 February	8 March	17	Shaw, 1925b
	47	1,350	MT	3	19 April	5 May	16	Betts, 1973
	50	1,470	ALB	6	21 April[d]	28 April	7	Murie and Harris, 1982[c]
S. elegans	41	2,175	WY	3	8 March	13 March	5	Clark, 1970, 1977
	40	2,350	CO	3	9 March	30 March	21	Fagerstone, 1982
S. franklinii	50	250	MAN	9	14 April	26 April	12	Sowls, 1948
	50	265	MAN	3	2 May	11 May	9	Iverson and Turner, 1972
S. lateralis	39	1,840	CA	3	14 April	12 May	38	Bronson, 1980
	39	2,730	NE	3	12 May	28 May	16	Bronson, 1980
S. parryii	61	800	YUK	3	15 April	24 April	9	Green, 1977
	62	600	AK	5	21 April	27 April	6	Hock, 1960
S. richardsonii	47	280	ND	3	1 April	22 April	21	Quanstrom, 1968
	50	250	MAN	9[e]	20 March	7 April	18	Sowls, 1968

Species	Latitude °N	Altitude m	Location[a]	Years studied	Date of emergence[b] Earliest	Latest	Range (days)	Source
S. richardsonii	50	870	ALB	5	13 February	7 March	22	Michener, 1983a[c]
	50	1,235	ALB	4	22 March	14 April	23	Michener, 1979[c]
S. tereticaudus	32	740	AZ	3	7 January	17 January	10	Dunford, in litt.
S. townsendii	39	1,200	NE	4	13 February	21 February	8	Alcorn, 1940
	41	1,300	UT	4	20 February[g]	4 March	12	Rickart, 1982
S. tridecemlineatus	34	230	TX	3	12 March	12 March	0	McCarley, 1966
	41	2,175	WY	3	31 March	6 April	6	Clark, 1971, 1977
S. variegatus	41	~1,500	UT	3	19 February	3 March	12	Juelson, 1970
Cynomys leucurus	41	2,175	WY	3	9 February	21 February	12	Clark, 1977
Marmota monax	40	200	PA	13	29 January	13 February	15	Davis, 1977
	43	~320	ONT	3	5 March	9 March	4	de Vos and Gillespie, 1960
	44	~150	VT	3	13 March	5 April	23	Smith, 1931

a Abbreviated name of state or province.
b Date of first emergence by adult males is given, when available, since this emergence date is the one most frequently provided in published reports.
c Also includes information on mean or median emergence date.
d Median emergence dates of adult male cohort.
e Emergence data collected in seven of the nine years.
f First emergence dates of adult females.
g Dates on which "majority" of females are active.

First, early emergers that resume homeothermy when food is scarce and inclement weather is common experience high mortality (e.g., Morton and Sherman, 1978). Second, offspring born to animals that emerge and breed late have low survival (e.g., Armitage et al., 1976).

The endogenous rhythm of alternating bouts of torpor and arousal during hibernation appears to promote emergence at an opportune time. Because arousals are short and infrequent in midwinter but increase in duration and frequency later in the hibernation season (Drescher, 1967; French, 1982; Jameson, 1964; Pengelley and Fisher, 1961; Wang, 1973, 1979), the probability that an animal is homeothermic increases as spring approaches. This pattern presumably permits an animal to monitor and respond to ambient conditions.

Although a relation between time of vernal emergence and air temperature has been noted for several species (Knopf and Balph, 1977; Michener, 1977, 1979; Murie and Harris, 1982; Tileston and Lechleitner, 1966; Yahner and Svendsen, 1978), such a relation has been sought but not found in other studies (Clark, 1977; Davis, 1967, 1977; McCarley, 1966). Several factors may account for an apparent lack of association between emergence and air temperature: (1) animals in underground hibernacula may not be responding directly to air temperature; even if they do monitor surface conditions periodically, air temperature tends to be an unreliable cue because it fluctuates with time of day and with transient atmospheric systems; (2) correlating emergence on a specific day with air temperature on that day may not be meaningful if animals are responding to trends in weather conditions spanning several days or weeks; (3) because animals undergo alternating bouts of torpor and arousal, they are not always physiologically capable of reacting immediately to appropriate environmental cues; and (4) attempts to correlate first emergence with climatic factors may not be fruitful if the first emerging animal is not representative of the majority of its cohort (see Davis, 1967). During a five-year study of vernal emergence by Richardson's ground squirrels in the prairie region of southern Alberta, I found that the date of first emergence can be misleading if used as an indicator of the time of emergence of an entire cohort (Michener, 1983a). From 1979 to 1983 the discrepancies between the dates of first emergence and median emergence were 5, 14, 2, 18, and 7 days for adult males (n = 22, 21, 21, 23, and 24), and 6, 5, 10, 12, and 17 days for adult females (n = 16, 18, 38, 85, and 104).

Most emergence dates reported in the literature are for the first animal seen aboveground (Table 4.1). To understand the role that environmental parameters play in determining the time of vernal emergence, I suggest that the entire emergence sequence be monitored and compared with temporal trends in a suite of climatic variables including maximum air temperature, soil temperature at various depths, snow cover, and snow depth.

Although vernal emergence occurs when air and soil temperature are increasing and snow cover is decreasing, sympatric species do not necessarily emerge in response to the same weather conditions. Clark (1977) found that on the Laramie Plains of Wyoming white-tailed prairie dogs emerged in mid-February, Wyoming ground squirrels in mid-March, and thirteen-lined ground squirrels in early April. Similarly, Sowls (1948) noted that at Delta, Manitoba, the first Richardson's ground squirrels appeared 2–3 weeks before the first Franklin's ground squirrels, and Michener (1977) reported that in the foothills of the southern Alberta Rocky Mountains Richardson's ground squirrels emerged and bred 3–4 weeks in advance of Columbian ground squirrels. As yet neither mechanistic nor adaptive explanations have been proposed for species-specific differences in time of emergence from hibernation under the same environmental conditions.

Vernal Emergence Sequences

Typically adult males resume aboveground activity in spring before females (Table 4.2, see also Davis, 1976). Differences in time of vernal emergence of males and females have long been recognized (e.g., Shaw, 1925*b*; Stockard, 1929; Wade, 1927), but because most studies present data only on first emergence dates, the range and magnitude of sex differences have rarely been quantified. Several studies that have monitored the entire emergence period over several years (Knopf and Balph, 1977; Michener, 1983*a*; Morton and Sherman, 1978; Murie and Harris, 1982) demonstrate that, despite some temporal overlap in emergence schedules, the mean (or median) date of emergence of males is significantly earlier than that of females. Males usually emerge 1–2 weeks before females in obligately hibernating species of *Spermophilus*, except for *S. tereticaudus*, which has a 3–4 week sex difference. Only a few exceptions to the male-before-female pattern of adult emergence have been reported for *Spermophilus* (Table 4.2); additional quantitative data are required to confirm that female precedence is typical for *S. variegatus* and for some populations of *S. beecheyi* and *S. tridecemlineatus*.

A 2–3 week sex difference in time of vernal emergence occurs among adult *Cynomys leucurus*. King (1955) reported that *C. ludovicianus* is active aboveground on all but the most inclement days during winter; he did not indicate if males come aboveground more frequently or for longer periods than females.

Adult male *Marmota monax* emerge 3–4 weeks in advance of adult females.

TABLE 4.2. Species of ground-dwelling squirrels for which a sex difference
in vernal emergence of adults has been reported

Species	Source
	Adult males emerge before adult females
Spermophilus armatus	Amend, 1970;[a] Balph, this volume;[a] Knopf and Balph, 1977[a]
S. beecheyi	Linsdale, 1946, Table 4
S. beldingi	Loehr and Risser, 1977; Morton, 1975; Morton and Sherman, 1978[a]
S. columbianus	Manville, 1959; Michener, 1977; Murie and Harris, 1982;[a] Shaw, 1925*b*
S. dauricus	Fei et al., 1975
S. elegans	Clark, 1970, 1977, Fig. 31; Fagerstone, 1982
S. franklinii	Iverson and Turner, 1972; Sowls, 1948
S. lateralis	Bronson, 1980;[b] McKeever, 1964, Fig. 1; Skryja and Clark, 1970
S. musicus	Emelianov et al., 1982
S. parryii	Green, 1977, Fig. 5; Hock, 1960; McLean and Towns, 1981;[a] Mitchell, 1959
S. richardsonii	Davis, 1982;[a] Dorrance, 1974;[a] Michener, 1974; Michener, 1977, 1979, 1983*a;* Nellis, 1969; Yeaton, 1972
S. spilosoma	Streubel, 1975
S. tereticaudus	Dunford, 1977; Neal, 1965*b*
S. townsendii	Alcorn, 1940; Rickart, 1982; Smith and Johnson, in press
S. tridecemlineatus	Beer, 1962; Clark, 1971; Foster, 1934; Johnson et al., 1933; Moore et al., 1934; Wade, 1927
Cynomys leucurus	Bakko and Brown, 1967; Clark, 1977; Stockard, 1929; Tileston and Lechleitner, 1966
Marmota monax	Davis, 1967; Snyder and Christian, 1960; Snyder et al., 1961
Eutamias minimus	Criddle, 1943; Sheppard, 1969
E. sibiricus	Kawamichi, 1983
Tamias striatus	Allen, 1938; Schooley, 1934; Smith and Smith, 1972
	Adult females emerge before adult males
Spermophilus beecheyi	Edge, 1931; Storer et al., 1944; Stroud, 1983
S. tridecemlineatus	McCarley, 1966[c]
S. variegatus	Juelson, 1970

[a] Includes quantitative data additional to first emergence dates.

[b] Bronson (1980) noted a sex difference of 3 weeks in first emergence dates at 1,460 m but no sex difference at 2,730 m. The first emergence date was estimated as the midpoint of the interval between inspections when squirrels were not and then were active; since this interval was 5, 13, and 12 days at the high-elevation site in the three-year study (Bronson, in litt.) a sex difference in first emergence dates could have been masked.

[c] McCarley (1966) noted that "the earliest appearing individuals were not always male," and his data for 1964 in Fig. 1 suggest that some females appear 1–2 weeks before males.

Information on sex differences in emergence by *M. caligata, M. flaviventris*, and *M. olympus* is notably absent in the literature. In these three species marmots live in small social groups, usually composed of one adult male, one to several adult females, and several subadults; groups members often hibernate communally and apparently emerge synchronously in spring (Andersen et al., 1976; Armitage, 1974; Barash, 1973, 1974; Downhower and Armitage, 1971; Holmes, this volume; Johns and Armitage, 1979). Possibly a sex difference in terminal arousal from torpor occurs but is not manifest as a sex difference in resumption of activity because early arousers either wait for or stimulate arousal in other hibernaculum members. Armitage (1962) indicated that the male was the second animal to resume aboveground activity in a colony composed of one adult male and nine adult female yellow-bellied marmots. Because marmot groups typically contain only one adult male, data from many groups are required to quantify the relation between sex and time of vernal emergence.

Age does not affect time of vernal emergence in species in which yearlings of both sexes are reproductively competent upon emergence from hibernation at 11 months old. For such species (e.g., *S. parryii, S. richardsonii*) the vernal emergence sequence is simply males > (before) females (McLean and Towns, 1981; Michener, 1983*a*). Yearling males of *S. armatus, S. beldingi,* and *S. townsendii idahoensis* are usually sexually immature, whereas most or all yearling females reproduce. In these three species, the vernal emergence sequence is adult male > adult female > yearling female > yearling male (Knopf and Balph, 1977; Morton and Sherman, 1978; Smith and Johnson, in press). The only ground squirrel in which yearling females are also usually sexually immature is *S. columbianus;* I noted that the first yearling male Columbian ground squirrels appeared aboveground before the first females (Michener, 1977), but Murie and Harris (1982) found no significant sex difference in yearling emergence. The emergence sequence for *S. columbianus* therefore is adult male > adult female > yearling male ≥ yearling female.

All yearling *M. flaviventris* are reproductively immature and most 2-year-olds do not reproduce (Armitage and Downhower, 1974). Both yearlings and 2-year-olds are immature in *M. olympus* and *M. caligata* (Barash, 1973; Holmes, this volume). An age difference in vernal emergence schedules has not been mentioned for these three species; apparently, reproductively immature animals of both sexes emerge at about the same time as breeding members of the colony.

Adaptive Significance of Vernal Emergence Schedules

Why do adult males emerge before females, and why do nonreproductive yearling males emerge after females in most species of *Spermophilus?* I propose that early vernal emergence by adult males is a strategy that maximizes their opportunities for successful reproduction. Female Richardson's, Columbian, and Belding's ground squirrels typically breed about 4 days after their spring emergence (Michener, 1980, 1983*a*, 1984; Murie and Harris, 1982; Sherman, 1976), and similar prompt breeding following emergence has been reported for other ground squirrels (Fagerstone, 1982; Hock, 1960; Knopf and Balph, 1977; McLean and Towns, 1981; Smith and Johnson, in press; Sowls, 1948). Because males typically hibernate in isolation from females, they can determine when females are active only by being aboveground to monitor their presence. Late emergence can be costly to males, because any females that have been active for several days are likely to have been inseminated by earlier-emerging males. For instance, in a population of *S. richardsonii* studied in 1981, I found that eight of 14 females active at the time the last resident male emerged on 4 March were already pregnant. Because 45 females bred that year, the potential breeding opportunities for the late male were reduced by 18% (see Michener, 1983*a,* for further details). In years in which the breeding season is unusually prolonged (e.g., when a snowstorm delays emergence or breeding by females; Morton and Sherman, 1978), late-emerging males may improve their reproductive success relative to earlier-emerging males if the latter experience a decline in sperm production before the end of the breeding season. However, the tendency for adult males to emerge before females suggests that there usually is little selective advantage to late emergence.

In addition to allowing males to locate females as they emerge, early emergence by adult males also may play a role in final maturation of the reproductive system. Liddle (1982) established that a period of homeothermy is essential for reproductive maturation in captive male *S. beldingi.* Under natural conditions, some male marmotines do not produce mature sperm until several days after emergence (Bakko and Brown, 1967; Hock, 1960; Mitchell, 1959; Neal, 1965*a*), whereas spermatogenesis is complete at the time of emergence in other species (Christian et al., 1972; Ellis et al., 1983; Morton and Gallup, 1975; Wells, 1935). For the latter species, reproductive maturation could occur during a period of homeothermy underground before the males appear on the surface. The length of homeothermic period necessary for reproductive maturation, and whether this period is effective underground or must be associated with aboveground activity, is not known for most sciurids.

Early emergence may permit males to establish territories before females appear, thereby enabling them to devote time and energy to intersexual rather than intrasexual interactions after female emergence. However, because males cannot predict which females will survive hibernation or which areas will contain the highest densities of estrous females until the females emerge, attempting to establish territories in advance of female emergence may not be a successful strategy. Several species of ground squirrels have a leklike mating system with dominance hierarchies and no defense of specific areas (Dobson, this volume); early male emergence in these species cannot be attributed to establishment of prebreeding territories. Males could use the prebreeding period to assess the identity and strength of other males and to establish loosely defined areas of site-dependent dominance, but intense intrasexual interactions and fine tuning of relative spatial positions of males are not likely to occur until estrous females appear. Few studies have specifically compared the behavior of males before female emergence versus during the breeding season. However, several reports indicate that male-male chases and fights, male excursions and intrusions, and injured males are most commonly observed in the breeding season (Bakko and Brown, 1967; Balph and Stokes, 1963; Clark, 1977; Kivett, 1975; Murie and Harris, 1978; Schwagmeyer and Brown, 1983; Wistrand, 1974). Paul (1977) noted that male *S. armatus* tend to move to areas occupied by females, and that dispersion of males in spring is partly a function of the distribution of females. Likewise, male *S. richardsonii* adjust the positions of their ranges from the pre-breeding to the breeding season such that they cluster around areas of greatest female density (Davis, 1982; Michener, 1983*a*).

The selective advantages of being active and producing mature sperm by the time the first female is sexually receptive presumably have resulted in adult males' emerging slightly (1–2 weeks) before adult females in most sperm-ophiles. Because of the probable metabolic costs associated with early resumption of homeothermy in cold climates, the lack of reproductive opportunities before the emergence of females, and the possibility that sperm production cannot be sustained over long periods, selection will tend to act against those males that emerge exceptionally early. For males that are not sexually mature there is no immediate reproductive cost to emerging after the adult male and female cohorts. Because the breeding season is a period of intense activity and social interaction, selection may have favored those subadults that avoid becoming targets of aggression from older, reproductive squirrels by emerging later than breeding conspecifics.

In mountain-dwelling marmots, adult males are typically associated with one to several adult females and may hibernate with the females; therefore males need not emerge before females to detect when females appear aboveground or to obtain access to estrous females. Hock and Cottini (1966) and Rausch and Rausch (1971) suggested that in some species of *Marmota* mating occurs in the

Annual Cycles

hibernaculum before vernal emergence. If so, aboveground activity is not necessary for males either to attain reproductive competency or to ensure breeding opportunities.

Autumnal Immergence Schedules

Only adults and subadults are present in the aboveground population during the first 2 months of each active season. The appearance of juveniles from the natal burrows results in a dramatic increase in population density. All age and sex classes are then simultaneously active and engaged in prehibernatory growth and/or fattening. Thereafter, animals return underground for the hibernation season. Obtaining accurate data on immergence is difficult because the disappearance of an animal could be due to death, dispersal, or submergence underground. Only when an animal is recovered the following spring can immergence be singled out as the reason for its disappearance. However, by using a combination of frequent monitoring of the active population and a criterion for the earliest possible immergence date (such as the earliest date of disappearance of a known survivor) immergence sequences of cohorts can be determined even though it may not be possible to verify that specific animals hibernated.

The most general sequence of autumnal immergence is adult male > (before) adult female > subadult > juvenile (Clark, 1977; Dorrance, 1974; Michener, 1974; Michener, 1977, 1979; Morton, 1975; Murie, 1973; Tileston and Lechleitner, 1966). Among adult females, reproduction affects fattening schedules and hence time of immergence; females that do not bear litters or do not rear young to weaning age commence hibernation earlier than females that wean litters (Barash, 1973, 1976; Kilgore and Armitage, 1978; Michener, 1978). Among juveniles, males immerge 2–3 weeks after females in *S. parryii* and *S. richardsonii* (McLean and Towns, 1981; Michener, 1979), species in which males are sexually active as yearlings. The prolonged active season of juvenile males may be a prerequisite for reproductive competence and success the following spring. Among species in which males typically initially breed as 2-year-olds, a sex difference in yearling immergence schedules, with males remaining aboveground later than females, has been noted for *S. armatus* and *S. columbianus* (Knopf and Balph, 1977; Michener, 1977), further suggesting that males prolong their active season relative to females of the same age in the year before first breeding. Because accurate data on immergence schedules are not available for most species of *Spermophilus*, the generality of the hypothesis that males remain active later than females in the year preceding sexual maturity cannot currently be tested.

92

Departures from the basic autumnal immergence sequence occur in Arctic, Uinta, and Wyoming ground squirrels; in these species adult males enter hibernation after adult females (Fagerstone, 1982; Green, 1977; Knopf and Balph, 1977; McLean and Towns, 1981). Because there is a sex difference in time of entry into hibernation among yearling *S. armatus*, though no consistent pattern among juveniles, the immergence sequence for this species is adult female > adult male ≥ yearling female > yearling male > juvenile. Among *S. parryii*, yearling and older adult cohorts are indistinguishable, and adult males remain active as late as juvenile females and sometimes as late as juvenile males, so the immergence sequence is adult female > juvenile female ≥ adult male ≥ juvenile male.

Among the mountain-dwelling *Marmota*, immergence apparently is relatively synchronous. Most studies of *M. caligata*, *M. flaviventris*, and *M. olympus* do not mention age or sex differences in autumnal disappearance. However, Barash (1973, 1976) and Kilgore and Armitage (1978) indicated that adult males and nonreproductive females enter hibernation 1–3 weeks before parous females, subadults, and juveniles.

In addition to variations in the sequence of immergence of cohorts among species, there are variations in the relative time of immergence of the various cohorts. In some species adults immerge sufficiently in advance of juveniles that there is a period of up to several months in each active season when only young of the year are aboveground (Clark, 1970, 1977; Dorrance, 1974; McCarley, 1966; Michener, 1974; Michener, 1977, 1979; Morton, 1975; Murie, 1973; Rickart, 1982; Skryja and Clark, 1970). In other species there is only a brief period in which juveniles are active in the absence of adults (Barash, 1973, 1976; Green, 1977; Kilgore and Armitage, 1978; McLean and Towns, 1981; Michener, 1977).

Perhaps the most extreme case of staggering of immergence among cohorts occurs in *S. richardsonii*. In populations of Richardson's ground squirrels studied in southern Saskatchewan (Michener, 1974), central Alberta (Dorrance, 1974), and the foothills of southern Alberta (Michener, 1979), adult males typically disappear in June to mid-July, adult females in late July and August, and juveniles in September and early October. Juvenile females entered hibernation earlier than juvenile males in all three populations. Asynchrony in immergence schedules means that adult males are active simultaneously with juveniles for only a few weeks and that juveniles spend most of their first summer of life unable to interact with adults of either sex.

To quantify the amount of coincidence of aboveground activity of cohorts in *S. richardsonii*, I recorded dates of litter emergence and dates of last sighting of

93

individuals in 1982 in a population under study since 1979 near Picture Butte, Alberta (49°52'N, 112°40'W, elevation 870 m). The range of emergence dates for 54 litters, determined by checking daily for the first appearance of young from known natal burrows, was 13 May–8 June. Immergence dates of adult males were estimated to ± 3 days by trapping and searching for males at weekly intervals; seven males were last seen 25 May–18 June. Four adult females that did not lactate were last sighted 31 May–9 June. The prehibernation population of parous females was considered to consist of the 53 mothers still resident after the last nonmother disappeared. Most mothers (44/53 = 83%) were last seen 18–30 June, and all had disappeared by the second week of July. Immergence of juveniles was monitored on a portion of the study area on which 31 litters (122 females, 121 males) had emerged in May. The sex ratio of the juvenile population remained at 1:1 in June and July, though the population declined to 52 squirrels (one immigrant and 25 locally born females, and 12 immigrant and 14 locally born males) by 21 July. By 4 August most juvenile females had disappeared, leaving a male-biased juvenile population aboveground (three females, 20 males). From 22 August to 22 September only juvenile males were active aboveground. The median date of litter emergence was 20 May, and the median dates of immergence for the four cohorts were estimated as 13 June (seven adult males), 27 June (53 mothers), 1 August (26 juvenile females), and 2 September (20 juvenile males). Based on these dates, 33% and 52% of the 73-day active season of juvenile females coincided with aboveground activity by adult males and by adult females, and 23% and 36% of the 105-day active period of juvenile males coincided with activity by adult males and by adult females. Juveniles therefore spent most of their first summer of life out of contact with adult conspecifics.

Adaptive Significance of Autumnal Immergence Sequences

Synchronous immergence of cohorts tends to characterize species that live at high elevations or northerly latitudes where the growing season is short and where the total active season for the species is less than 6 months; for example, *S. columbianus, M. caligata, M. flaviventris,* and *M. olympus*. Presumably forage and weather conditions have dictated that juveniles terminate their active season at about the same time as older cohorts. However, this leaves a season too short for juveniles both to attain adult size and to store sufficient fat for hibernation. Juveniles in these species require an additional one or two active seasons before achieving adult size.

Asynchronous immergence of cohorts is most pronounced in species living in habitats with growing seasons long enough to permit activity over a 7–8 month period; for example, *S. richardsonii*, *S. tereticaudus*, and *C. leucurus*. Because juveniles in such species continue aboveground activity and weight gain for many weeks after the disappearance of adults, inadequate food supplies or inclement weather cannot account for early adult immergence. Yeaton (1972) and Clark (1977) suggested that early entry into hibernation by adults is an adaptation to reduce intraspecific competition, particularly competition for food between adult males and juveniles. I reject this hypothesis on the grounds that the disappearance of males has only a negligible effect in providing additional food to juveniles (see also Michener, 1983*b*). In species with female-biased adult sex ratios there are relatively few males in the population compared with juveniles (Michener and Michener, 1977); as an extreme example, in the Richardson's ground squirrel population discussed above, seven adult males and 493 juveniles were resident in late May to early June of 1982. In species with a more nearly equal adult sex ratio, numbers of juveniles per male will tend to approximate the average litter size per female, that is, three to nine juveniles (Murie et al., 1980), and adult males will account for a significant fraction of the active population. In such species the disappearance of adult males could result in less competition for food, but this will increase food resources to young only if food is limited in quantity or accessibility. No studies have specifically measured the proportion of food energy available in summer that is consumed by adult males, but probably it is not significant because food is not considered a limiting resource in summer (e.g., Kilgore and Armitage, 1978). If termination of feeding by adult males does significantly increase food availability, either directly by reduced feeding pressure or indirectly by giving juveniles access to areas previously defended by males, early immergence by males should be an adaptive strategy only if the juveniles that profit are the male's own progeny. Thus the necessary correlates for early male immergence being an adaptation to reduce food competition appear to be a low ratio of juveniles to males and proximity of sires to their progeny. The species that best meet these conditions are the mountain-dwelling marmots, but immergence is relatively synchronous in these species.

The timing of immergence is presumably an adaptation for individual survival. Once animals have stored sufficient fat to have a reasonable chance of surviving hibernation, continued activity should occur only if the costs of remaining active are less than the costs of entering hibernation. Male *S. richardsonii* in the southern Alberta prairie population discussed earlier attain weights of 500–655 g in early June, a time when daily temperatures are approaching their maximum for the year. The risks of heat and water stress increase as the animals get fatter, and obese squirrels are not agile or readily able to enter small holes. Selection will favor early immergence if mortality resulting from environmental stress and predation is greater than that resulting from a lengthy period of dependence on deposits of body fat.

Late immergence by juveniles compared with adults can be attributed to the need for young both to grow and to fatten before their first hibernation. Sex differences in time of juvenile immergence occur in species that are reproductively mature as yearlings. Although juvenile males of *S. richardsonii* are heavier than same-aged juvenile females by midsummer (Dorrance, 1974; Michener, 1974), they store less fat, both absolutely and in proportion to body weight, than females (Dolman and Michener, 1983). Emergence weights of yearling males are not significantly lower than those of older males (Michener, 1984), suggesting that males virtually complete growth to adult size as juveniles. Prolonged activity and attainment of adult size in the first active season enable yearling males of *S. richardsonii* to compete successfully with older males during the breeding season (Michener, 1983a). Rickart (1982) likewise noted that juvenile male *S. townsendii mollis* remain active longer than females, attain higher weights but sequester fat at a slower rate, and are reproductively competent as yearlings.

Apparently, animals fatten and immerge as soon as possible. Energy that is required for reproduction and for growth cannot be diverted to fat deposition, so fattening is delayed if there are competing demands for energy. Consequently, immergence schedules reflect the chronological sequence in which individuals in different cohorts are able to commence fat deposition. Generally adult males begin to deposit fat shortly after the termination of the breeding season, whereas parous females usually do not commence fattening until about 40 days postpartum (Michener, 1978; Morton, 1975; Phillips, this volume). Adult females that fail to lactate typically fatten and immerge after adult males but before females that wean litters (Michener, 1978, unpubl. data). Subadults remain aboveground later than adults, and in the year preceding sexual maturity subadult males generally remain active later than do same-aged females. This sex difference apparently relates to the need for males to achieve greater size than females in preparation for the demands of intrasexual competition in the subsequent breeding season. For mountain-dwelling marmots, the short season available for growth and fattening results in relatively synchronous immergence of parous females, subadults, and juveniles and in postponement of sexual maturity until 2 or 3 years of age (Barash, 1973, 1976).

Arctic, Uinta, and Wyoming ground squirrels, species in which adult males enter hibernation after parous females (Fagerstone, 1982; Knopf and Balph, 1977; McLean and Towns, 1981; Zegers and Williams, 1977), are exceptions to

96

the general pattern that immergence sequences correspond with fattening sequences. McLean and Towns (1981) noted that adult male Arctic ground squirrels store food during late summer whereas adult females do not provision the hibernaculum with seed stores. By remaining active until early October, males amass food stores, postpone the commencement of dependence on fat reserves, shorten the period of hibernation, and consequently lose relatively little weight over winter. McLean and Towns (1981) proposed that food storage and delayed autumnal immergence by males relative to females, in both adult and juvenile cohorts, are adaptations to maximize male body mass in spring when males compete for access to estrous females. An additional advantage to males of delaying their immergence relative to that of females could be related to their assessing the locations of hibernacula used by females. Such information would permit males to focus their activity on areas where estrous females are likely to appear the following spring. Interspecific comparisons of the costs and benefits of early entry into hibernation versus a prolonged active season are required to ascertain why the time of immergence by males relative to females differs among species.

Implications for Sociality

The social organization of North American marmotines forms a continuum ranging from species in which individuals are asocial (e.g., Franklin's ground squirrel) to species in which individuals live in integrated, cohesive groups (e.g., Olympic marmot). I have identified five grades of sociality along this continuum (Michener, 1983*b*). The three primary features used to classify species were (1) the extent to which daughters are retained in or near the mother's range and hence the extent to which the ranges of mother and adult daughters and of adult sisters overlap; (2) the extent to which litters of such adjacent kin intermingle and hence the extent to which females from several generations and of varying degrees of kinship share ranges; and (3) the period over which adult males defend territories encompassing the ranges of adult females and hence the extent to which males associate with, and may protect, females and young (presumably their mates and offspring). Armitage (1981), who defined sociality in terms of the extent to which a group of individuals of differing sex and age share space, likewise identified five levels of sociality. Of 18 species that Armitage and I independently classified, 14 were assigned to the same social grade and the other four, although classified differently, were placed in adjacent categories.

Armitage (1981, Table 2) noted that the sociality index correlated significantly with age of sexual maturity ($r = 0.76$), age at dispersal ($r = 0.48$), and litter size ($r = -0.43$). These three factors were themselves intercorrelated and also were correlated with various body weight parameters. Armitage considered sociality to be a life history tactic that evolved in large-sized species living in habitats with growing seasons too short to permit maturity as yearlings. However, he found no correlation between sociality index and length of the active season. Species with the highest social indices (4 and 5 on Armitage's scale) include mountain-dwelling *Marmota* with total active seasons of 5 months or less and the black-tailed prairie dog, which does not hibernate; thus the lack of a statistical association between sociality and length of active season is not surprising. I suggest that an important factor to consider is not just the length of the active season but the extent to which the active seasons of various cohorts are synchronous (see Michener, 1983*b*, for further details).

Because recruitment of younger individuals, particularly females, into the social group is characteristic of species assigned high social indices, conditions promoting development of cohesive adult-young bonds may have been important in the evolution of sociality. Annual cycles characterized by lengthy periods in which young are not in contact with adults may limit the extent to which complex, integrative bonds develop among individuals of different ages. In contrast, annual cycles characterized by almost complete coincidence of the active seasons of adults and subadults permit constant reinforcement of social bonds. Such adult:subadult seasonal coincidence can be achieved in several ways, as is demonstrated by the two most social species, *M. olympus* and *C. ludovicianus*. Olympic marmots inhabit alpine meadows with short vegetative growing seasons, are obligate hibernators, and have a total annual active season of about 4.5 months (Barash, 1973), whereas black-tailed prairie dogs inhabit shortgrass prairie and are active all year (King, 1955). However, in both species young spend virtually all of their subadulthood simultaneously active with adults. Similarly, Columbian and Arctic ground squirrels live in divergent habitats with differing lengths of growing season, but both experience high adult:subadult seasonal coincidence and are relatively social (grade 3 in Michener, 1983*b*). *S. columbianus* live in mountain meadows, have an active season (in Alberta) of about 3.5 months, and mature sexually as 2-year-olds (Michener, 1977; Murie and Harris, 1982), whereas *S. parryii* live in subarctic meadows, have a total active season of about 6 months, and mature as yearlings (McLean and Towns, 1981). In both species, adult:subadult seasonal coincidence ranges from 70% to 95% depending on which sexes are considered.

Adult:subadult seasonal coincidence is typically greater than 70% among the seven species of ground-dwelling squirrels with social grades of 3–5, whereas seasonal coincidence is usually less than 70% among the 11 species classed as 1 or 2 (Michener, 1983*b*). The seven social species include three large ground

98

squirrels, two prairie dogs, and two marmots, whereas the 11 less social species include nine small and medium-sized ground squirrels, one prairie dog, and the woodchuck. I would modify Armitage's (1981) statement that social species are large and have short active seasons to say that social species are large and experience high synchrony in the timing of activity of cohorts. Extensive temporal overlap of aboveground activity between adult and nonadult cohorts may be the result of: (1) delayed immergence of adults, which prolongs their active season such that there is only a brief period during which no adults are active (e.g., Arctic ground squirrel); (2) delayed attainment of sexual maturity in habitats with short active seasons which prolongs subadulthood over several years (e.g., Olympic marmot), and (3) absence of obligate hibernation with consequent year-round activity (e.g., black-tailed prairie dog). Timing and sequencing of the annual cycle and, ultimately, environmental parameters that determined these patterns appear to be factors that influenced the evolution of sociality in ground-dwelling squirrels.

Temporal overlap of active seasons provides the opportunity for individuals from different cohorts to interact throughout most of their nonhibernating lives, but it does not imply that development of cohesive social bonds and sharing of space necessarily result. Many species of *Spermophilus* and *Ammospermophilus* that occur south of 30°N are active year-round, but there is little suggestion in the literature that these species are social. Rather than being the motive force for the evolution of sociality in ground-dwelling sciurids, seasonal coincidence may be an enabling mechanism that permits development of social tolerance and space sharing when the latter are of adaptive value. Thus the advantages of sociality need to be evaluated to determine why social groups evolved among northern species with extensive temporal overlap in activity among cohorts.

The extent to which temporal overlap of active seasons is critical for the development of integrated social groups depends on how and when social bonds are formed and on how frequently and in what ways such bonds need to be reinforced to maintain amicability among individuals. Ground squirrels demonstrate an ability to recognize familiar conspecifics after being separated over the hibernation period (Holmes and Sherman, 1982; Michener and Michener, 1973), so some social attachments can be retained for several months without reinforcement. Because little is known about the formation of social bonds in ground-dwelling sciurids, the relative importance of age of participants, intensity of interactions, and duration of exposure in development of social tolerance cannot yet be assessed. Such information is necessary to evaluate the extent to which temporal overlap of activity by mature and immature cohorts is accompanied by interactions essential for the formation of social groups.

99

To interpret more completely the role that synchrony of active seasons among cohorts may have played in promoting the evolution of sociality, more information is needed on the behavioral ecology of ground-dwelling sciurids. Accurate data on active seasons of natural populations are required to determine the extent of adult:subadult seasonal coincidence and to identify environmental pressures molding the duration of the active season of each cohort. Intraspecific variations in social systems require investigation to ascertain whether sociality and temporal coincidence of active seasons covary within a species. Additionally, the frequency and nature of social interactions require evaluation to understand the role that temporal and spatial overlap in opportunity to interact plays in development of social attachments and hence in the formation of social groups.

In summary, times of vernal emergence and autumnal immergence, and hence duration of the active season, vary among species and, within a species, vary with age and sex. Size of species and length of the active season have interactive effects determining the age of sexual maturity. Species in which subadults are active simultaneously with older cohorts typically are large, mature at 2 years or older (except *S. parryii*), and are classed as moderately to very social (grades 3 to 5 in Armitage, 1981, and Michener, 1983*b*). Species in which subadults remain active for at least several weeks after adults have hibernated are typically small (except *M. monax*), mature as yearlings (especially females), and are classed as asocial to slightly social (grades 1 and 2). Because species size, duration of the active season, temporal coincidence in activity of adults and nonadults, age at first reproduction, and degree of sociality are interrelated, an understanding of the evolution of sociality in ground-dwelling sciurids requires information on annual cycles of activity and on seasonal variation in the nature and frequency of social interactions.

Acknowledgments

I thank the following for generously providing me with unpublished information on annual cycles: D. Balph, M. Bronson, C. Dunford, J. Green, and W. Holmes. P. Larkin-Lieffers assisted with various aspects of manuscript preparation. This article was prepared while I held an NSERC of Canada University Research Fellowship at the University of Lethbridge.

Literature Cited

Alcorn, J. R. 1940. Life history notes on the Piute ground squirrel. J. Mamm., 21: 160–170.

Allen, E. G. 1938. The habits and life history of the eastern chipmunk, *Tamias striatus lysteri*. New York State Mus. Bull., 314:1–122.

Amend, L. R. 1970. On the population ecology of Uinta ground squirrels. Unpubl. M.S. thesis, Utah State Univ., Logan, 60 pp.

Andersen, D. C., K. B. Armitage, and R. S. Hoffmann. 1976. Socioecology of marmots: female reproductive strategies. Ecology, 57:552–560.

Armitage, K. B. 1962. Social behaviour of a colony of the yellow-bellied marmot (*Marmota flaviventris*). Anim. Behav., 10:319–331.

———. 1974. Male behaviour and territoriality in the yellow-bellied marmot. J. Zool. London, 172:233–265.

———. 1981. Sociality as a life-history tactic of ground squirrels. Oecologia, 48:36–49.

Armitage, K. B., and J. F. Downhower. 1974. Demography of yellow-bellied marmot populations. Ecology, 55:1233–1245.

Armitage, K. B., J. F. Downhower, and G. E. Svendsen. 1976. Seasonal changes in weights of marmots. Amer. Midland Nat., 96:36–51.

Bakko, E. B., and L. N. Brown. 1967. Breeding biology of the white-tailed prairie dog, *Cynomys leucurus*, in Wyoming. J. Mamm., 48:100–112.

Balph, D. F., and A. W. Stokes. 1963. On the ethology of a population of Uinta ground squirrels. Amer. Midland Nat., 69:106–126.

Barash, D. P. 1973. The social biology of the Olympic marmot. Anim. Behav. Monogr., 6:173–245.

———. 1974. The social behaviour of the hoary marmot (*Marmota caligata*). Anim. Behav., 22:256–261.

———. 1976. Pre-hibernation behavior of free-living hoary marmots, *Marmota caligata*. J. Mamm., 57:182–185.

Beer, J. R. 1962. Emergence of thirteen-lined ground squirrels from hibernation. J. Mamm., 43:109.

Betts, B. J. 1973. The adaptiveness of the social organization of a population of Columbian ground squirrels (*Spermophilus columbianus*). Unpubl. Ph.D. dissert., Univ. Montana, Missoula, 235 pp.

Bronson, M. T. 1980. Altitudinal variation in emergence time of golden-mantled ground squirrels (*Spermophilus lateralis*). J. Mamm., 61:124–126.

Christian, J. J., E. Steinberger, and T. D. McKinney. 1972. Annual cycle of spermatogenesis and testis morphology in woodchucks. J. Mamm., 53:708–716.

Clark, T. W. 1970. Richardson's ground squirrel (*Spermophilus richardsonii*) in the Laramie Basin, Wyoming. Great Basin Nat., 30:55–70.

———. 1971. Notes on the biology of the thirteen-lined ground squirrel in the Laramie Plains, Wyoming. Southwestern Nat., 15:495–505.

———. 1977. Ecology and ethology of the white-tailed prairie dog (*Cynomys leucurus*). Publ. Biol. Geol. Milwaukee Public Mus., 3:1–97.

Criddle, S. 1943. The little northern chipmunk in southern Manitoba. Canadian Field-Nat., 57:81–86.

Davis, D. E. 1967. The role of environmental factors in hibernation of woodchucks (*Marmota monax*). Ecology, 48:683–689.

———. 1976. Hibernation and circannual rhythms of food consumption in marmots and ground squirrels. Quart. Rev. Biol., 51:477–514.

———. 1977. Role of ambient temperature in emergence of woodchucks (*Marmota monax*) from hibernation. Amer. Midland Nat., 97:224–229.

Davis, L. S. 1982. Sociality in Richardson's ground squirrels *Spermophilus richardsonii*. Unpubl. Ph.D. dissert., Univ. Alberta, Edmonton, 152 pp.

de Vos, A., and D. Gillespie. 1960. A study of woodchucks on an Ontario farm. Canadian Field-Nat., 74:130–145.

Dolman, T. M., and G. R. Michener. 1983. Brown and white adipose tissue in relation to age and sex in juvenile Richardson's ground squirrels. Canadian J. Zool., 2789–2797.

Dorrance, M. J. 1974. The annual cycle and population dynamics of Richardson's ground squirrels. Unpubl. Ph.D. dissert., Univ. Wisconsin, Madison, 150 pp.

Downhower, J. F., and K. B. Armitage. 1971. The yellow-bellied marmot and the evolution of polygamy. Amer. Nat., 105:355–370.

Drescher, J. W. 1967. Environmental influences on initiation and maintenance of hibernation in the Arctic ground squirrel, *Citellus undulatus*. Ecology, 48:962–966.

Dunford, C. 1977. Behavioral limitation of round-tailed ground squirrel density. Ecology, 58:1254–1268.

Edge, E. R. 1931. Seasonal activity and growth in the Douglas ground squirrel. J. Mamm., 12:194–200.

Ellis, L. C., R. A. Palmer, and D. F. Balph. 1983. The reproductive cycle of male Uinta ground squirrels: some anatomical and biochemical correlates. Comp. Biochem. Physiol., 74A:239–245.

Emelianov, P. F., I. K. Vagner, A. M. Karmov, E. K. Titov, V. V. Ivanovsky, and N. N. Vasiliev. 1982. Biology of *Citellus musicus* (Rodentia, Sciuridae) in the central Caucasus. Zool. Zhur., 61:419–427.

Fagerstone, K. A. 1982. Ethology and taxonomy of Richardson's ground squirrels (*Spermophilus richardsonii*). Unpubl. Ph.D. dissert., Univ. Colorado, Boulder, 298 pp.

Fei, R. Z., C. Y. Li, C. K. Shang, and C. J. Yang. 1975. An ecological study of Daurian ground squirrels (*Citellus dauricus*). Acta Zool. Sin., 21:18–29.

Foster, M. A. 1934. The reproductive cycle in the female ground squirrel, *C. tridecemlineatus*. Amer. J. Anat., 54:487–511.

French, A. R. 1982. Intraspecific differences in the pattern of hibernation in the ground squirrel *Spermophilus beldingi*. J. Comp. Physiol., 148B:83–91.

Green, J. E. 1977. Population regulation and annual cycles of activity and dispersal in the Arctic ground squirrel. Unpubl. M.S. thesis, Univ. British Columbia, Vancouver, 193 pp.

Heller, H. C., and T. L. Poulson. 1970. Circannian rhythms. II. Endogenous and exogenous factors controlling reproduction and hibernation in chipmunks (*Eutamias*) and ground squirrels (*Spermophilus*). Comp. Biochem. Physiol., 33:357–383.

Hock, R. J. 1960. Seasonal variations in physiologic functions of Arctic ground squirrels and black bears. Bull. Mus. Comp. Zool., 124:155–171.

Hock, R. J., and V. Cottini. 1966. Mammals of the Little Susitna Valley, Alaska. Amer. Midland Nat., 76:325–339.

Holmes, W. G., and P. W. Sherman. 1982. The ontogeny of kin recognition in two species of ground squirrels. Amer. Zool., 22:491–517.

Iverson, S. L., and B. N. Turner. 1972. Natural history of a Manitoba population of Franklin's ground squirrel. Canadian Field-Nat., 86:145–149.

Jameson, E. W. 1964. Patterns of hibernation in captive *Citellus lateralis* and *Eutamias speciosus*. J. Mamm., 45:455–460.

Johns, D. W., and K. B. Armitage. 1979. Behavioral ecology of the alpine yellow-bellied marmot. Behav. Ecol. Sociobiol., 5:133–137.

Johnson, G. E., M. A. Foster, and R. M. Coco. 1933. The sexual cycle of the thirteen-lined ground squirrel in the laboratory. Kansas Acad. Sci., 36:250–269.

Juelson, T. C. 1970. A study of the ecology and ethology of the rock squirrel, *Spermophilus variegatus* (Erxleben) in northern Utah. Unpubl. Ph.D. dissert., Univ. Utah, Salt Lake City, 192 pp.

Kawamichi, M. 1983. Solitary society with age-dependent dominance rank in Siberian chipmunks. Proc. 18th Internat. Ethol. Conf., p. 15b (abstr.).

Kilgore, D. L., Jr., and K. B. Armitage. 1978. Energetics of yellow-bellied marmot populations. Ecology, 59:78–88.

King, J. A. 1955. Social behavior, social organization, and population dynamics in a black-tailed prairiedog town in the Black Hills of South Dakota. Contrib. Lab. Vert. Biol., Univ. Michigan, 67:1–123.

Kivett, V. K. 1975. Variations in integumentary gland activity and scent marking in Columbian ground squirrels (*Spermophilus c. columbianus*). Unpubl. Ph.D. dissert., Univ. Alberta, Edmonton, 137 pp.

Knopf, F. L., and D. F. Balph. 1977. Annual periodicity of Uinta ground squirrels. Southwestern Nat., 22:213–224.

Liddle, R. E. 1982. Effects of food and homeothermy on the reproductive development of male *Spermophilus beldingi*. Ann. Mtg. Amer. Soc. Mammal., Abstr. no. 133.

Linsdale, J. M. 1946. The California ground squirrel. Univ. California Press, Berkeley, 475 pp.

Loehr, K. A., and A. C. Risser. 1977. Daily and seasonal activity patterns of the Belding ground squirrel in the Sierra Nevada. J. Mamm., 58:445–448.

Manville, R. H. 1959. The Columbian ground squirrel in northwestern Montana. J. Mamm., 40:26–45.

McCarley, H. 1966. Annual cycle, population dynamics and adaptive behavior of *Citellus tridecemlineatus*. J. Mamm., 47:294–316.

McKeever, S. 1964. The biology of the golden-mantled ground squirrel, *Citellus lateralis*. Ecol. Monogr., 34:383–401.

McLean, I. G., and A. J. Towns. 1981. Differences in weight changes and the annual cycle of male and female Arctic ground squirrels. Arctic, 34:249–254.

Michener, D. R. 1974. Annual cycle of activity and weight changes in Richardson's ground squirrel, *Spermophilus richardsonii*. Canadian Field-Nat., 88:409–413.

Michener, G. R. 1977. Effect of climatic conditions on the annual activity and hibernation cycle of Richardson's ground squirrels and Columbian ground squirrels. Canadian J. Zool., 55:693–703.

———. 1978. Effect of age and parity on weight gain and entry into hibernation in Richardson's ground squirrel. Canadian J. Zool., 56:2573–2577.

———. 1979. The circannual cycle of Richardson's ground squirrels in southern Alberta. J. Mamm., 60:760–768.

———. 1980. Estrous and gestation periods in Richardson's ground squirrels. J. Mamm., 61:531–534.

———. 1983*a*. Spring emergence schedules and vernal behavior of Richardson's ground squirrels: why do males emerge from hibernation before females? Behav. Ecol. Sociobiol., 14:29–38.

———. 1983*b*. Kin identification, matriarchies, and the evolution of sociality in ground-dwelling sciurids. Pp. 528–572, *in* Recent advances in the study of mammalian behavior (J. F. Eisenberg and D. G. Kleiman, eds.). Spec. Publ., Amer. Soc. Mamm., 7:1–753.

———. 1984. Sexual differences in body weight patterns of Richardson's ground squirrels during the breeding season. J. Mamm., 65:59–66.

Michener, G. R., and D. R. Michener. 1973. Spatial distribution of yearlings in a Richardson's ground squirrel population. Ecology, 54:1138–1142.

———. 1977. Population structure and dispersal in Richardson's ground squirrels. Ecology, 58:359–368.

Mitchell, O. G. 1959. The reproductive cycle of the male Arctic ground squirrel. J. Mamm., 40:45–53.

Moore, C. R., G. F. Simmons, L. J. Wells, M. Zalesky, and W. O. Nelson. 1934. On the control of reproductive activity in an annual-breeding mammal (*Citellus tridecemlineatus*). Anat. Rec., 60:279–289.

Morton, M. L. 1975. Seasonal cycles of body weights and lipids in Belding ground squirrels. Bull. Southern California Acad. Sci., 74:128–142.

Morton, M. L., and J. L. Gallup. 1975. Reproductive cycle of the Belding ground squirrel (*Spermophilus beldingi beldingi*): seasonal and age differences. Great Basin Nat., 35:427–433.

Morton, M. L., and P. W. Sherman. 1978. Effects of a spring snowstorm on behavior, reproduction, and survival of Belding's ground squirrels. Canadian J. Zool., 56: 2578–2590.

Murie, J. O. 1973. Population characteristics and phenology of a Franklin ground squirrel (*Spermophilus franklinii*) colony in Alberta, Canada. Amer. Midland Nat., 90: 334–340.

Murie, J. O., and M. A. Harris. 1978. Territoriality and dominance in male Columbian ground squirrels (*Spermophilus columbianus*). Canadian J. Zool., 56:2402–2412.

———. 1982. Annual variation of spring emergence and breeding in Columbian ground squirrels (*Spermophilus columbianus*). J. Mamm., 63:431–439.

Murie, J. O., D. A. Boag, and V. K. Kivett. 1980. Litter size in Columbian ground squirrels (*Spermophilus columbianus*). J. Mamm., 61:237–244.

Neal, B. J. 1965*a*. Reproductive habits of round-tailed and Harris antelope ground squirrels. J. Mamm., 46:200–206.

———. 1965*b*. Seasonal changes in body weights, fat depositions, adrenal glands and temperatures of *Citellus tereticaudus* and *Citellus harrissii* (Rodentia). Southwestern Nat., 10:156–166.

Nellis, C. D. 1969. Productivity of Richardson's ground squirrels near Rochester, Alberta. Canadian Field-Nat., 83:246–250.

Paul, R. T. 1977. Social behavior and social organization in an unconfined population of Uinta ground squirrels. Unpubl. M.S. thesis, Utah State Univ., Logan, 74 pp.

Pengelley, E. T., and K. C. Fisher. 1961. Rhythmical arousal from hibernation in the golden-mantled ground squirrel, *Citellus lateralis tescorum*. Canadian J. Zool., 39:105–120.

Quanstrom, W. R. 1968. Some aspects of the ethoecology of Richardson's ground squirrel in eastern North Dakota. Unpubl. Ph.D. dissert, Univ. Oklahoma, Norman, 121 pp.

Rausch, R. L., and V. R. Rausch. 1971. The somatic chromosomes of some North American marmots (Sciuridae), with remarks on the relationships of *Marmota broweri* Hall and Gibson. Mammalia, 35:85–101.

Rickart, E. A. 1982. Annual cycles of activity and body composition in *Spermophilus townsendii mollis*. Canadian J. Zool., 60:3298–3306.

Schooley, J. P. 1934. A summer breeding season in the eastern chipmunk, *Tamias striatus*. J. Mamm., 15:194–196.

Schwagmeyer, P. L., and C. H. Brown. 1983. Factors affecting male-male competition in thirteen-lined ground squirrels. Behav. Ecol. Sociobiol. 13:1–6.

Shaw, W. T. 1925*a*. The seasonal differences of north and south slopes in controlling the activities of the Columbian ground squirrel. Ecology, 6:157–163.

———. 1925*b*. Duration of the aestivation and hibernation of the Columbian ground squirrel (*Citellus columbianus*) and sex relation to same. Ecology, 6:75–81.

Sheppard, D. H. 1969. A comparison of reproduction in two chipmunk species (*Eutamias*). Canadian J. Zool., 47:603–608.

Sherman, P. W. 1976. Natural selection among some group-living organisms. Unpubl. Ph.D. dissert., Univ. Michigan, Ann Arbor, 254 pp.

Skryja, D. D., and T. W. Clark. 1970. Reproduction, seasonal changes in body weight, fat deposition, spleen and adrenal gland weight of the golden-mantled ground squirrel, *Spermophilus lateralis lateralis* (Sciuridae) in the Laramie Mountains, Wyoming. Southwestern Nat., 15:201–208.

Smith, G. W., and D. R. Johnson. In press. Demography of a Townsend ground squirrel population in southwestern Idaho. Ecology.

Smith, L. C., and D. A. Smith. 1972. Reproductive biology, breeding seasons, and growth of eastern chipmunks, *Tamias striatus* (Rodentia: Sciuridae) in Canada. Canadian J. Zool., 50:1069–1085.

Smith, W. P. 1931. Calendar of disappearance and emergence of some hibernating mammals at Wells River, Vermont. J. Mamm., 12:78–79.

Snyder, R. L., and J. J. Christian. 1960. Reproductive cycle and litter size of the woodchuck. Ecology, 41:785–790.

Snyder, R. L., D. E. Davis, and J. J. Christian. 1961. Seasonal changes in the weights of woodchucks. J. Mamm., 42:297–312.

Sowls, L. K. 1948. The Franklin ground squirrel, *Citellus franklinii* (Sabine), and its relationship to nesting ducks. J. Mamm., 29:113–137.

Stockard, A. H. 1929. Observations of reproduction in the white-tailed prairie dog (*Cynomys leucurus*). J. Mamm., 10:209–212.

Storer, T. I., F. C. Evans, and R. G. Palmer. 1944. Some rodent populations in the Sierra Nevada of California. Ecol. Monogr., 14:165–192.

Streubel, D. P. 1975. Behavioral features of sympatry of *Spermophilus spilosoma* and *Spermophilus tridecemlineatus* and some aspects of the life history of *S. spilosoma*. Unpubl. D.A. dissert., Univ. Northern Colorado, Greeley, 130 pp.

Stroud, D. C. 1983. Seasonal activity, demography, dispersal, and a population simulation model of the California ground squirrel, *Spermophilus beecheyi*. Unpubl. Ph.D. dissert., Univ. California, Davis, 149 pp.

Tileston, J. V., and R. R. Lechleitner. 1966. Some comparisons of the black-tailed and white-tailed prairie dogs in north-central Colorado. Amer. Midland Nat., 75:292–316.

Wade, O. 1927. Breeding habits and early life of the thirteen-striped ground squirrel, *Citellus tridecemlineatus* (Mitchill). J. Mamm., 8:269–276.

———. 1950. Soil temperatures, weather conditions, and emergence of ground squirrels from hibernation. J. Mamm., 31:158–161.

Wang, L. C. H. 1973. Radiotelemetric study of hibernation under natural and laboratory conditions. Amer. J. Physiol., 224:673–677.

———. 1979. Time patterns and metabolic rates of natural torpor in the Richardson's ground squirrel. Canadian J. Zool., 57:149–155.

Wells, L. J. 1935. Seasonal and sexual rhythm and its experimental modification in the male of the thirteen-lined ground squirrel (*Citellus tridecemlineatus*). Anat. Rec., 62:409–447.

Wistrand, H. 1974. Individual, social, and seasonal behavior of the thirteen-lined ground squirrel (*Spermophilus tridecemlineatus*). J. Mamm., 55:329–347.

Yahner, R. H., and G. E. Svendsen. 1978. Effects of climate on the circannual rhythm of the eastern chipmunk, *Tamias striatus*. J. Mamm., 59:109–117.

Yeaton, R. I. 1972. Social behavior and social organization in Richardson's ground squirrel (*Spermophilus richardsonii*) in Saskatchewan. J. Mamm., 53:139–147.

Zegers, D. A., and O. Williams. 1977. Seasonal cycles of body weight and lipids in Richardson's ground squirrel, *Spermophilus richardsonii elegans*. Acta Theriol., 22:380–383.

JOHN A. PHILLIPS

San Diego Zoo

Chapter 5

Environmental Influences on
Reproduction in the
Golden-mantled Ground Squirrel

Abstract. The annual cycles of two populations of golden-mantled ground squirrels (*Spermophilus lateralis*) in the Sierra Nevada, California, were studied both
in the field and under laboratory conditions from 1976 to 1979. Even though both
field sites (Bodie and Castle Peak) were at a similar latitude (38°N and 39°N) and
the same altitude (2,650 m), the length of the aboveground active season was
25% to 40% shorter at Castle Peak than at Bodie. Emergence of adult squirrels at
both field sites was negatively correlated with the amount of snow cover. Squirrels from Castle Peak, the area with the greater variation in length of snow cover,
showed greater variation in dates of emergence (up to 20 days within a year; up to
59 days between years). During years with active seasons of average length, all
squirrels (males, nonpregnant and pregnant females) had no difficulty in attaining their prehibernation body mass (70 to 100 days at plateau body mass).
However, following a severe winter, males and nonpregnant females from the
temporally compressed environment at Castle Peak attained their plateau body
mass just before (10 to 25 days) hibernation. During that year the pregnancy rate
at that field site was extremely low (19% versus 70% average). Pregnancy delayed the onset of the prehibernation weight gain period by approximately 60
days. Growth and development of offspring were inversely related to litter size.
Because offspring have a short time to become independent and attain their prehibernation body mass, a lower fecundity in females from the temporally compressed environment appeared to allow these juveniles to develop faster.

The relation between the environment (especially, latitude, altitude, and microhabitat) and reproduction in the ground-dwelling sciurids of North America is
discussed.

Introduction

North American species of the genus *Spermophilus* are conspicuous residents of a variety of environments, ranging from desert to alpine habitats. Species or populations occupying areas with moderate climates experience long snow-free seasons compared with animals that inhabit more extreme environments, usually at higher latitudes or altitudes. During the months when snow denies access to vegetation or the quality of vegetation is poor, the majority of ground squirrel species help ensure survival through obligate seasonal hibernation. Hibernation is a mechanism that provides an alternative to the high cost of winter endothermy, yet overwintering success depends upon adjustments in metabolism and variations in reproductive expenditure that occurred during the previous season of activity and affected the extent of fat deposition. Because energetic and reproductive costs appear to be influenced by prevailing environmental conditions, the magnitude of physiological constraints on the ability to reproduce successfully are unique to each population (Blake, 1972; Bronson, 1980; Phillips, 1981). The components of the environment that influence the physiological adjustments in reproductive output may be either the extreme conditions per se or the amount of uncertainty (unpredictability) of those conditions (Levins, 1969).

An annual rhythm of hibernation, reproduction, and prehibernation weight gain has been documented for many of the ground-dwelling sciurids of North America. In many species the total cycle is controlled by an endogenous rhythm that persists in the laboratory in the absence of natural environmental cues (Davis, 1976; Kenagy, 1980; Mrosovsky, 1980; Pengelley and Fisher, 1963). Under naturally fluctuating conditions this internal rhythm appears to be temporally flexible and can be molded by the particulars of the local environment. Kenagy (1980) suggested two possible mechanisms that could account for variation in timing of the annual cycle among populations: (1) distinct genetic programs for annual rhythms may have evolved to match the physical constraints of local environments; or (2) selection pressures may have molded a general and highly plastic temporal program for annual rhythms that can be modified to the local environment during any particular year.

Many physiological processes, including reproduction, have approximately fixed durations in mammals. In obligate hibernators the timing of the reproductive sequence (mating, pregnancy, lactation, dispersal of young) is dependent upon the timing of emergence from hibernation (Kalabukhov, 1960). Hibernators, like all other species, must maximize their reproductive output while remaining within the physical and temporal limits imposed by both environmental and physiological constraints. Theoretically, reproductive effort should be increased to the point at which any further increase will reduce total fitness (Fisher, 1930; MacArthur and Pianka, 1966). Reproductive output in mammals can be increased in at least four ways: by breeding several times per season; by breeding over many seasons; by increasing litter size; or by increasing survival of offspring through parental care without increasing litter size. The possibility of breeding more often within each year probably plays a distant secondary role in shaping reproductive output in the hibernating ground squirrels because the temporal constraints imposed by middle to high elevations north of 30°N are severe enough that more than one reproductive event per year would be physiologically impossible. The exception to this observation is the thirteen-lined ground squirrel, *Spermophilus tridecemlineatus,* in which females may produce two litters per year in the southernmost portion of its range, Texas (McCarley, 1966). Increasing litter size does not increase reproductive output unless more young survive to reproduce, and similarly, reproductive output does not increase if an individual sacrifices future reproductive ability by increasing parental care of current offspring. Therefore one would expect that litter size and the amount of parental care exhibited should reflect the environmental conditions experienced by distinct populations. The final result should be to maximize reproductive output over the lifetime of the individual.

If we define fitness as the survival value and reproductive capacity of any given phenotype relative to all others in a population, then we can ask several questions about maximization of reproductive effort of animals in general, in this case the hibernating ground squirrels. First, How can female ground squirrels maximize their reproductive capacities within their environmental and physiological constraints? Second, Do the mechanisms for increasing reproductive capacity vary from one locale to another or vary from year to year within a local environment? Third, Are there mechanisms for maximizing reproduction that can be identified over the lifetime of the individual as well as annually?

This paper will attempt to answer these questions by examining two populations of golden-mantled ground squirrels (*Spermophilus lateralis*) with different lengths of active season. Particular attention will be given to the relation between temporal constraints (latitude, altitude, climate, and microhabitats) and the reproductive physiology of the two populations.

Study Areas, Populations, and Methods

The two field study sites (approximately 10 ha each) were on opposite sides of the Sierra Nevada at Castle Peak (Nevada County; 120°20'W, 39°20'N) and Bodie

(Mono County; 119°W, 38°10'N), California. The study populations at both sites were at an elevation between 2,550 and 2,750 m. The Castle Peak site was dominated by red fir/pine forest with open areas of grasses, whereas the Bodie site was a typical sagebrush community.

Climatological data were obtained from weather stations within 5 km of each study site (Central Sierra Snow Laboratory and Bodie State Historical Park) and by personal observation during the annual spring thaw. Soil temperatures, at the surface and at a depth of 50 cm, were measured (telethermometer, Yellow Springs Instruments) at 1200 h Pacific Standard Time in shaded areas at about monthly intervals at Castle Peak from June 1977 through May 1979. Access to Bodie was restricted during the winter months, and soil temperatures were not determined.

The populations were sampled by livetrapping from April 1976 to May 1979, with intensive sampling before and during the active season. Individual animals were sexed, weighed to the nearest 1.0 g, marked with numbered ear tags, and released at the site of capture. During subsequent sampling periods, the body mass and location of capture of each squirrel were noted, and previously uncaptured animals were eartagged.

A 300 m line transect (north-south) was established within the study area at Bodie in September 1976 and at Castle Peak in May 1977. Approximate dates (within 7 days at Bodie and 5 days at Castle Peak) of emergence and parturition were determined in spring 1977 for previously marked squirrels trapped within 25 m perpendicular to the transect (15,000 m^2). Previous trapping records indicated that up to 20 adult ($\geq$ 2 years) females could be expected within the trap grids. Areas of similar quality adjacent to the study populations were trapped intensively each spring, and squirrels from these areas were transferred to the laboratory. Males and nongravid females were individually housed in 25 by 15 by 30 cm wire-mesh cages, and pregnant females were housed individually in 25 by 90 by 90 cm enclosures. Each squirrel was provided with a nest box and bedding materials. Sunflower seeds, laboratory chow (Purina), and apples were available ad lib. The animal room temperature was 25 $\pm$ 2°C, and the photoperiod was simulated natural (38°N) and included ultraviolet light (Sylvania GL-40W). The room was maintained to the standards of the American Association for the Accreditation of Laboratory Animal Care. Disturbances were kept to a minimum throughout each year's experiments, and rooms were entered only during the photophase.

Males and nongravid females were weighed to the nearest 1.0 g at 5-day intervals until 50 days from the estimated date of emergence. Pregnant females were weighed at 5-day intervals until 50 days postpartum. All adult squirrels were

TABLE 5.1. Summary statistics for snow cover, emergence dates, and emergent body mass of adult (≥ 2 years) *Spermophilus lateralis* at Castle Peak and Bodie, California. Data are mean ± SD (N). Sample size for mean emergence dates is the sum of the sample size given with the male and female weight data.

	Castle Peak			Bodie		
	1975–1976	1976–1977	1977–1978	1975–1976	1976–1977	1977–1978
Days of snow cover[a]	140	170	209	112	104	159
Emergence date[b]	3 May ± 10	18 May ± 18	1 July ± 13	13 April ± 9	6 April ± 8	10 May ± 10
Body mass (g) ♂♂	144 ± 10 (9)	135 ± 6 (15)	122 ± 7 (20)	131 ± 4 (17)	145 ± 8 (20)	136 ± 3 (22)
Body mass (g) ♀♀	129 ± 5 (10)	138 ± 8 (18)	130 ± 6 (8)	140 ± 7 (13)	130 ± 7 (20)	128 ± 9 (15)

[a] Measured as last date of 100% snow cover minus date of first snowfall.
[b] Castle Peak was sampled at 5-day intervals, Bodie at 7-day intervals.

weighed at about 60, 70, 90, and 120 days after their estimated date of emergence (males and nongravid females) or parturition (pregnant females). The date of mating was estimated by backdating 27–28 days (Cameron, 1967; McKeever, 1965) from the known time of parturition.

On 1 September of each year the squirrels were transferred to walk-in environmental chambers (36 m^3). Each squirrel was housed in a 25 by 15 by 30 cm cage. Food types and availability, nesting materials, and lighting conditions were as before; however, the temperature of the chamber was gradually lowered from 25° ± 1°C to 7.5° ± 1°C from 1 September to 1 October of each year. The occurrence of arousal was determined by daily observation (see Pengelley and Fisher, 1961) and electronic monitoring (see Twente et al., 1977). Squirrels in an aroused state were weighed to the nearest 1.0 g.

All squirrels were returned to the field after one season in captivity; although many were trapped again at later dates, they were not used for further study. Methods and data for growth of litters can be found in Phillips (1981). Data for weight gain by individual squirrels were fitted to Gompertz curves (Ricklefs, 1967) for statistical analysis. Analysis of growth rates within populations was by analysis of variance. All two sample analyses between means were by the Student's *t*-test.

Results

Timing of emergence. Although both study sites were at the same elevation, the annual period of snow cover was up to 40% longer at Castle Peak than at Bodie, which is in the rain shadow of the Sierra Nevada (see Phillips, 1981, Fig. 1). Whereas 1975–1976 and 1976–1977 were drought years, when the Sierra Nevada received only a moderate snowfall, the winter of 1977–1978 was severe. Thus extremes in length of snow cover are represented in this study.

The mean date of emergence of adults from hibernation was related to the severity of the preceding winter (Table 5.1). There was a negative correlation (*r* = −0.79, Castle Peak; *r* = −0.63, Bodie) between the percentage of snow cover and the number of squirrels that had emerged in each area. Snowmelt at Bodie was relatively homogeneous owing to the level terrain, and squirrels in adjacent hibernacula emerged within 7 days of each other in 1977. At Castle Peak the rate of spring snowmelt was more heterogeneous, depending upon the slope's aspect and/or the density of trees in any particular area. As a result, neighboring squirrels at Castle Peak had emergence dates that differed by as much as 20 days in 1977. Since the winter of 1976–1977 was mild and the snowmelt was relatively uniform among microhabitats, the variation in emergence dates of squirrels at

113

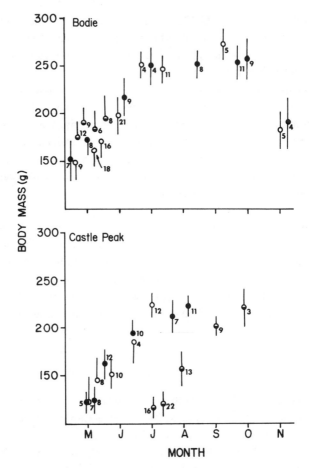

FIGURE 5.1. Body mass of adult male and nonpregnant female *Spermophilus lateralis* at Bodie and Castle Peak, California. ● 1976; ○ 1977; ◑ 1978; vertical lines are ± 2 SE; numerals are sample size.

Castle Peak probably represented a minimum. During the overwintering months (November through April) of 1977–1978, the soil temperature at Castle Peak 50 cm below the surface fluctuated between 3° and 6°C, whereas midday air temperature ranged from −22° to 7°C. When total snowmelt occurred in May 1977, the soil temperature increased about 6°C over a 10-day period. Emergence appeared to be cued by this rapid increase in soil temperature.

The body mass cycle in the field. There were no significant differences in the body mass (133 ± 7g) of recently emerged females in the study populations either between years or between study sites. The emergent body mass of males was not different between or within populations during 1976 and 1977; however, after the severe winter of 1978, Castle Peak males were significantly ($P < 0.05$) leaner than Bodie males (122 ± 7 g, n = 20; 136 ± 3 g, n = 22). Although field data for body mass after emergence were intermittent, Gompertz transformation of the growth curves revealed no significant differences in the shapes of the curves between sexes, populations, or years (Fig. 5.1).

The laboratory body mass cycle. Data for the laboratory body mass cycle were based on 38 pregnant females, 32 nonpregnant females, and 24 males. The increase in body mass of males and nongravid females did not vary between years or populations (Fig. 5.2); emergent body mass doubled at about 75 days from capture. The calendar date at which the animals first attained their plateau body mass was a function of the severity of the preceding winter (Table 5.2). A comparison of the timing of the increase in body mass following the moderate winter of 1976–1977 with that following the severe winter of 1977–1978 provides the best example. In 1977, females at Castle Peak emerged about 28 May, and those females that did not become pregnant that spring reached their plateau body mass by late July. Thereafter, the body mass of individual squirrels was basically unchanged until immergence into hibernation (a period of about 90 days). In late

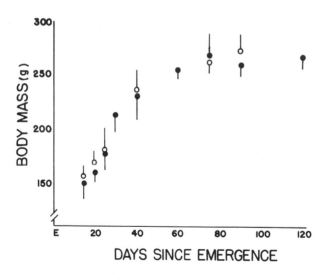

FIGURE 5.2. Body mass of captive adult nonpregnant female (●) and male (○) *Spermophilus lateralis*. The data are a composite of captive animals from Bodie and Castle Peak from 1976 to 1978. The sample sizes are 18 females and 24 males. Vertical lines are ± 2 SE.

TABLE 5.2. Dates of plateau body mass of captive nonpregnant female and male *Spermophilus lateralis* from Castle Peak and Bodie, California. Data are mean (SD).

			Sample size	First date at plateau weight	Days at plateau weight[a]
Bodie					
	1976	♀	—	—	—
		♂	4	22 June (11)	91 (12)
	1977	♀	4	28 June (13)	103 (10)
		♂	4	19 June (14)	88 (17)
	1978	♀	5	8 July (7)	82 (7)
		♂	4	30 June (10)	80 (9)
Castle Peak					
	1976	♀	3	3 August (11)	81 (8)
		♂	4	22 July (6)	71 (9)
	1977	♀	2	26 July (6)	90 (5)
		♂	4	28 July (15)	80 (12)
	1978	♀	4	3 September (4)	17 (12)
		♂	4	22 August (10)	23 (9)

[a] Date of first heterothermic bout minus initial date at plateau weight.

May of 1978 a minimum of 125 cm of snow covered the Castle Peak study site, and females did not emerge until after 22 June. Nonpregnant females in the laboratory did not attain their plateau mass until early September.

The general effect of producing a litter was to delay the onset of the increase in body mass. Females increased their body mass by approximately 15% between emergence and mating (Fig. 5.3). The average body mass at the time of mating was 152 ± 5 g (n = 6; all 1977; 3 Bodie, 3 Castle Peak). The average body mass at parturition was 208 ± 12 g (n = 32). Females lost approximately 10% of their body mass during the first 25 days of lactation and in most cases did not begin to regain this weight until 35 days postpartum. Females gained weight rapidly after weaning litters and attained their plateau body mass 55 ± 6 days postlactation.

Effect of the environment on reproduction. After the mild winters of 1975–1976 and 1976–1977 about 70% of adult (≥ 2 years) females at both study sites were pregnant (Table 5.3). However, after the severe winter of 1977–1978 only 19% of the females at Castle Peak were pregnant or had delivered by 15 August (about 6 weeks after emergence), whereas 83% of the females at Bodie were pregnant (Table 5.3). Thus the late thaw of 1978 severely restricted reproduction at Castle

Peak, but the increased precipitation and subsequent increased vegetational growth appear to have enhanced reproduction slightly at Bodie.

Growth of offspring. The following is a summary of the results of the physiological relations between females and their offspring (previously reported in Phillips, 1981). (1) Growth and development of young *S. lateralis* were inversely related to litter size in both populations. (2) Fecundity (average litter size at birth) was lower in females from Castle Peak (4.5 versus 6.0). (3) Offspring from small (≤ 5 young) litters were able to attain their prehibernation body mass sooner and hibernate earlier than offspring from larger litters. (4) Offspring that remained homeothermic throughout their initial overwintering period were always from large litters. (5) There was no significant difference between populations either in food consumption of mothers while lactating or in the amount of nutrition mothers provided to their litters.

Discussion

The adaptive significance of an annual rhythm is that it allows an animal to remain relatively synchronous with the environment. The advantage of being relatively

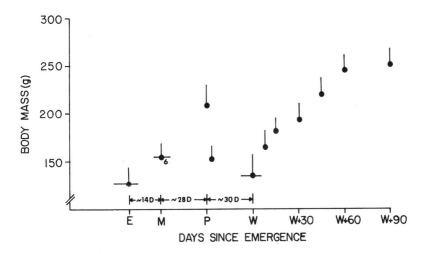

FIGURE 5.3. Body mass of captive pregnant *Spermophilus lateralis*. A composite of animals from Bodie and Castle Peak from 1976 to 1978. The date of emergence (E) and the interval between emergence and mating (M) are approximate owing to sampling intervals (values given are approximate mean and range). The value at weaning (W) is the mean and range. Vertical lines are ± 2 SE; n = 32 unless otherwise given.

117

TABLE 5.3. Percentage of female golden-mantled ground squirrels
pregnant at Bodie and Castle Peak

	1976 % N	1977 % N	1978 % N
Bodie	74 (34)	71 (38)	83 (36)
Castle Peak	67 (33)	73 (44)	19 (42)

synchronous (as opposed to absolutely synchronous) lies in the possibility of modifying the rhythm to adapt to existing conditions. As an example, a long snow-free season would allow hibernators to begin activity earlier and hence remain active longer than in years with early snowfall or late snowmelt, yet this adjustment would not destroy the basic rhythm.

The annual cycle of the adult pregnant female hibernator is composed of at least six major events: emergence, mating, pregnancy, lactation, prehibernatory weight gain, and hibernation. Mating, pregnancy, and lactation occur with predictable latencies after emergence and are not influenced by subsequent environmental conditions (except those so extreme as to kill the female; see Morton and Sherman, 1978). These components are both phasic and cyclic and must occur in synchrony with the appropriate environmental conditions to be successfully completed. If the synchrony is lost during any given year, the likely consequences are the loss of offspring and/or a decrease in the probability that the female will survive the overwintering period. The ultimate benefit of responding appropriately to the proximate environmental cues is an increased survivorship of offspring, which can occur annually or over the lifetime of the individual.

The specific environmental conditions that influence populations determine the time ''window'' available for the completion of each major event within the annual cycle of the female hibernator. Females inhabiting areas with severe or uncertain environments have less time or less margin for error within that constrained time base to accomplish the reproductive event. As a final consequence, one would expect that in highly unpredictable areas selection would favor individuals that exhibit behavioral plasticity such that their responses are synchronized with prevailing environmental conditions.

Climatic conditions influence the dates of emergence from hibernation by ground-dwelling sciurids (see Michener, this volume). Interspecific and intraspecific variation in dates of emergence has been attributed to differences associated with latitude, altitude, annual heterogeneity of snowfall, soil temperature, and air temperature. A comparison of populations of Richardson's ground squir-

118

rels (*S. richardsonii*) along a latitudinal gradient (42°–55°N) shows that the date of conception (and hence emergence) can vary by as much as a month (Clark, 1970; Michener, 1973; Nellis, 1969; Sheppard, 1972). Similar latitudinal influences on the dates of emergence have been reported for *S. lateralis* (Pengelley and Asmundson, 1975), *S. tridecemlineatus* (Choate and Fleharty, 1975; McCarley, 1966; Zimney, 1965), and *S. parryii* (Hock, 1960; Mitchell, 1959).

Emergence from hibernation in sciurid rodents is generally inversely correlated with altitude. Emergence of white-tailed prairie dogs (*Cynomys leucurus*) can vary by more than two months between low and high altitude populations (Bakko and Brown, 1967; Tileston and Lechleitner, 1966). Bronson (1980) found consistent 40–45-day differences in emergence dates within years in populations of *S. lateralis* inhabiting areas between 1,460 and 2,730 m. Blake (1972) found a similar relation in this species, and other field studies suggest that this may be a universal correlation among the Marmotini (*M. flaviventris:* Phillips, pers. obs.; *S. columbianus:* Murie and Harris, 1982).

Although there are relations between emergence and latitudinal and altitudinal gradients, a more substantial relation exists between the annual heterogeneity of snow cover and soil temperature in distinct macro- and microhabitats. The effect on macrohabitats can be nominal, as Michener (1977) found when comparing emergence dates of *S. richardsonii* and *S. columbianus* between years with winters of different intensity, or the effect can be extreme as Morton and Sherman (1978) noted in *S. beldingi*. In the latter case a severe spring snowstorm delayed the annual cycle of the entire population by more than one month. As shown in my study, the period of annual snow cover (and hence the increase in soil temperature associated with the spring thaw) can vary by as much as 40% between areas that are geographically close and altitudinally identical. Additionally, and perhaps more important, the unpredictability of the annual period of snow cover can vary considerably between locations. Between 1976 and 1978 at Castle Peak this variation was 59 days, whereas at Bodie the variation was only 34 days. Thus, both the average length of snow cover and the unpredictability of the period of snow cover influence the annual cycles of populations in distinct macrohabitats. Variations in emergence owing to environmental influence are also apparent at the microhabitat level. Shaw (1925) noted consistent differences in emergence dates between animals inhabiting north- or south-facing slopes in the same macrohabitat. The results of my study support Shaw's findings.

Regardless of the environmental factors that trigger emergence, most species of ground-dwelling sciurids exhibit sex- and age-related differences in date of emergence. Generally, adult males emerge before adult females (*S. beldingi:* Morton and Sherman, 1978; *S. columbianus:* Manville, 1959; Murie and Harris,

1982; *S. lateralis:* Bronson, 1980; *S. richardsonii:* Michener, 1983; *Cynomys leucurus:* Bakko and Brown, 1967; see Michener, this volume, for review). However, this sex difference is less apparent, generally, in the more temporally constrained environments (Bronson, 1980; Morton and Sherman, 1978), and specifically when the active season has been restricted by a severe winter (Knopf and Balph, 1977; Morton and Sherman, 1978). Adults of many species of sciurids emerge before subadults (Bronson, 1979; Knopf and Balph, 1977; Murie and Harris, 1982; Snyder and Christian, 1960). Because spermatogenesis in male Marmotini is initiated during dormancy, mating can occur as soon as adult females have emerged and become receptive. This latency to mating can vary considerably between species. *Marmota monax* can be active for a month or longer before mating occurs (Snyder and Christian, 1960), whereas *M. fla-viventris,* which inhabits more time-constrained habitats, mates almost immediately after emergence (Nee, 1969). Similarly, short latency periods of about 4 days have been documented for *S. richardsonii* (Michener, 1980) and *S. columbianus* (Murie and Harris, 1982). The severity of the preceding winter can also influence the latency period between emergence and mating (Morton and Sherman, 1978) and, as my results show, can actually inhibit reproduction (although not necessarily mating) entirely.

Because gestation and lactation are physiological processes, the time required for each event varies minimally between species and essentially not at all within species. In those species where back calculations have been possible, a period of about 1 month appears to be required for gestation (*M. monax* [32 days: Hoyt, 1952], *S. lateralis* [27−28 days: Cameron, 1967; McKeever, 1965], *S. columbianus* [24 days: Shaw, 1925], *S. richardsonii* [22.5 days: Michener, 1980], *C. leucurus* [30 days: Bakko and Brown, 1967]). The lactation period is more variable and appears to be influenced by the size of the litter (Phillips, 1981); however, young typically first emerge 3.5−4.5 weeks from birth (Ferron, this volume; Murie and Harris, 1982; Phillips, 1981).

The gain of body fat during the active season allows survival through the overwintering period. The rate of weight recovery varies between species, populations, and sexes, but once initiated two stages are apparent: a period of rapid weight gain and a plateau phase of little or no increase just before entry into hibernation. As is revealed in this study, during active seasons following "average" winters, male and nonpregnant female golden-mantled ground squirrels have little difficulty in attaining their prehibernation (or plateau) body mass far in advance of the next dormant season. This was true even at Castle Peak where the active seasons were short. However, after severe winters squirrels have low emergence weights and a relatively short season of activity, and these combine to compress the phase of plateau weight substantially. Because pregnancy decreases even further the time available for fattening, it might be physiologically impossible for females to attain sufficient body fat and wean a litter in years with extremely long winters. Perhaps this explains why fewer female ground squirrels are pregnant during years following severe winters (this study; Morton and Sherman, 1978). With few exceptions, the success of every population of ground-dwelling sciurids revolves around the female and her *single* annual litter. Yet even if female emergence is timed to coincide with male emergence this does not ensure that there will be sufficient time available to raise a litter. In a case where the preceding winter was extremely long and thus the probability of successfully raising a litter decreases, the female's total fitness may be increased by her not reproducing during that season.

The factors that influence growth in mammals change at birth and again at weaning. Preweaning growth is most dependent upon maternal input, whereas postweaning growth is most affected by the environmental conditions the offspring experience. Mayer and Roche (1954), Kalabukhov (1960), Clark (1970), and Pengelley (1966) suggested that accelerated development and accumulation of body fat would have survival value for offspring preparing for their initial overwintering period. A number of field and laboratory studies have confirmed this hypothesis, showing that (1) offspring from hibernating sciurids develop faster than their nonhibernating counterparts (Kiell and Millar, 1978; Maxwell and Morton, 1975; Pengelley, 1966); (2) within the hibernating species, those from habitats with severe climates grow faster than species from more equable habitats (Kiell and Millar, 1978); and (3) maternal input appears to be constant within populations, with growth rates of young being a function of litter size (Dolman, 1980; Phillips, 1981). This accelerated growth allows littermates from smaller litters to attain temporal advantage over the slower-developing offspring in that they are able to enter their own independent growth phase earlier, which allows them to disperse at an earlier age (if the species is characterized by dispersal of juveniles), and this allows them to reach their prehibernation level of body fat earlier (Phillips, 1981).

My laboratory results (Phillips, 1981) show that gestation in *S. lateralis* lasts 29–31 days. The lactation period is more variable, lasting between 28 and 35 days, depending upon litter size. The maximum combined range for reproduction is 57–66 days. If 180 days is the average length of an active season for a particular population and approximately 70 days are required for mating, gestation, and lactation, then 110 days remain for the independent growth of offspring. The 8-day difference in age at weaning noted above may seem insignificant compared with 110 days; however, over that 8-day period, offspring of golden-mantled ground squirrels in their weight-gain phase would gain about 20 g (or 8%) of their prehibernation weight. If a level of 30–40% body fat is required for successful hibernation (Blake, 1972), then this 8% could be significant in determining the success of the initial overwintering period. Additionally, the approximations above assume that there is an active season of 180 days, that the female emerged at the optimal time, and that the young were growing at the optimal rate. If, as during 1978 at Castle Peak, the length of the active season is drastically shortened owing to a late thaw, then females should not reproduce that year. This appeared to be what occurred. Although not reproducing in a year of delayed emergence decreases a female's fitness for that year, it may nonetheless increase her fitness over her lifetime by allowing her to be better prepared to survive the subsequent period of hibernation.

Acknowledgments

Original research reported in this paper was supported by grants from the Theodore Roosevelt Fund of the American Museum of Natural History and the Chancellor's Patent Fund of the University of California. I am grateful to W. Bloodgood, S. DeBecker, R. Hawley, and T. Stevens for their technical assistance in the field and laboratory.

Literature Cited

Adams, C. F. 1975. Nutritive values for American foods. U.S. Dept. Agric. Handb. no. 456.

Bakko, E. B., and L. N. Brown. 1967. Breeding biology of the whitetailed prairie dog, *Cynomys leucurus,* in Wyoming. J. Mamm., 48:100–112.

Blake, B. H. 1972. The annual cycle and fat storage in two populations of golden-mantled ground squirrels. J. Mamm., 53:157–167.

Bronson, M. T. 1979. Altitudinal variation in emergence time of golden-mantled ground squirrels (*Spermophilus lateralis*). J. Mamm., 61:124–126.

———. 1980. Altitudinal variation in the life history of golden-mantled ground squirrels (*Spermophilus lateralis*). Ecology, 60:272–279.

Cameron, D. M. 1967. Gestation period of the golden-mantled ground squirrel (*Citellus lateralis*). J. Mamm., 48:492–493.

Choate, J. R., and E. D. Fleharty. 1975. The mammals of Ellis County, Kansas. Occas. Papers Mus. Texas Tech. Univ., no. 37. 80 pp.

Clark, T. W. 1970. Early growth, development, and behavior of the Richardson's ground squirrel (*Spermophilus richardsonii elegans*). Amer. Midland Nat., 83:197–205.

Davis, D. E. 1976. Hibernation and circannual rhythms of food consumption in marmots and ground squirrels. Quart. Rev. Biol., 51:477–514.

Dolman, T. M. 1980. Development of thermoregulation in Richardson's ground squirrels, *Spermophilus richardsonii*. Canadian J. Zool., 58:890–895.

Fisher, R. A. 1930. The genetical theory of natural selection. Clarendon Press, Oxford, 272 pp.

Hock, R. J. 1960. Seasonal variations in physiologic functions of Arctic ground squirrels and black bears. Bull. Mus. Comp. Zool., 124:155–171.

Hoyt, S. F. 1952. Additional notes on the gestation period of the woodchuck. J. Mamm., 33:388.

Kalabuhkov, N. I. 1960. Comparative ecology of hibernating mammals. Bull. Mus. Comp. Zool., 124:45–74.

Kenagy, G. J. 1980. Interrelation of endogenous annual rhythms of reproduction and hibernation in the golden-mantled ground squirrel. J. Comp. Physiol., 135:333–339.

Kiell, D. F., and J. S. Millar. 1978. Growth of juvenile Arctic ground squirrels (*Spermophilus parryii*) at McConnell River, N.W.T. Canadian J. Zool., 56:1475–1478.

Knopf, F. L., and D. F. Balph. 1977. Annual periodicity of Uinta ground squirrels. Southwestern Nat., 23:213–224.

Levins, R. 1969. Dormancy as an adaptive behavior. Pp. 1–10, *in* Dormancy and survival. Symposia of the Society for Experimental Biology, 23. Academic Press, New York.

MacArthur, R., and E. Pianka. 1966. An optimal use of a patchy environment. Amer. Nat., 100:603–609.

Manville, R. H. 1959. The Columbian ground squirrel in Northwestern Montana. J. Mamm., 40:26–45.

Maxwell, C. S., and M. L. Morton. 1975. Comparative thermoregulatory capabilities of neonatal ground squirrels. J. Mamm., 56:821–828.

Mayer, W. V., and E. T. Roche. 1954. Development patterns in the Barrow ground squirrel, *Spermophilus undulatus barrowensis*. Growth, 18:53–59.

McCarley, H. 1966. Annual cycle, population dynamics, and adaptive behavior of *Citellus tridecemlineatus*. J. Mamm., 47:294–316.

McKeever, S. 1965. Reproduction in *Citellus beldingi* and *Citellus lateralis* in northeastern California. J. Reprod. Fert., 9:384–385.

Michener, G. R. 1973. Climatic conditions and breeding in Richardson's ground squirrel. J. Mamm., 54:499–503.

———. 1977. Effect of climatic conditions on the annual activity and hibernation cycle of Richardson's ground squirrels and Columbian ground squirrels. Canadian J. Zool., 55:693–703.

———. 1980. Estrous and gestation periods in Richardson's ground squirrels. J. Mamm., 61:531–534.

———. 1983. Spring emergence schedules and vernal behavior of Richardson's ground squirrels: Why do males emerge before females? Behav. Ecol. Sociobiol.,14:29–38.

Mitchell, O. G. 1959. The reproductive cycle of the male Arctic ground squirrel. J. Mamm., 40:45–53.

Morton, M. L., and P. W. Sherman. 1978. Effects of a spring snowstorm on behavior, reproduction, and survival of Belding's ground squirrels. Canadian J. Zool., 56: 2578–2590.

Mrosovsky, N. 1980. Circannual cycles in golden-mantled ground squirrels: experiments with food deprivation and effects of temperature on periodicity. J. Comp. Physiol., 136:355–360.

Murie, J. O., and M. A. Harris. 1982. Annual variation of spring emergence and breeding in Columbian ground squirrels (*Spermophilus columbianus*). J. Mamm., 63:431–439.

Nee, J. A. 1969. Reproduction in a population of yellow-bellied marmots (*Marmota flaviventris*). J. Mamm., 50:756–765.

Nellis, C. H. 1969. Productivity of Richardson's ground squirrels near Rochester, Alberta. Canadian Field-Nat., 83:246–250.

Pengelley, E. T. 1966. Differential developmental patterns and their adaptive value in various species of the genus *Citellus*. Growth, 30:137–142.

Pengelley, E. T., and S. M. Asmundson. 1975. Female gestation and lactation as Zeitgebers for circannual rhythmicity in hibernating ground squirrels, *Citellus lateralis*. Comp. Biochem. Physiol., 50A:621–626.

Pengelley, E. T., and K. C. Fisher. 1961. Rhythmical arousal from hibernation in the golden-mantled ground squirrel, *Citellus lateralis tescorum*. Canadian J. Zool., 39:105–120.

———. 1963. The effect of temperature and photoperiod on the yearly hibernating behavior of captive golden-mantled ground squirrels (*Citellus lateralis tescorum*). Canadian J. Zool., 41:1103–1120.

Phillips, J. A. 1981. Growth and its relationship to the initial annual cycle of the golden-mantled ground squirrel, *Spermophilus lateralis*. Canadian J. Zool., 59:865–871.

Ricklefs, R. E. 1967. A graphical method of fitting equations to growth curves. Ecology, 48:979–983.

Shaw, W. T. 1925. The seasonal differences of north and south slopes in controlling the activities of the Columbian ground squirrel. Ecology, 6:157–162.

Sheppard, D. H. 1972. Reproduction of Richardson's ground squirrels (*Spermophilus richardsonii*) in southern Saskatchewan. Canadian J. Zool., 50:1577–1581.

Snyder, R. L., and J. J. Christian. 1960. Reproductive cycle and litter size of the woodchuck. Ecology, 41:647–656.

Tileston, J. V., and R. R. Lechleitner. 1966. Some comparisons of the black-tailed and white-tailed prairie dogs in north-central Colorado. Amer. Midland Nat., 75:292–316.

Twente, J. W., J. Twente, and R. M. Moy. 1977. Regulation of arousal from hibernation by temperatures in three species of *Citellus*. J. Appl. Physiol., 42:191–195.

Zimney, M. L. 1965. Thirteen-lined ground squirrels born in captivity. J. Mamm., 46:521–522.

JANET E. JOY

University of Toronto

Chapter 6

Population Differences in Circannual Cycles of Thirteen-lined Ground Squirrels

Abstract. The endogenous circannual cycles that underlie seasonal activity cycles in ground squirrels were studied under constant laboratory conditions and compared between groups of thirteen-lined ground squirrels trapped in Michigan and Kansas. The body weight cycles of the Kansas ground squirrels were generally slower than those of the Michigan ground squirrels; their mean cycle lengths were 2 – 3 weeks longer than those of the Michigan ground squirrels. On average, the Michigan ground squirrels reached their first body weight peaks about 6 weeks earlier, their first trough weights earlier, and their second peak weights about 9 weeks earlier than the Kansas ground squirrels. Based on the form and phasing of their cycles, the Michigan ground squirrels appear to be programmed to enter hibernation earlier and more promptly and to hibernate longer. In general, the cycles of the Michigan ground squirrels appear to be adapted to longer winters. In addition to differing in the underlying form of their cycles, the Kansas and Michigan ground squirrels may also differ in their responses to environmental factors. I suggest that intraspecific population differences in seasonal activity patterns arc at least partly "underwritten" by differences in physiological programming.

Introduction

The typical annual cycle of hibernating sciurids is well known (see Davis, 1976; Michener, this volume). Males usually emerge from hibernation before females, and the breeding season begins shortly after females emerge (Beer, 1962; Knopf

125

and Balph, 1977; McKeever, 1964; Michener, 1983; Morton, 1975; Morton and Sherman, 1978; Murie and Harris, 1982; Scheck and Fleharty, 1980). Toward the end of summer, adult males usually enter hibernation first, followed by adult females, and finally young of the year (McCarley, 1966; Michener, 1977, 1979; Morton, 1975). There are exceptions to this pattern. In Texas, some female thirteen-lined ground squirrels (*Spermophilus tridecemlineatus*) may emerge before the males (McCarley, 1966). Male golden-mantled ground squirrels (*S. lateralis*) living at low elevations emerge from hibernation earlier than females, but males at higher elevations emerge at the same time as females (Bronson, 1980).

Timing of hibernation and breeding seasons varies considerably between species and populations and even from year to year (Bronson, 1977; Knopf and Balph, 1977; Michener, 1978, 1979, this volume; Murie and Harris, 1982; Wade, 1950), but we do not know exactly how it varies. Environmental factors are certainly important. Yearly variations in the timing of emergence from hibernation correlate with such factors as air temperature (Davis, 1977; Michener, 1979; Murie and Harris, 1982), soil temperature (Scheck and Fleharty, 1980; Wade, 1950), and snow cover (Bronson, 1977; Morton and Sherman, 1978; Shaw, 1925).

Although ground squirrels often emerge from hibernation late during a cold spring, there are limits to the delay imposed by cold weather. Even in the coldest springs, ground squirrels eventually emerge from their burrows. What is not always obvious from field studies is the role of the circannual cycle. Even in the absence of seasonal changes in weather, ground squirrels show a typical seasonal cycle. The sequence of emergence from hibernation, reproduction, prehibernatory fattening, and reentry into hibernation is driven by the underlying endogenous circannual cycle (see Davis, 1976; Pengelley and Asmundson, 1974, for reviews). In constant conditions these cycles free-run with periods that are generally less than a year and are probably adjusted to the calendar year by temperature cues during the spring phase (Davis, 1977; Heller and Poulson, 1970; Joy and Mrosovsky, 1983; Knopf and Balph, 1977; Michener, 1979).

Are the differences in the timing of seasonal activity based on differences in the circannual cycle? Interspecific differences in timing presumably are based on such differences. Even in areas of sympatry, different species may show marked differences in the timing of their seasonal activity patterns (McKeever, 1964; Michener, 1977). Pengelley and Kelly (1966) have shown that interspecific differences in the circannual cycles can be related to differences in seasonal activity patterns. In the laboratory, golden-mantled ground squirrels show much clearer circannual hibernation cycles than do Belding's ground squirrels, and in natural conditions they show more regular hibernation patterns (Heller and Poulson, 1970; Pengelley and Kelly, 1966). Yearly differences in timing within populations are presumably due to weather factors (Michener, this volume). What about the intermediate case—intraspecific differences between populations? Are such differences "underwritten" by differences in physiological programming, or are they attributable solely to regional differences in climate? If the differences were based strictly on immediate environmental factors, differences in the circannual cycles that underlie the annual cycles in the field would not be expected. If the cycles seen in the laboratory differed between populations, this would suggest that the population differences were physiologically based rather than environmentally based.

The thirteen-lined ground squirrel is one of the most cosmopolitan species among the ground squirrels, ranging from Manitoba to Texas (Hall, 1981). The timing of seasonal activity varies geographically. Thirteen-lined ground squirrels in Texas generally emerge from hibernation from about mid-March to the beginning of April (McCarley, 1966; Wistrand, 1974); in central Kansas they generally emerge between the end of March and the beginning of April (Scheck and Fleharty, 1980; Wade, 1930); and in Minnesota they generally do not emerge until the second half of April (Beer, 1962; Hohn and Marshall, 1966). Rongstad (1965) states that mean conception dates are 10 days earlier in western Kansas than in southern Wisconsin, where they are in turn 10 days earlier than in Manitoba. Although different studies vary greatly in sampling methods, sample size, and the number of years studied, the evidence indicates that the active seasons of the more northern populations of thirteen-lined ground squirrels begin later in the year.

Differences in seasonal activity patterns will have presumably arisen as a result of adaptations to the different climates. If such differences are based on differences in the underlying circannual cycle, we would expect to see differences in the circannual cycles of thirteen-lined ground squirrels that were trapped in areas where the climates were different. To test this, two different populations of thirteen-lined ground squirrels were studied in the laboratory under constant conditions.

Methods

Fifteen juvenile *Spermophilus tridecemlineatus* (six males and nine females) were trapped between 10 and 17 July 1978 in Leavenworth, Kansas; and 18 juveniles (four males and 14 females) were trapped between 20 and 22 July 1979 near East Lansing, Michigan. Ground squirrels in Michigan are exposed to longer and harsher winters than are those in Kansas. Based on means from 20-year records collected by the U.S. Department of the Interior Geological Survey (1970), the last killing frost is later in Michigan than in Kansas (10 May versus 20 April), the frost-free period is about a month shorter in Michigan (150 days versus 180 days), there are more days of snow cover (75 days versus 40 days), and the annual snowfall is about twice as great in Michigan as in Kansas (125 cm versus 50 cm).

The animals were kept in a warm room (21 ± 3°C) on a 12:12 light/dark schedule for at least 20 months. They were kept in individual cages and provided with nesting material and unlimited food (Purina Rodent Chow) and water. All animals were first weighed when they were brought into the laboratory (19 July 1978 for the Kansas animals and 25 July 1979 for the Michigan animals) and thereafter were weighed weekly to the nearest gram. Four of the 23 females failed to show clear body-weight cycles and were not included in the analyses.

The periods of the body weight cycles were calculated between successive body-weight peaks. A local weight maximum was considered a "peak" if it was followed by a weight-loss phase of at least 6 weeks. During a weight-loss phase an animal did not necessarily lose weight continuously. Occasionally an animal showed a "double" peak. After reaching a body weight peak, it lost weight for a few weeks, then reached the same weight a second time. In such cases the date of the first weight peak was used. "Trough" weights were the lowest weights between two peaks, and double troughs were treated in the same manner as double peaks.

Only the first cycles in captivity are compared. Results are analyzed using one-tailed Mann-Whitney U-tests and means are given plus-or-minus one standard deviation. Variances were compared using the Squared Ranks Test for Variance (Conover, 1980). Except where noted, results are analyzed separately by sex.

Results

Body-weight curves are shown for representative animals in Fig. 6.1. The form of the circannual cycle was different not only between the two populations, but also between males and females.

The cycles of the Kansas ground squirrels were generally slower than those of the Michigan ground squirrels. The mean cycle lengths of the Michigan ground squirrels were 2–3 weeks shorter than those of the Kansas ground squirrels, but this difference was statistically significant only for the comparison between

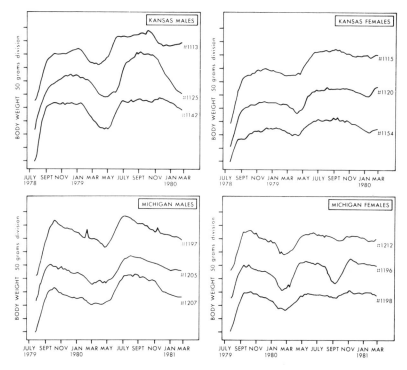

FIGURE 6.1. Individual body weight cycles for representative thirteen-lined ground squirrels kept at 25°C and light/dark 12:12. Note that ordinate shows relative, not actual, weight.

females (Table 6.1). On average the Michigan ground squirrels reached their first body-weight peak about 6 weeks earlier than the Kansas ground squirrels, their first trough weight earlier, and their second peak weight about 7 weeks earlier (Table 6.1).

The Kansas ground squirrels were more likely to show a weight plateau than the Michigan ground squirrels. Among the Michigan ground squirrels, only some of the females showed a plateau phase. Both male and female Kansas ground squirrels showed a plateau phase.

The shape of the peak body-weight phase was analyzed by comparing the mean slopes of the body-weight cycles calculated for each of the 5 weeks preceding and the 5 weeks following a peak weight. The cycles of the Michigan males showed more sharply defined peaks than those of Kansas males (Table 6.2). Similar patterns were seen in the females, but females showed greater individual variability than males in peak sharpness, and the differences fell short of statisti-

TABLE 6.1. Mean dates (± SD) of peak and trough body weights and
mean (± SD) cycle length. Probability values are given for one-tailed Mann-Whitney *U*-tests
of within-sex comparisons between populations; n.s. indicates *P* > 0.05.

	First peak date	Trough date	Second peak date	Cycle length (days)
Males				
Kansas	15 November 1978	3 April 1979	9 October 1979	327 (± 65)
(N = 6)	(± 40)	(±22)	(± 29)	
Michigan	30 September 1979	13 March 1980	5 August 1980	309 (± 26)
(N = 4)	(± 7)	(± 23)	(± 26)	
	P = 0.033	*P* = 0.057	*P* = 0.005	n.s.
Females				
Kansas	8 November 1978	8 March 1979	17 August 1979	282 (± 27)
(N = 6)	(± 36)	(± 51)	(± 41)	
Michigan	2 October 1979	12 February 1980	18 June 1980	257 (± 45)
(N = 13)	(± 14)	(± 8)	(± 48)	
	P = 0.014	*P* = 0.011	*P* = 0.014	*P* = 0.022

cal significance. When they were first brought into the laboratory, ground squirrels in both populations showed similarly steep weight-gain phases, but upon reaching prehibernation weights they adopted different strategies. Michigan ground squirrels promptly entered the weight-loss phase; Kansas ground squirrels often switched to a phase of very gradual weight gain or simply remained stable at high weights. Michigan males showed more sharply defined peaks than females ($P < 0.05$, for comparisons between the weight-gain slope and steepness), but the shape of the peaks was not significantly different between Kansas males and females (Table 6.2).

With the exception of the Kansas females, which lost only about 15% of their body weight, the other groups of squirrels lost 30–37% of their body weight during the weight-loss phase. In both sexes the weight-loss phase lasted 2–3 weeks longer in the Michigan ground squirrels than in the Kansas ground squirrels (Table 6.3). Michigan ground squirrels tended to spend more time losing weight, and the weight-loss phase occupied a larger proportion of the circannual cycle. The population differences among the males for both absolute and relative duration of the weight-loss phase were close to, but fell short of, conventional statistical limits ($P = 0.10$ in both cases). The sample sizes, however, were rather small, which means that the power of the test was relatively low. Since the

TABLE 6.2. Mean slopes (± SD) for the five weeks of the body-weight cycle preceding and the 5 weeks following peak body weights. Slopes are the means of weekly changes in weight divided by time between weighings (g/day). "Steepness" is the difference between the mean weight-gain and weight-loss slopes. Probability values are given as in Table 6.1.

	Weight-gain slope	Weight-loss slope	Steepness
Males			
Kansas (N = 6)	0.30 ± 0.13	−0.43 ± 0.27	0.73 ± 0.36
Michigan (N = 4)	1.48 ± 0.66	−0.74 ± 0.07	2.23 ± 0.67
	$P = 0.005$	$P = 0.057$	$P = 0.005$
Females			
Kansas (N = 6)	0.50 ± 0.41	−0.36 ± 0.34	0.86 ± 0.57
Michigan (N = 13)	0.81 ± 0.68	−0.43 ± 0.25	1.24 ± 0.73
	n.s.	n.s.	n.s.

results were consistent with those for the females, a test with a larger sample would most likely have fallen within conventional statistical limits.

In both populations, the weight-loss phase of females was 3–4 weeks shorter than that of the males, but their cycles were also shorter than those of the males, and the differences in the percentage of the cycle spent losing weight were not significant. Michigan males generally lost weight steadily for a long time, whereas Kansas males did not lose much weight until almost 2 months after the Michigan males had begun losing weight (Fig. 6.1).

Kansas ground squirrels tended to show more individual variability (Table 6.1). Both male and female Kansas ground squirrels showed significantly greater variance in the first peak date and in the duration of the first weight-loss phase; female Kansas ground squirrels showed greater variance in trough date than did the Michigan females; and Kansas males showed greater variance in cycle length than the Michigan males (Tables 6.1 and 6.3; $P < 0.01$ for all cases; Squared Ranks Test for Variance). Michigan ground squirrels did not show significantly greater variance for any of the variables relating to the timing of the cycles.

The weights of the ground squirrels from Kansas and Michigan were not significantly different when they were first brought into the laboratory (Table 6.4). In the laboratory, they showed similar linear growth curves for about 2 months.

Annual Cycles

TABLE 6.3. Means (± SD) for different parameters of the initial weight-loss phase. Probability values are given as in Table 6.1.

	Duration of the weight-loss phase (days)	Percentage of cycle spent losing weight	Percentage weight loss
Males			
Kansas (N = 6)	139 ± 46	41 ± 9	30 ± 10
Michigan (N = 4)	164 ± 21	54 ± 12	37 ± 7
	n.s.	n.s.	n.s.
Females			
Kansas (N = 6)	119 ± 34	42 ± 10	15 ± 5
Michigan (N = 13)	133 ± 13	53 ± 10	31 ± 7
	n.s.	$P = 0.017$	$P = 0.003$

However, when averaged over 20 months the Kansas ground squirrels showed a higher average growth rate and weighed more on average than the Michigan ground squirrels. The average growth rates for female Kansas and Michigan ground squirrels were 172 ± 60 mg/day and 108 ± 51 mg/day, respectively ($P = 0.006$). There was one unusual male in the Kansas group that showed a negative growth rate. If this male is excluded, the average growth rate for male Kansas and Michigan ground squirrels is 166 ± 52 mg/day and 90 ± 33 mg/day, respectively ($P = 0.032$). This estimate of growth is not ideal, however, since it is influenced by both the period and the form of the cycle. In addition, because I recorded only body mass, fat storage could not be distinguished from skeletal growth.

Kansas ground squirrels reached higher peak weights and weighed more at lowest body weights than the Michigan ground squirrels (Table 6.4). Although the differences are not statistically significant for all phases of the cycle (Table 6.4), the average weights for the 20 months of the study are significantly different for the two populations. Average weights for female Kansas and Michigan ground squirrels were 243 ± 46 g and 198 ± 21 g, respectively ($P = 0.011$); for male Kansas and Michigan ground squirrels, they were 253 ± 24 g and 214 ± 21 g, respectively ($P = 0.019$).

TABLE 6.4. Means (± SD) for initial, peak, and trough body weights.
Probability values are given as in Table 6.1.

	Initial body weight (g)	First peak body weight (g)	Trough body weight (g)	Second peak body weight (g)
Males				
Kansas (N = 6)	75 ± 17	279 ± 56	191 ± 23	327 ± 27
Michigan (N = 4)	84 ± 14	248 ± 30	171 ± 10	272 ± 36
	n.s.	$P = 0.129$	$P = 0.129$	$P = 0.057$
Females				
Kansas (N = 6)	75 ± 8	242 ± 47	206 ± 38	298 ± 54
Michigan (N = 13)	93 ± 2	218 ± 19	150 ± 24	224 ± 25
	n.s.	n.s.	$P = 0.001$	$P = 0.001$

Discussion

Fall phase: differences in peak weights. Michigan ground squirrels reached their first peak body weights earlier than the Kansas ground squirrels, which suggests that the Michigan ground squirrels are programmed to enter hibernation at an earlier date (or perhaps at an earlier age) than the Kansas ground squirrels. This is consistent with what is expected on the basis of the climatic differences between the two localities. Phillips (1981) compared laboratory-reared golden-mantled ground squirrels (*S. lateralis*) and found a similar pattern. The ground squirrels whose mothers had been trapped in an area where snowfall was greater entered hibernation at an earlier date than those whose mothers had been trapped in an area where there was normally less snowfall.

Ward and Armitage (1981) also reported population differences in the timing of peak body weights in yellow-bellied marmot (*Marmota flaviventris*) populations. They state that marmots from the milder climate (lowland xeric) reached their peak weights 2 months earlier than those from the harsher climate (montane mesic), which is opposite to the finding in the present study. Unfortunately, comparing their results with mine is not easy. Their experiments with the two groups of marmots were initiated at different phases of the circannual cycles

(August and December), and the two groups had been in the laboratory different lengths of time, with the cycles of individual marmots presumably free-running with different periods. It is not entirely clear if the weight peaks they compared are the first peaks in captivity for both the populations. Based on weight, all the marmots probably were adults. Additionally, there is no mention of sexes, which appear to be pooled. If yellow-bellied marmots show sex differences similar to those of thirteen-lined ground squirrels, this would have greatly biased the results.

In both Kansas and Michigan populations, females reached their first peak weights at roughly the same time as the males, but they reached their second body weight peaks about 6 weeks earlier ($P < 0.05$ for both populations) (Table 6.1). The cycle lengths of the females were also $5-7$ weeks shorter than those of the males ($P < 0.05$ for both populations).

Perhaps females reach their second body weight peaks earlier than males because of the artificial constraints placed on the normal behavior of these ground squirrels. A rather obvious consequence of individual caging is that females cannot breed and bear young. This deprivation may account for the sex difference in the cycles. Pregnancy and lactation have been shown to delay cycles of golden-mantled ground squirrels in the laboratory by about a month (Pengelley and Asmundson, 1975), and of Richardson's ground squirrels in the field by about 3 weeks (Michener, 1978). Alternatively, the earlier peaks of the males could be due to sex differences in responses to temperature. Perhaps the same temperature cues normally lengthen the cycles of females by a greater amount than those of the males. This is supported by the observation that cold (4°C) delays the date of lowest body weights in females more than in males (Joy, 1983). These possibilities are not mutually exclusive, and further investigation is necessary to evaluate them.

Shape of the peak weight phase. Ground squirrels generally do not hibernate until they have gained considerable weight. Once they attain high body weights, however, they do not necessarily hibernate or even enter a weight-loss phase. Some squirrels reach high body weights and then, instead of entering the weight-loss phase, show a plateau in the body weight cycle (Armitage and Shulenberger, 1972; Hall, 1969; Phillips, 1981). The shape of a weight peak could provide an index to the duration of a period of facultative hibernation. If this is the case, Kansas ground squirrels may be more opportunistic in the decision when to enter the weight-loss phase and Michigan males may be the least likely to show opportunistic responses to a typically mild winter.

Although Michigan males showed more sharply defined peaks than females, the shape of the peaks was not significantly different between Kansas males and females (Table 6.2). Although there was considerable individual variation, particularly among females, both males and females in the present study showed plateau phases (Fig. 6.1). Armitage and Shulenberger (1972) studied thirteen-lined ground squirrels that were trapped in the same area as the Kansas ground squirrels in this study. They state that males showed a prolonged plateau phase but females did not. Their study is not strictly comparable with this one, because they used adult ground squirrels and seven of their 13 females had borne litters. The figures presented in their paper show grouped data, which do not necessarily provide reliable estimates of cycle phases. For example, the peak date of an average weight curve calculated for female Kansas ground squirrels in this study occurs 50 days later than the mean peak date calculated using peak dates of individual squirrels. In contrast, the peak date on the average curve for female Michigan squirrels is only 2 days earlier than the mean peak date calculated using individual dates. The difference between the results of Armitage and Shulenberger's (1972) study and this study could be due to age differences of the squirrels, individual variability, or the use of grouped data.

Winter phase: differences in the first weight-loss phase. The ground squirrels from the harsher climate (Michigan) showed larger-amplitude cycles (greater percentage of weight loss), which is what Ward and Armitage (1981) found in yellow-bellied marmots and Blake (1972) found in golden-mantled ground squirrels in similar laboratory studies.

If the period of steady weight loss can be interpreted as indicating a more obligate phase of hibernation, the Michigan ground squirrels appear to be pre-programmed for longer winters. If Michigan ground squirrels have a proportionately shorter "facultative" hibernation phase, then they should show less year-to-year variability in the hibernation period than Kansas ground squirrels. Because they are "scheduled" for longer winters—or more continuously and consistently colder winters—the Michigan ground squirrels may be less likely to show abbreviated hibernation seasons during warm winters (and in warm laboratory conditions) than the Kansas ground squirrels. Several authors have reported that ground squirrels living in areas where winters tend to be colder and longer are sometimes more regular (or emerge from hibernation over a narrower time span) in their seasonal schedule than their conspecifics in areas where the climate is milder (Bronson, 1980; Fitch, 1948; but see Murie and Harris, 1982).

The longer weight-loss phase seen in the ground squirrels from the colder

135

climate (Michigan) contrasts with Blake's (1972) results. In her study of golden-mantled ground squirrels, those from the milder climate (Oregon) showed longer hibernation seasons than the ground squirrels from the colder climate (Colorado). She measured the end of the hibernation season by the onset of reproductive recrudescence rather than by the trough weights used in the present study. The Kansas males in this study came into reproductive condition earlier than the Michigan males, but reproductive status was not known for females (pers. obs.). Perhaps the differences between the two studies lie in interspecific and population differences in the phase relation between trough body weights and the onset of reproduction. The differences between these two studies may, however, reflect methodological differences more than species differences. Although generally kept warm (22–25°C), the squirrels in Blake's study were occasionally exposed to temperatures as low as 16°C; they were not weighed at regular intervals, making estimates of cycle phases imprecise; and the sample sizes were small (n = 2, 3, 3, and 6).

One might wonder if the population differences in mean peak dates were mainly due to differences in the form of the peak phase. However, at least two different estimates of cycle phase yield results that are consistent with those based on comparisons between peak dates. The first comparison was based on the mean of the first date when a weight loss was recorded for individual animals (i.e., the end of the phase of maximum weight gain), and the second comparison was based on the mean date of the first maximum residual of the linear regression calculated using all the recorded weights for individual animals (unpubl. obs.). Thus, although the date of maximum weight is a rather arbitrary measure of cycle phase, the results obtained by this method are fairly robust.

Because the ground squirrels were trapped as juveniles, their cycles are unlikely to have been directly modified by exposure to the different climates of Kansas and Michigan.

Based on reports of breeding dates in the wild for this species, the ground squirrels were probably about 80–100 days old when they were brought into the laboratory (Hall, 1969; Johnson et al., 1933; Rongstad, 1965; Zimny, 1965). Their precise birth dates are not known. Ground squirrels from both populations were from different litters, so their ages undoubtedly varied within and perhaps between the two populations. Michener (pers. comm.) reports that the date of first entry into hibernation by juvenile Richardson's ground squirrels (*S. richardsonii*) is influenced by their birth date, and Hall (1969) found that juvenile thirteen-lined ground squirrels trapped in two different years reached their first peak weights at about the same age. Although we do not know whether animals from different populations would necessarily reach their first peak weights at the same age, these results suggest that within a population the phasing of cycles is influenced by birth date.

If the weight of the ground squirrels when they were first brought into the laboratory is a reliable index of age, the differences seen in the initial stages of the circannual cycles in this study are probably not due strictly to age differences between the two populations. The correlation of initial weight with peak date is not significant for either the Kansas or the Michigan ground squirrels ($r = -0.219$ and $r = -0.269$, respectively; $P > 0.10$ for both cases). When groups were analyzed separately by both population and sex, only the Michigan males showed a significant correlation ($r = -0.970$, $P < 0.05$). Thus, if initial weight is a reliable index of age, the age range of the animals in this study was probably not great enough to account for the population differences. Because postemergent juvenile growth rates within field populations can show significant yearly variation, at best the initial weights can give only a general idea of age (Boag and Murie, 1981; Hohn and Marshall, 1966). Additionally, we cannot assume that different populations will reach their peak weights at the same age.

If there had been a greater range of ages, an age effect for the initial phases of the cycle might have been more apparent. Population differences in such aspects of the cycle as period, phasing (e.g., proportion of the cycle spent in the weight-loss phase), amplitude (e.g., percentage weight loss), and level (average weight) are unlikely to have been influenced by possible age differences between the two populations. While information on the precise ages of the ground squirrels would help in interpreting the differences found in this study, clearly there are differences in the cycles between the two populations.

The differences in mean dates of peak body weights probably are not because the squirrels were trapped in different years. In their seven-year field study, Boag and Murie (1981) found that the mean date of peak weight for juvenile Columbian ground squirrels (*S. columbianus*) showed yearly variations, but never more than 1 week. However, Boag and Murie presented grouped data, and perhaps the yearly variation is underestimated. In laboratory studies using adult golden-mantled ground squirrels trapped in four different years, I found that the time of the first body-weight peak in captivity varied depending on the year in which the animals were trapped (Joy, 1982). However, the maximum difference in mean peak dates was about 4 weeks. Thus, in the most extreme case in the four-year sample, the differences in mean peak dates that are attributable to trapping year is less than the 6-week difference in mean peak dates between the Kansas and Michigan ground squirrels.

Trapping animals from different populations in the same year would not provide an adequate control for yearly weather variations, because relevant weather factors are not necessarily correlated geographically. In the same year spring could be relatively cold in Michigan but relatively warm in Kansas. A laboratory study of animals trapped in several different years at a given location would be necessary to evaluate this effect. Even if the yearly differences in weather also influence the form of the circannual cycle, sufficient data are not available to assess this influence.

The intent of the present study was to compare the underlying circannual cycles of animals that are adapted to different climates. It would be interesting to know if the different populations show different thresholds for response to environmental cues. Perhaps the Michigan ground squirrels are normally induced to arouse from hibernation when the weather is colder than it is when the Kansas ground squirrels arouse. Although spring weather conditions influence the timing of seasonal activity, the time at which spring weather exerts an effect is unknown. Perhaps the phase of the cycle at which the ground squirrels are most responsive to weather cues occurs at slightly different times for the two populations. Although the endogenous cycles of the Kansas and Michigan ground squirrels differ, the functional implications of these differences are not clear. Speculations have been offered in the previous discussion, but further study is needed to analyze the direct effect of environmental conditions on circannual cycles.

Conclusion

Circannual cycles of thirteen-lined ground squirrels trapped in Kansas and Michigan differ in the form in which they are expressed in constant conditions; that is, the endogenous cycles that underlie the annual cycles are different in the two populations. In general, the cycles of the Michigan ground squirrels appear to be adapted to longer winters. These squirrels seem to be programmed to enter hibernation earlier and more promptly and to hibernate longer. These population differences generally correspond to what we would expect the animals to do in the field. However, Michigan ground squirrels reached their lowest body weights earlier than did the Kansas ground squirrels. In addition to differing in the underlying form of their cycles, the Kansas and Michigan ground squirrels may also differ in their response to environmental factors. Such differences are probably quantitative rather than qualitative. To answer the original question: yes, the underlying circannual cycles that drive the annual cycles of the two populations are different. Population differences in life-cycle patterns are at least partly "underwritten" by differences in physiological programming. The extent to which these intrinsic differences are molded by environmental circumstance remains to be uncovered.

Acknowledgments

I would like to thank K. B. Armitage, J. M. Ward, Jr., and A. E. Muchlinski for help in obtaining the animals studied; T. Tallerico-Melnyk, Y. Korent, and K. Davis for help with animal care; and G. R. Michener and an anonymous reviewer for editorial comments. Financial support was provided by Ontario Graduate Scholarships to me and a grant from the Natural Sciences and Engineering Research Council of Canada to N. Mrosovsky.

Literature Cited

Armitage, K. B., and E. Shulenberger. 1972. Evidence for a circannual metabolic cycle in *Citellus tridecemlineatus,* a hibernator. Comp. Biochem. Physiol., 42A:667–688.

Beer, J. R. 1962. Emergence of thirteen-lined ground squirrels from hibernation. J. Mamm., 43:109.

Blake, B. H. 1972. The annual cycle and fat storage in two populations of golden-mantled ground squirrels. J. Mamm., 53:157–167.

Boag, D. A., and J. O. Murie. 1981. Weight in relation to sex, age, and season in Columbian ground squirrels (Sciuridae: Rodentia). Canadian J. Zool., 59:999–1004.

Bronson, M. T. 1977. Altitudinal variation in the annual cycle and life history of the golden-mantled ground squirrel (*Spermophilus lateralis*). Unpubl. Ph.D. dissert., Univ. California, Berkeley, 134 pp.

———. 1980. Altitudinal variation in emergence time of golden-mantled ground squirrels (*Spermophilus lateralis*). J. Mamm., 61:124–126.

Conover, W. J. 1980. Practical nonparametric statistics. John Wiley, New York, 493 pp.

Davis, D. E. 1976. Hibernation and circannual rhythms of food consumption in marmots and ground squirrels. Quart. Rev. Biol., 51:477–513.

———. 1977. Role of ambient temperature in emergence of woodchucks (*Marmota monax*) from hibernation. Amer. Midland Nat., 97:224–229.

Fitch, H. S. 1948. Ecology of the California ground squirrel on grazing lands. Amer. Midland Nat., 39:513–596.

Hall, E. R. 1981. The mammals of North America. Vol. 1. Second ed. John Wiley, New York, pp. 381–415.

Hall, K. D. 1969. Effects of light and temperature on seasonal events in the life cycle of the 13-lined ground squirrel, *Citellus tridecemlineatus*. Unpubl. Ph.D. dissert., Univ. Kansas, Lawrence, 72 pp.

Heller, H. C., and T. L. Poulson. 1970. Circannian rhythms. II. Endogenous and exogenous factors controlling reproduction and hibernation in chipmunks (*Eutamias*) and ground squirrels (*Spermophilus*). Comp. Biochem. Physiol., 33:357–383.

Hohn, B. M., and W. H. Marshall. 1966. Annual and seasonal weight changes in a thirteen-lined ground squirrel population, Itasca State Park, Minnesota. J. Minnesota Acad. Sci., 33:102–106.

Johnson, G. E., M. A. Foster, and R. M. Coco. 1933. The sexual cycle of the thirteen-lined ground squirrel in the laboratory. Trans. Kansas Acad. Sci., 36:250–269.

Joy, J. E. 1982. Resetting of circannual cycles in golden-mantled ground squirrels by spring weather conditions. 62nd Ann. Mtg. Amer. Soc. Mamm., Abstr. 287.

———. 1983. Circannual cycles in ground squirrels. Unpubl. Ph.D. dissert., Univ. Toronto, Toronto, 255 pp.

Joy, J. E., and N. Mrosovsky. 1983. Circannual cycles in golden-mantled ground squirrels: lengthening of period by low temperatures in the spring phase. J. Comp. Physiol., Ser. A., 150:233–238.

Knopf, F. L., and D. F. Balph. 1977. Annual periodicity of Uinta ground squirrels. Southwestern Nat., 22:213–224.

McCarley, H. 1966. Annual cycle, population dynamics and adaptive behavior of *Citellus tridecemlineatus*. J. Mamm., 47:294–316.

McKeever, S. 1964. The biology of the golden-mantled ground squirrel, *Citellus lateralis*. Ecol. Monogr., 34:383–401.

Michener, G. R. 1977. Effect of climatic conditions on the annual activity and hibernation cycle of Richardson's ground squirrels and Columbian ground squirrels. Canadian J. Zool., 55:693–703.

———. 1978. Effect of age and parity on weight gain and entry into hibernation in Richardson's ground squirrels. Canadian J. Zool., 56:2573–2577.

———. 1979. The circannual cycle of Richardson's ground squirrels in Southern Alberta. J. Mamm., 60:760–768.

———. 1983. Spring emergence schedules and vernal behavior of Richardson's ground squirrels: why do males emerge from hibernation before females? Behav. Ecol. Sociobiol., 14:29–38.

Morton, M. L. 1975. Seasonal cycles of body weights and lipids in Belding ground squirrels. Bull. So. California Acad. Sci., 74:128–143.

Morton, M. L., and P. W. Sherman. 1978. Effects of a spring snowstorm on behavior, reproduction, and survival of Belding's ground squirrels. Canadian J. Zool., 56:2578–2590.

Murie, J. O., and M. A. Harris. 1982. Annual variation of spring emergence and breeding in Columbian ground squirrels (*Spermophilus columbianus*). J. Mamm., 63:431–439.

Pengelley, E. T., and S. J. Asmundson. 1974. Circannual rhythmicity in hibernating animals. Pp. 95–160, *in* Circannual clocks—annual biological rhythms (E. T. Pengelley, ed.). Academic Press, New York, 523 pp.

———. 1975. Female gestation and lactation as Zeitgebers for circannual rhythmicity in the hibernating ground squirrel, *Citellus lateralis*. Comp. Biochem. Physiol., 50A:621–625.

Pengelley, E. T., and K. H. Kelly. 1966. A "circannian" rhythm in hibernating species of the genus *Citellus* with observations on their physiological evolution. Comp. Biochem. Physiol., 19:603–617.

Phillips, J. A. 1981. Growth and its relationship to the initial annual cycle of the golden-mantled ground squirrel, *Spermophilus lateralis*. Canadian J. Zool., 59:865–871.

Rongstad, O. J. 1965. A life history of thirteen-lined ground squirrels in Southern Wisconsin. J. Mamm., 46:76–87.

Scheck, S. H., and E. D. Fleharty. 1980. Subterranean behavior of the adult thirteen-lined ground squirrel (*Spermophilus tridecemlineatus*). Amer. Midland Nat., 103:191–195.

Shaw, W. T. 1925. The seasonal differences of north and south slopes in controlling the activities of the Columbian ground squirrel. Ecology 6:157–162.

U.S. Department of the Interior Geological Survey. 1970. The National Atlas of the United States of America. Washington, D.C.

Wade, O. 1930. The behavior of certain spermophiles with special reference to aestivation and hibernation. J. Mamm., 11:160–188.

———. 1950. Soil temperatures, weather conditions, and emergence of ground squirrels from hibernation. J. Mamm., 31:158–161.

Ward, J. M., Jr., and K. B. Armitage. 1981. Circannual rhythms of food consumption, body mass, and metabolism in yellow-bellied marmots. Comp. Biochem. Physiol., 69A:621–626.

Wistrand, H. 1974. Individual, social, and seasonal behavior of the thirteen-lined ground squirrel (*Spermophilus tridecemlineatus*). J. Mamm., 55:329–347.

Zimny, M. L. 1965. Thirteen-lined ground squirrels born in captivity. J. Mamm., 46:521–522.

GARY L. BINTZ

Eastern Montana College

Chapter 7

Water Balance, Water Stress, and the Evolution of Seasonal Torpor in Ground-Dwelling Sciurids

Abstract. Although the adaptive significance of hibernation generally is thought to be a reduced energy requirement, water stress also may have been a selective factor in evolution of torpor. During the early part of the active season, sciurid hibernators maintain water balance without the need to drink by relying largely upon succulent vegetation and the humid burrow. As summer progresses vegetation dries and consumption of other foods, including seeds, fruits, insects, and tissues of other animals, increases. Water balance through the winter is not possible on these foods because some contain insufficient water (seeds, dry vegetation) and others are transient (insects and animal tissues). Many hibernators store large quantities of fat, and although water balance from fat catabolism may be possible in euthermia when the animal remains in its burrow, insufficient fat is stored for survival over the winter if the animal maintains euthermia. Hibernation allows reduced fat use, reduced vapor pressure gradients between the animal and its environment, and therefore approximate water balance over several months in the burrow. Although several factors probably were involved in the evolution of hibernation, the conclusion that water stress was one of them appears inescapable.

Introduction

Low ambient temperature and the consequent need for large amounts of metabolic energy to maintain euthermia are the conditions most often cited as directing the evolution of hibernation (Hudson, 1978). Accordingly, torpor in the burrow allows avoidance of extreme temperatures and conserves energy. Hibernation also conserves water, though this is less well recognized than hibernation as an adaptation for energy conservation. Many rodents must survive several months when little water is available, and several species of sciurid hibernators survive the entire season of torpor apparently without eating or drinking. In particular, maintaining water balance appears most difficult in summer, when drying of vegetation and high ambient temperatures decrease water availability and increase water loss, and during fall and winter, when water availability may be intermittent. Among some northern species of ground-dwelling sciurids, for example, *Spermophilus richardsonii* in Alberta, adult males and females enter hibernation as early as June and July when ambient temperatures are still increasing (Michener, 1977, 1979, this volume). Such early immergence suggests that seasonal torpor may have adaptive value in addition to energy conservation during periods of cool ambient temperatures.

The hypothesis considered in this chapter is that water stress is one factor that selected for torpor in many ground-dwelling sciurids. The question whether sciurid hibernators could remain in water balance throughout fall and winter while euthermic and depending on available resources is central to this hypothesis. Therefore I discuss water sources, routes of water loss, problems of water balance for animals remaining euthermic throughout fall and winter, and water metabolism in different microenvironments occupied by a single species.

Another means of evaluating the role of water stress in the evolution of hibernation is to compare water metabolism in hibernators to that of relatives that do not hibernate. In several cases hibernating species are less efficient in water conservation than closely related nonhibernators, which has led to the suggestion that hibernation in some groups may have evolved because the animals cannot adapt sufficient water conservation mechanisms to maintain water balance in euthermia during fall and winter (Bakko, 1977).

Availability of Water

Succulent food often satisfies the water requirements of many ground-dwelling sciurids; consequently, water and energy are ingested simultaneously in the natural environment. The availability of drinking water separately from dry food is one of the unnatural aspects of a laboratory, and laboratory experiments designed to test effects of food or water deprivation may not always approximate field conditions.

Many ground-dwelling sciurids appear able to live independent of drinking water (Linsdale, 1946). Water is often drunk when available (Grinnell and Dixon, 1918; Linsdale, 1946), but in many habitats standing water is so infrequent that it may be discounted as a necessity for survival of many species. Food may be the only source of water for many animals, as preformed water and water from oxidation of hydrogen in food. It follows that an animal undergoing starvation should experience water deprivation.

The diet of hibernators: the relation between food and water. Many studies have described qualitatively the diets of several sciurid species, and most species depend largely on green vegetation, especially early in the season of activity (Iverson and Turner, 1972; Linsdale, 1946; Rogers and Gano, 1980; Shaw, 1921; Vorhies, 1945). Several authors have made quantitative investigations of sciurid diets. Clark (1968) studied the diet of the Wyoming ground squirrel (*Spermophilus elegans*), an obligate hibernator, and found that from April to August green plant material decreased from 96% to 34%, seeds increased from 1% to 42%, and animal tissues increased from 3% to 24% of stomach contents. Over the whole period of study, green plant material constituted 73%, seeds 11%, animal tissues 14%, and insects 2% of total stomach contents. Similarly, Hawbecker (1947) observed that green plant material constituted 70% to 80% of the stomach contents of the Nelson antelope ground squirrel (*Ammospermophilus nelsoni*), a nonhibernator, from mid-December to May, the time of availability of green material, whereas insects represented 90% of the stomach contents during the remainder of the year. Succulent herbage also was the primary component of the diet of the California ground squirrel (*Spermophilus beecheyi*), a permissive hibernator, from February to May, the period when this material was available; from June to November flower buds, grasses, seeds, acorns, and insects were eaten (Linsdale, 1946). Kelso (1939) recorded stomach contents of 247 black-tailed prairie dogs (*Cynomys ludovicianus*), a nonhibernator, and 169 white-tailed prairie dogs (*C. leucurus*), an obligate hibernator, throughout the year. Vegetable matter composed essentially the entire diet of both species except in May, when cutworms formed 10% of the stomach contents of black-tailed prairie dogs, and July, when cutworms were 9% of the stomach contents of white-tailed prairie dogs. Fagerstone et al. (1981) reported that grasses and forbs represented more than 99% of the stomach contents of black-tailed prairie dogs during December to February and during May, June, and September. Furthermore, in January and February, when succulent grasses were unavailable, prickly pear cactus (80% water) was the most prevalent dietary item.

Ground-dwelling sciurids eat small vertebrates when available. California ground squirrels ate trapped birds (Linsdale, 1946). Franklin's ground squirrels, *Spermophilus franklinii*, killed and ate laboratory mice (Iverson and Turner,

1972) and ate duck eggs under natural conditions (Sowls, 1948). Thirteen-lined ground squirrels, *S. tridecemlineatus,* have been reported to kill and eat a variety of vertebrates, including mice, rabbits, and birds (Bridgewater and Penny, 1966). Cannibalism has been observed in several species, including yellow-bellied marmots, *Marmota flaviventris* (Armitage et al., 1979), and Arctic ground squirrels, *S. parryii* (Holmes, 1977). Richardson's ground squirrels eat road-killed conspecifics (pers. obs.). Although opportunistic consumption of vertebrates by ground-dwelling sciurids is common, few species appear to de-pend regularly upon this source of food. Franklin's ground squirrels may be an exception. Sowls (1948) observed that animal material other than insects com-posed one-third of the diet of *S. franklini* throughout the year.

In summary, the diets of ground-dwelling sciurids reflect the following: (1) succulent vegetation composes most of the diet when it is available; (2) when succulent vegetation is unavailable consumption of other food sources with a high water content, such as insects and animal matter, increases; (3) dry foods (e.g., seeds) rarely compose a majority of the diet at any season; (4) although most species are perhaps opportunistic carnivores, few species normally acquire more than approximately 15–20% of their energy requirements from other verte-brates; and (5) there appears to be little relation between diet and the pattern (obligate or facultative) of hibernation. Landry (1970) reviewed the omnivorous nature of rodents, including several species of *Spermophilus.*

Ground-dwelling sciurids depend heavily upon succulent vegetation, though in doing so many species use only a small portion of the total forage available. Kilgore and Armitage (1978) reported that yellow-bellied marmots ate only 0.8% to 3.1% of the available net primary production. Zegers and Williams (1979) noted that energy consumption by *S. elegans* accounted for 0.68% to 0.79% of the available primary production. Schitoskey and Woodmansee (1978) reported that an *S. beecheyi* population of 8.4 animals per ha required only 0.6, 0.4, and 0.2% of the forage biomass available in February, March, and April, respectively. It is difficult to describe hibernation as a response only for energy conservation when so much of the available forage is unused.

For several species, especially those in northern latitudes, emergence occurs when little green herbage is available, and animals rely temporarily upon remain-ing body fat (Galster and Morrison, 1976; Kiell and Millar, 1980).

Water in food. With the exception of seeds, the common foods of ground-dwelling sciurids have a very high water content. Succulent grasses contain 68% to 77% water; but water content of these grasses may decrease to 7% to 10% in the dry season (Hayward, 1961), and this may account for the transition to other food sources such as arthropods and vertebrates, which have a water content of 60% to 75%.

Water content plays an important role in sciurids' food selection. The round-tailed ground squirrel (*Spermophilus tereticaudus*) depends on succulent grasses and annuals and makes little use of fruit and dry seeds or cactus (Vorhies, 1945). California ground squirrels began feeding on seeds and acorns as herbage dried seasonally (Linsdale, 1946). Arctic ground squirrels did not eat vegetation that had less than 50% water, and three-fifths of that eaten had a water content of at least 70% (Batzli and Sobaski, 1980). Nelson antelope ground squirrels will eat turpentine weed and snakeweed only when other greens are unavailable (Haw-becker, 1947). Presumably the unpalatability of these two species is secondary to their water content when other succulents are absent. *S. pygmaeus* may be exceptional in that it consumes plant material with as little as 30% water (Formozov and Kodachova, 1961). Additional studies on the water content of the diet of sciurids are necessary to determine if water intake changes as the active season progresses and as available vegetation matures and seeds ripen.

Several species, including some hibernators, cache food. Temporary under-ground storage may increase water content of dry foods such as seeds. *Xerus inauris,* a ground squirrel of southern Africa, depends upon food stored under-ground during the dry season but not during the wet season (Marsh et al., 1978). *S. mexicanus* stores food for the hibernating season (Fisher and Manery, 1967). Shaw (1926) noted that 21 of 41 hibernation dens of the Columbian ground squir-rel contained food stores.

Water Loss

Water is lost through the alimentary canal, the urine, and insensibly through the skin and from pulmonary passages. The importance of these routes of water loss changes with season and activity. For example, active, well-fed rodents lose most water via the kidney or via the kidney and by evaporation, whereas in starved animals evaporation represents the major means of water loss (Bintz et al., 1979; Schmidt-Nielsen and Schmidt-Nielsen, 1951). During hibernation evaporation may be the only significant route of water loss.

Fecal water loss. Fecal water loss in most mammals varies with the amount of undigested material passing through the large intestine and the amount of water consumed. Reduction of food intake, whether caused directly or indirectly through self-imposed starvation brought about by water deprivation, reduces fecal water loss.

Fecal water content is often low in animals that are adapted to xeric conditions. On a diet of pearled barley, feces of laboratory rats averaged 68% water, whereas feces of kangaroo rats, *Dipodomys merriami*, were only 45% water (Schmidt-Nielsen and Schmidt-Nielsen, 1951). Contrarily, Blackwell and Pivorun (1979) observed no differences in fecal water content of three parapatric species of *Peromyscus* at the same ambient temperature, even though *P. polionotus* lives in an area with less precipitation than *P. maniculatus* and *P. leucopus*. Within each species there was an inverse relation between fecal water content and air temperature.

Little study has been done on fecal water loss of ground-dwelling sciurids. Daily fecal water loss in *Spermophilus richardsonii* averaged 6.3, 0.08, and 0.03 ml respectively for control animals, animals starved 7 days, and animals starved and water-deprived 7 days (Bintz and Mackin, 1980). Fecal water content was 45% to 50% in starved and water-deprived animals, similar to that of water-deprived kangaroo rats. Because hibernation is also a state of starvation, fecal water loss would be essentially nonexistent during hibernation and would probably be insignificant during the onset of hibernation. Data regarding possible changes in fecal water loss as diets change during the active season would be useful.

Urinary water loss. The ability to concentrate urine is an important adaptation of many desert-dwelling rodents, in particular those that can survive on dry diets. Maximum urine concentrations of desert-dwelling rodents are among the highest known for mammals (Table 7.1), and concentrations above 4,000 milliosmols/l have been reported for several species (Hewitt et al., 1981; Schmidt-Nielsen and O'Dell, 1961; Smith, 1951). Even wild house mice are capable of producing urine of 4,500 milliosmols/l (Haines et al., 1973), which is approximately 50% greater than the maximum urine osmolarity of domesticated mice.

Ground-dwelling sciurids are incapable of concentrating urine to the extent observed for many heteromyid and dipodid rodents. Most ground squirrels can produce urine between 2,500 and 3,800 milliosmols/l (Table 7.1). Maximum urine concentrations in chipmunks, marmots, and prairie dogs appear to average slightly lower than in ground squirrels. Within ground-dwelling sciurids there is a relation between aridity of the environment and maximum urine osmolarity. The antelope ground squirrel, *Ammospermophilus leucurus,* which occupies arid environments, produces urine up to 3,730 milliosmols/l (Hudson, 1962),

TABLE 7.1. Maximum urine osmolarity of rodents

Species	Maximum mosm/l	Source
Desert dwellers		
Nonsciurids		
Dipodomys merriami	5,600	Smith, 1951
Notomys alexis	6,230	Hewitt et al., 1981
Jaculus jaculus	6,500	Schmidt-Nielsen and O'Dell, 1961
Psammomys obesus	5,000	Schmidt-Nielsen and O'Dell, 1961
Neotoma albigula	3,295	Schmidt-Nielsen et al., 1948
Sciurids		
Ammospermophilus leucurus	3,730	Hudson, 1962
Non-desert-dwelling sciurids		
Spermophilus beecheyi	2,886	Baudinette, 1974
S. lateralis	2,425	Blake, 1977
S. richardsonii	3,000–3,300	Bintz and Roesbery, 1978
Tamias striatus	2,591	Blake, 1977
Cynomys leucurus	2,300	Bakko, 1977
C. ludovicianus [a]	2,800	Bakko, 1977
C. ludovicianus		Pfeiffer et al., 1979
Summer SWD 41 days [b]	2,781	
Winter SWD 56 days	1,640	
S. columbianus		
Dehydrated	2,800	Moy, 1971
Hibernating	1,518	Moy et al., 1972
Arousing	2,792	Moy et al., 1972
Marmota flaviventris		
Hibernating	611	Zatzman and South, 1975
Arousing	1,264	

[a] Not an obligate hibernator.
[b] SWD = starved and water-deprived.

which is the highest for any ground squirrel. The antelope ground squirrel posesses a kidney in which the glomeruli, proximal and distal convoluted tubules, and long renal papillae resemble those of the kangaroo rat (Hudson, 1962). On the other hand, the montane golden-mantled ground squirrel, *Spermophilus lateralis,* has a maximum urine concentration of 2,425 milliosmols/l (Blake, 1977). Even intraspecific differences in renal characteristics occur in different habitats. Relative medullary thickness in *Eutamias* spp. varied directly with dryness of habitat (Blake, 1977), and Bakko (1975) observed a greater relative medullary thickness in upland forest red squirrels, *Tamiasciurus hudsonicus,* than in river bottom conspecifics.

Some data suggest certain sciurid species capable of hibernation have maximum urine osmolarities lower than those of closely related nonhibernating species. For example, *A. leucurus* is generally not regarded as a hibernator, but it excretes a more concentrated urine than most other ground squirrels. When deprived of water in the laboratory, black-tailed prairie dogs, which do not hibernate, demonstrated greater urine concentrating ability (2,800 milliosmols/l) than white-tailed prairie dogs (2,300 milliosmols/l), which are capable of hibernation, even though the former species inhabits a more mesic environment (Bakko, 1977). The difference in urine osmolarities was not as great under field conditions. Maximum urine concentration also varies with season. Pfeiffer et al. (1979) recorded urine of 2,781 milliosmols/l in laboratory dehydrated summer black-tailed prairie dogs and only 1,640 milliosmols/l in laboratory dehydrated winter animals.

Maximum urine concentrations are usually observed from animals that have been water deprived under laboratory conditions, and urine from field animals is often less concentrated (Bakko, 1977; Baudinette, 1974). The occurrence of submaximal urine osmolarities under field conditions suggests that animals are not severely water stressed in the field.

Evaporative water loss. Evaporative water loss (EWL) is a major means of water loss from rodents. EWL occurs through pulmonary passages and from the skin. The rate of evaporation is determined by the surface area over which evaporation occurs and the vapor pressure gradient. The surface area for evaporation may vary somewhat in rodents and considerably in bats (Chew and White, 1960) with changes in body position. Vapor pressure gradient depends upon temperature of the surfaces from which evaporation occurs, temperature of surrounding air, and ambient humidity. The temperature gradient between skin and air is not the same as that between pulmonary passages and air. For a euthermic rodent in an air temperature of 22° to 24°C, skin temperature may be 30° to 32°C, whereas temperature of the air in the nasal passages may be only 1.0°C greater than ambient air (Schmid, 1976). Michener (1979) reported mean maximum temperatures of 26°C in July in the habitat of southern Alberta populations of Richardson's ground squirrels. In our laboratory temperatures of 27° to 29°C were measured at a depth of 0.5 cm in the nasal passages of *S. richardsonii* when the rectal temperature was 39°C and the air temperature was 26°C. Temperature in nasal passages decreases as air temperature falls; consequently, EWL decreases with lowered air temperature (Baudinette, 1972; Blackwell and Pivorun, 1979; Hudson and Deavers, 1973; Lindstedt, 1980; Studier and O'Farrell, 1976; Withers et al., 1979).

149

Annual Cycles

Evaporative water loss from skin has been compared with that from pulmonary passages. We calculated that evaporation from skin was similar to that from pulmonary passages for Richardson's ground squirrels at an air temperature of 22° or 24°C (Bintz et al., 1979). Baudinette (1972) calculated that 63% of the total evaporative loss by *S. beecheyi* occurred from pulmonary passages and the remainder from the skin. On the other hand, Schmidt-Nielsen and Schmidt-Nielsen (1952) concluded that nearly all of the EWL from kangaroo rats occurred via pulmonary passages.

Evaporative water loss is influenced by the amount of water available to the animal. Water restriction resulted in decreased EWL from *Peromyscus leucopus* (Deavers and Hudson, 1979), spiny mice, *Acomys cahirinus* (Daily and Haines, 1981), *S. richardsonii* (Bintz et al., 1979), and *S. beecheyi* (Baudinette, 1974). After 5 days of starvation and water deprivation, *S. richardsonii* reduced EWL 31% when expressed as a function of oxygen consumption (Bintz and Roesbery, 1978).

Comparing EWL between species is difficult because there has not been great consistency in the ambient humidity or air temperature under which EWL has been measured. Despite this, it can be concluded that EWL is usually lowest in desert-dwelling rodents (Table 7.2). Evaporative water loss is somewhat higher in ground-dwelling sciurids; EWL ranges between approximately 0.5 and 1.5 mg H_2O/ml O_2 at temperatures between 21° and 24°C (Table 7.2). Within the sciurids there is an indirect relation between EWL in dry air and aridity of the habitat. For example, Hudson and Deavers (1973) noted that Townsend's ground squirrel, *Spermophilus townsendii,* and the spotted ground squirrel, *S. spilosoma,* which inhabit arid environments, had lower EWL than three other species of sciurids that inhabit moister environments. Although *Ammospermophilus leucurus* has a low EWL (Hudson, 1962), there is no other evidence that nonhibernators have lower EWL than closely related hibernators.

The proportion of total water loss attributed to evaporation increases with water restriction. When ground squirrels are water deprived, the concentration of urine increases and urine volume decreases. These changes are of considerable magnitude; for example, urine volume of *S. richardsonii* decreased from 16.8 ml/day when unlimited water was available to 6 ml/day and 1.0 ml/day after 1 and 7 days of food and water deprivation (Bintz and Mackin, 1980). Reduction in fecal water loss was of even greater relative magnitude, being 6.3 ml/day by control ground squirrels and 0.03 ml/day after 7 days of food and water deprivation (Bintz and Mackin, 1980). Reduction in EWL under similar conditions is much less. Bintz and Mackin (1980) reported EWL of 12.3 ml/day by control Richardson's ground squirrels and 9.6 ml/day after 7 days of starvation and

Water Balance, Water Stress, and Seasonal Torpor

TABLE 7.2. Evaporative water loss by rodents

Species	Mg H_2O/ml O_2	T_a,°C[a]	Source
Desert dwellers			
Nonsciurids			
Dipodomys merriami	0.54	22–24	Schmidt-Nielsen and Schmidt-Nielsen, 1950
D. spectabilis	0.57	22–24	Schmidt-Nielsen and Schmidt-Nielsen, 1950
Sciurids			
Ammospermophilus leucurus	0.53	22	Hudson, 1962
	1.38	28	
Non-desert-dwellers			
Nonsciurids			
Mus musculus	0.85	22–24	Schmidt-Nielsen and Schmidt-Nielsen, 1950
Rattus norvegicus, domesticated	0.94	22–24	Schmidt-Nielsen and Schmidt-Nielsen, 1950
Sciurids			
Spermophilus beecheyi	0.52	15[b]	Baudinette, 1972
	1.60	20[c]	
S. spilosoma	0.5–0.8	9–11	Hudson and Deavers, 1973
	0.6–1.1	19–21	
S. townsendii	0.5–1.0	9–11	Hudson and Deavers, 1973
	0.5–1.2	19–21	
S. lateralis	0.5–0.8	9–11	Hudson and Deavers, 1973
	0.6–1.0	19–21	
S. armatus	0.5–1.2	9–11	Hudson and Deavers, 1973
	0.6–1.4	19–21	
S. beldingi	0.5–1.0	9–11	Hudson and Deavers, 1973
	0.6–1.4	19–21	
S. richardsonii			
Control	1.74	24	Bintz and Mackin, 1980
Starved and water deprived 7d	1.18	24	
S. tridecemlineatus			
Euthermic	0.78	7	Deavers and Musacchia, 1980
Torpid	0.94	7	

[a] All measurements were made in dry air except where noted.

[b] 7.8 mm Hg WVP

[c] 10.7 mm Hg WVP

151

water deprivation. During starvation and water deprivation, EWL is by far the greatest means of water loss (Bintz and Mackin, 1980); therefore EWL and an animal's ability to reduce it probably represent the limiting factors in tolerance when water intake is severely restricted. Occupancy of the burrow and reducing body temperature are the most important responses for reducing EWL by ground-dwelling sciurids.

Can Ground-Dwelling Sciurids Maintain Water Balance Through Fall and Winter Without Hibernating?

To evaluate the influence of water stress on evolution of hibernation in sciurids, we must examine the extent to which animals actually are stressed by the amount of water available. It may be unlikely that hibernation could have evolved as a response to water stress if hibernators were able to remain euthermic and in water balance throughout the fall and winter (assuming energy balance was possible). Accordingly, if hibernation is a response to water stress: (1) hibernators should be unable to maintain water balance on foods available during the drier seasons; (2) hibernators should be unable to maintain water balance and survive for a hibernating season while euthermic and starving; and (3) hibernators should be able to maintain water balance through the period of unavailability of succulent food when depending on stored body energy and torpor. An alternative hypothesis, that once hibernation evolved the selective pressure for water conservation was relaxed and hibernators became less capable of water conservation than their nonhibernating counterparts, is not considered here.

During fall and winter, water is available consistently from two sources — food and water in the animal's body tissues. Although rain and snow are potential sources of water for sciurids in certain environments, in other habitats precipitation in fall and winter occurs so infrequently that the availability of water cannot be depended upon; consequently, precipitation and standing water are excluded from consideration.

Use of available foods and water balance. In many habitats there is probably sufficient dry vegetation to supply energy requirements of ground-dwelling sciurids throughout fall and winter (Kilgore and Armitage, 1978; Schitoskey and Woodmansee, 1978; Zegers and Williams, 1979). At such times dry vegetation and seeds represent the most abundant, if not the only source of food for several species, and much of the time these would be the only external sources of water. If the composition of food is known, an animal's ability to maintain water balance on that food source can be calculated (Table 7.3). In the spring and early summer

Spermophilus richardsonii eats hound's-tongue, *Cynoglossum officinale,* and the following discussion is based upon use of this plant alone, though many other plant species are also eaten under natural conditions. Leaves of fresh hound's-tongue contain 84.5% water, 3.7% lipid, and 4.5% protein. The remainder, discounting ash, is considered to be carbohydrate. (Analyses were done in our laboratory.) The succulent nature of this plant allows water balance during spring and early summer by Richardson's ground squirrels (Table 7.3). Air-dried plants contained only 12% water, and this water content approximates that of other plants later in summer when precipitation is infrequent (Hayward, 1961). Richardson's ground squirrels could not maintain water balance on dehydrated hound's-tongue (Table 7.3). Richardson's ground squirrels also eat *Cryptantha interrupta, Cynoglossum* sp., *Mertensia paniculata, Lomatium ambiguum, Lomatium* sp., *Lepidum perfoliatum, Penstemon albidus, Hypericum perforatum,* and *Draba* sp. in Montana. Although the water content of these plants is high in early summer, presumably any combination of these plant species would not allow water balance when they are dried. Other foods with high water content must be eaten if ground squirrels are to maintain water balance and remain aboveground in mid to late summer.

Although the laboratory has major differences from the natural environment, including drinking water, ad lib. food with a high nitrogen content (stock diets), and absence of the burrow, there are enough similarities so we can discuss the ability of animals to maintain water balance in the field based on laboratory studies if the differences can be quantified. Standard laboratory chow is approximately 7% to 8% water, 20% protein, 4% lipid, and 60% digestible carbohydrate. On such a diet with no drinking water, golden-mantled ground squirrels lost weight as rapidly as when both food and water were unavailable (Riedesel et al., 1964). Spotted ground squirrels, which inhabit more arid environments than golden-mantled ground squirrels, lost weight rapidly when only dry food was available, but not as rapidly as when both food and water were absent, or as rapidly as golden-mantled ground squirrels when only dry food was available (Riedesel et al., 1964). Round-tailed ground squirrels could not maintain body weight at 22–27°C when allowed only dry seeds and commercial rat food (Hudson, 1964), despite an ambient humidity of 40% to 60%. Even antelope ground squirrels, which do not hibernate, could not maintain weight on food alone when the food contained only 10% water. Since dried vegetation has a water content similar to laboratory stock diets, it is doubtful that ground squirrels could maintain water balance on dried vegetation even if the vegetation were stored in the burrow to increase its water content or the animal spent much time in the burrow to reduce EWL.

TABLE 7.3. Estimated water availability and water balance for *Spermophilus richardsonii* on a diet of *Cynoglossum officinale*

Material for metabolic requirements/day (g)	Water available (ml)				Water loss/day (ml)				Net water balance (ml)
	kcal[c]	Preformed	Oxidative[d]	Total	EWL[e]	Fecal[f]	Urine[g]	Total	
Fresh leaves[a] 30.6	24.2	26.0	2.7	28.7	11.6	6.3	4.2	22.1	+ 6.6
Air-dried leaves[b] 5.0	24.2	0.6	2.7	3.3	11.6	6.3	4.2	22.1	− 18.8

[a] Plants were collected in May shortly after sprouting. Water content, 84.5%.

[b] Plants were collected in May and air dried at 24°C and 30% humidity to constant weight. Water content after air drying, 12%.

[c] Based upon a 400 g animal with a metabolic rate of 0.6 ml O_2 $g^{-1} h^{-1}$ (Baudinette, 1972).

[d] Calculated from Peters and Van Slyke (1946): 1.0 g of protein, fat, and carbohydrate would produce 0.40, 1.07, and 0.56 g of oxidative water, respectively.

[e] EWL = evaporative water loss, measured in the laboratory when humidity was 30% and air temperature was 22–24°C (Bintz et al., 1979).

[f] The value is for laboratory-acclimated animals that had free access to drinking water and were fed 15 g of Wayne Lab Blox/day (Bintz et al., 1979).

[g] Based upon a maximum urine concentration of 3,000 mosm/l, about two-thirds of which is urea (Bintz and Roesbery, 1978). The volume of urine is the minimum required to excrete the nitrogen present in the diet.

Use of stored fat. Adipose tissue of obese *S. richardsonii* contains approximately 3% protein, 4% water, and 92% lipid (Bintz and Mackin, 1980). As lipid is depleted the proportions of water and protein increase; consequently lipid appears to be selectively removed when adipose tissue serves as a source of energy. One gram of lipid produces 1.07 g of water but requires 2.01 l of O_2 for oxidation (Peters and Van Slyke, 1946); therefore an animal oxidizing fat could evaporate no more than 0.54 mg H_2O/ml O_2 and still maintain water balance from fat catabolism alone. Under laboratory conditions and in dry air EWL of starved, water-deprived Richardson's ground squirrels was more than twice this rate (Bintz and Mackin, 1980). Even at 30% humidity in the laboratory, obese ground squirrels without water lose weight rapidly.

A humid environment would decrease EWL and perhaps allow water balance from fat catabolism without need of becoming torpid. In burrows of *S. beecheyi* humidity was 68% to 87% in August and 78% to 95% in December (Baudinette, 1972). Baudinette also measured EWL by *S. beecheyi* under conditions that approximated a burrow environment. Evaporative water loss was 0.52 mg H_2O/ml O_2 at 15°C air temperature and 60% humidity. Therefore an animal could maintain water balance from fat catabolism while remaining euthermic if a humid environment with a moderately low ambient temperature was available. Even though an animal may maintain water balance under such conditions, there is not enough fat stored by a hibernator to last through fall and winter in euthermia, despite the extensive prehibernatory fattening of some animals. *S. parryii,* for example, accumulates adipose tissue up to 40% of total body weight (Galster and Morrison, 1976). Assuming the animal remains in the burrow and has an average metabolic rate of 0.6 ml $O_2 g^{-1} h^{-1}$ (Baudinette, 1972), a 400 g animal would require 24.2 kcal/day. That amount of energy would be supplied by 2.6 g of lipid, or about 3.0 g of adipose tissue. Even if a 400 g ground squirrel stored 200 g of adipose tissue (Morrison, 1960), the lipid stores would be depleted in 67 days in these circumstances. Hibernators are underground much longer. The inactive season for adult female *S. richardsonii* averaged 234 to 258 days (Michener, 1979). There is simply insufficient adipose tissue stored to survive the winter in euthermia without supplementary food.

The possibility exists that animals could remain euthermic and maintain water balance by combining use of stored lipid and dry vegetation. Since it appears that ground squirrels could only maintain water balance (and not gain water) through use of lipid and would probably be in negative water balance when depending upon dry vegetation and seeds, it is unlikely that this combination could result in overall water balance.

Selective tissue catabolism and water balance. Lipid catabolism alone disallows water balance (Chew, 1965), but the catabolism of lean body mass, which contains much free water, in combination with lipid oxidation allows water balance during starvation and water deprivation (Bintz and Mackin, 1980). Therefore one may consider whether a euthermic animal might achieve water balance through fall and winter by relying on catabolism of lean body mass and adipose tissue. In dry air and during euthermia a great deal of lean body mass must be catabolized to maintain water balance, and *S. richardsonii* does not survive more than several days even though dehydration does not occur (Bintz et al., 1979; Bintz and Riedesel, 1967). In a more humid environment or at lower body temperature when EWL would be less, as might occur when a burrow is available, such a mechanism may be of more adaptive value to an animal faced with periodic starvation and water deprivation. Other sciurids appear more tolerant of starvation and water deprivation than *S. richardsonii*. Spotted ground squirrels survived 42 days without food and water (Riedesel et al., 1964), and black-tailed prairie dogs (nonhibernators) were alive after 56 days of starvation and water deprivation (Pfeiffer et al., 1979). It is doubtful, however, that there is sufficient lean body mass and lipid to survive fall and winter without some other means of acquiring water and energy or reducing their consumption.

In summary, although a euthermic hibernator may be able to maintain water balance throughout fall and winter by remaining in the burrow and relying on oxidative water, there is insufficient stored energy if the animal remains euthermic. More work is necessary on the ability of different sciurids to maintain water balance on the foods available in fall and winter, but it does not appear from present data that most sciurids can maintain water balance on foods available throughout the year. The role of the burrow in water balance for hibernating and active sciurids is an important area for future research.

Water Balance during Hibernation

During hibernation an animal uses lipid as nearly the sole source of energy (Kayser, 1961). With the large amount of metabolic water from lipid oxidation and the low EWL resulting from a very low vapor pressure gradient between the animal and its burrow environment, the possibility of overhydration during hibernation was considered (Fisher and Manery, 1967). Intolerable dilution of body fluids would result if all metabolic water were retained; however, overhydration does not appear to occur during hibernation. Riedesel et al. (1964) measured water content of spleen, kidney, lung, and skeletal muscle in active, water-deprived, and hibernating *S. spilosoma* and *S. lateralis*. Skeletal muscle dehydrated during hibernation, whereas water content of other tissues was similar to that of the same tissues in active animals with ad lib. water. Mayer and Schaeffer (1914–1915) observed similar results in hibernating and active woodchucks. Therefore the percentage of body water does not change markedly during hibernation. Even though vapor pressure gradients in hibernation would be low, evaporation probably removes much of the water formed from oxidation of lipid.

Water Balance from Fat Catabolism at Different Body Temperatures

In well-fed animals, torpor often occurs in association with decreased ambient temperature. As ambient temperature falls below the thermoneutral zone, metabolic energy would be required to remain euthermic; consequently, considerable energy is saved by torpor. Krumbiegel (1955, cited in Kayser, 1961) described the upper thermal limit compatible with hibernation as 20° to 22°C for several species of ground squirrels. Observations of *S. lateralis* in our laboratory have yielded similar results. During January and February of 1972 we observed 22 *S. lateralis* in a room in which air temperature fluctuated between 17° and 25°C. For days on which air temperature was above 22°C (23–25°C), an average of only 41% of the animals were torpid, whereas on days when air temperature was ≤22°C (17–22°C) an average of 81% of the animals were torpid. During the two months of observation the air temperature was never above or below 22°C for more than three days consecutively. Although torpor clearly seems related to air temperature, water metabolism may be an additional factor in the onset of torpor at a temperature near 22°C. Fat is the source of energy and water during hibernation, and water balance from fat catabolism is allowed if EWL is less than 0.54 mg H_2O/ml O_2. This rate of water loss was achieved by *S. lateralis* when body temperature fell to 21–23°C (Table 7.4), which is a body temperature one might expect if an animal became torpid in an ambient temperature of 20–22°C. Thus the air temperature at which *S. lateralis* became hypothermic is also the body temperature that allows water balance from fat catabolism. At higher body temperatures too much water was evaporated to allow water balance with adipose tissue as the sole source of water (Table 7.4). These observations are based on EWL measured in dry air, and further conservation of water would be expected in the burrow. In comparison with euthermia, torpor not only increases the likelihood that fat deposits will be sufficient to last through the hibernating season but assures that water balance will be maintained during that period.

　　Water-deprived and starved euthermic ground squirrels maintain water balance by catabolizing lean body mass and adipose tissue, whereas hibernating animals consume lipid and suffer modest dehydration at most. By comparison,

TABLE 7.4: Body temperature, metabolic rate, and evaporative water loss of
Spermophilus lateralis at different ambient temperatures

Temperature (°C)		Metabolic rate	Evaporative water loss
Air	Rectal	$(Ml\ O_2\ g^{-1}h^{-1})$	$(Mg\ H_2O/ml\ O_2)$
21	34.5–36.6	1.38 ± 0.07	1.09 ± 0.09
18	21.0–23.4	0.39 ± 0.04	0.57 ± 0.08
8–10	11.6–13.2	0.16 ± 0.06	0.49 ± 0.09

euthermic laboratory rats that were starved and water deprived consumed lipid primarily and dehydrated (Bintz et al., 1971; Bintz and Riedesel, 1967). Given the relation among body temperature, EWL, and fat metabolism, it is reasonable that hibernation may be a response not only to conserve energy, but also to allow water balance from the source of energy.

Does Water Deprivation Induce Hibernation?

Several authors have suggested that lack of drinking water may bring about hibernation. Kalabukhov (1960) observed that dry food induced torpor in several sciurid species. California ground squirrels decreased activity when humidity fell below 30% (Linsdale, 1946), although the behavior may have been a response to the high temperatures that normally accompanied lowered humidity. Shaw (1921) believed that dehydration of the vegetation eaten by Townsend's ground squirrels led to their hibernation. Foster et al. (1939) studied the effects of food and water deprivation on entrance into hibernation by thirteen-lined ground squirrels, *S. tridecemlineatus*, in September. Of the food- and water-deprived animals 74% entered hibernation compared with only 12% of those deprived of food but allowed water. *Peromyscus eremicus* became dormant in summer when water resources were minimal (MacMillen, 1965), although starvation may also have been a factor.

Despite these reports, other authors have postulated that water deprivation alone is not a good stimulus for hibernation. Hudson (1964) suggested that food deprivation was more effective than water deprivation in inducing torpor in round-tailed ground squirrels. Davis (1967) concluded that drinking water deprivation alone did not stimulate torpor in woodchucks, *Marmota monax*, whereas food deprivation was effective in precipitating torpor. In all of these studies attempts were made to segregate food and water deprivation. Such a situation may not exist in the field. Hudson (1978) described difficulties in drawing conclusions about the natural environment based upon laboratory studies. Furthermore, one must be cautious in extending observations on short-term responses to conclusions regarding evolutionary adaptations. A stimulus that brings about a response actually may be peripheral to the adaptive nature of that response. For example, seasonal changes in pelage of many mammals may be triggered by photoperiod, whereas the adaptive value may concern temperature regulation (Beck, 1963). Similarly, studies relating food or water deprivation to induction of hibernation are not necessarily instructive regarding the role of each in the evolution of hibernation, especially since food and water intake are rarely separated in the field. The failure of water deprivation to bring about hibernation in many species does not remove water stress from the list of factors that may have directed the evolution of torpor.

The Evolution of Seasonal Torpor in Response to Water Stress

If hibernation in many rodents is a primitive phenomenon as Cade (1964) proposed, one cannot argue that hibernation evolved in response to water stress, or to many other stresses. On the other hand, Twente and Twente (1964) suggested that hibernators evolved from strict homeotherms, and Hudson (1973) raised the possibility that hibernation is derived as physiological neoteny of certain altricial mammals. Hudson (1973) also described the paradox between the apparent morphologically primitive nature of species that hibernate and the sophisticated (suggesting more advanced) adaptations of hibernation.

Regardless of the phyletic origin of hibernation in sciurids, water metabolism appears to have played a role, assuming a more modern evolution of hibernation than that suggested by Cade. There are many differences in behavior and physiology among rodent hibernators; however, within the sciurids there are certain features that are reasonably consistent. Most hibernating sciurids appear incapable of maintaining water balance on dried vegetation alone, most store lipids and do not eat during the hibernating season but do not store sufficient energy as lipids or food in the burrow to survive the hibernating season in euthermia, and most cannot maintain water balance on lipid catabolism alone while euthermic. Both water balance and conservation of energy depend upon torpor. Black-tailed prairie dogs, although they are not obligate hibernators, may be exceptional in that they can tolerate starvation for many weeks without becoming torpid. Water stress may not be the trigger for induction of torpidity, but it could well be one selective factor in the evolution of hibernation. Entry into hibernation in May – June by adult Townsend's ground squirrels in Utah (Rickart, 1982) and in June –

July by adult Richardson's ground squirrels in southern Alberta (Michener, 1977, 1979, this volume) suggests that seasonal torpor is a response to more than just the increased energetic demands of the cold winter months. Both water stress and the need to conserve energy probably played a role in the evolution of hibernation.

Other attempts have been made to link water stress to the evolution of torpidity. Bakko (1977) described the greater maximum urine osmolarity under laboratory conditions, the greater relative renal medullary thickness, and the longer survival when water deprived of black-tailed versus white-tailed prairie dogs, despite the white-tailed prairie dogs' occupancy of more xeric areas. Bakko's suggestion that the poorer ability of white-tailed prairie dogs to cope with water stress may have led to their evolving the ability to hibernate, whereas black-tailed prairie dogs did not, is reasonable if we assume that white-tailed prairie dogs were actually water stressed more when hibernation evolved in this species. The extent to which animals are actually water stressed in the field is not known. Other sciurid species that do not hibernate are more capable of water conservation than closely related species that hibernate, but the adaptation for hibernation may not be the result of differences in water metabolism. For example, *Ammospermophilus leucurus* does not hibernate, concentrates urine more than any other sciurid, has a very low EWL, and maintains water balance while remaining active throughout the year. However, adaptations of the difference in water conserving ability between antelope ground squirrels (*Ammospermophilus*) and those species of ground squirrels (*Spermophilus*) capable of hibernation may have little to do with hibernation. North American deserts are geologically recent (Sellers, 1965), and desert-dwelling sciurids such as *A. leucurus* may have evolved their water-conserving abilities recently in response to these environments as opposed to a relationship with hibernation.

There is great variety of responses to water stress within the rodents, and many of these are certainly independent of hibernation. The kangaroo rat, *Dipodomys merriami*, and the wood rat, *Neotoma albigula*, occupy similar habitats (Vorhies, 1945) and do not hibernate, yet the former species has evolved extreme water conservation in response to the xeric conditions, whereas the wood rat eats succulent cacti and is much less capable of water conservation. Thus the kangaroo rat and the wood rat have evolved two distinct means of coping with an arid environment without dependence on seasonal torpidity. In the case of ground-dwelling sciurids, as succulent food becomes less available in summer there is little alternative to hypothermia for maintaining water balance, and water stress appears to have been a factor in the evolution of seasonal torpidity.

Literature Cited

Armitage, K., D. Johns, and D. Andersen. 1979. Cannibalism among yellow-bellied marmots. J. Mamm., 60:205–207.

Bakko, E. B. 1975. A field water balance study of gray squirrels (*Sciuris carolinensus*) and red squirrels (*Tamiasciurus hudsonicus*). Comp. Biochem. Physiol. 51A: 759–768.

———. 1977. Field water balance performances in prairie dogs (*Cynomys leucurus* and *C. ludovicianus*). Comp. Biochem. Physiol., 56A:443–451.

Batzli, G. O., and S. T. Sobaski. 1980. Distribution, abundance, and foraging patterns of ground squirrels near Atkasook, Alaska. Arctic Alp. Res., 12:501–510.

Baudinette, R. V. 1972. Energy metabolism and evaporative water loss in the California ground squirrel. J. Comp. Physiol., 81:57–72.

———. 1974. The physiology of chronic water deprivation in the California ground squirrel (*Spermophilus beecheyi*): relevance to natural populations. J. Zool. London, 173:159–171.

Beck, S. D. 1963. Animal photoperiodism. Holt, Rinehart, and Winston, New York, 124 pp.

Bintz, G. L., and W. W. Mackin. 1980. The effect of water availability on tissue catabolism during starvation in Richardson's ground squirrels. Comp. Biochem. Physiol., 65A:181–186.

Bintz, G. L., and M. L. Riedesel. 1967. Water content of ground squirrel and laboratory rat tissues. Comp. Biochem. Physiol., 22:75–80.

Bintz, G. L., and H. W. Roesbery. 1978. Evaporative water loss by control and starved laboratory rats and *Spermophilus richardsonii*. Comp. Biochem. Physiol., 59A: 275–278.

Bintz, G. L., L. B. Bintz, and M. L. Riedesel. 1971. Respiratory quotient as an index of selective tissue catabolism by water-deprived laboratory rats and *Spermophilus lateralis*. Comp. Biochem. Physiol., 38A:121–127.

Bintz, G. L., D. L. Palmer, W. W. Mackin, and F. Y. Blanton. 1979. Selective tissue catabolism and water balance during starvation in Richardson's ground squirrels. Comp. Biochem. Physiol., 64A:399–403.

Blackwell, T. L., and E. B. Pivorun. 1979. Influence of temperature on the water balance of three parapatric species of *Peromyscus*. J. Mamm., 60:70–75.

Blake, B. H. 1977. The effects of kidney structure and the annual cycle on water requirements in golden-mantled ground squirrels and chipmunks. Comp. Biochem. Physiol., 58A:413–419.

Bridgewater, D. D., and D. F. Penny. 1966. Predation by *Citellus tridecemlineatus* on other vertebrates. J. Mamm., 47:345–346.

Cade, T. J. 1964. The evolution of torpidity in rodents. Ann. Acad. Sci. Fenn., Ser. A., 4:88–112.

Chew, R. M. 1965. Water metabolism of mammals. Pp. 44 – 178, *in* Physiological mammalogy, vol. 2. (W. V. Mayer and R. G. Van Gelder, eds.) Academic Press, New York, 326 pp.

Chew, R. M., and H. E. White. 1960. Evaporative water losses of the pallid bat. J. Mamm., 41:452 – 458.

Clark, T. W. 1968. Food uses of the Richardson ground squirrel (*Spermophilus richardsonii elegans*) in the Laramie Basin of Wyoming. Southwestern Nat., 13:248 – 249.

Daily, C. S., and H. B. Haines. 1981. Evaporative water loss and water turnover in chronically and acutely water-restricted spiny mice (*Acomys cahirinus*). Comp. Biochem. Physiol., 68A:349 – 354.

Davis, D. E. 1967. The role of environmental factors in hibernation of woodchucks (*Marmota monax*). Ecology, 48:638 – 689.

Deavers, D. R., and J. W. Hudson. 1979. Water metabolism and estimated field water budgets in two rodents (*Clethrionomys gapperi* and *Peromyscus leucopus*) and an insectivore (*Blarina brevicaudus*) inhabiting the same mesic environment. Physiol. Zool., 52:137 – 152.

Deavers, D. R., and X. J. Musacchia. 1980. Water metabolism and renal function during hibernation and hypothermia. Fed. Proc., 39:2969 – 2973.

Fagerstone, K. A., H. P. Tietjen, and O. Williams. 1981. Seasonal variation in the diet of black-tailed prairie dogs. J. Mamm., 62(4):820 – 824.

Fisher, K. C., and J. F. Manery. 1967. Water and electrolyte metabolism in heterotherms. Pp. 235 – 279, *in* Mammalian hibernation, vol. 3 (K. C. Fisher et al., eds.). American Elsevier, New York, 535 pp.

Formozov, A. N., and K. S. Kodachova. 1961. Les rongeurs vivant en colonies dans la steppe Eurasienne et leur influence sur les sols et la végétation. Terre et Vie, 108: 116 – 129.

Foster, M. A., R. C. Foster, and R. K. Meyer. 1939. Hibernation and the endocrines. Endrocrinology, 24:603 – 612.

Galster, W., and P. Morrison. 1976. Seasonal changes in body composition of the Arctic ground squirrel, *Citellus undulatus*. Canadian J. Zool., 54:74 – 78.

Grinnell, J., and J. Dixon. 1918. California ground squirrels. Mo. Bull. California St. Comm. Hort., 7(11 and 12):597 – 708.

Haines, H., C. Ciskowski, and V. Harms. 1973. Acclimation to chronic water restriction in the wild house mouse *Mus musculus*. Physiol. Zool., 46:110 – 128.

Hawbecker, A. C. 1947. Food and moisture requirements of the Nelson antelope ground squirrel. J. Mamm., 28:115 – 125.

Hayward, J. S. 1961. The ability of the wild rabbit to survive conditions of water restriction. CSIRO Wildl. Res., 6:160 – 175.

Hewitt, S., J. F. Wheldrake, and R. V. Baudinette. 1981. Water balance and renal function in the Australian desert rodent *Notomys alexis:* the effect of diet on water turnover rate, glomerular filtration rate, renal plasma flow and renal blood flow. Comp. Biochem. Physiol., 68A:405 – 410.

Holmes, W. G. 1977. Cannibalism in the Arctic ground squirrel (*Spermophilus parryii*). J. Mamm., 58:437–438.

Hudson, J. W. 1962. The role of water in the biology of the antelope ground squirrel *Citellus leucurus*. Univ. California Publ. Zool., 64:1–56.

———. 1964. Temperature regulation in the round-tailed ground squirrel, *Citellus tereticaudus*. Ann. Acad. Sci. Fenn., Ser. A., 4:218–233.

———. 1973. Torpidity in mammals. Pp. 97–165, *in* Comparative physiology of thermoregulation. Vol. 3. Special aspects of thermoregulation (G. C. Whittow, ed.). Academic Press, New York, 278 pp.

———. 1978. Shallow daily torpor: a thermoregulatory adaptation. Pp. 67–108, *in* Strategies in cold: natural torpidity and thermogenesis (L. C. H. Wang and J. W. Hudson, eds.). Academic Press, New York, 715 pp.

Hudson, J. W., and D. R. Deavers. 1973. Metabolism, pulmocutaneous water loss and respiration of eight species of ground squirrels from different environments. Comp. Biochem. Physiol., 45A:69–100.

Iverson, S. L., and B. N. Turner. 1972. Natural history of a Manitoba population of Franklin's ground squirrels. Canadian Field-Nat., 86:145–149.

Kalabukhov, N. I. 1960. Comparative ecology of hibernating mammals. Bull. Mus. Comp. Zool. Harvard, 124:45–74.

Kayser, C. 1961. The physiology of natural hibernation. Pergamon Press, London, 325 pp.

Kelso, L. H. 1939. Food habits of prairie dogs. U.S. Dept. of Agric., Circ. no. 529:1–15.

Kiell, D. J., and J. S. Millar. 1980. Reproduction and nutrient reserves of Arctic ground squirrels. Canadian J. Zool., 58:416–421.

Kilgore, D. L., Jr., and K. B. Armitage. 1978. Energetics of yellow-bellied marmot populations. Ecology, 59:78–88.

Krumbiegel, I. 1955. Biologie der Säugetiere. Agis Verlag, Krefeld, Baden-Baden, p. 591. Cited in Kayser (1961), pp. 53 and 75.

Landry, S. O., Jr. 1970. The Rodentia as omnivores. Quart. Rev. Biol., 45:351–372.

Lindstedt, S. L. 1980. Energetics and water economy of the smallest desert mammal. Physiol. Zool., 53:82–97.

Linsdale, J. M. 1946. The California ground squirrel. Univ. California Press, Berkeley, 475 pp.

MacMillen, R. E. 1965. Aestivation in the cactus mouse, *Peromyscus eremicus*. Comp. Biochem. Physiol., 16:227–248.

Marsh, A. C., G. Louw, and H. H. Berry. 1978. Aspects of renal physiology, nutrition, and thermoregulation in the ground squirrel *Xerus inauris*. Madoqua, 2(2):129–135.

Mayer, A., and G. Schaeffer. 1914–1915. Variations de la teneur en lipides et activité physiologique des tissus: l'ère partie. J. Physiol. Path. Gen., 16:325–336.

Michener, G. R. 1977. Effect of climatic conditions on the annual activity and hibernation cycle of Richardson's ground squirrels and Columbian ground squirrels. Canadian J. Zool., 55:693–703.

————. 1979. The circannual cycle of Richardson's ground squirrels in southern Alberta. J. Mamm., 60:760–768.

Morrison, P. 1960. Some interrelations between weight and hibernation function. Bull. Mus. Comp. Zool. Harvard, 124:75–91.

Moy, R. M. 1971. Renal function in the hibernating ground squirrel, *Spermophilus columbianus*. Amer. J. Physiol., 220:747–753.

Moy, R. M., R. W. Lesser, and E. W. Pfeiffer. 1972. Urine concentrating ability of arousing and normothermic ground squirrels (*Spermophilus columbianus*). Comp. Biochem. Physiol., 41A:327–337.

Peters, J. P., and D. D. Van Slyke. 1946. Quantitative clinical chemistry: interpretations. Second ed., vol. 1. Williams and Wilkins, Baltimore, 1041 pp.

Pfeiffer, E. W., L. N. Reinking, and J. D. Hamilton. 1979. Some effects of food and water deprivation on metabolism in black-tailed prairie dogs, *Cynomys ludovicianus*. Comp. Biochem. Physiol., 63A:19–22.

Rickart, E. A. 1982. Annual cycles of activity and body composition in *Spermophilus townsendii mollis*. Canadian J. Zool., 60:3298–3306.

Riedesel, M. L., L. R. Klinestiver, and N. R. Benally. 1964. Tolerance of *Citellus lateralis* and *C. spilosoma* for water deprivation. Ann. Acad. Sci. Fenn., Ser. A., 4: 377–388.

Rogers, L. E., and K. A. Gano. 1980. Townsend ground squirrel diets in the shrub-steppe of southwestern Washington. J. Range Mgmt., 33:463–465.

Schitoskey, F., Jr., and S. R. Woodmansee. 1978. Energy requirements and diet of the California ground squirrel. J. Wildl. Mgmt., 42:373–382.

Schmid, W. D. 1976. Temperature gradients in the nasal passage of some small mammals. Comp. Biochem. Physiol., 54A:305–308.

Schmidt-Nielsen, B., and K. Schmidt-Nielsen. 1950. Evaporative water loss in desert rodents in their natural habitats. Ecology, 31:75–85.

————. 1951. A complete account of the water metabolism in kangaroo rats and an experimental verification. J. Cell. Comp. Physiol., 38:165–181.

Schmidt-Nielsen, B., and R. O'Dell. 1961. Structure and concentrating mechanism in the mammalian kidney. Amer. J. Physiol., 200:1119–1124.

Schmidt-Nielsen, B., K. Schmidt-Nielsen, A. Brokaw, and H. Schneiderman. 1948. Water conservation in desert rodents. J. Cell. Comp. Physiol., 32:331–360.

Schmidt-Nielsen, K., and B. Schmidt-Nielsen. 1952. Water metabolism of desert mammals. Physiol. Rev., 32:135–166.

Sellers, W. D. 1965. Physical climatology. Univ. Chicago Press, Chicago, 272 pp.

Shaw, W. T. 1921. Moisture and altitude as factors in determining the seasonal activities of the Townsend ground squirrel in Washington. Ecology, 2:189–192.

————. 1926. The storing habits of the Columbian ground squirrel. Amer. Nat., 60: 367–373.

Smith, H. W. 1951. The kidney: structure and function in health and disease. Oxford Univ. Press, London, 1049 pp.

Sowls, L. K. 1948. The Franklin ground squirrel, *Citellus franklini* (Sabine), and its relationship to nesting ducks. J. Mamm., 29:113–137.

Studier, E. H., and M. J. O'Farrell. 1976. Biology of *Myotis thysanodes* and *M. lucifugus* (Chiroptera: Vespertilionidae). III. Metabolism, heart rate, breathing rate, evaporative water loss and general energetics. Comp. Biochem. Physiol., 54A:423–432.

Twente, J. A., and J. W. Twente. 1964. An hypothesis concerning the evolution of heterothermy in bats. Ann. Acad. Sci. Fenn., Ser. A, 4, 71:435–442.

Vorhies, C. T. 1945. Water requirements of desert animals in the southwest. Arizona Univ. Exp. Sta., Tech. Bull., no. 107:487–525.

Withers, P. C., A. K. Lee, and R. W. Martin. 1979. Metabolism, respiration and evaporative water loss in the Australian hopping-mouse *Notomys alexis* (Rodentia: Muridae). Aust. J. Zool., 27:195–204.

Zatzman, M. L., and F. E. South. 1975. Concentration of urine by the hibernating marmot. Amer. J. Physiol., 228:1326–1340.

Zegers, D. A., and O. Williams. 1979. Energy flow through a population of Richardson's ground squirrels. Acta Theriol., 24:221–235.

3. Communication

DONALD H. OWINGS AND DAVID F. HENNESSY

University of California at Davis

Chapter 8

The Importance of
Variation in Sciurid Visual
and Vocal Communication

Abstract. This paper develops a view of communication as an ongoing process that we call a "management" view. In the management view, communicative behavior is an aspect of the behavioral process that functions to regulate an individual's social circumstances. Such a regulative view treats communication as an ongoing process of adjustment to ongoing situational changes rather than as a linear chain of discrete signals and reactions. Its utility becomes apparent when the management view is applied to the problem of signal variation.

Our discussion of sciurid vocal communication is organized around the issue of variation in alarm signaling and its functional significance. We argue against a unitary treatment of alarm calling. Instead, we develop a view of alarm calling as multifunctional and structurally variable at multiple levels.

Our discussion of sciurid visual communication also emphasizes a multifunctional and structurally variable view of signaling. We point out that not all visually perceivable aspects of social behavior necessarily function exclusively as communicative behavior. In some cases the behavior may function to extract information from another (e.g., greeting). In other cases it may facilitate nonsignaling activities such as locomotion (e.g., tail movement).

Introduction

The theme of this paper is that communicative behavior is most profitably viewed as an ongoing process rather than as a linear chain of discrete signals and reactions (Overton and Reese, 1981). The utility of a process view becomes apparent when

169

it is applied to the problem of signal variation (see Barlow, 1977; Green and Marler, 1979). Our goals are to develop a process view of communication, which we will call a "management" view. We will then use this view as a framework for reviewing selected topics on variation in sciurid vocal and visual communication.

A Process View of Communication

The apparent purposiveness of behavior is often accounted for by appealing to the ultimate explanation of natural selection (Lorenz, 1970). One can also account for apparent purposiveness in a proximate sense by developing an analogy to general systems concepts like homeostasis (in the broad sense; see Toates, 1980). A homeostatic system is a negative feedback system that acts to minimize the difference between desired and actual states of some regulated quantity. In an analogy to communication, the regulated quantity is the behavior of another animal, and each communicant is a negative feedback system. In accord with this analogy, the behavior of each participant in a social interaction is both cause and effect of the other's behavior, that is, proximate causation is two-way (Bateson, 1979). Each exchange in an interaction is difficult to understand in isolation and is better understood in terms of the regulatory problems each participant faces. These regulatory problems are analogous to functions, but in a proximate sense. Signaling behavior is an aspect of a behavioral process that functions to regulate an individual's social circumstances. Regulation is an ongoing process of adjustment to ongoing situational changes, not a chain of discrete events. We emphasize variation in signaling because regulatory process implies variation.

An animal can regulate the behavior of another animal either through direct physical manipulation or by signaling (Dawkins and Krebs, 1978). Signaling accomplishes one's social ends "nontrophically," whereas more forcible social activities like pushing and carrying accomplish social ends "trophically" (Jander, 1975). "Trophic" and "nontrophic" are not categorically distinct but represent two ends of a continuum of behavioral variation. Some actions, like thrusting sand at a distant opponent, are not readily classifiable as either "signaling" or "nonsignaling" social behavior, because they fall at intermediate points on this continuum.

Signaling is just one facet of an individual's ongoing process of regulating its social circumstances. Thus, parallel ongoing changes in posture, locomotion, head orientation, and vocalization by a male California ground squirrel may together function to keep another male away from an estrous female (pers. obs.).

At any given moment, different facets of an individual's behavior may fall at different points on a trophic/nontrophic continuum; that is, a squirrel may run (trophic) while calling (nontrophic). To understand the function(s) of some aspect of an individual's behavior, such as signaling, one should view it in the context of the animal's concomitant behavior. We will argue later, for example, that the use of chatter vocalizations by young and adult California ground squirrels during snake encounters is functionally different because their concomitant behaviors differ. This point seems especially relevant to the study of vocal communication because calls can be recorded and objectively (sonagraphically) described in the absence of any other information about the signaler.

A functional description of an individual's signaling and concomitant behavior is inadequate without a description of its circumstances. In their studies of rat aggression, Blanchard and Blanchard (1981) describe the following common pattern of interaction between an alpha resident male and an intruding adult male. After olfactory investigation the alpha bites the dorsum of the intruder, who flees; the alpha gives chase, and the intruder adopts a bipedal "boxing" stance; the alpha then continues his efforts to bite the intruder's dorsum by lateral attack, and the intruder gradually drops to a supine position; the alpha then stands on the intruder's ventrum, continuing to aim biting attempts at his dorsum. The Blanchards argue against a common traditional interpretation of, for example, "lying-on-the-back" as a "submissive" signal and "lateral orientation" as a "threat" signal. They demonstrate quantitatively that resident males have a strong "preference" for biting on the dorsum and rarely bite on the ventrum. (We propose that this is because the resident is more vulnerable to retaliatory bites during ventral biting than during dorsal biting.) These agonistic acts are not static postures. During each defensive act, the intruder twists and turns to keep the ventrum most and the dorsum least accessible. The corresponding shift in behavior by the resident represents the best countermeasure for continuing to work for biting access to the intruder's dorsum. Thus they argue that attack and defensive behaviors have coevolved. The best way to understand the functional significance of each attack behavior is to realize the preference for backbiting and *to refer to the defensive act that it counters*.

In summary, one discovers the functions of signaling by studying the signaler's concomitant behavior, which is described in terms of the signaler's situation. The regulatory aspect of this view implies, metaphorically, that individuals make "judicious use of means to accomplish an end": this is one definition of the term "management." For this reason we have chosen "management" as a metaphor of the process of communication (Hennessy et al., 1981).

171

Communication

Multiple Levels of Variation in Signaling

Different investigators report different levels of situational specificity of sciurid vocal behavior. King (1955), for example, distinguished between the black-tailed prairie dog's general warning bark, often used in the presence of terrestrial predators, and its hawk-warning bark. The general warning bark is a "short, nasal yip that varies in intensity and frequency with the stimulus that produces it." The hawk-warning bark differs in being "faster, more intense, of higher pitch and of shorter duration." These descriptions indicate King's sensitivity to two levels of variation in vocal behavior—the structure of individual barks (e.g., more intense, of higher pitch), and the temporal patterning of bark series (e.g., hawk-warning barks are faster). In an early sonographic study of black-tailed prairie dog vocalizations, Waring (1970) detected no differences in sonograms of barks elicited by aerial and ground predators. The brevity of the aerial-predator bark series was treated as a by-product of the rapidity of the raptor's maneuver. Such emphasis on the structure of individual emissions (e.g., barks), and deemphasis on the temporal organization of series of emissions, has been characteristic of most studies of sciurid vocal behavior (e.g., Leger, Owings, and Gelfand, 1980; Owings and Leger, 1980). This approach may partly be a by-product of the tangible record of individual emissions that results from sonographic analysis. A management view disposes one to modify traditional approaches to the study of sciurid vocal behavior in two ways. First, one might recognize that there are multiple levels of organization of vocal behavior, for example, the organization (structure) of individual emissions and the temporal organization of series of emissions (see also Beer, 1977). Second, one might characterize signaling at each level not in terms of static structural properties, but in terms of the parameters of variation at that level (Table 8.1). Black-tailed prairie dogs, for example, have been characterized as engaging in both "individual" and "continuous" barking. Individual barks vary in "shape," duration, and harshness. Continuous barking varies in the interval between barks (Smith et al., 1977; compare levels 1 and 2*Ab* in Table 8.1). Sciurid signaling can vary in at least one additional way: different vocal elements can be used in the same call series (Table 8.1, level 2*B*). Mixing of signal elements can also occur between channels, for example, the jump-yip of black-tailed prairie dogs (Smith et al., 1976). Future efforts to describe the concomitant behavior of callers are likely to reveal many more examples of such cross-channel mixing of signaling behavior. Black-tailed prairie dogs (Waring, 1970) and California ground squirrels (Hennessy et al., 1981), for example, often move their tails while vocalizing (Fig. 8.1).

Characterizing signaling at multiple levels has profound implications for the

172

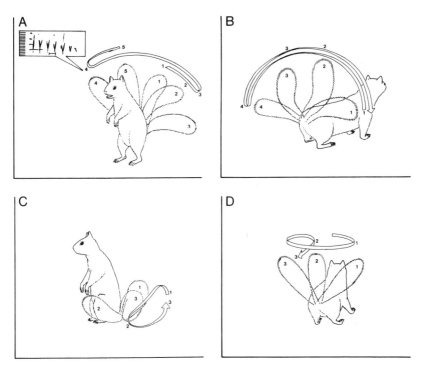

FIGURE 8.1. Variation in the form of tail movement and its combination with vocalization by California ground squirrels. A, This squirrel has just spotted a dog and is "chatter" calling while moving her tail as depicted. Similar tail movements are at times combined with chattering while dealing with snakes. Marks on the vertical axis of the sonogram represent 1-kHz intervals. The horizontal bracket represents 100 msec. B, This squirrel is facing a snake as she tail flags silently. C–D, Tail movement during pauses in running as a red-tailed hawk flew over. These latter two movements were brief and virtually masked by the running that was almost coincident with them. Adapted from Hennessy et al. (1981).

study of sciurid signaling behavior. If sciurids can vary both the structure and the mix of signaling elements as well as the temporal organization of signal emission, then the potential for variability in signaling is enormous.

How a Management View Differs from Alternative Views of Communication

The two prevailing alternatives to a management view have been called "informing" and "manipulating" views (see Owings and Leger, 1980). In both views the study of the functions of signaling entails decomposing communication into constituent elements. In the "informing" view, these are sender (signaler), information (signal), and receiver ("target"). The causal antecedent of the signal

173

Communication

TABLE 8.1. Hierarchy of organization of ground squirrels' long-distance vocalizations. No single species is likely to exploit all levels and sublevels, but the taxon as a whole covers the whole range, and each species probably covers a substantial portion of this hierarchy.

Vocal unit	How that unit varies	Examples
1. Continuous spectrographic tracings	In duration, fundamental frequency, spectral "spread," and pattern and degree of frequency modulation	*Spermophilus beecheyi* "single-notes" (Leger et al., 1980) *Cynomys ludovicianus* "barks" (Smith et al., 1977)
2A. Series of similar spectrographic tracings	In temporal patterning: *a.* Tracings emitted in small enough numbers and spaced irregularly enough that they are easily viewed as several separate decisions to call. May grade into *b*.	*Cynomys ludovicianus* "hawk-warning," "defense," or "individual" barks (King, 1955; Smith et al., 1977)
	b. Tracings emitted at regular time intervals, but in large enough numbers and with wide enough spacing to be viewed as separate emissions with a "higher-order" temporal patterning. Tracings vary in spacing and number. May grade into *c*.	*Spermophilus beecheyi* "chatting" or "repetitive calling" (Owings and Virginia, 1978; this paper) *Cynomys ludovicianus* "continuous barks" (Smith et al., 1977)
	c. Tracings emitted at fairly regular time intervals, but spaced widely enough to sound like separate emissions. Tracings occur in discrete clumps, temporally separate from other clumps. May grade into *d*.	*Cynomys gunnisoni* "barks" or "alarm calls" (Slobodchikoff and Coast, 1980; Waring 1970) *Spermophilus tereticaudus* "clustered rapid peeps" (Dunford, 1977b)
	d. A series of tracings spaced closely enough to sound like a single pulsed emission. Separate pulses may even get "slurred" into a single, long tracing.	*Spermophilus armatus* "churr" (Balph and Balph, 1966) *Spermophilus beldingi* "trill" (Robinson, 1981)

continue

is its referent or message. The response of a receiver to a signal is its meaning (e.g., Leger et al., 1980; Owings and Leger, 1980; Smith, 1977). In the "manipulating" view the elements of communication do not imply the mutualistic sharing of information: the elements are actor (signaler), releaser (signal), and reactor (target). The causal antecedent of a signal is some triggering event. The typical reaction to a signal is its function (Dawkins and Krebs, 1978; Hinde, 1981).

The informing view appears inadequate on at least two bases. First, information is a nontrophic resource, as valuable to animals as are such trophic resources

TABLE 8.1. *continued*

Vocal unit	How that unit varies	Examples
Series of more than one form of spectrographic tracing	In temporal patterning, much like 2*A* *a–d* above "2*A* types" may grade into corresponding "2*B* types." These also vary in the particular tracings combined.	*Spermophilus beecheyi* changes call structure in a series as dog changes behavior (Owings and Virginia, 1978); "preface" syllables in *S. beecheyi* "chatters" (Owings and Leger, 1980) and *S. armatus*, "churrs" (Koeppl et al., 1978) *Spermophilus armatus, columbianus, elegans, richardsonii* "combinations" (Balph and Balph, 1966; Koeppl et al., 1978)
Series of series of spectrographic tracings	Series like 2*Ac*, 2*Ad*, 2*Bc*, amd 2*Bd* may themselves be emitted repeatedly, possibly with variation like that described in 2*Aa*, 2*Ab* and 2*B*.	*Cynomys gunnisoni* "alarm barks" (Slobodchikoff and Coast, 1980; Waring, 1970), *Spermophilus beecheyi* "chatters" (Owings and and Virginia, 1978), *Spermophilus tridecemlineatus* "trills" (Schwagmeyer, 1980), and *Spermophilus beldingi* "trills" (Robinson, 1981) may be sounded repeatedly

as food (Jander, 1975). Since animals are naturally selected to act in their own genetic self-interest, we need to formulate special explanations for seemingly unselfish acts like information sharing (e.g., Axelrod and Hamilton, 1981). Second, particular classes of signals have properties that are difficult to understand strictly on the basis of the information they "make available" (Dawkins and Krebs, 1978). The remarkable diversity of song types in the repertoires of some birds, for example, has spawned a variety of functional hypotheses based on concepts other than information provision (Krebs, 1977; Morton, 1982).

Dawkins and Krebs (1978) have published an explicit challenge to this informing view (see also Morton, 1982). They propose that "manipulation" might be a more appropriate view. Although this first challenge to the "informing" view has been an important one, we also find problems with the "manipulating" view. First, Dawkins and Krebs overemphasize the conflict of interest between signaler and perceiver, as is indicated by the following quotation: "actors do sometimes succeed in *subverting* [italics added] the nervous systems of reactors, and adaptations to do this are the phenomena which we see as animal signals" (1978:

309). Their focus on agonistic behavior is consistent with this assumption of strong conflicts of interest. We have indicated elsewhere (Owings and Leger, 1980) that in many nonagonistic situations the compatibility of interest between signaler and perceiver is high, for example, where a target of an alarm signal is a relative (Dunford, 1977a; Hoogland, 1980; Schwagmeyer, 1980; Sherman, 1977; Smith, 1978). The manipulating view, with its clear negative connotations, seems inappropriate where compatibility of interest is high. Second, Dawkins and Krebs maintain that to understand the functional significance of signaling, one should consider only benefit *to the signaler;* benefit *to the target* is, they contend, irrelevant. They then write as though the target does not constrain signaling at all, for example, by treating signaling as synonymous with communication (1978: 283). Such a position is again consistent with their strong conflict-of-interest view. However, Blanchard and Blanchard's (1981) work on rat fighting demonstrates clearly that even when animals are fighting the behavior of each fighter strongly constrains the behavior of the other. Third, the "manipulating" view provides little basis for understanding the adaptive significance of the high "referential specificity" (Marler, 1977) of animal signals revealed by recent field studies (e.g., Seyfarth et al., 1980). Graded covariation between signal structure and situation is an especially difficult problem for the manipulating view (Dawkins and Krebs, 1978:300).

The management view and alternative views differ most fundamentally in how they conceptualize the organism. In the alternative views, the organism *reacts* to information in the signal (stimulus). In the management view, the organism *acts* on a difference between desired and actual conditions. The conceptualization of an organism as a reactive animal constrains one to depend on information transfer as a stimulus for receiver behavior. Ironically, Dawkins and Krebs, while advocating that we drop considerations of information in communication, evince continued dependence on the concept of information transfer in at least two ways. First, their discussion of the transmission of deceitful information implies the transmission of valid information. Second, they finish their discussion of graded signals by puzzling over why graded information should be made available (1978:300). In the management view, both signaler and target are active in communication, but they face different problems. The signaler needs to obtain a particular performance from an active target not by transmitting information, but by operating on the target's expectancies (an acceptable term for an active organism; see Mason, 1978). Signals therefore do not have referents or messages. On the basis of its awareness of correlations between signal structure and situation, the active target must extract, not react to, behaviorally relevant information. These correlations between signal structure and situation, that is, the information in signals, arise from the signaler's ongoing adjustments to ongoing situational changes, especially in the target's behavior. This constraining influence of targets on signaling distinguishes the management view from the manipulating view. Such an appeal to situational constraints on the management process accounts for situational specificity of signaling and thereby accounts for apparently informative signaling. The management view accomplishes this while maintaining a selfish signaler that regulates circumstances in its own interests.

In the remainder of this chapter we will review selected topics in sciurid vocal and visual communication and interpret these phenomena in terms of the management view.

Vocal Communication

Like many other vertebrates, ground squirrels often vocalize while dealing with predators (Harvey and Greenwood, 1978). The functional significance of emitting these signals has been one of the major themes of recent studies of squirrel vocalizations (e.g., Owings and Leger, 1980; Schwagmeyer, 1980; Sherman, 1977, 1980a). Our discussion of sciurid vocal communication is organized around the issue of variation in alarm signaling and its functional significance (Hennessy et al., 1981).

The intrinsic interest of alarm signaling relates to its apparent riskiness for the signaler and the apparent benefits to perceivers of the signals. Such behavior seems phenotypically altruistic (Sherman, 1977; but see Hennessy, 1982) and thus may demand "special" explanations, like kin selection (Maynard Smith, 1965; Sherman, 1977, 1980a; but see Shields, 1980). Indeed, the prevailing conclusion with respect to ground squirrel alarm calling has been that such vocalizing is nepotistic, selectively benefiting descendant and/or nondescendant relatives. Such a conclusion has been based on several demonstrations of positive correlations between the presence of relatives and the tendency to vocalize when terrestrial predators are detected (Dunford, 1977a; Hoogland, 1980; Owings and Leger, 1980; Owings, unpubl. data; Schwagmeyer, 1980; Sherman, 1977, 1980a; 1980b; Smith, 1978).

This important first step in assessing the functional significance of calling by ground squirrels raises some intriguing questions. In the studies cited above, the treatment of variation in alarm calling has concentrated on whether or not individuals emit a particular call. In the following sections we will argue that calling is not structurally unitary but varies at multiple levels and correlates with variation in calling situations.

TABLE 8.2. Those cases in which the same class of call is used both during an intraspecific interaction and during an encounter with a predator.

Species	Class of call	Circumstances of use	Sources
Spermophilus armatus	Churr	Social: Threat by ♀ ♀ only Antipredator: Ground predators	Balph and Balph, 19▮
	Chirp	Social: Threat, or agonistic advertisement by ♀ ♀ and ♂ ♂ Antipredator: Aerial predators	
S. columbianus	Soft chirp	Social: Such use occurs, but situational details not available Antipredator: Often follow shrill chirps in the aftermath of an encounter with a predator or occur alone at "mild threats" (Betts and Koeppl, et al. differ in their reports on differences in the circumstances of use of soft and shrill chirps; we report Betts' opinion here)	Betts, 1976; Harris ▮ al., 1983; Koeppl et al., 1978
	Shrill chirp, or basic and dissonant chirp	Social: No such use has been reported Antipredator: Aerial and ground predators	
	Churr	Social: Apparently no such use Antipredator: Emitted at bolt into burrow and away from human disturbance; "high-intensity alarm"	
S. beldingi	Trill, or churr	Social: Chase Antipredator: Aerial and terrestrial predators, but possibly more terrestrial than aerial (compare Turner with Robinson)	Robinson, 1981; Sh▮ man, 1977; Turner, ▮
	Chirp, or hawk alarm	Social: Chase Antipredator: Predominantly aerial predators, but also terrestrial	
S. tereticaudus	Whistle, or peep	Social: Threat by ♂ ♂ and ♀ ♀ Antipredator: Possibly just ground predators, but not clear (but social whistles are repeated, antipredator whistles apparently are not)	Dunford, 1977a, 19▮
S. tridecemlineatus	Trill	Social: During breeding and agonistically Antipredator: Aerial and terrestrial predators (but social and antipredators uses occur in separate seasons)	Harris, 1967; Matoc 1977; Schwagmeye▮ 1980; Schwagmeye▮ and Brown, 1981

continu▮

TABLE 8.2. *continued*

Species	Class of call	Circumstances of use	Sources
S. beecheyi	Chatter / chat or long call	Social: All seemingly agonistic; during chases, either chaser or chased may call; during their times of peak aggression, both males and females call ''spontaneously'' and repeatedly from promontories Antipredator: Occasionally to distant aerial predators, more frequently to snakes, and commonly to mammalian predators (Levy reports frequent chatters to distant raptors)	Leger et al., 1980; Levy, 1977; Owings and Leger, 1980; Owings and Virginia, 1978
	Whistle	Social: By chased during agonistic chase Antipredator: Often to low-flying raptors, less frequently when apparently startled by very near mammalian predator	
Cynomys ludovicianus	Jump-yip	Social: Used widely, but most often during territorial boundary challenges, especially by adult males; used in many other social situations in which the animal is beginning to ''relax'' after a disturbance Antipredator: Occurs after a predator has passed, or while harassing snakes	Halpin, 1983; King, 1955; Owings and Owings, 1979; Smith et al., 1973, 1976, 1977 Waring, 1970
	Bark	Social: Partly a threat to aggressive conspecifics, partly recruits help from coterie mates in dealing with intruders Antipredator: Aerial and terrestrial predators (but all sources indicate differences in the temporal patterning of barking in different circumstances)	
Marmota caligata	Medium call, or ascending calls, chirps, accelerating chirps	Social: Yes, but specific circumstances not known Antipredator: Emitted during flyover by model golden eagle	Noyes and Holmes, 1979 Taulman, 1977

The social use of vocalizations. In at least eight species, including five known to call nepotistically, the calls used during encounters with predators are often structurally very similar to those used during predominantly agonistic social interactions (Table 8.2). To the extent that relatives of callers cannot distinguish social uses from antipredator uses, social calling might be expected to dilute warning or other antipredator functions. This may actually represent a pseudo-problem for two reasons. First, intraspecies predation on young is common in Belding's ground squirrels and may be frequent in other sciurids as well (Sherman, 1981, 1982; but see Michener, 1982). Thus, some cases of "social" calling may be functionally similar to calling in the presence of a weasel or ferret. Furthermore, the threat of injury can be quite real even during agonistic interactions between adults (Sherman, 1976), which is the most common social situation for using "alarm" calls (Table 8.2). Thus there may be many parallels between the social and predatory problems that sciurids deal with by vocalizing. We will elaborate this line of argument later. The second point has to do with variability in signals and signaling. Given the potential for variation in calling documented in Table 8.1 and the fact that social and predatory threats are not identical, apparently similar calling in these two situations is likely to differ. In California ground squirrels, social "whistles" differ from alarm "whistles," and social "chatters" differ from alarm "chatters" (Leger et al., 1980; Owings and Leger, 1980; Table 8.2).

Diverse forms of threat posed by different terrestrial predators. All evidence of nepotistic antipredator calling by sciurids has dealt with terrestrial predators, which are not a unitary lot. Different kinds pose different qualities and quantities of threat to sciurids. Canids and felids, for example, do not have ready access to sciurids' burrows, but mustelids and snakes do. Most canids and felids are dangerous to both adults and young, whereas many snakes and mustelids (weasels and ferrets) are much more dangerous to young than to adults (Fitch, 1948). Sciurids treat these predators differently. When canids and felids appear, squirrels are likely to retreat to the vicinity of burrows, stand erect or mount a promontory, watch the predator intently, call at times, and enter the burrow only when the predator gets very close (King, 1955; Owings, unpubl. data; pers. obs. of yellow-bellied marmots). In contrast, weasels, ferrets, and snakes are much more likely to be confronted and even harassed (Henderson et al., 1974; Hennessy et al., 1981; Owings and Coss, 1977; Owings and Owings, 1979; Waring, 1966). In the management view, alarm signaling simply represents the nontrophic aspect of the full spectrum of parallel antipredator activities ranging along the trophic/nontrophic continuum. Consequently, signaling should co-vary with nonsignaling antipredator behavior and thus differ for terrestrial predators posing different sorts of threats (cf., Seyfarth et al., 1980). Snake-elicited chatters by California ground squirrels are structurally different from chatters elicited by mammalian predators (Owings and Leger, 1980). Similarly, whereas barking is the usual vocalization used by black-tailed prairie dogs while dealing with mammalian predators (King, 1955; Smith et al., 1977), these sciurids are much more likely to jump-yip while dealing with snakes (Halpin, 1983; Owings and Owings, 1979). Such adjustments in signal structure can be quite subtle, and they correlate with subtle differences in the nature of the predators being dealt with. For example, the structure of badger-elicited chatters by California ground squirrels differed from canid/felid-elicited chatters (Owings and Leger, 1980). Recently we have discovered acoustic differences in the jump-yips of black-tailed prairie dogs dealing with different sizes and species of snakes (Owings, unpubl. data). In summary, sciurids organize their behavior in different ways for different terrestrial predators and use structurally different vocalizations. Structurally different calls probably are functionally different.

Calls at aerial versus terrestrial predators: not different signs, but products of different time constraints. Researchers have for some time been aware of a "coarser" level of adjustability of sciurid alarm vocalizations than that described above. A number of species have been reported to use structurally different calls for aerial versus terrestrial predators (e.g., "whistles" versus "chatters" of Arctic and California ground squirrels; see Melchior, 1971; Owings and Virginia, 1978; also Turner, 1973; Fig. 8.2, on three-note versus whistle). However, the notion that the differences in these calls are *specific* to the aerial-terrestrial predator difference has been questioned (Leger et al., 1980; Levy, 1977; Owings and Leger, 1980; Robinson, 1981; J. F. Taulman, pers. comm.). "Aerial predator" calls usually occur when raptors arrive low and fast and thus

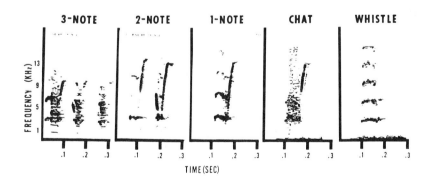

FIGURE 8.2. Variants of California ground squirrel vocalizations used in a playback study. Note that the progression "three-note," "two-note," "one-note," "whistle" represents consecutive positions in a structurally graded series; three-notes and two-notes are also called chatters. Adapted from Leger and Owings (1978).

181

are also associated with "urgency," or relatively little time to deal with an important event. Mammalian predators usually arrive less suddenly, often yielding less urgency, that is, more time to deal with the situation. Consistent with the urgency idea is the fact that some sciurids also emit "aerial predator" calls when they suddenly find themselves close to a mammalian predator and "terrestrial predator" calls when they detect a distant flying hawk (e.g., Leger et al., 1980; Owings and Leger, 1980; Robinson, 1981). These call structure differences may be viewed as being the product of the differential time constraints (urgency) in the two classes of calling situations rather than as functioning to differentiate aerial and terrestrial predators.

The following observations are consistent with this "differential urgency" view. (1) California ground squirrels respond to whistle playbacks as though they expect an urgent situation, that is, by apparently minimizing their conspicuousness and preparing to bolt into a burrow. Chatter playbacks, on the other hand, elicit conspicuous bipedal postures and scanning. Such behavior apparently indicates that they expect a less urgent situation (Leger and Owings, 1978). (2) The reduced spectral spread of "high urgency" calls should make them less localizable, and thus the whistler less conspicuous, than the "low-urgency," or chatter caller (as in Marler's 1955 classic argument; see also Melchior, 1971; Owings and Virginia, 1978; Fig. 8.2). (3) When dealing with a hawk flyover, Belding's ground squirrels run to the closest burrow. In contrast, when a dog approaches they "take the time" to pass one-entrance burrows to reach multiple-entrance burrow systems (Turner, 1973). This general argument illustrates the management view of the problem of the situational specificity of signaling (cf. "referential specificity," Marler, 1977). High situational specificity of signaling is the product not of selection to "make specific information available," but of specificity in the constraints of signaling situations that make only certain forms of behavior workable (Hennessy et al., 1981).

Antipredator vocalizing: an ongoing process. One of the differences between high- and low-urgency encounters with predators is the duration of vocalizing. Rapidly unfolding but often brief, high-urgency encounters with predators frequently involve a brief period of calling. On the other hand, in more slowly developing, low-urgency encounters, sciurids often use the greater time available by calling for prolonged periods (Fitzgerald and Lechleitner, 1974; King, 1955; Leger et al., 1980; Owings and Virginia, 1978; Robinson, 1981; Waring, 1970). Prolonged calling may begin with a few, irregularly spaced calls (as in Table 8.1, level 2*Aa*), apparently on first detecting the source of danger. Calling may then grade into or abruptly become a "repetitive pattern," that is, regularly

182

spaced in time and composed of a series of structurally similar emissions (Smith et al., 1977, as in Table 8.1, level 2*Ab*).

Such "repetitive" calling is common among sciurids (e.g., Barash, 1973; Robinson, 1981; Waring, 1966). This pattern of calling often seems futile or nonfunctional because it can go on even after the source of danger has departed. The observation that most squirrels in the vicinity quickly cease to respond overtly to such calling if they can detect no danger to themselves reinforces one's sense of the lack of utility of this behavior (e.g., Waring, 1970; but Betts, 1976, indicates that such animals may glance up more frequently). We have quantitatively documented the differential impact of naturally occurring repetitive and "nonrepetitive" calls during encounters between California ground squirrels and a dog. Potential target squirrels reacted overtly to a significantly higher proportion of nonrepetitive than repetitive calls. We have also documented the following differences in repetitive and nonrepetitive calling situations (Owings, unpubl. data). (1) Nonrepetitive calling was much more likely when the dog was trotting or running: repetitive calling was more likely when the dog was stationary or walking. (2) Squirrels were always oriented toward the dog while calling nonrepetitively but were more frequently oriented away from the dog while calling repetitively (Fig. 8.3). (3) Nonrepetitive callers were more likely to be off than on a boulder, whereas repetitive callers were just as often on as off a boulder. (4) Although the frequency of calling nonrepetitively at dogs increased on first emergence of young from natal burrows there was no change in repetitive calling. This differential impact of these two classes of calling, combined with clear differences in their situations of use (Smith et al., 1977; and below), indicates that repetitive and nonrepetitive calling are functionally distinct. As Smith et al. (1977) pointed out, the clear patterning of repetitive calls through time, contrasted with the apparent absence of such patterning of nonrepetitive calls, suggests that repetitive calling might represent a more "tonic" communicatory effort than nonrepetitive calling (as in Schleidt, 1973). That nonrepetitive calling is more likely early during encounters and more consistently elicits an immediate reaction suggests that it is an appropriate candidate for one or more of the typical functions accorded alarm signals, that is, warning relatives (see Sherman, 1977); confusing or distracting the predator with the pandemonium of mass flight to refuge (Charnov and Krebs, 1975; Sherman, 1977); and dissuading the predator (Alcock, 1975; Curio, 1978; Smythe, 1970). On the other hand, repetitive calling may be organized to *maintain* a particular activity in targets rather than to elicit some immediate reaction. Since "out of sight" is not equivalent to "gone" for many squirrel predators (Barash, 1973; pers. obs.; D. S. Zezulak, pers. comm.), repetitive callers may be maintaining the level of vigilance in the squir-

FIGURE 8.3. Typical postural differences of squirrels who are calling nonrepetitively (left), and repetitively (right). The nonrepetitive caller is facing the predator, whereas the repetitive caller is looking away from the predator. The marks on the vertical axis of the sonograms are at 1-kHz intervals. The two marks on the horizontal axis bracket 100 msec. Drawing by A. Gladney.

rels around them. The caller could benefit by getting quicker feedback about the location of the predator if one of these more vigilant targets spots it. We have not tested this hypothesis. Our general point, though, is that calling in the presence of predators is an *ongoing* process. Although the initial calls in an area may, as a first approximation, be characterized as functioning to "warn," subsequent calling in that same area falls on the ears of "already warned" individuals and thus is likely to be functionally different. The management view has been important in part because it has drawn our attention to multiple levels of organization of signaling.

How, then, are sciurids using alarm vocalizations to their own benefit? We have already proposed that there may be parallels between social and antipredator calling situations. The most obvious parallel is that most "social" calling is agonistic (Table 8.2) and thus involves a level of conflict of interest comparable in many cases to that existing between predator and prey. Furthermore, during interactions between sciurids and their less immediately dangerous predators (e.g., snakes, weasels, ferrets), squirrels approach and even make contact with the predator: such interactions can have the same probabilistic predictability as intraspecific agonistic "rituals" (as in Eibl-Eibesfeldt, 1970: 314–325). For example, the timing of barking, jump-yipping, recruiting help, and close-quarter interaction is relatively predictable while black-tailed prairie dogs deal with both conspecific intruders and snakes (King, 1955; Owings and Owings, 1979). It is possible, therefore, that one can develop some insight into the use of alarm calls by noting how a similar structural class of calls is used socially (see also Frankenberg, 1981).

The best sources of information about how sciurids use vocalizations while interacting with conspecifics are King's (1955) and Smith et al.'s (1973, 1976, 1977) papers on black-tailed prairie dogs. Female and subadult black-tailed prairie dogs often bark "continuously" when they encounter a conspecific intruder into their coterie (Table 8.1, level 2*Ab*). Such continuous barking influences at least two different classes of targets: the intruder is repelled directly, and the resident male is recruited. On the other hand, black-tailed prairie dogs use "individual" barks while interacting agonistically with members of their own coterie (Table 8.1, level 2*Aa;* Smith et al., 1977). The following points are germane to the functional significance of calling. (1) Calling when a nonresident intrudes may do more than simply warn other coterie members; it may help the caller directly, for example, by recruiting aid. (2) The same calls may simultaneously serve to dissuade the intruder. (3) Therefore, we do not need to choose between different potential targets of calling: multiple targeting may be a regular feature of sciurid calling. (4) The form of calling varies with the relationship between caller and target (e.g., resident versus nonresident of caller's coterie).

Although a "recruiting help" hypothesis (point 1 above) has not been proposed for sciurid alarm calls, another class of calls has routinely been viewed as a recruiting signal — calls used during predator harassment, or mobbing behavior (see Curio, 1978). Sciurids often use the same class of calls while harassing predators that they do while dealing with more immediately dangerous felid and canid predators (Coss and Owings, 1978; Owings and Leger, 1980; Table 8.2), and conspecifics are often recruited by such harassment (Owings and Coss, 1977, 1981; Owings and Owings, 1979). Furthermore, harassment and other styles of antipredator behavior are not categorically distinct; they intergrade (Hennessy, 1982). Therefore calling "at" more immediately dangerous predators might also serve a recruiting function. When both parents and their young call "at" predators (e.g., Schwagmeyer, 1980), we propose that they may be calling for very different reasons: parents may be protecting young, but young may be recruiting help. For example, both adult and young California ground squirrels chatter and chat while dealing with snakes, but otherwise they behave differently. Adults approach and confront the snake. Young stay farther back, often on promontories, and appear to recruit squirrels and keep track of the snake (Owings, unpubl. data; Owings and Coss, 1981). The "recruiting help" idea is a member of a broader class of functional hypotheses dealing with all cases of the use of alarm calls to influence the behavior of conspecifics to one's own benefit. The "vigilance maintenance" hypothesis of repetitive calling (see above), Charnov and Krebs's (1975) "manipulation" hypothesis, and "grouping facilitation" hypotheses (Hirth and McCullough, 1977; Owens and Goss-Custard, 1976) are all members of this general functional class.

If social calling can be multiply targeted (points 2 and 3 above), then perhaps alarm calling can too. One may not need, therefore, to distinguish between "predator target" and "conspecific target" hypotheses about alarm calling (compare Sherman, 1977, with Curio, 1978). Since there has been no serious challenge to the contention that conspecifics are targets of these calls (Sherman, 1980*a*), our primary task here is to make credible the idea that predators are also targets. We have already argued (above) for continuity between predator-harassment situations and more immediately dangerous predatory situations. Harassment is clearly targeted on predators, and vigilance is just as clearly targeted on predators who are not harassed. Calling is then a facet of a process that is partly targeted on predators, including, for example, coyotes and bobcats. As Smith et al. (1977) have pointed out, the details of sciurid/predator interaction clearly indicate that each influences the other's behavior. The structure, patterning, and rate of calling vary as a function of the predator's behavior and proximity (Smith et al., 1977; Owings and Virginia, 1978; Owings, unpubl. data). In turn, predators often orient toward and charge calling sciurids (Owings, unpubl. data; Sherman, 1977, 1980*a*). The notion of multiple functions of signals readily follows from the idea of multiple targets of signals (see also DeWaal and Van Hooff, 1981; Frankenberg, 1981).

Signaling may also serve multiple functions with respect to a single target. In his listing of the possible functions of alarm calling, Sherman (1977) included the following two alternatives: discouragement of predator pursuit and reduction of the likelihood of later attacks by the same predator. We propose that calling could simultaneously serve both functions in the following sense. Discouragement of predator pursuit is one *immediate* way to build a *long-term* reduction in the likelihood of later attacks by the same predator. Such an argument follows from a process view in the following way. As we argued earlier, particular signal-response exchanges are difficult to understand in isolation from the ongoing process of interaction between active organisms. On a longer time scale, one could argue analogously that particular interactions, for example, between squirrel and predator, are difficult to understand in isolation from the continuously developing relationship between active organisms such as predator and squirrel. Such a conceptualization is hierarchical in the following sense: each signal / response exchange both contributes to an interaction and is influenced by the nature of the interaction. Interactions, in turn, both contribute to and are influenced by the long-term relationship between the participants. A dominance relationship, for example, can be viewed as the outcome of past interactions and a constraint on current interactions (Bernstein, 1981). In dealing with why an animal emits a particular signal, one should consider both immediate and long-term functions, not choose between them. Although this conceptualization comes from the literature on intraspecies relations (Anderson and Mason, 1974; Hinde, 1976; Simpson, 1973), the idea extends readily to interspecies relations. Clearly there is evidence of long-term consequences for the *predator* of predator/prey interactions: the literature on aversion learning (e.g., Gustavson, 1977), aposematic coloration, and mimicry (Edmunds, 1974) provides examples. Among sciurids, killing gopher snakes too small to be dangerous (Fitch, 1948), evoking several consecutive unsuccessful attacks by a coyote (Barash, 1973), and repeatedly bowling over a red-tailed hawk as it eats a prairie dog (Stromberg, 1974), may all represent antipredator behavior with long-term functional consequences. Similarly, there is both direct and indirect evidence of long-term consequences for the *prey* of predator/prey interactions. Gulls stay farther away from a fox model after seeing it associated with a dead gull (Kruuk, 1976). European blackbirds learn to mob a stuffed nonraptorial bird after observing mobbing by conspecifics in the model's vicinity (Curio et al., 1978). In sciurids, young and adults call differently in potential predatory situations (Owings, unpubl. data; Robinson, 1981), and snakes are treated differently by squirrels from populations with different histories of snake predation (Hennessy, 1982; Owings and Coss, 1977; Owings and Owings, 1979).

We view behavior, including alarm calling, as complexly multifunctional, because it is organized to manage multiple targets and to achieve long- and short-term functional outcomes for each target. For this reason we propose that the term "alarm" call be dropped as too functionally specific. In making this recommendation we assume that "alarm" is typically used functionally, as in "to sound an alarm" or "warn." Such a label does not consider longer-term functions with respect to squirrel targets or any functions with respect to predator targets. For calls associated with predators, we propose the less specific functional label "antipredator" calls, because such calls are used to deal with the presence of predators, perhaps by warning conspecifics, dissuading predators, and so on (Hennessey et al., 1981). This "multiply-targeted, multifunctional" view has profound implications for the problem of variation in calling. All targets, as well as long- and short-term functions of calling, are potential sources of variation in calling. Such variation is likely to be revealed at several levels in the organization of calling (Table 8.1).

Visual Communication

Differences between Visual and Vocal Signaling

The temporal open-endedness of some visual signals. The easiest signals to deal with are temporally discrete ones, that is, signals with readily identifiable onset and termination. However, not all activities of social significance are so temporally discrete. The tail, for example, is used in such relatively discrete activities as "flicking" and "flagging." However, other more static features of tail use also appear to be socially important, for example, the position in which the tail is held (high versus low, or toward versus away from another squirrel) or the extent of erection of tail hairs (e.g., Balph and Stokes, 1963; Betts, 1976; Owings et al., 1977; Wistrand, 1974). Although the *act* of adjusting the tail to a particular state is relatively discrete, such a state may be held for highly variable periods. Other examples are the direction of gaze, posture (e.g., quadrupedal versus bipedal), or position relative to another individual. Although discrete signals are amenable to a particulate view of behavior (a signal-response chain), activities that can be maintained through time are more amenable to a view of behavior as a regulatory process. That is, tail positions (especially high ones), postures (especially erect ones), and distances from others (especially moving others) are states that require active maintenance.

Such a realization is fostered more by the study of visual than vocal signaling. Constant vocal output is tightly constrained by the amount of air that can be stored for the process. Therefore the elements of acoustic communication are usually temporally discrete. Although some visual signals are also discrete, maintaining a relatively constant visual configuration is feasible. The most permanent configurations are morphological rather than behavioral and are often called "signs" or "badges" rather than signals (Smith, 1977: 239), but even these can often be displayed or turned on and off behaviorally. Thus, the elements of visual signaling have a wider range of time courses of change than vocal elements.

188

*Greater trophic/nontrophic intergradation of visually perceivable social be-
havior.* We find utility in the ethological idea that many signals can be viewed as
derived from preparations for social action (e.g., intention movements, auton-
omic changes: cf. Andrew, 1972; see also Daanje, 1951; Morris, 1956; Moynihan, 1955). Vocalizations probably derive in part from trophic preparation of the
respiratory apparatus for social action (Andrew, 1963). Since such respiratory
adjustments are not apparent to others, animal behaviorists do not have as much
opportunity to discover the ''trophic'' origins of vocal behavior (see Morton,
1982). In contrast, trophic sources of visual signals are visually perceivable and
therefore easily linked to corresponding signals. Thus the ''aggressive upright''
posture of gulls (Tinbergen, 1959) prepares the wings and beak for offensive use.
If such postural preparation dissuades the opponent, no other interaction may be
necessary. If the opponent persists, however, the wings and beak may be brought
into action (a fight occurs), and we can watch actual gradation between nontrophic posturing and trophic activity like pecking and striking with the wings.
So, visually perceivable facets of social behavior grade along a much greater
portion of the trophic/nontrophic continuum than does vocal behavior. Vocal
output is therefore usually readily distinguishable from more trophic social behavior, but the greater intergradation of visually perceived social behavior makes
that distinction much more difficult. This is probably why Blanchard and Blanchard (1981), for example, questioned the signal status of rat agonistic postures.
For this reason the following sections deal with visually perceivable social behavior, without major concern over whether such behavior reflects exploitation
of the visual channel to manage the behavior of others, that is, visual signaling.
As in the vocal sections, we review here selected topics in a management
framework.

Greeting

The identification problem. The management view implies two facets to social
behavior—*influencing* target behavior while simultaneously *extracting information* on how best to exert that influence. A useful analogy to these two facets
can be found in the general systems concepts of the *control* and *identification*
problems, respectively (Arbib, 1972:80–81):

At the heart of control theory is *the control problem:* ''Given reasonably
accurate descriptions of a system and some performance required of it, to find
inputs which, when applied to the system, will elicit (a reasonable approximation to) the desired performance.''

Communication

A common situation which complicates the control problem is that the controlled system may not be known accurately—it may even change its character somewhat with time. . . . [Therefore, the controlling system] must continually solve . . . *the identification problem:* "To use repeated experiments upon the input-output behavior of a system to build up a state-variable description for a system which yields similar behavior."

How one behaves toward another individual depends not only on a broad characterization of that individual (e.g., adult male), but also on more specific details, that is, the relationship of the individuals (e.g., resident versus established neighbor versus transient versus potential immigrant; see Anderson and Mason, 1974). Some social behavior appears organized to acquire such information—to deal with the identification problem. Thus, staring intently at a conspecific (e.g., Owings et al., 1977) may not only be a form of threat but may also serve to gather more specific information about who the individual is and what it is doing (Coss, 1978). Some information acquisition can be more interactive; for example, olfactory inspection may require close approach that often evokes a response by the target, resulting in a pattern of interaction called "greeting" (e.g., Barash, 1973) or "kissing" (e.g., King, 1955), in which nose-to-nose, mouth-to-mouth, or nose-to-mouth contact occurs. Information about an individual's identity can be extracted from glandular secretions during greeting (Harris and Murie, 1982). The concept of feedback raises the possibility of an even more interactive form of information extraction, which might be called "probing." Adult male black-tailed prairie dogs appear to distinguish between residents and nonresidents of their coterie at some distance by rushing at the individual in question, whose reaction aids the male in identification: nonresidents usually flee, but residents crouch, wag their tails, and open their mouths in apparent anticipation of kissing (King, 1955). We propose that many social inputs function in part to elicit behavior on which to base further target assessment. (See Clutton-Brock and Albon, 1979, and Trivers, 1972, for alternative treatments of the role of assessment in social behavior.)

Selfish participation in greeting. Among some of the more social sciurids the functions of engaging in greeting often appear to differ for the two participants. As for black-tailed prairie dogs, adult male Olympic marmots frequently approach other individuals but often abort the interaction if the target attempts to engage in greeting. The animal approached is likely to take the initiative, though, and apparently to attempt to set up a greeting interaction. Barash (1973) discussed the seeming paradox that adult males frequently approach the vicinity of others and frequently participate in greeting but much less often actually *initiate*

190

greeting. The paradox might be resolved by proposing that adult males are probing and thus can terminate interaction before greeting if the target proves to be a
resident. In contrast, other members of the unit may be engaging in the more tonic
process of ensuring that they remain familiar to the males and others by ''insist-
ing'' on greeting interactions. Barash's (1973) report that infants are the most
frequent initiators of greeting and that yearlings are second is consistent with this
view. The prolonged allogrooming often associated with greeting does not seem
immediately functional (Barash, 1973) but may act in a more tonic fashion to
cultivate or maintain relationships.

Greeting is an interaction, not a signal. The interests of a particular individual
are not stable across greeting interactions but vary with that individual's relationship with the other participants. The behavior leading into a greeting, the
actual form of the greeting, and what follows greeting should vary with this
relationship. Fisler (1976) clearly described such covariation between relationship and the form and behavioral context of greeting by antelope ground
squirrels, and Barash (1973, 1974) emphasizes the complex variability of marmot greeting.

In the face of all this variability both in what precedes and in what follows
greeting (Barash, 1973, 1974), as well as in the relative orientations of the participants during greeting (Fisler, 1976), the superimposition of noses, of mouths,
or of nose on mouth seems to form a ''node'' of stability, like Golani's ''joint''
(1976), which draws one's attention to this part of the interaction. This consistency of points of superimposition, and the participation of both individuals in
achieving this superimposition, probably accounts for the treatment of greeting
as a signal at some times and an interaction at other times (Fisler, 1976; Nowicki
and Armitage, 1979). To label greeting a signal could dispose one to treat this
interaction as a product of a ''cooperative'' effort, thereby reducing the investigator's sensitivity to differences or even conflicts in the interests of participants.
The relative consistency of superimposition can further foster such ''cooperative'' thinking. Consistency in superimposition of body parts, or temporal coupling of social activities, was probably responsible for the development of the
ethological concept of agonistic ''rituals'' (e.g., Eibl-Eibesfeldt, 1970:314–
325) and ultimately for the development of an ''interactional'' or ''informing''
perspective on communication (as discussed earlier, see also Smith, 1977:11–
14). We have already pointed out that such a perspective can be criticized as
non-Darwinian for failing to treat interacting individuals explicitly as acting in
their own interests. A management view accounts for temporal and spatial coupling of the behavior of individuals, especially during agonistic encounters, as

resulting from selfish action and effective counteraction (as described earlier for rat fighting; Blanchard and Blanchard, 1981). More generally, such coupling can be explained with the management idea that the behavior of each participant constrains the behavior of the other in the interaction.

Use of the Tail in Signaling

Many sciurid biologists have mentioned use of the tail in signaling at least briefly, but the phenomenon has received little systematic attention. Sufficient information is available, however, to indicate that tail use is not a simple matter. Tail movement has been related to (1) a state of "uneasiness" (Betts, 1976; King, 1955); (2) investigatory behavior (Grubitz, 1963; Wistrand, 1974); (3) the presence of predators (Hennessy et al., 1981; King, 1955; Rongstad, 1965); (4) vocalizing (Hennessy et al., 1981; King, 1955; Waring, 1970); (5) locomotion (Barash, 1973; Betts, 1976; Hennessy et al., 1981; Quanstrom, 1971; Watton and Keenleyside, 1974); and (6) sexual, agonistic, or amicable interaction (Armitage, 1974; Barash, 1973; King, 1955; Wistrand, 1974). One's sense of the ambiguous functional status of tail movement is intensified by the observation that it often seems to have no immediate effect on nearby squirrels (Betts, 1976; Watton and Keenleyside, 1974; pers. obs.).

One may begin to deal with such ambiguity by using an approach that seemed profitable when applied to sciurid vocalization. Tail movement is not structurally unitary but varies in movement axis, duration, speed, speed modulation, amplitude, and directedness (where movement is "aimed"), as well as in the extent of piloerection, the "stiffness" of the tail, and the patterning of movement bouts through time (Armitage, 1974; Balph and Stokes, 1963; Betts, 1976; Hennessy et al., 1981; Owings et al., 1977; Owings and Coss, 1977; Quanstrom, 1971; Wistrand, 1974; Fig. 8.1). Such structural variability raises the possibility of functional variability, which has been confirmed in our studies of snake-elicited tail flagging by California ground squirrels (Hennessy et al., 1981).

Tail flagging is highly variable. Individual squirrels adjust their tail flagging as a function of whether they are dealing with the snake alone or are accompanied by another snake-directed squirrel; whether or not a rattlesnake rattles; and whether they are just beginning, in the process of, or finishing a bout of dealing directly with the snake. Our comparisons of one-, two-, and three-cycle bouts of tail flagging yielded some remarkable findings. The profile of behavior concomitant with one-cycle bouts was the reverse of the three-cycle profile, and the two-cycle profile was intermediate between the two.

Tail movement as multifunctional behavior. The most consistently reported correlate of tail movement has been locomotion. This is not surprising, since the tail is an extension of the vertebral column, which is flexed during locomotion (Kiley-Worthington, 1976). Tail movement probably has trophic utility in locomotion, for example, as an aid to balance (Hildebrand, 1974, pp. 514 and 560). Some fairly subtle tail movements, often coincident with locomotion, may function primarily to facilitate locomotion (Fig. 8.1C, D). Other tail movements, although temporally close to bouts of locomotion, are so conspicuous and socially effective that signaling functions seem obvious, for example, snake-elicited tail flagging (Fig. 8.1B). Signaling tail movements may be associated with locomotion because they are derived from locomotor "intention" movements (Daanje, 1951). The management view differs from this ethological view in at least one important way (see also Andrew, 1972; Kiley-Worthington, 1976). Tail movement may be used *simultaneously* for locomotor and signaling functions, and some graded changes in tail movement may reflect shifts in relative emphasis of these two functions. We are currently testing this idea by seeking features of tail use that covary with locomotion and postural changes and other features of tail use that covary with the behavior of potential targets. This is a specific case of our earlier proposal that different but simultaneous characteristics of an individual's behavior can fall at different points on the trophic/nontrophic continuum. At any point in time an individual can validly be characterized as signaling or not signaling, depending on what aspect of its behavior is described.

An intriguing conclusion follows from an extension of the argument above to other "sources" of "derived" activities. These "sources" can all be characterized as the signaler operating on itself. "Intention" movements are postural preparations for action. Autonomically mediated changes such as piloerection are thermoregulatory preparations for action (Morris, 1956). "Displacement" activities such as preening, feeding, and drinking might be viewed as aspects of "multiplex" behavior in that, for example, thirst is being slaked during the resolution of a social problem (see Manning, 1979:182, for citation of relevant studies). If squirrels are simultaneously doing the things above *and* influencing others, the signaler itself is typically one target of its own behavior. The "identification" problem in the management view, Andrew's (1972) "recognition comparison," and Chance's (1962) "cut-off" hypothesis are special cases of this general argument. At any point an individual's behavior can validly be characterized as targeted on itself or on others, depending on what aspect of its behavior is described.

Conclusion

A process view of communication focuses on variation at multiple levels of organization of signaling behavior. Furthermore, signaling behavior is not treated typologically but is viewed as intergrading with nonsignaling social behavior along a trophic / nontrophic continuum. In our efforts to understand the functional significance of this variation, we have identified the following potential sources of variation: multiple targets of signaling; multiple functions with respect to each target; the use of signals as probes; and the effect of self-regulation on signal structure. Operationally, the influence of these sources on variation is sought through the use of multiple descriptions of signaling, each with respect to different facets of the signaling situation.

Acknowledgments

Preparation of this article was aided by National Science Foundation Grants BNS 78-17770 to Owings and BNS 82-10065 to Owings and Hennessy and by Faculty Research Grant D-819 from the University of California at Davis to Owings. We thank the following people for their helpful comments and suggestions: D. M. Balph, R. G. Coss, M. A. Harris, D. W. Leger, D. F. Lott, W. J. Loughry, J. O. Murie, R. M. Murphey and the students in Animal Behavior 201 during fall 1982. We are especially grateful to W. A. Mason for introducing us to a process view of behavior.

Literature Cited

Alcock, J. 1975. Animal behavior: an evolutionary approach. Sinauer Associates, Sunderland, Massachusetts, 547 pp.

Anderson, C. O., and W. A. Mason. 1974. Early experience and complexity of social organization in groups of young rhesus monkeys (*Macaca mulatta*). J. Comp. Physiol. Psych., 87:681–690.

Andrew, R. J. 1963. Evolution of facial expression. Science, 142:1034–1041.

———. 1972. The information potentially available in mammal displays. Pp. 179–204, *in* Non-verbal communication (R. A. Hinde, ed.). Cambridge University Press, Cambridge, 443 pp.

Arbib, M. A. 1972. The metaphorical brain: an introduction to cybernetics as artificial intelligence and brain theory. Wiley-Interscience, New York, 243 pp.

Armitage, K. B. 1974. Male behaviour and territoriality in the yellow-bellied marmot. J. Zool. London, 172:233–265.

Axelrod, R., and W. D. Hamilton. 1981. The evolution of cooperation. Science, 211:1390–1396.

Balph, D. F., and A. W. Stokes. 1963. On the ethology of a population of Uinta ground squirrels. Amer. Midland Nat., 69:106–126.

Balph, D. M., and D. F. Balph. 1966. Sound communication of Uinta ground squirrels. J. Mamm., 47:440–450.

Barash, D. P. 1973. The social biology of the Olympic marmot. Anim. Behav. Monogr., 6:171–245.

———. 1974. The social behavior of the hoary marmot (*Marmota caligata*). Anim. Behav., 22:256–261.

Barlow, G. W. 1977. Modal action patterns. Pp. 98–134, *in* How animals communicate (T. A. Sebeok, ed.). Indiana University Press, Bloomington, 1,128 pp.

Bateson, G. 1979. Mind and nature: a necessary unity. E. P. Dutton, New York, 238 pp.

Beer, C. G. 1977. What is a display? Amer. Zool., 17:155–165.

Bernstein, I. S. 1981. Dominance: the baby and the bathwater. Behav. Brain Sci., 4: 419–457.

Betts, B. J. 1976. Behavior in a population of Columbian ground squirrels, *Spermophilus columbianus columbianus*. Anim. Behav., 24:652–680.

Blanchard, R. J., and D. C. Blanchard. 1981. The organization and modeling of animal aggression. Pp. 529–563, *in* The biology of aggression (P. F. Brain and D. Benton, eds.). Sijthoff and Noordhoff, Rockville, Maryland, 637 pp.

Chance, M. R. A. 1962. An interpretation of some agonistic postures: the role of "cut-off" acts and postures. Symp. Zool. Soc. London, 8:71–89.

Charnov, E. L., and J. R. Krebs. 1975. The evolution of alarm calls: altruism or manipulation? Amer. Nat., 109:107–112.

Clutton-Brock, T. H., and S. D. Albon. 1979. The roaring of red deer and the evolution of honest advertisement. Behaviour, 69:145–169.

Coss, R. G. 1978. Perceptual determinants of gaze aversion by the lesser mouse lemur (*Microcebus murinus*), the role of two facing eyes. Behaviour, 64:248–270.

Coss, R. G., and D. H. Owings. 1978. Snake-directed behavior by snake naive and experienced California ground squirrels in a simulated burrow. Z. Tierpsychol., 48:421–435.

Curio, E. 1978. The adaptive significance of avian mobbing. I. Teleonomic hypotheses and predictions. Z. Tierpsychol., 48:175–183.

Curio, E., U. Ernst, and W. Vieth. 1978. The adaptive significance of avian mobbing. II. Cultural transmission of enemy recognition in blackbirds: effectiveness and some constraints. Z. Tierpsychol., 48:184–202.

Daanje, A. 1951. On locomotory movements in birds and the intention movements derived from them. Behaviour, 3:48–98.

Dawkins, R., and J. R. Krebs. 1978. Animal signals: information or manipulation? Pp. 282–309, *in* Behavioural ecology: an evolutionary approach (J. R. Krebs and N. B. Davies, eds.). Sinauer Associates, Sunderland, Massachusetts, 494 pp.

DeWaal, F. B. M., and J. A. R. A. M. Van Hooff. 1981. Side-directed communication and agonistic interactions in chimpanzees. Behaviour, 77:164–198.

Dunford, C. 1977a. Kin selection for ground squirrel alarm calls. Amer. Nat., 111: 782–785.

Communication

————. 1977*b*. Social system of round-tailed ground squirrels. Anim. Behav., 25: 885–906.

Edmunds, M. 1974. Defence in animals. Longman Group, Essex, 357 pp.

Eibl-Eibesfeldt, I. 1970. Ethology: the biology of behavior. Holt, Rinehart and Winston, San Francisco, 530 pp.

Fisler, G. F. 1976. Agonistic signals and hierarchy changes of antelope squirrels. J. Mamm., 57:94–102.

Fitch, H. S. 1948. Ecology of the California ground squirrel on grazing lands. Amer. Midland Nat., 39:513–596.

Fitzgerald, J. P., and R. R. Lechleitner. 1974. Observations on the biology of Gunnison's prairie dog in central Colorado. Amer. Midland Nat., 92:146–163.

Frankenberg, E. 1981. The adaptive significance of avian mobbing. IV. "Alerting others" and "perception advertisement" in blackbirds facing an owl. Z. Tierpsychol., 55:97–118.

Golani, I. 1976. Homeostatic motor processes in mammalian interactions: a choreography of display. Pp. 69–134, *in* Perspectives in ethology (P. P. G. Bateson and P. H. Klopfer, eds.). Plenum Press, New York, 352 pp.

Green, S., and P. Marler. 1979. The analysis of animal communication. Pp. 73–158, *in* Social behavior and communication (P. Marler and J. G. Vandenbergh, eds.). Handbook of behavioral neurobiology, Plenum Press, New York 3:1–411.

Grubitz, G. 1963. The social behavior of the thirteen-lined ground squirrel (*Citellus tridecemlineatus*). Unpubl. M.S. thesis, Univ. Oklahoma, Norman, 57 pp.

Gustavson, C. R. 1977. Comparative and field aspects of learned food aversions. Pp. 23–44, *in* Learning mechanisms in food selection (L. M. Barker, M. R. Best, and M. Domjan, eds.). Baylor Univ. Press, Waco, Texas, 632 pp.

Halpin, Z. 1983. Naturally-occurring encounters between black-tailed prairie dogs (*Cynomys ludovicianus*) and snakes. Amer. Midland Nat., 109:50–54.

Harris, J. 1967. Voice and associated behavior in *Citellus tridecemlineatus* and other ground squirrels. Unpubl. Ph.D. dissert., Univ. Michigan, Ann Arbor, 91 pp.

Harris, M. A., and J. O. Murie. 1982. Responses to oral gland scents from different males in Columbian ground squirrels. Anim. Behav., 30:140–148.

Harris, M. A., J. O. Murie, and J. A. Duncan. 1983. Responses of Columbian ground squirrels to playback of recorded calls. Z. Tierpsychol. 63:318–330.

Harvey, P. H., and P. J. Greenwood. 1978. Anti-predator defence strategies: some evolutionary problems. Pp. 129–151, *in* Behavioural ecology: an evolutionary approach (J. R. Krebs and N. B. Davies, eds.). Sinauer Associates, Sunderland, Massachusetts, 494 pp.

Henderson, F. R., P. F. Springer, and R. Adrian. 1974. The black-footed ferret in South Dakota. Tech. Bull. 4, South Dakota Dept. Fish, Game and Parks, Pierre, South Dakota, 32 pp.

Hennessy, D. F. 1982. Paradigmatic constraints on explaining predator harassment: risky versus conservative snake harassment by California ground squirrels. Pp. 6–63, *in*

Functional significance of variation in predator harassment. Unpubl. Ph.D. dissert., Univ. California, Davis, 65 pp.

Hennessy, D. F., D. H. Owings, M. P. Rowe, R. G. Coss, and D. W. Leger. 1981. The information afforded by a variable signal: constraints on snake-elicited tail flagging by California ground squirrels. Behaviour, 78:188–226.

Hildebrand, M. 1974. Analysis of vertebrate structure. John Wiley, New York, 710 pp.

Hinde, R. A. 1976. Interactions, relationships, and social structure. Man, 11:1–17.

———. 1981. Animal signals: ethological and games-theory approaches are not incompatible. Anim. Behav., 29:535–542.

Hirth, D. H., and D. R. McCullough. 1977. Evolution of alarm signals in ungulates with special reference to white-tailed deer. Amer. Nat., 111:31–42.

Hoogland, J. L. 1980. Nepotism and cooperative breeding in the black-tailed prairie dog (Sciuridae: *Cynomys ludovicianus*). Pp. 283–310, *in* Natural selection and social behavior: recent research and theory (R. D. Alexander and D. W. Tinkle, eds.). Chiron Press, New York, 532 pp.

Jander, R. 1975. Ecological aspects of spatial orientation. Ann. Rev. Ecol. Syst., 6: 171–188.

Kiley-Worthington, M. 1976. The tail movements of ungulates, canids and felids with particular reference to their causation and function as displays. Behaviour, 56: 69–115.

King, J. A. 1955. Social behavior, social organization, and population dynamics in a black-tailed prairiedog town in the Black Hills of South Dakota. Contrib. Lab. Vert. Biol., Univ. Michigan, 67:1–123.

Koeppl, J. W., R. S. Hoffman, and C. F. Nadler. 1978. Pattern analysis of accoustical behavior in four species of ground squirrels. J. Mamm., 59:677–696.

Krebs, J. R. 1977. The significance of song repertoires: the Beau Geste hypothesis. Anim. Behav., 25:475–478.

Kruuk, H. 1976. The biological function of gulls' attraction towards predators. Anim. Behav., 24:146–153.

Leger, D. W., and D. H. Owings. 1978. Responses to alarm calls by California ground squirrels: effects of call structure and maternal status. Behav. Ecol. Sociobiol., 3: 177–186.

Leger, D. W., D. H. Owings, and D. L. Gelfand. 1980. Single-note vocalizations of California ground squirrels: graded signals and situation-specifity of predator and socially evoked calls. Z. Tierpsychol., 52:227–246.

Levy, N. 1977. Sound communication in the California ground squirrel. Unpubl. M.S. thesis, California State Univ., Northridge, 63 pp.

Lorenz, K. 1970. Inductive and teleological psychology. Pp. 351–370, *in* Studies in human and animal behavior, vol. 1 (K. Lorenz, ed.). Harvard University Press, Cambridge, 403 pp.

Manning, A. 1979. An introduction to animal behavior. Addison-Wesley, London, 329 pp.

Communication

Marler, P. 1955. Characteristics of some animal calls. Nature, 176:6–8.

———. 1977. Primate vocalization: affective or symbolic? Pp. 85–96, in Progress in ape research (G. H. Bourne, ed.). Academic Press, New York, 300 pp.

Mason, W. A. 1978. Social experience and primate cognitive development. Pp. 233–251, in The development of behavior: comparative and evolutionary aspects (G. M. Burghardt and M. Bekoff, eds.). Garland Publishing, New York, 443 pp.

Matocha, K. G. 1977. The vocal repertoire of Spermophilus tridecemlineatus. Amer. Midland Nat., 98:482–487.

Maynard Smith, J. 1965. The evolution of alarm calls. Amer. Nat., 99:59–63.

Melchior, H. R. 1971. Characteristics of Arctic ground squirrel alarm calls. Oecologia, 7:184–190.

Michener, G. R. 1982. Infanticide in ground squirrels. Anim. Behav., 30:936–938.

Morris, D. 1956. The feather postures of birds and the problem of the origin of social signals. Behaviour, 9:75–113.

Morton, E. S. 1982. Grading, discreteness, redundancy and motivation—structural rules. Pp. 183–212, In Acoustic communication in birds. Vol. 1. Production, perception and design features of sounds (D. E. Kroodsma, E. H. Miller, and H. Ouellet, eds.). Academic Press, New York, 371 pp.

Moynihan, M. 1955. Remarks on the original sources of displays. Auk, 72:240–246.

Nowicki, S., and K. B. Armitage. 1979. Behavior of juvenile yellow-bellied marmots: play and social integration. Z. Tierpsychol., 51:85–105.

Noyes, D. H., and W. G. Holmes. 1979. Behavioral responses of free-living hoary marmots to a model golden eagle. J. Mamm., 60:408–411.

Overton, W. F., and H. W. Reese. 1981. Conceptual prerequisites for an understanding of stability-change and continuity-discontinuity. Internat. J. Behav. Develop., 4:99–123.

Owens, N. W., and J. D. Goss-Custard. 1976. The adaptive significance of alarm calls given by shorebirds on their winter feeding grounds. Evolution, 30:397–398.

Owings, D. H., and R. G. Coss. 1977. Snake mobbing by California ground squirrels: adaptive variation and ontogeny. Behaviour, 62:50–69.

———. 1981. How do ground squirrels repel rattlesnakes? Anima, 6:37–43.

Owings, D. H., and D. W. Leger. 1980. Chatter vocalizations of California ground squirrels: predator- and social-role specificity. Z. Tierpsychol., 54:163–184.

Owings, D. H., and S. C. Owings. 1979. Snake-directed behavior by black-tailed prairie dogs (Cynomys ludovicianus). Z. Tierpsychol., 49:35–54.

Owings, D. H., and R. A. Virginia. 1978. Alarm calls of California ground squirrels (Spermophilus beecheyi). Z. Tierpsychol., 46:58–70.

Owings, D. H., M. Borchert, and R. Virginia. 1977. The behaviour of California ground squirrels. Anim. Behav., 25:221–230.

Quanstrom, W. R. 1971. Behaviour of Richardson's ground squirrel, Spermophilus richardsonii richardsonii. Anim. Behav., 19:646–652.

Robinson, S. R. 1981. Alarm communication in Belding's ground squirrels. Z. Tierpsychol., 56:150–168.

Rongstad, O. J. 1965. A life-history of thirteen-lined ground squirrels in southern Wisconsin. J. Mamm., 46:76–87.

Schleidt, W. M. 1973. Tonic communication: continual effects of discrete signs in animal communication systems. J. Theor. Biol., 42:359–386.

Schwagmeyer, P. L. 1980. Alarm calling behavior of the thirteen-lined ground squirrel, *Spermophilus tridecemlineatus*. Behav. Ecol. Sociobiol., 7:195–200.

Schwagmeyer, P. L., and C. H. Brown. 1981. Conspecific reaction to playback of thirteen-lined ground squirrel vocalizations. Z. Tierpsychol., 56:25–32.

Seyfarth, R. M., D. L. Cheney, and P. Marler. 1980. Vervet monkey alarm calls: semantic communication in a free-ranging primate. Anim. Behav., 28:1070–1094.

Sherman, P. 1976. Natural selection among some group-living organisms. Unpubl. Ph.D. dissert., Univ. Michigan, Ann Arbor, 254 pp.

———. 1977. Nepotism and the evolution of alarm calls. Science, 197:1246–1253.

———. 1980a. The meaning of nepotism. Amer. Nat., 116:604–606.

———. 1980b. The limits of ground squirrel nepotism. Pp. 505–544, *in* Sociobiology: beyond nature/nurture? (G. W. Barlow and J. Silverberg, eds.). Westview Press, Boulder, 627 pp.

———. 1981. Reproductive competition and infanticide in Belding's ground squirrels and other animals. Pp. 311–331, *in* Natural selection and social behavior: recent research and new theory (R. D. Alexander and D. W. Tinkle, eds.). Chiron Press, New York, 532 pp.

———. 1982. Infanticide in ground squirrels. Anim. Behav., 30:938–939.

Shields, W. M. 1980. Ground squirrel alarm calls: nepotism or parental care? Amer. Nat., 116:599–603.

Simpson, M. J. A. 1973. Social displays and the recognition of individuals. Pp. 225–279, *in* Perspectives in ethology (P. P. G. Bateson and P. H. Klopfer, eds.). Plenum Press, New York, 336 pp.

Slobodchikoff, C. N., and R. Coast. 1980. Dialects in the alarm calls of prairie dogs. Behav. Ecol. Sociobiol., 7:49–53.

Smith, S. F. 1978. Alarm calls, their origin and use in *Eutamias sonomae*. J. Mamm., 59:889–893.

Smith, W. J. 1977. The behavior of communicating: an ethological approach. Harvard Univ. Press, Cambridge, 545 pp.

Smith, W. J., et al. 1973. Behavior of a captive population of black-tailed prairie dogs. Annual cycle of social behavior. Behaviour, 46:189–220.

Smith, W. J., S. L. Smith, J. G. Devilla, and E. C. Oppenheimer. 1976. The jump-yip display of the black-tailed prairie dog *Cynomys ludovicianus*. Anim. Behav., 24:609–621.

Smith, W. J., S. L. Smith, E. C. Oppenheimer, and J. G. Devilla. 1977. Vocalizations of the black-tailed prairie dog, *Cynomys ludovicianus*. Anim. Behav., 25:152–164.

Smythe, N. 1970. On the existence of "pursuit invitation" signals in mammals. Amer. Nat., 104:491–494.

Stromberg, M. R. 1974. Group response in black-tailed prairie dogs to an avian predator. J. Mamm., 55:850–851.

Taulman, J. F. 1977. Vocalizations of the hoary marmot, *Marmota caligata*. J. Mamm., 58:681–683.

Tinbergen, N. 1959. Comparative studies of the behaviour of gulls (*Laridae*): a progress report. Behaviour, 15:1–70.

Toates, F. 1980. Animal behaviour: a systems approach. John Wiley, New York, 299 pp.

Trivers, R. L. 1972. Parental investment and sexual selection. Pp. 136–179, *in* Sexual selection and the descent of man, 1871–1971 (B. Campbell, ed.). Aldine, Chicago, 378 pp.

Turner, L. W. 1973. Vocal and escape responses of *Spermophilus beldingi* to predators. J. Mamm., 54:990–993.

Waring, G. H. 1966. Sounds and communications of the yellow-bellied marmot. Anim. Behav., 14:177–183.

———. 1970. Sound communications of black-tailed, white-tailed, and Gunnison's prairie dogs. Amer. Midland Nat., 83:167–185.

Watton, D. G., and M. H. R. Keenleyside. 1974. Social behavior of the Arctic ground squirrel, *Spermophilus undulatus*. Behaviour, 50:77–99.

Wistrand, H. 1974. Individual, social and seasonal behavior of the thirteen-lined ground squirrel (*Spermophilus tridecemlineatus*). J. Mamm., 55:329–347.

ZULEYMA TANG HALPIN

University of Missouri – St. Louis

Chapter 9

The Role of Olfactory
Communication in the Social Systems of
Ground-Dwelling Sciurids

Abstract. Ground squirrels (*Spermophilus*), prairie dogs (*Cynomys*), and marmots (*Marmota*) possess a variety of specialized scent glands, including oral,
anal, and dorsal glands. These glands may be used to deposit scent passively
during the animal's daily, routine activities and also actively during stereotyped
scent-marking behaviors. In addition, many social and "greeting" behaviors
appear to involve the investigation of scent-producing areas, suggesting that
these scents may play a role in olfactory communication.

The available evidence from observation and experimentation suggests that
the biological odors produced by ground-dwelling sciurids may be particularly
important in agonistic interactions and in individual and group recognition. Anal
glands are generally extruded during stressful and agonistic situations, but the
significance of this behavior is not well understood. Oral and dorsal gland secretions may be involved in individual and group recognition. Moreover, these and
other odor sources, such as urine, may communicate information on sexual
identity, reproductive condition, or dominance status. Unfortunately, the paucity of experimental work on sciurid biological odors makes it impossible to
reach more definitive conclusions regarding the function and evolutionary significance of these odors. Simple field and laboratory experiments that may help to
remedy this situation are discussed.

Chemical Communication: An Introduction

The study of animal communication has been an integral part of the investigation
of animal behavior almost since the inception of the field of ethology (Lorenz,

201

1935; Tinbergen, 1959; von Frisch, 1923). Early studies of vertebrate communication concentrated almost entirely on the visual and auditory sensory modalities, and little if any attention was given to olfactory modes of communication (but see von Frisch, 1941, for an exception). However, since the 1950s it has become clear that chemical communication is widespread among virtually all animal phyla, and olfaction is now considered one of the most important modalities used for communication among mammals (Brown, 1979; Eisenberg and Kleiman, 1972).

Initially, chemical signals used in intraspecific communication (pheromones) were classified as either releasers or primers (Wilson and Bossert, 1963). A releaser effect was defined as "involving the classical stimulus-response mediated wholly by the central nervous system." In other words, releaser pheromones produce an immediate behavioral response. A primer effect, on the other hand, is one in which "the endocrine and reproductive (and possibly other) systems are altered physiologically."

Unfortunately, while such a conceptual framework described reasonably well the responses to pheromones found among many insects (and there are exceptions even here), it did not fare as well when applied to mammalian responses to odors. Among mammals, responses to odors are varied and do not always involve either an alteration of the endocrine/reproductive systems or a stimulus-response type of change in behavior.

Bronson (1974) suggested that for mammals the term "signaling pheromone" might be more appropriate than releaser pheromone. He argued that, among mammals, pheromones communicate information but do not generally trigger an immediate and stereotyped response. Muller-Schwarze (1977) also stressed this point and suggested that the term "informer pheromone" be used for chemical substances that communicate information but do not release any particular behavioral or physiological response. Bronson's signaling pheromones and Muller-Schwarze's informer pheromones were invaluable concepts, and their introduction marked a turning point in our thinking by emphasizing that the dichotomy between primers and releasers is not always realistic. Beauchamp et al. (1976) further emphasized the chemical and behavioral complexity of mammalian pheromonal systems and concluded that chemical signals do not function in a way fundamentally different from other modalities used in communication. All signals used in communication, regardless of their mode of action, basically communicate information, and the responses to a signal will always depend on the receiver's "interpretation" of that information.

Marler (1961) suggested that five categories of information are particularly important in animal communication: information that conveys species identity, individual identity, sexual identity, motivational state, and information regarding important environmental parameters or variables. Smith (1977) broadly classified messages (the information content of a signal) as behavioral and nonbehavioral. Nonbehavioral messages included information on species, individual, sexual, and reproductive identity as well as information on group identity and location of the sender. Behavioral messages provided information on the behaviors most likely to be performed by the communicator and on how (e.g., intensity, stability) these behaviors would be performed. Although the methods of classification are different, Smith's nonbehavioral messages seem to overlap broadly with Marler's first four designative messages, and his behavioral messages could be interpreted as communicating information on motivational state.

Scent glands and scent-marking behaviors are common among the ground squirrels, marmots, and prairie dogs, but to date few studies have examined the possible information content or the functions of the biological odors produced by these sciurids. In this chapter I will attempt to briefly review the distribution and morphology of the scent glands, describe the scent marking and other scent-related behaviors of these species, and discuss the types of information that may be contained in sciurid biological odors and the possible functions of these odors, particularly as they relate to the social organization of these ground-dwelling sciurids.

Scent Glands

Oral and anal glands appear to be ubiquitous among the ground-dwelling sciurids. Dorsal glands, on the other hand, have been reported only among the ground squirrels (*Spermophilus* spp.). Some confusion appears to exist in the literature regarding oral and cheek glands. For example, Armitage (1976), Barash (1973), and others refer to "cheek marking" in marmots, but their descriptions suggest that the gland involved is in the oral angle at the corner of the mouth. Meier et al. (1982) looked for cheek glands in *Marmota monax* but found only oral angle glands. Kivett et al. (1976) use the term cheek glands only in relation to a group of glands below the ears in certain species of ground squirrels; this concentration of glands appears to be an extension of the dorsal gland field on the backs of the animals. To avoid further confusion, in this chapter I will use the term "oral gland" to refer to the glands in the oral angle. Cheek glands (sensu Kivett et al., 1976) will not be discussed separately and will be considered an extension of the dorsal gland field.

Communication

Oral glands. Scent marking with oral glands is common among ground squirrels and marmots, and it is likely that these glands also occur in the prairie dogs (see section on scent marking and scent-related behaviors). However, the morphology and histology of the oral glands have been described in detail only in the ground squirrels and in *Marmota monax* (See Halpin, in press; Kivett, 1978; Kivett et al. 1976; Meier et al., 1982; Quay, 1965). In all species, the oral glands are immediately posterior to the corners of the mouth and extend into the lower dermis and hypodermis of the oral angle. The gland is of the apocrine sudoriferous type and consists of one or more lobes, each composed of coiled, branched tubules lined with cuboidal or columnar epithelium. A separate excretory duct originates from each lobe and empties into a hair follicle or directly onto the surface of the skin. The number of lobes and the size of the gland may differ among species.

Both males and females of all species examined (but in *S. franklinii* only males were examined) possess oral glands. The description given by Kivett et al. (1976) does not indicate if glands are sexually dimorphic in size, but Meier et al. (1982) report that in *M. monax* the glands are largest in adult males during the spring.

The effects of hormones on oral gland size and activity have been examined only in male *Spermophilus columbianus* (Kivett, 1975). Castration resulted in a reduction in the size of the gland and in the frequency of scent marking; replacement therapy with testosterone restored gland size and marking frequency. Females were not examined, but females scent mark more during pregnancy and lactation (Kivett, 1975), suggesting that estrogen, progesterone, or prolactin may affect scent marking.

Anal glands. Although anal glands have been reported in virtually all species of ground squirrels, prairie dogs, and marmots, they have been described in detail only for *Spermophilus richardsonii* (Sleggs, 1926), *S. columbianus* (Kivett, 1978), *Marmota monax* (Smith and Hearn, 1979), and *Cynomys ludovicianus* (Jones and Plakke, 1981). In all four species the anal gland consists of three separate glandular masses or lobes within the walls of the anal canal. The lobes of the gland are normally retracted and hidden within the anal walls, but they can be everted through the anus and made to pulsate. In the everted state, the gland appears as three nipplelike papillae that protrude from the anus.

Histological studies (Jones and Plakke, 1981; Kivett, 1978; Sleggs, 1926; Smith and Hearn, 1979) showed that each lobe of the anal gland consists of a central channel or reservoir and of both holocrine sebaceous and apocrine glandular elements. The central channel of each lobe narrows into a duct that opens into the walls of the anus. Differences between the species examined are minimal and seem to be limited to the exact location of the glandular elements within the lobes. With the exception of Salmon (1979) who found that female *S. beecheyi* have larger glands than males (but male glands contained more secretion), no one has reported sexual dimorphism in gland size.

When both glandular elements are active, the secretions of the anal gland probably consist of a combination of secretory products from both sebaceous and apocrine elements. Jones and Plakke (1981) reported that the sebaceous elements of the black-tailed prairie dog anal gland secrete a combination of neutral lipids and proteins. The chemical composition of anal gland secretions of other species is not known.

Dorsal glands. Dorsal glands have been described only in the genus *Spermophilus* (Hatt, 1926; Kivett, 1978; Kivett et al., 1976) and have not been found in any other sciurid species so far examined (e.g., chipmunks: Yahner et al., 1979). A large number of individual dorsal glands (e.g., 60 individual glands in *S. columbianus*) make up a ''dorsal gland field'' that extends down the animal's back behind the scapular region. In all species examined (Kivett et al., 1976) the individual dorsal glands consist of coiled, branched tubules lined with cuboidal or columnar secretory epithelial cells.

Kivett et al. (1976) found differences in the distribution of dorsal glands among the six species they studied. In *S. columbianus* and *S. parryii* the gland field extends anteriorly and terminates ventral to the ears; in *S. franklini* and *S. lateralis* the glands terminate in the shoulder region. Sexual dimorphism in gland size is present in all species, with males having larger glands than females (Kivett et al., 1976).

The size and activity of the dorsal glands appear to be under androgenic control. Kivett (1975) found that in castrated male Columbian ground squirrels injections of testosterone propionate resulted in an increase in the size and secretory activity of the dorsal glands. The hormonal control of the dorsal glands in females is not known.

Other sources of odors. Kivett (1978) has described pedal sweat glands consisting of coiled unbranched tubules in the foot pads of *S. columbianus*. Other possible sources of odors in the ground-dwelling sciurids include saliva, urine, and feces, but no studies have been conducted on these substances to determine if they are involved in chemical communication.

TABLE 9.1. Biological odors of ground-dwelling sciurids

Source of biological odor	Genera in which found	Mode of deposition or transfer	Context of usage or implied function[a]
Oral glands	*Spermophilus* *Marmota* *Cynomys*	Rubbed on substrate. Transfer to self or conspecifics may occur during self- and allogrooming and during greetings.	Greeting behaviors; possibly involved in individual or group identification. Scent marking most frequent among dominant individuals.
Dorsal glands	*Spermophilus*	Actively rubbed on substrate (twist marking). Passively deposited when animal's back touches overhanging objects or walls of burrow.	May indicate occupancy of an area (individual identity?). Marking frequency highest among dominant individuals and during agonistic encounters; may imply threat.
Anal glands	*Spermophilus* *Marmota* *Cynomys*	Odor may be released into the air when glands are extruded. Secretions may be deposited on substrate during ventral or anal drag.	Gland extrusion occurs when animal appears frightened and during agonistic encounters. Ventral/anal drag most frequent during the breeding season, suggesting a sexual function.
Urine	*Spermophilus* *Marmota* *Cynomys*	May be deposited as a trail during ventral or anal drag (reported only in *Spermophilus*).	Same as ventral/anal drag above.
Pedal glands	*Spermophilus* (but other genera have not been examined)	Presumably deposited on substrate as animal walks in its environment. May be deposited during scratching behaviors preceding agonistic encounters.	Generally unknown. May deposit a trail; during scratching may imply threat.

[a] See text for additional information and clarification.

Scent Marking and Scent-Related Behaviors

In this section I review the available information on the use of scent glands for scent marking and other scent-related behaviors. The emphasis will be on the use of the glands discussed in the previous section. To avoid speculation that may be unfounded, I will limit discussion of rubbing behaviors involving areas of the body that have not been demonstrated to contain specialized glandular tissues to the section on "comfort behaviors." The possible evolutionary antecedents of scent marking and scent-related behaviors of the ground-dwelling sciurids will not be considered in this chapter. For discussions of this topic, the reader is referred to Ferron (1977), Halpin (in press), Kivett et al. (1976), and Steiner (1975).

Oral glands. Active scent marking with glands in the oral angle sometimes referred to as mouth or cheek rubbing) is widespread among the terrestrial sciurids and appears to be particularly common among the ground squirrels (Ferron, 1977; Kivett, 1978; Kivett et al., 1976; Steiner, 1974) and marmots (Armitage, 1976; Barash, 1973; Meier et al., 1982). It has not, however, been reported among the prairie dogs, except perhaps as what appears to be part of a comfort movement (Halpin, pers. obs. for *Cynomys ludovicianus;* C. N. Slobodchikoff, pers. comm. for *C. gunnisonii).*

The pattern followed during marking with oral glands is similar in all species. The animal approaches and sniffs the object to be marked, then rapidly moves its head in a forward and sideways motion, pressing the sides and corners of its mouth against the object. In some species both sides of the face are usually rubbed, but in others (e.g., *Spermophilus lateralis,* Ferron, 1977) it is more common for only one side to be rubbed. The animal may rub only once or may perform the behavior repeatedly. Once the behavior is completed, the animal usually again sniffs the area where it has marked. In the woodchuck (*M. monax*) gnawing of the marked sites is often interspersed with scent-marking behavior (Meier et al., 1982). Gnawing may provide a visual marker, add saliva to the substrate, or both.

Almost any object that is accessible to the animal may be marked, including rocks and stones, low-growing branches or roots, and burrow entrances or mounds. Often, several squirrels within the same social group will repeatedly scent mark at the same location.

The oral glands may also be involved in self-oriented and conspecific-oriented behaviors. During self-grooming, for example, the animal generally begins by licking its fore paws and rubbing them along the corners of the mouth. Secretions from the oral glands (and saliva?) may be picked up on the paws and spread over the rest of the body as grooming continues, resulting in self-marking or "self-anointing." During allogrooming the groomer pats, licks, and nibbles another individual. This behavior suggests that transfer of oral gland secretions may occur and that the behavior may in part involve the scent marking of conspecifics. Furthermore, Armitage (pers. comm.) reports that during agonistic encounters yellow-bellied marmots (*M. flaviventris*) sometimes engage in what appears to be self-anointing. Self-anointing and conspecific marking are known to occur in other species of mammals (e.g., Brockie, 1976; Eisenberg and Gould, 1970; Mykytowycz, 1965; Schultze-Westrum, 1969). However, although Steiner (1974) and Kivett et al. (1976) discussed the possible involvement of oral glands in self- and allogrooming, there is no experimental evidence that conspecific marking and self-anointing actually occur among the sciurids.

207

Virtually all social ground squirrels, prairie dogs, and marmots have been reported to perform a "greeting" behavior in which one animal approaches and makes naso-oral contact with another (see Armitage, 1962; Balph and Stokes, 1963; Barash, 1973; King, 1955; Quanstrom, 1971; Steiner, 1975; Watton and Keenleyside, 1974). This behavior, which in prairie dogs has been called the "kiss" (King, 1955), appears to involve olfactory investigation of the oral glands. Most commonly, the animal that is approached opens its mouth, and the other animal pushes its nose and muzzle into its partner's mouth until actual contact is made between the nose of the sniffer and the mouth corners of the partner (Steiner, 1975). Sometimes both animals open their mouths and olfactory investigation appears to be mutual. This behavior, which precedes many other social interactions and occurs with a higher frequency among members of the same social group, almost certainly involves the oral glands (see next section for a discussion of possible functions).

The importance of the oral glands in the social behaviors of the ground-

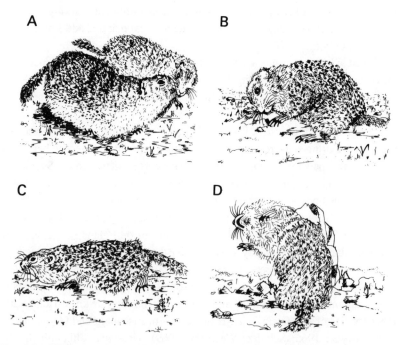

FIGURE 9.1. Illustration of the most commonly seen scent-marking and scent-related behaviors of terrestrial sciurids. A, "greeting" behavior; B, marking with oral glands; C, ventral drag; D, marking with the dorsal glands (twist marking), seen only in *Spermophilus*. (Redrawn from Steiner, 1974, 1975)

dwelling sciurids is further evidenced by the interest these animals show in the cheeks and mouth corners of conspecifics. Investigatory, amicable, and aggressive behaviors, for example, are frequently directed to these areas (see Kivett et al., 1976; Steiner, 1974), at least among the ground squirrels.

Dorsal glands. Scent marking with the dorsal gland field is limited to the ground squirrels and may be either active or passive. In passive scent marking, dorsal gland secretions are deposited as the animal's back passively makes contact with overhanging branches, rock outcroppings, or burrow walls (Kivett et al., 1976). In such cases, scent deposition results from the normal, routine activities of the animals, and no specialized scent-marking behavior is present.

Active scent marking with the dorsal glands involves a behavior that has been called "twist marking." Generally the squirrel begins by marking with the oral glands, then moves forward with a spiral or twisting motion of the body during which the side of the face, the shoulders, and the back are rubbed against the substrate. The behavior is not always performed in its complete form; in some cases, particularly if the object to be marked is in a vertical or elevated position, the squirrel may rub only the cheek and shoulder regions against it; in other cases, for example when the squirrel is marking a flat or horizontal surface, the animal is more likely to roll over completely in a rapid spiral motion so that the back also touches the substrate (Ferron, 1977; Kivett et al., 1976; Steiner, 1974). Twist marking is usually preceded and followed by sniffing of the substrate; at times, particularly when it is associated with an agonistic encounter such as a territorial intrusion, the marking behavior may be preceded by vigorous clawing and scratching of the substrate (Steiner, 1974).

Scent marking with the dorsal gland field is frequently performed against vertical or sloping substrates such as rocks, tree stumps, mounds of dirt or grass, and burrow entrances (Steiner, 1974). Typically, one class of animal (e.g., dominant males in *S. columbianus* and *S. parryii*) does most of the marking, and an individual visits and marks the same sites day after day. Intruders frequently place their own marks on such "signposts," which are then vigorously remarked by the resident animal once the intruder has been detected (Steiner, 1974). Virtually all species of social or gregarious ground squirrels show twist marking (*S. columbianus, S parryii, S. richardsonii:* Kivett et al., 1976; *S. lateralis:* Ferron, 1977; Kivett et al., 1976; *S. armatus:* Balph and Stokes, 1963; *S. beecheyi:* Linsdale, 1946; and *S. spilosoma:* Steiner, 1974). The behavior has not been observed in either *S. tridecemlineatus* or *S. franklinii* (Kivett et al., 1976), both of which are generally considered less social than the aforementioned species.

209

Communication

Anal gland. Although a number of terrestrial sciurids show an anal or ventral drag behavior, it is not clear at present whether scent marking with the anal gland is involved (J. Murie, pers. comm.). Steiner (1974) describes the "anal drag" of Columbian and Arctic ground squirrels as a behavior during which the squirrel presses its hindquarters against the substrate and then, while retaining this "squatting" position, moves forward slowly, dragging and rubbing the anogenital region against the substrate. This behavior, which is usually preceded by thorough sniffing of the substrate, can deposit a liquid trail with a strong musky odor. According to Steiner (1974) and Kivett (1975), this trail may consist of urine but also, possibly, of anal gland secretions. J. Murie (pers. comm.), however, believes there is no distinctive behavior pattern that can be classified as an "anal drag" because it is the entire belly region (rather than the anogenital region specifically) that is pressed against the substrate. Furthermore, in discussing the belly or anal drag, Kivett et al. (1976) suggest that if scent is deposited, it is likely to be done so only passively as a result of comfort activities. Murie (pers. comm.) also believes that while urine is often deposited during the ventral drag, it is less likely that anal gland secretions are involved. Clearly, additional studies on this behavior and on its relevance to scent marking and chemical communication in other *Spermophilus* are needed.

Among prairie dogs, C. N. Slobodchikoff (pers. comm.) reports that a behavior essentially similar to the anal drag described by Steiner (1974) is performed by adult male, female, and juvenile *Cynomys gunnisonii* (see discussion, next section). A behavior like the ventral drag is also occasionally performed by black-tailed prairie dogs, *C. ludovicianus*. However, the behavior occurs so rarely that it is likely to be only a comfort movement (Halpin, pers. obs.). Scent marking with the anal glands has not been reported for any of the marmot species.

In some sciurids the anal glands are used as part of agonistic displays during territorial disputes and other aggressive encounters (e.g., Armitage, 1976, for *Marmota flaviventris;* Haslett, 1973, for *M. monax;* King, 1955, for *C. ludovicianus;* Kivett, 1978, for *Spermophilus columbianus*). During such displays the anal glands are extruded through the anus and made to pulsate. In some species (*S. armatus, C. ludovicianus* and *M. flaviventris*), extrusion of the anal glands may be accompanied by elevation and piloerection of the tail and the anal region. The displaying animal may then turn and present its anal region and extruded anal glands toward the face of its opponent. Possible functions of this behavior will be discussed in the following section. Extrusion of the anal glands also commonly occurs when a squirrel is handled or is frightened. Extrusion of anal glands during such situations may be a general pattern among terrestrial sciurids; the same

210

behavior has been observed in the highly solitary eastern chipmunk, *Tamias striatus* (Halpin, pers. obs.).

Pedal glands. As I mentioned earlier, during territorial disputes of ground squirrels, vigorous scratching of the substrate often precedes twist marking (Steiner, 1974). During such scratching, secretions from the pedal sweat glands may be deposited on the substrate. However, scratching may also serve as a visual signal or be used to remove odors left by a territorial opponent. Since the presence of pedal glands has been confirmed only for *S. columbianus* (Kivett, 1978), more general interpretations of scratching as scent marking may be premature. Secretions from pedal glands may also be deposited passively as the animal moves about its environment, digs at the ground, or grooms itself or a conspecific.

Comfort behaviors. Sciurids often perform comfort behaviors (activities associated with grooming and pelage maintenance) or rub the chin, throat, or belly against the substrate while basking, dust-bathing, or resting at the entrance to a burrow. During such comfort behaviors odors may be deposited on the substrate (Steiner, 1974). However, experimental evidence for scent deposition is lacking, and no specialized scent glands have been reported in those areas of the body (Kivett et al., 1976).

Certain other comfort movements almost surely involve the passive deposition of odors. For example, sciurids sometimes rub the sides of the face and mouth against the substrate after eating or after biting an opponent (Steiner, 1974). Although this behavior probably serves a cleaning function, secretions from the oral (and cheek?) glands may be left behind. Likewise, as discussed previously, the ventral drag may occur as a comfort behavior, but biologically meaningful odors may nonetheless be passively transferred to the substrate (Kivett et al., 1976).

Scent marking and sociality. Kivett et al. (1976) have suggested that among ground squirrels (*Spermophilus* spp.) there is a correlation between frequency of scent marking and degree of sociality. Among the six species they studied, *S. parryii* and *S. columbianus* are considered to have the highest level of sociality and also show the highest frequency of scent marking with oral and dorsal glands. *S. franklinii,* on the other hand, shows little evidence of active scent marking and is also considered the least social of the six species. The other three species (*S. lateralis, S. richardsonii,* and *S. tridecemlineatus*) are intermediate both in degree of sociality and in frequency of scent marking. However, even though *S.*

richardsonii and *S. tridecemlineatus* are roughly comparable in terms of social organization and degree of sociality (Kivett et al., 1976), *S. richardsonii* shows a much higher frequency of scent marking than does *S. tridecemlineatus*. In the latter species, marking with oral glands occurred only occasionally, and twist marking was never observed; comfort behaviors, including chin, throat, and belly rubbing, were the predominant scent-related activities in this species.

The frequency of "greeting" behaviors also shows a positive correlation with degree of sociality in these six species. That is not surprising, however, since frequency of "greetings" (and other amicable behaviors) is one of the criteria used to determine degree of sociality (Kivett et al., 1976).

Among the marmots no evidence exists of a correlation between degree of sociality and frequency of scent marking, but quantitative, comparative data on these species are not available. Virtually all species of marmots, from the highly social *Marmota olympus* (Barash, 1973) to the more solitary *M. monax* (Meier et al., 1982) have been reported to scent mark with the oral glands, but no studies have attempted to examine frequency of scent marking as a function of social organization.

Very little information is available regarding scent marking and sociality among the prairie dogs. Black-tailed prairie dogs (*Cynomys ludovicianus*), among the most social of all sciurids, appear to do little if any active scent marking (Halpin, pers. obs.). *C. gunnisonii,* a less social species, is reported to scent mark extensively by means of the ventral or anal drag (C. N. Slobodchikoff, pers. comm.). To my knowledge there is no information available on scent marking in the other prairie dog species, *C. leucurus, C. parvidens,* and *C. mexicanus,* making further comparisons impossible.

In summary, at present it is not possible to formulate a general hypothesis relating frequency of scent marking to degree of sociality. Among the ground squirrel species that have been examined, the evidence is highly suggestive, but additional species should be considered. Among the prairie dogs and marmots, the relatively scant evidence available does not support such a correlation; no quantitative data are available for marmot species, and among the prairie dogs the more solitary *C. gunnisonii* appears to scent mark more than the highly social *C. ludovicianus*.

Since scent-marking behaviors may serve a variety of functions in different species, it may not be realistic to expect a clear correlation between frequency of scent marking and level of sociality. For example, among solitary species, individuals are likely to encounter each other infrequently and odors may be the most efficient means of communicating information (e.g., individual identity, aggressive motivation, reproductive condition) about the resident of a particular area.

212

Among social species odors may provide similar information, but because of the close proximity of individuals, scent marking of the substrate may not be as prevalent; interindividual olfactory interactions, on the other hand, may be more frequent. Clearly, a better understanding of the functions of biological odors in different sciurid species is necessary before more broadly based predictions or generalizations can be made.

Variations in patterns of scent marking. Although comparable data are not available for many species, a few general statements can be made regarding variations in patterns of scent marking as a function of sex, age, reproductive condition, and social status. Sexual dimorphism in frequency of scent marking appears to be the rule, with males generally having larger glands and scent marking more than females (*S. columbianus* and *S. parryii:* Kivett et al., 1976; *M. monax:* Meier et al., 1982; and *M. marmota;* Koenig, 1957). In *S. richardsonii,* however, Wehrell (cited in Steiner, 1974) reported that, at least under certain conditions, females mark more than males. Frequency of scent marking in male and female *S. lateralis* is comparable, and no sexual dimorphism has been reported in *M. olympus* (Barash, 1973), *M. flaviventris* (Armitage, 1976), or *C. gunnisonii* (C. N. Slobodchikoff, pers. comm.). However, a finer and more quantitative analysis may be necessary before a definitive statement can be made for the last three species.

Information on other factors affecting frequency of scent marking is extremely limited. In general, juvenile sciurids appear to perform a variety of scent-related comfort behaviors (Steiner, 1974) but little if any active scent marking. Exceptions to this may be juvenile *C. gunnisonii,* which frequently perform the ventral or anal drag (C. N. Slobodchikoff, pers. comm.). Yearling (but not juvenile) *M. flaviventris* have also been reported to scent mark with the oral glands (Armitage, 1976). Among the species that have been examined (*S. columbianus, S. parryii,* and *S. richardsonii:* Kivett et al., 1976) scent marking reaches a peak during the breeding season in males and during pregnancy and lactation in females. Steiner (1974) reports that among Columbian and Arctic ground squirrels frequency of scent marking is related to dominance, with the dominant males doing most of the marking. Armitage (1976) also found that marking with the oral glands was most common among dominant male and female *M. flaviventris.*

Information Content and Function of Biological Odors

One of the most challenging difficulties in the study of animal communication is that it is impossible to ascertain directly either the information content (messages) or the function of the signals used in communication. Instead, the researcher must attempt to deduce message and function by observing the context in which a signal occurs and the responses of conspecifics to it. On the basis of such repeated observations it becomes possible to propose a hypothesis that can then be tested experimentally.

A confounding problem in the study of vertebrate chemical communication has been a failure by many researchers to distinguish adequately among the information content of a signal, the responses it elicits among conspecifics, and its function or adaptive significance. Furthermore, the context in which the signal is used has often been equated with its information content or function. It is essential to remember that the responses given to a chemical signal and the context in which the signal occurs may be used by the researcher to help elucidate the information content and function of the signal, but that response, context, information content, and function are neither equivalent nor synonymous.

It may also be valuable to reemphasize that, among mammals, responses to biological odors are generally not stereotyped, and that one message may evoke different responses in different receivers. The receiver plays an essential role by interpreting the message and determining what response to give. In any particular situation the response given to a signal will vary depending on the physiological state, motivation, and past experience of the receiver and also on the context in which the interaction is taking place.

In this section I consider Marler's (1961) and Smith's (1977) categories of messages, then review the correlational (context and conspecific responses) and experimental evidence that supports each category. This approach will, I hope, provide new insights but, owing to the incomplete nature of the available data, will not allow definitive conclusions in all cases. Consequently, much of the following discussion must remain tentative and speculative. An alternative, but still controversial, analysis of communication systems proposed by Dawkins and Krebs (1978) will not be considered here.

Species identification. No direct experimental evidence indicates that the biological odors of terrestrial sciurids carry information on species identity. Most sciurids show a great deal of interest in the scent marks deposited by conspecifics, suggesting that the odor is recognized as a biologically significant (e.g., species-specific?) signal. However, although almost by definition (an *intraspecific* chemical signal) pheromones are assumed to carry information on species identity, only a few studies have tested this assumption for any mammalian species. Experimental studies examining the ability of terrestrial sciurids to distinguish between own-species odors and the odors of other closely related species are clearly needed.

Sexual identity. As in the case of species identity, the role of odors in communicating information on sexual identity has often been assumed but rarely tested. Among some sciurids, scent marking increases during the breeding season in males and during pregnancy and lactation in females. Although the biological odors produced at this time probably carry information on reproductive condition and motivation (see below), sexual identity may also be communicated. Moreover, in species that show sexual dimorphism in frequency of scent marking, the frequency with which a particular scent mark is encountered may provide indirect information on the sex of the marker. There have been no experimental studies on sexual recognition by odor among ground squirrels, prairie dogs, and marmots, but Keevin et al. (1981) demonstrated that the eastern chipmunk, *Tamias striatus,* can distinguish between male and female conspecifics on the basis of odor. When simultaneously presented with male and female odors, male chipmunks spent more time investigating female odors, and females spent more time investigating male odors. Sexual identification by odors is also likely to occur among the more social and gregarious members of this family. Additional studies are obviously necessary.

Individual identity. Individual identification by odor appears to be widespread among mammals (see Halpin, 1980), and much of the available evidence suggests that may also be true among the sciurids. In an interesting field experiment, Harris and Murie (1982) monitored the responses of male and female *Spermophilus columbianus* to plastic cubes containing oral gland scent from male conspecifics. Their results showed that both male and female squirrels were able to distinguish between their own odors (odor of the resident male in the case of female subjects) and those of other conspecific males, and also between the odors of neighboring and strange males. Likewise, based on differences in sniffing frequencies and sequential patterns of sniffing at different glands, Salmon (1979) concluded that the anal glands of *S. beecheyi* may be important in individual or group recognition. These results are compatible with the hypothesis that the glandular scents of ground squirrels may contain information on individual identity. The same may be true of the other sciurid species discussed, and it is tempting to conclude that glandular secretions may function in individual recognition, or at least in the recognition of familiar versus unfamiliar conspecifics.

The involvement of the oral glands in individual identification is also suggested by the prevalence among social sciurids of the "greeting" behaviors discussed previously (Steiner, 1975). These nose-to-mouth greetings are performed by individuals of all ages but are more common between members of the same social group. Between such animals, greetings are likely to lead to amicable behaviors such as allogrooming, playing, or resting together. Between members of different social groups, on the other hand, greetings are rare, are usually performed hesitantly, and are likely to be followed by agonistic interactions. This pattern of behavior suggests that greetings may merely identify an individual; after identification and depending on the social relationship of the two animals, either agonistic or friendly behaviors will be the most likely to follow.

Other sciurid biological odors (e.g., dorsal glands, urine) may also contain information on individual identity. Unfortunately, only one other sciurid species has been examined experimentally. Using whole body odors contained in soiled bedding, Keevin et al. (1981) determined that both male and female chipmunks, *T. striatus,* can distinguish individual differences in the odors of male and female conspecifics. It would be most interesting to test the ability of prairie dogs and marmots to distinguish individual differences in the odors of conspecifics. Studies on the dorsal glands of ground squirrels (see below) are also needed.

The results of the preceding study on the eastern chipmunk indicate that individual differences in odors are not found only among social species. Rather, the presence of individual odors may be ubiquitous among rodents and may serve a variety of functions in both social and solitary species. Data from other families of rodents support this generalization; individual differences in odors have been reported not only among social murid and cricetid rodents but also among more solitary species (e.g., *Mesocricetus auratus,* Halpin, unpubl. data; *Dicrostonyx groenlandicus,* Huck and Banks, 1979).

Group identification. Group identification is generally thought to occur from the mixing or sharing of the individual odors produced by members of the same social group. Alternatively, one individual within the group may mark all others, and that individual's scent may then come to be recognized as the group's odor. Among social sciurids, the opportunity for scent sharing is widespread. Animals may share scents when allogrooming, when sleeping or resting in contact with one another, and when scent marking or body rubbing in an area where another animal has already scent marked. Furthermore, Steiner (1975) has suggested that during nose-to-mouth greetings scent may be shared. The sniffer, for example, may pick up on its muzzle the scent of its partner; this scent, as well as the sniffer's own scent, could then be passed on to the next animal that is investigated. Thus, if all group members engage in nose-to-mouth "greetings," the oral gland scents of all group members can be shared and mixed, thereby creating a unique group odor. In some species (e.g., *S. columbianus:* Steiner, 1974, 1975) one dominant individual performs most of the scent marking and greeting behaviors. Possibly other group members pick up and share that one individual's odors, which then become the group's identifying odor.

The existence of group identifying odors is feasible and appealing. However, among the sciurids no experimental studies have examined this hypothesis. If group odors do exist, they may be most likely to occur among the more social species (e.g., *C. ludovicianus, M. olympus, S. parryii*) and species that have female kin groups as the basic unit of social organization.

Motivational state. Signals that provide information on motivational state indicate to the receiver which behaviors the sender is most likely to perform. Among sciurids, chemical signals may provide information on reproductive condition and on aggressive motivation or dominance status.

The ability of biological odors to communicate reproductive condition in many species of mammals is well known (reviews by Eisenberg and Kleiman, 1972; Brown, 1979). In general, any chemical substance that is under hormonal control and increases gradually, with a peak at the time of maximum sexual receptivity, could communicate the sexual status and motivation of the producer. Among females, sex pheromones composed of mixtures of several different chemical substances could have some of their components responsive to increases in estrogens and other components responsive to changes in circulating levels of progestins. Fluctuations in the ratio of these two components could then provide information on sexual receptivity and reproductive condition.

Among the sciurids strong circumstantial evidence suggests that chemical cues may indicate reproductive condition. In at least some species of ground squirrels (*S. columbianus, S. richardsonii, S. parryii:* Kivett et al., 1976) scent marking reaches a peak during the breeding season in males and during pregnancy and lactation in females. Furthermore, Kivett (1975) has demonstrated that the size and secretory activity of the oral and dorsal glands of *S. columbianus* are under androgenic control. Among black-tailed prairie dogs, the apocrine elements of the anal glands are active only during the breeding season (Jones and Plakke, 1981). All of these correlations suggest that the presence of certain odors and/or the rate of deposition of odors change during the reproductive cycle and may therefore communicate information on the reproductive status and sexual motivation of the sender.

It is not clear if the odors produced by terrestrial sciurids during the breeding season only contain information on breeding condition or whether they also serve as sexual excitants or attractants. In *S. columbianus*, for example, the odor trails deposited by the ventral drag of males during the breeding season appear to be highly attractive to both male and female conspecifics (Steiner, 1974). Furthermore, M. Harris and J. Murie (pers. comm.), using plastic cubes containing vaginal secretions, demonstrated that under field conditions male *S. columbianus* are more strongly attracted to the genital odors of estrous and preestrous females than to those of postestrous females.

Unfortunately, few other studies have directly examined the responses of male and female sciurids to the odors produced by the opposite sex during the breeding season. Likewise, there is no information on the chemical composition of sciurid pheromones during different stages of the breeding cycle or on the hormonal control of odors in females.

The increase in scent marking during the breeding season in males and during pregnancy and lactation in females may be related not only to reproductive condition but also to dominance status or aggressive motivation. Ralls (1971) has argued in favor of a positive correlation between the frequency of scent marking and dominance or aggressive motivation in mammals. Among at least some sciurid species, aggression is highest during the breeding season in males and during pregnancy and lactation in females (females may, for example, defend a natal burrow against all other conspecifics) (Kivett, 1974; Steiner, 1974).

Among some ground squirrels (e.g., *S. columbianus, S. parryii:* Steiner, 1974) and marmots (e.g., *M. flaviventris:* Armitage, 1976) scent marking with dorsal or oral glands or both is more common among dominant, more aggressive individuals and among territory owners. The association between aggression and scent marking is further supported by the fact that scent marking frequently occurs immediately before or immediately after agonistic interactions (Armitage, 1976; Steiner, 1974). In some species (e.g., *S. columbianus:* Steiner, 1974) scent marking before an aggressive encounter may be accompanied by conspicuous displays, such as vigorous scratching of the substrate, which are likely to make the marker and the scent-marking behavior more obvious to the opponent. Although scent marking is common among territorial individuals, there is little evidence that scent marks function directly in territorial defense. Squirrels are known to mark not only their own territories but also those of their neighbors, and scent marks do not appear to deter territorial intrusions (Kivett et al., 1976; Steiner, 1974). However, the "hesitant" behavior of intruders suggests that they are aware that they are within another animal's territory (J. O. Murie, pers. comm.).

Thus, although no experimental data are available, the correlation between scent marking, dominance, and aggression suggests that, among sciurids, marking with the oral and dorsal glands may serve to communicate aggressive intention or threat. The receiver may be able to determine the aggressive motivation of the sender not only by the presence of the odor, but also by the frequency of scent deposition. In the latter case, the receiver may gain information in one of the two ways: by directly observing (visually) the frequency of scent marking by the sender, and by the frequency of its encounters with previously deposited scent marks, even if the marker is no longer present. Visual signals, then, are potentially important and may help to explain the conspicuous and stereotyped movements and displays so often associated with scent marking.

In the system described above, the odor deposited during scent marking and the frequency of scent marking may convey totally different messages. The secretions of the dorsal glands, for example, could simply communicate individual and sexual identity, but the frequency with which the message is deposited could provide information on the motivational state (e.g., aggression) and probable behavior of the sender. In addition, the age of the scent mark may provide information of how much time has elapsed since the marker was in the area. Although this discussion is purely speculative, it suggests the possible complexity of sciurid chemical communication and emphasizes the need for additional studies.

Whereas scent marking with oral and dorsal glands appears to be related to dominance or aggression, extrusion of the anal glands may be associated with fear or submission. Most sciurids extrude the anal glands when they are cornered or handled, situations that presumably evoke fear and during which the animal might be expected to give a submissive display. Additionally, Haslett (1973) demonstrated that in paired encounters between woodchucks, *M. monax,* those animals that are least likely to extrude the anal papillae are the most likely to become dominant. He concluded that the secretions of the anal glands most likely communicate fear or alarm (see below). However, in some species (e.g., blacktailed prairie dogs, Halpin, pers. obs.) both animals involved in an agonistic interaction may extrude and display the anal glands. In such cases determining which animal is dominant is not easy, particularly when agonistic encounters occur at territorial boundaries (as is often the case), where the two animals may repeatedly shift from one territory to the other. Also, Balph and Stokes (1963) suggested that anal gland extrusion in the Uinta ground squirrel (*S. armatus*) communicates threat, and C. N. Slobodchikoff (pers. comm.) reports that in *C. gunnisonii* the anal drag (which may involve the anal glands) is most commonly performed by territory owners at territorial boundaries. Last, the extrusion of anal glands when a squirrel is frightened might even be reinterpreted as a threat display. Thus, in view of the equivocal and contradictory nature of the data, the significance of anal gland secretions and anal gland extrusion must remain in doubt.

Environmental parameters. The kinds of environmental information most frequently conveyed by animal signals concern either the presence and location of food or the presence and detection of predators. Among sciurids there is little direct or experimental evidence that scent marking communicates information about food. Possibly, however, food carried in the cheek pouches may become passively marked with oral gland secretions (Kivett et al., 1976). Such olfactory cues could then be used by other squirrels to locate food caches.

Although anal gland extrusion usually occurs during frightening or alarming situations, conspecifics do not generally respond in a manner that suggests alarm or fright. In the one case in which the responses of conspecifics to anal gland secretions have been examined experimentally, Haslett (1973) found that secretions from both male and female woodchucks inhibited the activity of other woodchucks. Although such a response may represent alarm, other interpretations are also possible, and the question of an alarm pheromone among sciurids must remain open.

Chemical communication systems may be extremely complex, and the preceding discussion probably oversimplifies the situation. The evidence available suggests that the biological odors of terrestrial sciurids may be most important in communicating individual and sexual identity, reproductive condition, and aggressive motivation. As discussed previously, the same signal (odor or glandular secretion) may carry several different messages, and different odors may be redundant in the information they carry. The possibility also exists that different glands may be used in combination (e.g., oral marking followed by twist marking) to create more complex messages such as a combination of individual identity (or occupancy of an area) and threat (Kivett, 1975). Table 9.1 summarizes information on sciurid scent glands and the contexts in which they are used.

The responses of conspecifics even to the same message may vary depending on the sex, age, physiological state, and previous experience of the receiver. For example, an odor may be attractive to members of the same social group but aversive to outsiders. Likewise, an odor that communicates only individual identity may be avoided after the receiver has had one or more negative experiences with the producer of the odor. The effectiveness of most odors employed in a territorial context probably depends on such learned aversions.

Most of this discussion has centered on the role of biological odors in intraspecific communication. However, biological odors may also have important effects on their producers. Ewer (1968), for example, has suggested that scent marking may increase the level of familiar odors within an animal's environment, thereby reducing its level of anxiety. Thus, an increase in scent marking that communicates aggressive motivation to conspecifics may also have the concomitant function of "reassuring" the marker.

Last, in discussing the adaptive significance or function of biological odors, the essential question is how the production of the odor contributes to the reproductive success of the sender. Each odor can be analyzed with respect to its information content and the responses it elicits from conspecifics. From such information, the function of the odor in terms of its evolutionary significance to the sender may be hypothesized. In social species, benefits accrued through kin selection must also be considered. Among terrestrial sciurids, since so little is known about the information content of odors, definitive statements about adaptive significance are not yet possible. Most of the evidence suggests that sciurid odors may be particularly important in recognizing group members and maintaining social groups (e.g., information on individual identity), in competitive interactions and the spacing individuals within the populations (e.g., information on dominance and aggressive motivation), and in reproductive processes and intrasexual competition (e.g., information on sexual identity and reproductive condition). However, until additional information is forthcoming, both on the uses and information content of biological odors and on the variety and complexity of sciurid social organization, much of the preceding discussion and analysis must remain conjectural.

Some of the ideas suggested in this review may be tested by designing specific studies that combine laboratory and field techniques. A habituation-preference paradigm such as that employed by Keevin et al. (1981) with the eastern chipmunk could be used to test for individual odors in other sciurid species. Field observations and experimentation (e.g., Harris and Murie, 1982) could then be used to demonstrate that animals can also distinguish individual differences in odors under field conditions. Studies in which animals are allowed to show a preference between two odors could provide information on the ability to distinguish species and sex differences (e.g., Keevin et al., 1981) and reproductive condition (M. A. Harris and J. O. Murie, pers. comm.).

Experiments to test the role of odors and scent-associated behaviors in agonistic interactions and dispersion may be more difficult to design. However, a number of simple studies could provide valuable, if still preliminary, information: (1) The responses (e.g., attraction, avoidance, scent-marking, and agonistic behaviors) of both males and females to male and female odors presented in laboratory and field contexts need to be determined. Specifically, do dominant and subordinate individuals within the same social group respond differently to the same odors and, conversely, are there different responses to the odors of dominant versus subordinate individuals? Are there age and sex differences in responses? (2) The use of the anal glands or scent marking or both during agonistic encounters needs to be described in detail. In particular, it is essential to know if there is any reliable correlation between social rank (dominance/subordinance) and extrusion of the anal glands or frequency of scent marking. Haslett (1973) can serve as a model for additional studies on this question. (3) Hormonal and experiential manipulations may be used to alter the dominance status of individuals. It can then be determined if frequency of scent-marking behaviors or responses to conspecific odors can also be altered in a predictable fashion that correlates with social rank.

The studies suggested above would provide valuable information that could be used as a framework for designing more sophisticated studies addressing the question of function and evolutionary significance. A variety of sciurid species with different social organizations must be examined; biological odors among the sciurids may serve many different functions, and only by studying a cross section of species and taking into account differences in their ecology, social structure, and behavioral ontogeny can we hope to arrive at more comprehensive generalizations.

Acknowledgments

I thank Jan Murie and Dietland Muller-Schwarze for their valuable comments and suggestions on the manuscript. Elizabeth Cohen drew the figure.

Literature Cited

Armitage, K. B. 1962. Social behaviour of a colony of the yellow-bellied marmot (*Marmota flaviventris*). Anim. Behav., 10:319–331.
————. 1976. Scent marking by yellow-bellied marmots. J. Mamm., 57:583–584.
Balph, D. F., and A. W. Stokes. 1963. On the ethology of a population of Uinta ground squirrels. Amer. Midland Nat., 69:106–126.
Barash, D. P. 1973. The social biology of the Olympic marmot. Anim. Behav. Monogr., 6:171–245.
Beauchamp, G. K., R. L. Doty, D. G. Moulton, and R. A. Mugford. 1976. The pheromone concept in mammalian chemical communication: a critique. Pp. 144–160, *in* Mammalian olfaction, reproductive processes and behavior (R. L. Doty, ed.). Academic Press, New York, 344 pp.

222

Brockie, R. 1976. Self-anointing by wild hedgehogs, *Erinaceus europaeus*, in New Zealand. Anim. Behav., 24:68–71.

Bronson, F. H. 1974. Pheromonal influences on reproductive activities in rodents. Pp. 344–365, *in* Pheromones (M. Birch, ed.). Elsvier, New York, 495 pp.

Brown, R. E. 1979. Mammalian social odors: a critical review. Adv. Study Behav., 10:103–162.

Dawkins, R., and J. R. Krebs. 1978. Animal signals: information or manipulation? Pp. 282–309, *in* Behavioural ecology (J. R. Krebs and N. B. Davies, eds.). Sinauer Associates, Sunderland, Massachusetts, 494 pp.

Eisenberg, J. F., and E. Gould. 1970. The tenrecs: a study in mammalian behavior and evolution. Smithsonian Contrib. Zool., 27:1–137.

Eisenberg, J. F., and D. G. Kleiman. 1972. Olfactory communication in mammals. Ann. Rev. Ecol. Syst., 3:1–32.

Ewer, R. F. 1968. Ethology of mammals. Logos Press, London, 418 pp.

Ferron, J. 1977. Le comportement de marquage chez le spermophile à mante dorée (*Spermophilus lateralis*.) Nat. Canadien, 104:407–418.

Frisch, K. von. 1923. Über die ''Sprache'' der Bienen, eine tierpsychologische Untersuchung. Zool. Jb. Physiol., 40:1–186.

———. 1941. Über einen Schreckstoff der Fischhaut und seine biologische Bedeutung. Z. Vergl. Physiol. 29:46–145.

Halpin, Z. T. 1980. Individual odors and individual recognition: review and commentary. Biol. Behav., 5:233–248.

———. In press. Chemical communication among sciurid rodents: a review. *In* Social odours in mammals (R. E. Brown and D. Macdonald, eds.). Oxford University Press, Oxford.

Harris, M. A., and J. O. Murie. 1982. Responses to oral gland scents from different males in Columbian ground squirrels. Anim. Behav., 30:140–148.

Haslett, G. W. 1973. The significance of anal scent marking in the eastern woodchuck. Bull. Ecol. Soc. Amer. (abstr.), 54:43–44.

Hatt, R. T. 1926. A new dorsal gland in ground squirrels, *Callospermophilus*, with a note on its anal gland. J. Morph. Physiol., 42:441–451.

Huck, W., and E. Banks. 1979. Behavioral components of individual recognition in the collared lemming (*Dicrostonyx groenlandicus*). Behav. Ecol. Sociobiol., 6:85–90.

Jones, T. R., and R. K. Plakke. 1981. The histology and histochemistry of the perianal scent gland of the reproductively quiescent black-tailed prairie dog (*Cynomys ludovicianus*). J. Mamm., 62:362–368.

Keevin, T. M., Z. T. Halpin, and N. McCurdy. 1981. Individual and sex-specific odors in male and female eastern chipmunks (*Tamias striatus*). Biol. Behav., 6:329–338.

King, J. A. 1955. Social behavior, social organization, and population dynamics in a black-tailed prairiedog town in the Black Hills of South Dakota. Contrib. Lab. Vert. Biol., Univ. Michigan., 67:1–123.

Kivett, V. K. 1975. Variations in integumentary gland activity and scent marking in

Columbian ground squirrels (*Spermophilus c. columbianus*). Unpubl. Ph.D. dissert., Univ. Alberta, Edmonton, 133 pp.

———. 1978. Integumentary glands of Columbian ground squirrels (*Spermophilus columbianus*): Sciuridae. Canadian J. Zool., 56:374–381.

Kivett, V. K., J. O. Murie, and A. L. Steiner. 1976. A comparative study of scent-gland location and related behavior in some northwestern Neartic ground squirrel species (Sciuridae): an evolutionary approach. Canadian J. Zool., 54:1294–1306.

Koenig, L. 1957. Beobachtungen über Reviermarkierung sowie Droh-Kampf und Abwehrverhalten des Murmeltieres (*Marmota marmota* L.). Z. Tierpsychol., 14:510–521.

Linsdale, J. M. 1946. The California ground squirrel. Univ. California Press, Berkeley, 475 pp.

Lorenz, K. 1935. Der Kumpan in der Umwelt des Vogels. J. Ornithol., 83:137–213.

Marler, P. 1961. The logical analysis of animal communication. J. Theor. Biol., 1: 295–317.

Meier, P. T., J. M. Walro, and G. Svendsen. 1982. The oral angle scent gland of woodchucks (*Marmota monax*): histology and associated behaviors. Paper presented at the Conference on Sociality in Ground Squirrels. Banff, Alberta (abstr.).

Muller-Schwarze, D. 1977. Complex mammalian behavior and pheromone bioassay in the field. Pp. 413–432, *in* Chemical signals in vertebrates (D. Muller-Schwarze and M. M. Mozell, eds.). Plenum Press, New York, 609 pp.

Mykytowycz, R. 1965. Further observations on the territorial function and histology of the submandibular cutaneous (chin) glands in the rabbit, *Oryctolagus cuniculus* (L). Anim. Behav., 13:400–412.

Quanstrom, W. R. 1971. Behavior of Richardson's ground squirrel, *Spermophilus richardsonii*. Anim. Behav., 19:646–652.

Quay, W. B. 1965. Comparative survey of the sebaceous and sudoriferous glands of the oral lips and angle in rodents. J. Mamm., 46:23–37.

Ralls, K. 1971. Mammalian scent marking. Science, 171:443–449.

Salmon, T. P. 1979. The anal gland of the California ground squirrel *Spermophilus beecheyi*. Ph.D. dissert., Univ. California, Davis, 151 pp.

Schultze-Westrum, T. G. 1969. Social communication by chemical signals in flying phalangers *Petaurus breviceps papuanus*. Pp. 268–277, *in* Olfaction and taste, vol. 3 (C. Pfaffman, ed.). Rockefeller University Press, New York, 648 pp.

Sleggs, G. F. 1926. The adult anatomy and histology of the anal glands of the Richardson ground squirrel, *Citellus richardsonii* Sabine. Anat. Rec., 32:1–44.

Smith, J. D., and G. W. Hearn. 1979. Ultrastructure of the apocrine sebaceous anal scent gland of the woodchuck, *Marmota monax:* evidence of apocrine and merocrine secretion by a single cell type. Anat. Rec., 193:269–292.

Smith, W. J. 1977. The behavior of communicating—an ethological approach. Harvard University Press, Cambridge, 545 pp.

Steiner, A. L. 1974. Body-rubbing, marking, and other scent-related behavior in some ground squirrels (Sciuridae): a descriptive study. Canadian J. Zool., 52:889–906.

———. 1975. "Greeting" behavior in some sciuridae, from an ontogenetic, evolutionary and socio-behavioral perspective. Nat. Canadien, 102:737–751.

Tinbergen, N. 1959. Comparative studies of the behaviours of gulls (Laridae): a progress report. Behaviour, 15:1–70.

Watton, D. G., and M. H. A. Keenleyside. 1974. Social behaviour of the Arctic ground squirrel, *Spermophilus undulatus*. Behaviour, 50:77–99.

Wilson, E. O., and W. H. Bossert. 1963. Chemical communication among animals. Recent Prog. Hormone Res., 19:673–716.

Yahner, R. H., B. L. Allen, and W. J. Peterson. 1979. Dorsal and anal glands in the eastern chipmunk, *Tamias striatus*. Ohio J. Sci., 79:40–43.

4. Mating Systems

F. STEPHEN DOBSON

University of Michigan

Chapter 10

Environmental Influences
on Sciurid
Mating Systems

Abstract. The influence of social and ecological factors on the behavioral tactics of adult males during the mating season is evaluated in the sciurid rodents of North America. The type of polygyny varies among sciurids, especially among ground squirrels (genera *Spermophilus* and *Cynomys*). These polygynous mating systems can be divided into two types: in male defense polygyny, territories are defended by dominant adult males during the mating season; in nondefense polygyny adult males do not defend territories. The hypothesis that variation in the type of polygyny in ground squirrel species is influenced by historical origin is not supported, nor is the variation in type of polygyny explained by hypotheses that invoke the influence of competition among males for mates, the length of the mating season, the operational sex ratio, or the visual complexity of the habitat. The best-supported relationship is between the type of polygyny and local density of adults (both sexes). To account for this relationship, I present a new hypothesis that invokes the influence of the costs that adult males incur while monitoring and interacting with male and female conspecifics.

Introduction

The term "mating system" can be defined as "the general behavioral strategy employed in obtaining mates" (Emlen and Oring, 1977: 222). The identity of the limiting sex (the one in demand) and the manner of mate acquisition by the limited sex can be used to differentiate and typify mating systems. Other relevant characteristics of a mating system are the number of mates acquired, the presence and characteristics of pair bonds, patterns of parentage, and characteristics of parental care.

The sciurid rodents of North America exhibit a variety of mating systems. Monogamy occurs in some populations (Holmes, this volume), but polygyny (in which females are limiting) is far more widespread. The mating systems that are currently described as polygynous are extremely variable. For example, males defend territories that include groups of females (harems) in yellow-bellied marmots, *Marmota flaviventris* (Armitage, 1974; Downhower and Armitage, 1971), and black-tailed prairie dogs, *Cynomys ludovicianus* (Hoogland, 1981; King, 1955). In Belding's ground squirrels (*Spermophilus beldingi*), however, males do not defend resource-based territories or mates, and promiscuity (in which both sexes mate multiply) is common (Hanken and Sherman, 1981; Sherman, 1976).

Several recent reviews (Alcock, 1980; Borgia, 1979; Bradbury, 1980, 1981; Emlen and Oring, 1977; Wittenberger, 1979) have recognized two basic types of polygynous (and polygynous but somewhat promiscuous) mating systems. In one type males defend an area (or territory) that contains mates or resources that mates need. I term this "male defense polygyny." In "nondefense polygyny" males compete for female mating choices or for undisturbed mating opportunities, and males may form dominance hierarchies. These two types of mating systems differ in the character of male dominance during the mating season. In male defense polygyny, dominance among males is site related, but in nondefense polygyny it is not.

I have treated male defense and nondefense polygyny as distinct alternatives among species. There is evidence, however, that male tactics vary within local populations; some male Columbian ground squirrels defend territories, whereas others (subordinates) do not (Murie and Harris, 1978; pers. obs.). Moreover, rates of social interaction are variable in different areas and years, even within a population (Armitage, 1977). My reference to alternative types of polygyny, therefore, is a simplification for the purpose of testing possible explanations.

The dominance system in populations during the mating season is a result of the behavioral tactics that individual males use to compete for mates. The tactics of males are often easy to observe and quantify. Female mating tactics are often more difficult to ascertain, but they are likely to be strongly influenced by male tactics (i.e., if males restrict the choices of mates directly or by controlling resources; Borgia, 1979). Patterns of male parentage might also correlate with male behavioral tactics. Multiple male parentage of a litter appears to occur frequently in species with nondefense polygyny and infrequently in species with male defense polygyny (see Foltz and Hoogland, 1981; Hanken and Sherman,

1981; Hoagland and Foltz, 1982; Schwagmeyer, this volume; Schwartz and Armitage, 1980). The behavioral tactic that males adopt within the context of a polygynous mating system may depend on factors in the ecological and social environment. I will examine some hypothesized relationships between ecological and social factors, and the occurrence of territorial defense as a mating tactic of males. Predictions drawn from the hypotheses will be tested with comparative data from the literature on North American sciurid rodents, emphasizing the ground squirrels. A perfect agreement between the interspecific data and the predictions is not expected, but the lack of significant agreement will constitute evidence for the rejection of a hypothesis as a general explanation.

Methods

I used descriptions of male behaviors during the mating season to classify local populations (and to typify species) as exhibiting male defense or nondefense polygyny (references and data for ground squirrels are given in Appendix 10.1). Populations were classed as having male defense polygyny if at least some adult males were territorial during the mating season. These adult males exhibited either significant site-related dominance (e.g., Murie and Harris, 1978) or dominance along a territorial boundary (e.g., McLean, 1981). If site-related defense of mates or of the resources that mates need did not occur, I classed populations as exhibiting nondefense polygyny.

Ranges of parameters (taken over several years, from different areas, or in different studies) are reported to indicate variability (Appendix 10.1). Densities were estimated by dividing the number of potentially breeding adults (or adult males) by the area under observation during the mating or breeding season. The number of adults observed was estimated from figures in three cases (Dunford, 1977a; Green 1977; Slade and Balph, 1974).

For *Spermophilus beldingi* the minimum and maximum number of adults on a "lekking" area (sensu Alexander, 1975) during a year of high density was used to estimate local density (P. W. Sherman, 1976, pers. comm.). The estimated upper end of the range in adult density in *Cynomys ludovicianus* is from Hoogland (1981), and the season of measurement was not specified. King's (1955) data suggested that the local density of adults increases after the mating season, so the value adapted from Hoogland (1981) may be an overestimate. The estimated upper end of the range of adult male density in *C. ludovicianus* is from a mean value given by Hoogland (1981) and may be an underestimate.

The body size of adult males was estimated from the mean greatest length of skull from specimens at the Museum of Zoology, University of Michigan, the Museum of Vertebrate Zoology, University of California, and the Department of Zoology, University of Alberta. The area of origin of specimens was restricted and was as close as possible to the location of relevant behavioral studies.

The length of the mating season was estimated from reports in the literature. Additional data were obtained on *S. richardsonii* from captive births (Michener, 1973) and on *S. beecheyi* and *S. columbianus* from the period over which young emerged from natal burrows in local populations that I have studied (unpubl. data). Minimum estimates for *S. tereticaudus* and *C. ludovicianus* were calculated from the reported period over which pregnant females were trapped, minus the estimated gestation period (King, 1955; Neal, 1965). Sex ratios of adults during the mating season were estimated from the literature in a manner similar to the method used to estimate adult density.

Historical Origin

The hypothesis. Before I evaluate contemporary social and ecological factors that might influence the type of polygyny exhibited by sciurid species, I will consider the possibility that the observed pattern of behavioral variation among species is strongly influenced by inheritance of characteristics from ancestors. If different behavioral types (e.g., male defense and nondefense polygyny) correlate closely with phylogeny, then they might represent genetically invariant adaptations to past environments. The behavioral character of territorial defense by males, therefore, might be constrained by phylogenetic inheritance.

The "historical origin" hypothesis predicts that male defense or nondefense polygyny is characteristic of some set of taxa at a level between the family and the population (i.e., one type of polygyny is a synapomorphy defining a group of related taxa).

To examine whether behavioral variability correlates with phylogeny, the distribution of types of polygyny among squirrel species must be compared with a well-supported cladogram. I constructed a cladogram of North American sciurids that includes only the relevant taxa (Fig. 10.1). Except for the precise placement of *Cynomys* (see Nadler et al., 1971), the historical relationships are well corroborated (Black, 1963; Bryant, 1945; Hafner, this volume; Hight et al., 1974; Moore, 1959; Nadler et al., 1982).

The test. In the "mating bouts" of tree squirrels (*Sciurus* and *Tamiasciurus*), adult males follow and fight over estrous females (see Heaney, this volume). Neither the estrous female, nor the area she occupies, is successfully defended by

232

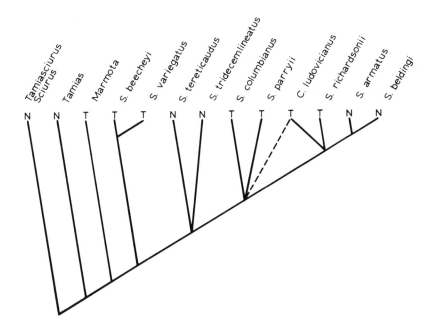

FIGURE 10.1. A hypothesis of the historical origin of marmotine taxa for which data on the behavioral tactics of adult males during the mating season are available. An alternative origin of *Cynomys ludovicianus* is indicated by a dashed line. N, nondefense polygyny, T, male defense (territorial) polygyny, S, *Spermophilus*, C, *Cynomys*.

a dominant male. Thus tree squirrels exhibit nondefense polygyny, though previous territorial behavior may increase a male's dominance in a mating bout (Koford, 1982). The eastern chipmunk, *Tamias striatus*, appears to have mating bouts similar to those of tree squirrels (Elliot, 1978; Yahner, 1978). Based on these "outgroups," the primitive condition for marmotine rodents appears to be nondefense polygyny.

Male defense of territory (the colony area) during and after the mating season occurs in the hoary marmot, *Marmota caligata* (Holmes, this volume), the yellow-bellied marmot (Armitage, 1974), and the Olympic marmot, *M. olympus* (Barash, 1973). Hoary marmots are monogamous in some populations (Holmes, this volume), but males still show territorial defense, albeit with a single mate. Woodchucks, *M. monax*, have social relationships that differ markedly from those of the other North American marmots (see Michener, 1983), but they have not been observed closely during the mating season (e.g., Bronson, 1964; Grizzell, 1955).

As predicted, adult males in all species of marmots studied have a similar

233

behavioral tactic during the mating season. The outgroup comparison with chipmunks and tree squirrels indicates that this may be a synapomorphy. Thus the hypothesis that the type of polygyny exhibited by the marmots is the result of a common historical origin is not rejected.

A test of the historical origin hypothesis can also be made in the monophyletic group that contains the genera *Spermophilus* and *Cynomys*. The pattern of behavioral types in the ground squirrel species requires more than one independent evolutionary origin of male defense and nondefense polygyny, regardless of which type of polygyny is considered primitive (Fig. 10.1). Thus, the hypothesis can be rejected as an explanation for the pattern of sharing of type of polygyny by the members of this clade, and hypotheses based on adaptation to environmental factors may be considered.

Competition Among Males

The hypothesis. Davis (1958), in an experimental study, found that house mice form territories at low density and dominance hierarchies at high density. Subsequently, Brown (1964) suggested that territories must be economically defensible for defense to occur (i.e., the benefits of defense must exceed the costs). Emlen and Oring (1977) were the first to apply the concept of economic defensibility to polygynous mating systems. Specifically, they hypothesized that as local density increases so does the number of male competitors, making the defense of mates or the resources needed to attract mates more difficult and favoring nondefense polygyny.

This "density-male competition" hypothesis is supported by comparative studies of bats (Bradbury, 1980, 1981), elephant seals (LeBoeuf, 1974), topi (Monfort-Braham, 1975), Uganda kob (Leuthold, 1966), and many non-mammalian taxa (e.g., Alcock, 1980; Alexander, 1961; C. K. Sherman, 1980; Snow, 1973). The hypothesis predicts that nondefense polygyny will occur in species that exhibit relatively high local densities during the mating season.

The test. The prediction of higher density in nondefense species is upheld for all the ground squirrel species except the thirteen-lined ground squirrel, *S. tridecemlineatus* (Fig. 10.2). Belding's ground squirrels occur over a wide range of densities during the mating season. Because ground squirrels that defend territories do so for the entire mating season (see Michener, 1983), it may be important that Belding's ground squirrels occur at higher densities during part of the mating season than the highest value for territorial species. If only thirteen-lined ground squirrels are considered anomalous, then more species support the prediction than would be expected at random ($P = 0.02$, one-tailed binomial test). If Belding's ground squirrels are also considered anomalous, then the fit of the data to the prediction approaches significance ($P = 0.09$, one-tailed binomial test).

The ground squirrel species are of different body sizes and thus might be expected to have different densities and home range sizes. I examined the natural log of local density plotted against the natural log of the cubed mean greatest length of skull of adult males (an indicator of body size). McNab (1963) claimed that metabolic scaling (slope $= 0.75$) obtains between the natural logs of body size and home range size (the average area per adult, which can be estimated by the inverse of local density for group living ground squirrels). His results, however, were equally consistent with isometric scaling (slope $= 0.67$). I scale body size and local density isometrically (slope $= -0.67$) and thus avoid assumptions about metabolic relationships.

Species with male defense polygyny should occur below an isometric scaling

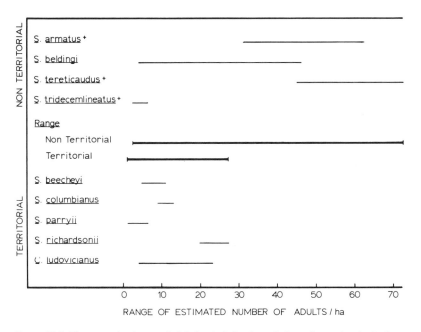

FIGURE 10.2. The range of estimates of adult density in local populations of ground squirrels. Superscript crosses indicate populations that were studied on mowed lawns. The ranges of values for species (populations) that exhibit male defense and nondefense polygyny appear in the middle of the figure. References and data are given in Appendix 10.1.

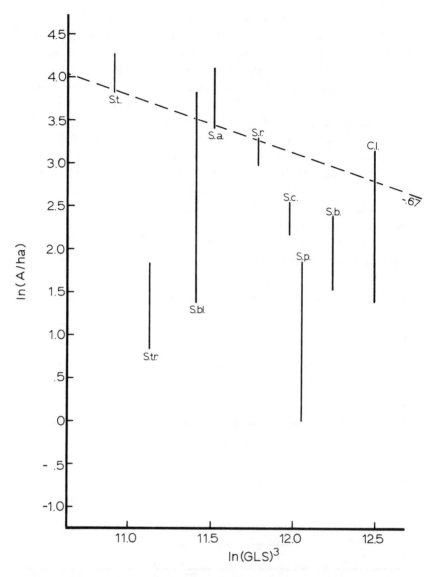

FIGURE 10.3. The range of the natural log of the local density (adults per hectare) estimates for adult ground squirrels, plotted against the natural log of the mean greatest length of skull (GLS) cubed for adult males. Local population density increases with increasing values on the vertical axis. The horizontal axis indicates increasing body size. One example of an isometric scaling line (slope = −0.67) is given. Ranges labeled at the top indicate male defense polygyny; ranges labeled at the bottom indicate nondefense polygyny. S. a., *S. armatus;* S. b., *S. beecheyi;* S. bl., *S. beldingi;* S. c., *S. columbianus;* S. p., *S. parryii;* S. r., *S. richardsonii;* S. t., *S. tereticaudus;* S. tr., *S. tridecemlineatus;* C. l., *C. ludovicianus.* References and data are given in Appendix 10.1.

236

line, and species with nondefense polygyny should occur above the scaling line (density is lower below, and higher above, such a line, as in Fig. 10.3). No placement of an isometric scaling line completely separates the data in the predicted direction (Fig. 10.3). Again, the data for thirteen-lined ground squirrels do not corroborate the hypothesis, but the data on other species are generally supportive. Metabolic scaling (slope $= -0.75$) or other empirical scaling (slope $= -1.02$; see Harestad and Bunnell, 1979) gives a poorer resolution of the data than isometric scaling.

The prediction of Emlen and Oring (1977) invoked the influence of intrasexual competition by males. This prediction has been supported by previous comparisons of adult densities for other taxa (e.g., Alcock, 1980; Bradbury, 1980, 1981; Emlen and Oring, 1977), and the predicted relationship between type of polygyny and local density of adults is consistent with much of the data on ground squirrels (Figs. 10.2 and 10.3). I believe, however, that this relationship is not the best test of the hypothesis. The local density of adult males should be a more accurate parameter for examination than the density of all adults.

Neither the actual ranges of male densities nor the data adjusted for body size gives better resolution of different types of polygyny on the predicted sides of any placement of an isometric scaling line (Appendix 10.1, Fig. 10.4). In fact, there appears to be no consistent relationship between local density of adult males and type of polygyny when body size is taken into account. Thus the more detailed analysis, and better test, fails to support the density-male competition hypothesis as a general explanation of the type of polygyny in different ground squirrel species.

Length of the Mating Season

The hypothesis. The territories of male ground squirrels are defended before, during, and perhaps somewhat beyond the mating season (see Michener, 1983). As the mating season continues, the cumulative cost of defense increases. At some point individual females might come into estrus over so long a period that continuous territorial defense is no longer profitable, and a nondefense behavioral tactic is adopted by adult males during the breeding season (Emlen 1976). This hypothesis predicts that male defense polygyny will occur in species with relatively short mating seasons and nondefense polygyny will occur where the mating season is long.

The test. The length of the mating season in local populations of ground squirrels overlaps extensively in species with male defense and nondefense polygyny

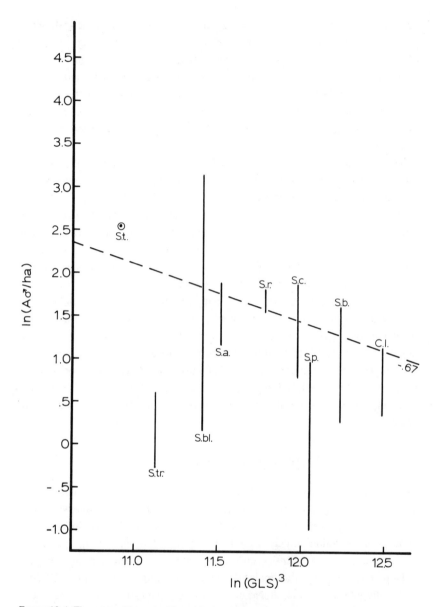

FIGURE 10.4. The range of the natural log of the local density estimates for adult male ground squirrels, plotted against the natural log of the mean greatest length of skull (GLS) cubed for adult males. Axes and labels as in Fig. 10.3. One exemplary scaling line is shown. References and data are given in Appendix 10.1.

(Fig. 10.5). There is no tendency for species with nondefense polygyny to have longer mating seasons (but see McCarley, 1966, for an apparently rare case of two litters per year for some females in a thirteen-lined ground squirrel population). Thus the hypothesis concerning the influence of the length of the mating season is not supported as a general explanation of the type of polygyny in different ground squirrel species.

Operational Sex Ratio

The hypothesis. Emlen (1976: 309) defines the operational sex ratio as "the ratio of receptive females to potential mating males at any one time." Three factors can cause a skew toward males in the operational sex ratio: a relatively long mating season, relatively short and asynchronous receptive periods of estrous females, and an actual skew in the sex ratio of sexually active adults.

Because territorial male ground squirrels appear to defend for an entire mating season (see references, Appendix 10.1), I will take one mating season to be the period over which operational sex ratios are measured (dividing by the length of the mating season does not change the relationships among the ratios). For the few species examined, the receptive period of estrous females has been found to occur over a few hours on a single day (Sherman, 1976; Hoogland, 1981; Schwagmeyer and Brown, 1983). Comparative data on the synchrony of estrus are not available. The operational sex ratio in ground squirrels 'therefore' is estimated by the ratio of females to males among the potentially breeding adults (see also Clutton-Brock and Harvey, 1976).

As the operational sex ratio (females/male) decreases, the number of competitors for female mates increases, the number of female mates decreases, or both. The result of these two factors is to increase the intensity of competition among males for mates, favoring nondefense polygyny (Emlen and Oring, 1977). The "operational sex ratio" hypothesis predicts that species with nondefense polygyny will have lower operational sex ratios than species with male defense polygyny.

The test. There is considerable variation within some species and among species in the operational sex ratios of ground squirrels (Fig. 10.6). The species with nondefense polygyny do not have the lowest operational sex ratios. In fact, three of the species have relatively high sex ratios. Therefore the operational sex ratio hypothesis is not supported as an explanation of the type of polygyny in different ground squirrel species.

239

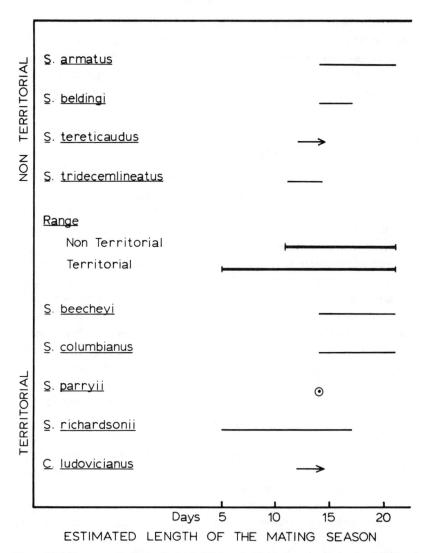

FIGURE 10.5. The range of estimates (in days) of the length of the mating season in local populations of ground squirrels. The ranges of values for species (populations) that exhibit male defense and non-defense polygyny appear in the middle of the figure. Arrows indicate possible underestimates (see Methods). References are given in Appendix 10.1.

Habitat Structure

The hypothesis. Ground squirrel species might use scent, hearing, or sight to locate each other aboveground. The most frequently used of these is probably sight (vision is highly developed in ground squirrels; Jacobs 1978). As the visual structure of the habitat becomes more complex (has more obstructions), it should become more difficult for a dominant male to perceive intruding males that are competing for mates. Thus defense becomes more difficult, favoring nondefense polygyny.

The "habitat structure" hypothesis predicts that in habitats with greater visual complexity, nondefense polygyny will occur. This prediction should be especially applicable to a comparison between ground dwellers (which use primarily two dimensions) and arboreal sciurids (which use three dimensions extensively in a visually complex habitat).

The test. The habitats of tree squirrels (parklike woodland, coniferous forest, and tropical forest) are visually complex. Chipmunks are much less arboreal than tree squirrels, but they do regularly climb, and the deciduous forests they occupy are

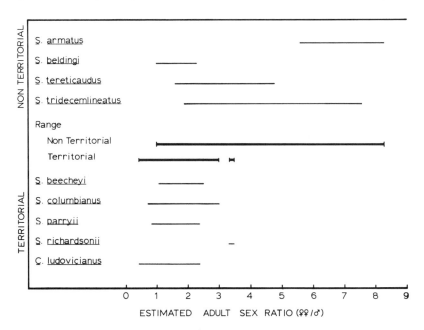

FIGURE 10.6. The range of estimates of sex ratio of adults (females/male) in local populations of ground squirrels. The range of values for species (populations) that exhibit male defense and nondefense polygyny appear in the middle of the figure. References and data are given in Appendix 10.1.

also visually complex. Chipmunks and tree squirrels that live in deciduous forests may breed under relatively good visibility conditions (e.g., in late winter), but the habitat still has an extensive three-dimensional nature. The characteristics of the behavioral tactics of adult males during the mating season in tree squirrels, chipmunks, marmots, and ground squirrels have been described above. Territorial defense by males does not occur during the mating seasons of any of the more arboreal sciurids, but it does occur in several ground-dwelling species. Thus comparison between sciurid groups just below the subfamily level supports the hypothesis.

Three of the ground squirrels have been studied on mowed lawns (Fig. 10.2), where visibility should be excellent relative to more pristine habitats. Contrary to prediction, all three species exhibit nondefense polygyny. Quantitative data on relative visibility of different ground squirrel habitats are needed for more complete testing, but the preliminary test fails to support the hypothesis for the ground squirrels.

Additional Hypotheses

Density threshold. A hypothesis to explain a lack of defense at low density can be adapted from the territory-threshold model of Carpenter and MacMillen (1976). If adult female home ranges are relatively scattered at low local population densities, the cost of territorial defense of such large areas by males may exceed the benefits, and nondefense polygyny would be favored. When body size is taken into account, however, thirteen-lined ground squirrels occur at relatively low local population densities, but no lower than those of territorial populations of Arctic ground squirrels (Figs. 10.3, 10.4). There is no indication that female home ranges are more clumped in Arctic ground squirrels; in fact, the reverse may be true (McLean, 1981; Silverman, 1981). Thus the hypothesis derived from Carpenter and MacMillen (1976) is not supported as an explanation of the type of polygyny exhibited by thirteen-lined ground squirrels.

Relative home range size. Bradbury (1981) suggested that when the home ranges of adult females are larger than those of adult males, nondefense polygyny will be favored because males do not range far enough to control females or appreciable amounts of the resources females need. This hypothesis predicts that, during the mating season, female home ranges will be as large as or larger than male home ranges in species with nondefense polygyny. Males of six ground squirrel species expand their ranges during the mating season (Dunford, 1977*b;* Johnson, 1981;

McLean, 1981; Michener, 1979; Murie and Harris, 1978; Silverman, 1981). In all cases male home ranges appear to be larger than female home ranges, including two species that exhibit nondefense polygyny. Although more estimates of home range sizes during the mating season are needed, the preliminary results do not support Bradbury's hypothesis.

Discussion

I have presented a preliminary examination of several hypotheses that might serve as general explanations of the variability that occurs in the behavioral tactics of adult male sciurid rodents during the mating season (and therefore the characteristic type of polygyny), emphasizing the ground squirrels. The hypothesis of historical origin is tentatively rejected as an interspecific explanation for the distribution of types of polygyny in ground squirrels (Fig. 10.1). The density-male competition hypothesis was rejected as a general explanation of the type of polygyny when the local density of adult males was examined (Fig. 10.4). The hypotheses that the type of polygyny is influenced primarily by the length of the mating season (Fig. 10.5), by the operational sex ratio (Fig. 10.6), or by the visual complexity of the habitat were also rejected as general explanations of the variability in ground squirrels. Preliminary tests of the density threshold and relative home range size hypotheses failed to support them.

Bradbury (1981) claimed to falsify Emlen and Oring's (1977) density-male competition hypothesis with a review of data on grouse. It was not clear whether Bradbury calculated local densities of adults on leks (as for Belding's ground squirrels in the present study) or average adult densities over much larger areas. In any case, he did not consider the possible influence of the length of the mating season and the operational sex ratio. The present study, therefore, may be the first rejection of the hypotheses of Emlen (1976) and Emlen and Oring (1977) as general explanations of the type of polygyny found in a group of related taxa.

The most interesting finding among these rejections is the generally supported relationship between overall local population density and type of mating system (Figs. 10.2, 10.3). I propose an addition to the density-male competition hypothesis to explain this generality. Territorial males must exclude competing males *and* monitor the condition and location of potential mates that might come into estrus. If females are coy, or if they try to mate with males from off the territory, territorial males might incur considerable costs in attracting, monitoring, and perhaps sequestering mates. Thus, as density increases, the cost of territorial behavior as a successful mating tactic for males increases. Note that under this overall "density" hypothesis the density of adult males or females alone is unimportant, as is the sex ratio of adults in the population.

The density hypothesis might prove to be a good generalization for ground squirrels and perhaps for other taxa that exhibit a relationship between local density and type of polygyny. The hypothesis is not, however, consistent with all of the interspecific data, especially when body size is taken into account (Fig. 10.3). The density hypothesis fails to explain the mating system of thirteen-lined ground squirrels (Figs. 10.2, 10.3). The social and ecological factors that influenced the evolution of nondefense polygyny in this species might not be generally applicable.

Tests of the density hypothesis might best be conducted within species that exhibit variability in the density of local populations and the behavioral tactics of adult males during the mating season. If changes in local density do not correspond to predicted changes in the success of the territorial tactic of males, then the hypothesis could be rejected as an explanation of the type of polygyny in particular cases. Such tests would have the advantage of being conducted on evolving units (local populations or demes). Factors in the social and ecological environment that influence the type of polygyny exhibited by the evolving units of a species are most likely to indicate which evolutionary pressures could have caused existing interspecific variation.

Acknowledgments

This work is the direct result of instruction and encouragement by numerous tutors. I have learned relevant sciurid biology from D. F. Balph, D. E. Davis, L. S. Davis, J. E. Green, L. R. Heaney, W. G. Holmes, G. R. Michener, J. O. Murie, P. L. Schwagmeyer, and P. W. Sherman. For relevant theoretical discussions I thank the scholars named above and R. D. Alexander, G. K. Crieghton, W. G. Eberhard, M. J. West-Eberhard, P. R. Grant, J. L. Hoogland, A. G. Kluge, B. Lundrigan, P. Myers, R. W. Redding, M. Robertson, and R. W. Wrangham. My wife, J. D. Kjelgaard, assisted in the research and drew the figures. R. D. Alexander, L. S. Davis, L. R. Heaney, W. G. Holmes, A. G. Kluge, B. Lundrigan, G. R. Michener, J. O. Murie, P. Myers, P. L. Schwagmeyer, P. W. Sherman, and J. F. Wittenberger read and helped to improve the manuscript. I thank L. S. Davis, J. E. Green, J. O. Murie, and R. M. Zammuto for ground squirrel specimens and P. W. Sherman for providing me with unpublished data on *S. beldingi*. I am grateful to J. O. Murie (Department of Zoology, University of Alberta), P. Myers (Museum of Zoology, University of Michigan), and J. L. Patton (Museum of Vertebrate Zoology, University of California) for allowing me to measure ground squirrel specimens. I owe special thanks to G. R. Michener and J. O. Murie for suggesting that I write on the topic.

Literature Cited

Alcock, J. 1980. Natural selection and the mating systems of solitary bees. Amer. Sci., 68:146–153.

Alexander, R. D. 1961. Aggressiveness, territoriality, and sexual behavior in field crickets (Orthoptera: Gryllidae). Behaviour, 17:130–223.

———. 1975. Natural selection and specialized chorusing behavior in acoustical insects. Pp. 35–77, *in* Insects, science, and society (D. Pimental, ed.). Academic Press, New York, 284 pp.

Armitage, K. B. 1974. Male behaviour and territoriality in the yellow-bellied marmot. J. Zool. London, 172:233–265.

———. 1977. Social variety in the yellow-bellied marmot: a population-behavioural system. Anim. Behav., 25:585–593.

Balph, D. F., and A. W. Stokes. 1963. On the ethology of a population of Uinta ground squirrels. Amer. Midland Nat., 69:106–126.

Barash, D. P. 1973. The social biology of the Olympic marmot. Anim. Behav. Monogr., 6:173–245.

Bickford, C. E. 1979. Aspects of the social structure of the California ground squirrel (*Spermophilus beecheyi*) in western Oregon. Unpubl. M.A. thesis, Oregon State Univ., Corvallis, 56 pp.

Black, C. C. 1963. A review of the North American tertiary Sciuridae. Bull. Mus. Comp. Zool., 130:109–248.

Borgia, G. 1979. Sexual selection and the evolution of mating systems. Pp. 19–80, *in* Sexual selection and reproductive competition in insects (M. F. Blum and N. Blum, eds.). Academic Press, New York, 463 pp.

Bradbury, J. W. 1980. Foraging, social dispersion and mating systems. Pp. 189–207, *in* Sociobiology: beyond nature/nurture? (G. W. Barlow and J. Silverberg, eds.). Westview Press, Boulder, Colorado, 627 pp.

———. 1981. The evolution of leks. Pp. 138–169, *in* Natural selection and social behavior (R. D. Alexander and D. W. Tinkle, eds.). Chiron Press, New York, 532 pp.

Bronson, F. H. 1964. Agonistic behaviour in woodchucks. Anim. Behav., 12:470–478.

Brown, J. L. 1964. The evolution of diversity in avian territorial systems. Wilson Bull., 76:160–169.

Bryant, M. D. 1945. Phylogeny of Nearctic Sciuridae. Amer. Midland Nat., 33:257–390.

Carpenter, F. L., and R. E. MacMillen. 1976. Threshold model of feeding territoriality and test with a Hawaiian honeycreeper. Science, 194:639–642.

Clutton-Brock, T. H., and P. H. Harvey. 1976. Evolutionary rules and primate societies. Pp. 195–237, *in* Growing points in ethology (P. P. G. Bateson and R. A. Hinde, eds.). Cambridge Univ. Press, Cambridge, 548 pp.

Davis, D. E. 1958. The role of density in aggressive behaviour of house mice. Anim. Behav., 6:207–210.

Mating Systems

Dobson, F. S. 1983. Agonism and territoriality in the California ground squirrel. J. Mamm., 64:218–225.

Downhower, J. F., and K. B. Armitage. 1971. The yellow-bellied marmot and the evolution of polygamy. Amer. Nat., 105:355–370.

Dunford, C. 1977a. Behavioral limitation of round-tailed ground squirrel density. Ecology, 58:1254–1268.

———. 1977b. Social system of round-tailed ground squirrels. Anim. Behav., 25:885–906.

Elliot, L. 1978. Social behavior and foraging ecology of the eastern chipmunk (Tamias striatus) in the Adirondack Mountains. Smithsonian Contrib. Zool., 265:1–107.

Emlen, S. T. 1976. Lek organization and mating strategies in the bullfrog. Behav. Ecol. Sociobiol., 1:283–313.

Emlen, S. T., and L. W. Oring. 1977. Ecology, sexual selection, and the evolution of mating systems. Science, 197:215–223.

Foltz, D. W., and J. L. Hoogland. 1981. Analysis of the mating system in the black-tailed prairie dog (Cynomys ludovicianus) by likelihood of paternity. J. Mamm. 62: 706–712.

Green, J. E. 1977. Population regulation and annual cycles of activity and dispersal in the Arctic ground squirrel. Unpubl. M.A. thesis, Univ. of British Columbia, Vancouver, 193 pp.

Grizzell, R. A. 1955. A study of the southern woodchuck, Marmota monax monax. Amer. Midland Nat., 53:257–293.

Hanken, J., and P. W. Sherman. 1981. Multiple paternity in Belding's ground squirrel litters. Science, 212:351–353.

Harestad, A. S., and F. L. Bunnell. 1979. Home range and body weight—a reevaluation. Ecology, 60:389–402.

Hight, M. E., M. Goodman, and W. Prychodko. 1974. Immunological studies of the Sciuridae. Syst. Zool., 23:12–25.

Hoogland, J. L. 1981. Nepotism and cooperative breeding in the black-tailed prairie dog (Sciuridae: Cynomys ludovicianus). Pp. 283–310, in Natural selection and social behavior (R. D. Alexander and D. W. Tinkle, eds.). Chiron Press, New York, 532 pp.

Hoogland, J. L., and D. W. Foltz. 1982. Variance in male and female reproductive success in a harem-polygynous mammal, the black-tailed prairie dog (Sciuridae: Cynomys ludovicianus). Behav. Ecol. Sociobiol., 11:155–163.

Jacobs, G. H. 1978. Spectral sensitivity and colour vision in the ground-dwelling sciurids: results from golden mantled ground squirrels and comparisons for five species. Anim. Behav., 26:409–421.

Johnson, K. 1981. Social organization in a colony of rock squirrels (Spermophilus variegatus, Sciuridae). Southwestern Nat., 26:237–242.

King, J. A. 1955. Social behavior, social organization, and population dynamics in a black-tailed prairiedog town in the Black Hills of South Dakota. Contrib. Lab. Vert. Biol., Univ. Michigan, 67:1–123.

Koford, R. K. 1982. Mating system of a territorial tree squirrel (*Tamiasciurus douglasii*) in California. J. Mamm., 63:274–283.

LeBoeuf, B. J. 1974. Male-male competition and reproductive success in elephant seals. Amer. Zool. 14:163–176.

Leuthold, W. 1966. Variations in territorial behavior of Uganda kob *Adenota kob thomasi* (Neumann 1896). Behaviour, 27:215–258.

McCarley, H. 1966. Annual cycle, population dynamics and adaptive behavior of *Citellus tridecemlineatus*. J. Mamm., 47:294–316.

McLean, I. G. 1981. Social ecology of the Arctic ground squirrel, *Spermophilus parryii*. Unpubl. Ph.D. dissert., Univ. of Alberta, Edmonton, 149 pp.

McLean, I. G., and A. J. Towns. 1981. Differences in weight changes and the annual cycle of male and female Arctic ground squirrels. Arctic, 34:249–254.

McNab, B. K. 1963. Bioenergetics and the determination of home range size. Amer. Nat., 97:133–139.

Michener, G. R. 1973. Climatic conditions and breeding in Richardson's ground squirrel. J. Mamm., 54:499–503.

———. 1979. Spatial relationships and social organization of adult Richardson's ground squirrels. Canadian J. Zool., 57:125–139.

———. 1983. Kin identification, matriarchies, and the evolution of sociality in ground-dwelling sciurids. Pp. 528–572, *in* Recent advances in the study of mammalian behavior (J. F. Eisenberg and D. G. Kleiman, eds.). Spec. Publ., Amer. Soc. Mamm., 7:1–753.

Monfort-Braham, N. 1975. Variations dans la structure sociale du topi, *Damaliscus korrigum* Ogilby, au Parc National de l'Akagera, Rwanda. Z. Tierpsychol., 39:332–364.

Moore, J. C. 1959. Relationships among living squirrels of the Sciurinae. Bull. Amer. Mus. Nat. Hist., 118:153–206.

Morton, M. L., and P. W. Sherman. 1978. Effects of a spring snowstorm on behavior, reproduction, and survival of Belding's ground squirrels. Canadian J. Zool., 56:2578–2590.

Murie, J. O., and M. A. Harris. 1978. Territoriality and dominance in male Columbian ground squirrels (*Spermophilus columbianus*). Canadian J. Zool., 56:2402–2412.

Nadler, C. F., R. S. Hoffmann, and J. J. Pizzimenti. 1971. Chromosomes and serum proteins of prairie dogs and a model of *Cynomys* evolution. J. Mamm., 52:545–555.

Nadler, C. F., et al. 1982. Evolution in ground squirrels. II. Biochemical comparisons in Holarctic populations of *Spermophilus*. Z. Saugetierk. 47:198–215.

Neal, B. J. 1965. Reproductive habits of round-tailed and Harris antelope ground squirrels. J. Mamm. 46:200–206.

Owings, D. H., M. Borchert, and R. Virginia. 1977. The behaviour of California ground squirrels. Anim. Behav., 25:221–230.

Schwagmeyer, P. 1980. Alarm calling behavior in the thirteen-lined ground squirrel, *Spermophilus tridecemlineatus*. Behav. Ecol. Sociobiol., 7:195–200.

Schwagmeyer, P. L., and C. H. Brown. 1983. Factors affecting male–male competition in thirteen-lined ground squirrels. Behav. Ecol. Sociobiol. 13:1–6.

Schwartz, O. A., and K. B. Armitage. 1980. Genetic variation in social mammals: the marmot model. Science, 207:665–667.

Sherman, C. K. 1980. A comparison of the natural history and mating system of two anurans: Yosemite toads (*Bufo canorus*) and black toads (*Bufo exsul*). Unpubl. Ph.D. dissert., Univ. Michigan, Ann Arbor, 410 pp.

Sherman, P. W. 1976. Natural selection among some group-living organisms. Unpubl. Ph.D. dissert., Univ. Michigan, Ann Arbor, 254 pp.

———. 1980. The limits of ground squirrel nepotism. Pp. 504–544, *in* Sociobiology: beyond nature/nurture? (G. W. Barlow and J. Silverberg, eds.). Westview Press, Boulder, Colorado, 627 pp.

Silverman, D. L. 1981. The behavioral ecology of the thirteen-lined ground squirrel (*Spermophilus tridecemlineatus*). Unpubl. M.S. thesis, Univ. Michigan, Ann Arbor, 45 pp.

Slade, N. A., and D. F. Balph. 1974. Population ecology of Uinta ground squirrels. Ecology, 55:989–1003.

Snow, B. K. 1973. The behavior and ecology of hermit hummingbirds in the Kanaku Mountains, Guyana. Wilson Bull., 85:163–177.

Tileston, J. V., and R. R. Lechleitner. 1966. Some comparisons of the black-tailed and white-tailed prairie dogs in north-central Colorado. Amer. Midland Nat., 75:292–316.

Wittenberger, J. F. 1979. The evolution of mating systems in birds and mammals. Pp. 271–349, *in* Handbook of behavioral neurobiology, vol. 3 (P. R. Marler and J. G. Vandenbergh, eds.). Plenum, New York. 427 pp.

Yahner, R. H. 1978. The adaptive nature of the social system and behavior in the eastern chipmunk. Behav. Ecol. Sociobiol., 3:397–427.

Yeaton, R. I. 1972. Social behavior and social organization in Richardson's ground squirrel (*Spermophilus richardsonii*) in Saskatchewan. J. Mamm., 53:139–147.

Environmental Influences on Sciurid Mating Systems

APPENDIX 10.1. Estimates of parameters for *Spermophilus* and *Cynomys* species from the literature

Species	Mating system	Greatest length of skull: adult males (mm)	Adult density (adults/ha)		Adult male density (males/ha)		Adult sex ratio (females/male)	
			From	To	From	To	From	To
Spermophilus armatus	Nondefense	46.5 (N = 12)	31.1	62.2	3.3	6.7	5.6	8.3
S. beldingi	Nondefense	44.7 (N = 12)	4.0	46.1	1.2	23.0	1.0	2.3
S. tereticaudus	Nondefense	38.0 (N = 16)	45.0	72.5		12.5	1.6	4.8
S. tridecemlineatus	Nondefense	40.9 (N = 9)	2.3	6.4	0.7	1.8	1.9	7.5
S. beecheyi	Male defense	59.1 (N = 20)	4.7	11.0	1.3	5.0	1.2	2.5
S. columbianus	Male defense	54.1 (N = 9)	8.9	13.0	2.2	6.5	0.7	3.0
S. richardsonii	Male defense	50.6 (N = 9)	19.7	27.3	4.6	6.1	3.3	3.5
S. parryii	Male defense	55.5 (N = 20)	1.0	6.4	0.4	2.7	0.8	2.4
Cynomys ludovicianus	Male defense	64.3 (N = 14)	3.9	23.3	1.4	3.1	0.4	2.4

SOURCES:

S. armatus: Balph, this volume; Balph and Stokes, 1963; Slade and Balph, 1974.
S. beecheyi: Bickford, 1979; Dobson, 1983, unpubl. data; Owings et al., 1977.
S. beldingi: Morton and Sherman, 1978; P. W. Sherman, 1980, pers. comm.
S. columbianus: Dobson, unpubl. data; Murie and Harris, 1978.
S. parryii: Green 1977; McLean 1981; McLean and Towns, 1981.
S. richardsonii: L. Davis, pers. comm.; Michener, 1973, 1979; Yeaton, 1972.
S. tereticaudus: Dunford, 1977a, 1977b; Neal, 1965.
S. tridecemlineatus: Schwagmeyer, 1980; Schwagmeyer and Brown, 1983; Silverman, 1981.
C. ludovicianus: Hoogland, 1981; King, 1955; Tileston and Lechleitner, 1966.

WARREN G. HOLMES

University of Michigan

Chapter 11

The Ecological Basis
of Monogamy in
Alaskan Hoary Marmots

Abstract. Data were collected during five field seasons on the behavioral ecology
of a population of hoary marmots (*Marmota caligata*) living in south-central
Alaska. In each of 11 colonies, I observed a single adult male/female pair and
their two to five offspring. Characteristics of these monogamous sciurids included (1) perennial association between individual males and females for up to 4
years, (2) bi- or triennial breeding by most females, (3) a single nonadult age class
per colony with young typically dispersing as 2- or 3-year-olds, and (4) frequent
amicable social interactions among colony residents but infrequent interactions
among marmots living in colonies that abutted each other. I hypothesize that
monogamy occurs in the Alaskan population primarily as a result of interactions
between two ecological factors. First, distances between nearest-neighbor hibernacula made it impossible for a male to control more than one such winter burrow, which was used yearly by all colony residents. Second, vegetation (forage)
sufficient to support two females and their young did not appear to be associated
with each hibernaculum. Males did not directly aid their young, suggesting that
monogamy was not based on the need for biparental care. Finally, I found that the
female:male breeding ratio in populations from three other marmot species was
negatively related to interhibernaculum distance and positively related to vegetation biomass within a colony's boundaries. This suggests that these two ecological variables may be important factors in marmot mating systems.

Introduction

The evolution of anisogamy, sexual reproduction, and parental care affected many aspects of male and female behavior. In general, a female's reproductive success is constrained by the time and energy she can devote to gamete and offspring production rather than by her number of mates. In contrast, a male's reproductive success is generally limited by the number of mates he acquires (Orians, 1969; Trivers, 1972, Williams, 1966). Thus males are fundamentally polygynous, and monogamy will evolve only if certain selective pressures exist (Emlen and Oring, 1977; Wittenberger, 1979; Wittenberger and Tilson, 1980).

Although monogamy is common in birds (Lack, 1968), it is rare among mammals, in which 97% of species breed polygynously (Kleiman, 1977). This generalization will probably remain valid, although it is based mainly on data from large, conspicuous, diurnal species and overlooks the smaller, nocturnal ones (Dewsbury, 1981; Foltz, 1981).

Because mammals that breed monogamously are relatively rare, they provide important opportunities to examine how ecological factors constrain or overcome the evolutionary tendency toward polygyny. Here I present results from a five-year field study on the behavior and ecology of the hoary marmot (*Marmota caligata*) in south-central Alaska. The population's basic social unit was an adult male/female pair and their two to five offspring. I examine how monogamy in this population was affected by low vegetation (food) density and large distances between burrows suitable for hibernation. These two ecological variables are also examined in relation to female:male breeding ratios in other species of marmots.

Terminology

I use the following terms: (1) Mating system: the general pattern of male/female associations for breeding purposes that includes the number of mates for each sex, how mates are attracted, chosen, and defended, the characteristics (if any) of pair bonds (below), and the features (if any) of parental care of young. (2) Pair bond: an ongoing association between an adult male and female for breeding purposes that is characterized by greater proximity, social tolerance, and coordinated behavior than occurs between other adults. (3) Monogamy: a male and female maintain a single pair bond only with each other. Monogamy is not dependent on the nature or frequency of social interactions between mates (Kleiman, 1977) other than that they will be unique when compared with interactions between other adults. (4) Polygyny: a male maintains pair bonds with two (or more)

251

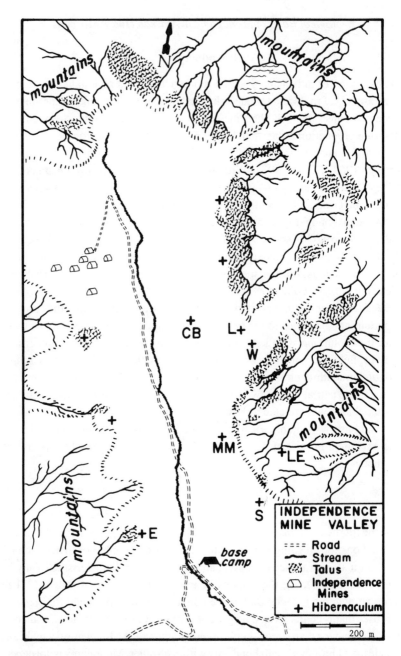

FIGURE 11.1. The study site in the Independence Mine Valley of south-central Alaska, about 65 km north of Anchorage. The single hibernaculum in each colony (n = 11 colonies) is shown. In addition, the most intensively studied colonies (see text) are indicated by letters: CB = Can't Be, L = Lorien, W = Wilderland, MM = Misty Mountain, LE = L'Escarpé, S = Source, and E = Eldorado.

females simultaneously. (5) ''Colony'' has referred to a variety of social groupings in *Marmota* (Armitage, 1962; Barash, 1973; Downhower and Armitage,
1971). To describe Alaskan hoary marmots, I use ''colony'' to refer to a male and
his mate, and their associated young, that live in a circumscribed area with relatively fixed boundaries. All colonies I studied had at least one contiguous neighboring colony (Fig. 11.1). Nevertheless, more than 95% of all social interactions
were intracolonial, and animals spent at least 85% of their foraging time feeding
within the boundaries of their own colony's home range (Holmes, 1979). I classify hoary marmots as infants (confined to their natal burrow), juveniles (active
aboveground in their first summer), yearlings (active in their second summer),
2-year-olds (active in their third summer), or adults (active more than three summers). ''Young'' refers collectively to juveniles, yearlings, and 2-year-olds unless specified otherwise.

Methods

I observed hoary marmots in the Independence Mine Valley of south-central
Alaska for three field seasons (early May through early September, 1974–1976)
and made 2-week visits to the study site in May 1977 and July 1978. The Independence Mine Valley (hereafter IMV) is 65 km north of Anchorage and 8 km
east of Grubstake Gulch in the Talkeetna Mountains (61°47'N, 149°17'W). The
valley (elevation 990 m, ca. 300 m above treeline) is approximately 1.6 km wide
and 3.2 km long and is surrounded on three sides by peaks rising abruptly to 1,400
m (Fig. 11.1). A relatively flat meadow over the valley floor is typical of slow-
growing, high-latitude, short mesophytic grasslands (Bliss et al., 1973). The
meadow is visually ''open'' (vegetation ranging from 5 to 75 cm in mid-July) and
''bumpy,'' with numerous hummocks and boulders about 0.5 m high scattered
across it. Talus piles occur widely (especially where the surrounding peaks meet
the flatter meadow) and are used by marmots as activity centers (details in
Holmes, 1979).

I observed marmots for 1,115h (1974–1976, excluding trapping time and
colony vegetation surveys) and concentrated my observations in the morning
(0630–1100 h, Anchorage Standard Time, 48% of all hours) and evening
(1700–2200 h, 31% of all hours) when most social and foraging behavior occurred. I used preconstructed tally sheets to record the location (grids with 10 by
10 m squares were marked on four colonies) and behavior of each colony member
at 5-min intervals (Altmann, 1974) (hereafter, 5-min census data).

Animals were trapped in early May by placing a single-door live trap into the
snow tunnel leading to each colony's single hibernation burrow (hibernaculum).

Mating Systems

After snowmelt in mid-June, trapping was difficult (23 trapping h / marmot), and only one of 15 baits (human urine) attracted marmots into traps. Animals were lightly anesthetized with ether, weighed, and individually marked with an ear tag (permanent identification), Nyanzol fur dye, and colored construction flagging (8 cm long) sewn between the shoulders. All animals (n = 29) were individually marked in five colonies (hereafter the "marked" colonies). Six more colonies were observed, but individual identification of each marmot (n = 30) was not always possible.

The behavioral data reported below come only from individually recognizable animals observed from 1974 to 1976. These animals included eight adult males, eight adult females, 14 juveniles, 10 yearlings, and 14 2-year-olds that lived in eight different colonies. All of these marmots were individually recognizable as a result of dye marking or unique pelage patterns. Other information (e.g., duration of pair bonds, age at dispersal of young, breeding schedules of females) comes from the 1974–1976 observations and additional data gathered during 2-week periods in 1977 and 1978 on individually recognizable animals. Data collection was often hampered by trapping difficulties, low rates of litter production (below), and the low density of animals in the valley compared with other species of marmots (Holmes, 1979). These problems preclude certain statistical comparisons (e.g., age or sex differences in behavior) and limit sample sizes in some cases.

Means (± SE) and sample sizes (n) are presented in the text, tables, and figures for those data most relevant to the mating system of IMV marmots. Standard parametric and nonparametric statistics were used to compare groups depending on sizes and distributions of samples (Blalock, 1972; Siegel, 1956). Details of methodology and additional information on the behavioral ecology of the population are in Holmes (1979).

Results

General Biology

Seasonal activity pattern. Marmots in the five marked colonies entered hibernation in mid to late September (Hock and Cottini, 1966) and emerged from hibernation between 2 May and 8 May (range for 1975–1977). All animals in a colony appeared within 1 day of the first resident's emergence, and all members of a colony emerged from the same hibernaculum entrance. Mating occurred during the first 2 weeks aboveground (hereafter the breeding period), based on the first appearance of juveniles (n = 8 litters) between 28 June and 30 July

254

(1974–1976), assuming a 25–30-day gestation and 25–30-day lactation period as occurs in other species of marmots (Armitage, 1981).

Colony composition and dispersal. I identified 11 colonies in the valley (Fig. 11.1) and determined their composition by trapping (n = 5 colonies) or by detailed observation (n = 6 colonies, more than 50h of observation per colony). There was a single adult male/female pair in the eight colonies in which all individuals were recognizable, along with their associated young (Table 11.1). (In 1975 one colony had a second adult male living on its periphery who was gone in 1976.) Colonies contained only one nonadult age class each year owing to dispersal patterns and the breeding schedules of females (below).

Although I did not observe copulations, I assumed that a colony's adult male and female produced the juveniles emerging in their colony. Insemination of a female by a male other than her mate was unlikely, because I observed only five instances in three years of males' visiting other colonies during the breeding period (cf. Barash, 1981). There was no change between years in either member of the breeding pair at the five marked colonies (four years' data from three colonies and three years' data from two colonies). Thus I conclude that the mating system of IMV hoary marmots was "perennial monogamy" (Brown, 1975).

I trapped and marked all 14 juveniles seen to emerge aboveground in five colonies (1974–1976), 10 of which survived their first winter. All 10 yearlings lived in and survived hibernation in their natal colony. During the next summer, 14 2-year-olds (four first identified as yearlings) were resident in their natal col-

TABLE 11.1. Mean (± SE) number of hoary marmots in eight colonies containing individually recognizable animals in south-central Alaska

Class	Juveniles resident (N = 13 cases)[a]	Yearlings resident (N = 13 cases)[a]	2-year-olds resident (N = 10 cases)[a]
Adult males	1.0 ± 0.0	1.0 ± 0.0	1.0 ± 0.0
Adult females	1.0 ± 0.0	1.0 ± 0.0	1.0 ± 0.0
Juveniles	3.1 ± 0.2	—	—
Yearlings	—[b]	2.8 ± 0.3	—
2-year-olds	—	—	2.6 ± 0.4

[a] Some colonies had this age class resident in more than one year.

[b] Only one nonadult age class lived in a colony at one time owing to patterns of dispersal and breeding schedules of adult females.

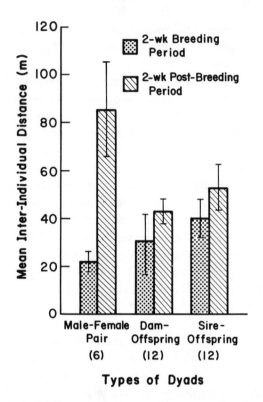

FIGURE 11.2. The mean (±SE) distance between various hoary marmots (based on 5-min scan samples) during the 2-week breeding period (95 h of observation) and the subsequent 2-week period (105 h of observation). Number of pairs is shown in parentheses and explained in the text. Data are from the 1975 and 1976 field seasons.

ony; two disappeared (dispersed?) in June when their juvenile siblings came aboveground, and two remained on the periphery of their colony when their dam brought her litter aboveground in early July. The 10 remaining 2-year olds (living in three colonies) stayed in their natal colony through the summer, and their dams did not bring litters aboveground. As 3-year-olds they were all observed on the periphery of their natal colony, each of which contained juveniles.

The dispersal data are meager because individual females produced litters infrequently. Litters were spaced 2 (n = 1 female), 3 (n = 4) or 4 (n = 4) years apart or 3.3 ± 0.2 years between litters (n = 9 females). However, the data do suggest that dispersal from the natal colony was affected by the presence of juvenile siblings and was delayed relative to most other marmots that disperse as juveniles (*M. monax:* de Vos and Gillespie, 1960; Grizzell, 1955), yearlings or

2-year-olds (*M. flaviventris:* Downhower and Armitage, 1981; Johns and Armitage, 1979), or as 2- or 3-year-olds (*M. olympus:* Barash, 1973).

Social Behavior

Male/female relations. Pair bonds between IMV marmots were "loose" as revealed by data on spatial proximity and male/female interactions. Results for adults are based on six males and their mates (n = 6 male/female pairs). Each of these adults was also observed with two of their young (n = 12 sire/offspring and dam/offspring pairs). First, the mean distance between a male and his mate during the 2-week breeding period was significantly less (*P* < 0.001) than the mean distance for the following 2-week period; in contrast, neither the mean dam/offspring nor the mean sire/offspring distance varied significantly between these periods (*P* > 0.1 both comparisons, Fig. 11.2). Second, the three most common kinds of encounters between members of a mated pair occurred much more frequently during the 2-week breeding period than the following 2-week period (Fig. 11.3): (1) nose-body contact (one animal investigates the other by making

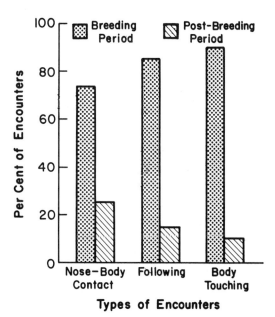

FIGURE 11.3. The percentage of nose-body contacts (n = 65 total contacts), following (n = 40) and body touching (n = 27) that occurred between members of mated pairs of hoary marmots during the 2-week breeding period and the subsequent 2-week period. Encounters and sample sizes are explained in the text. Data are from the 1974–1976 field seasons.

257

repeated nasal contacts with the recipient's head, back, flanks, or anal region); (2) following (one animal remains within 5 m of the other by moving whenever the "leader" does); and (3) body touching (animals maintain direct body contact for at least 5 s, including lying side by side, fur chewing, or mounting). Thus, members of pairs of *M. caligata* remained closest to each other during the breeding period and confined most of their social interactions to this period. A male was significantly more likely to follow (n = 28 of 34 follows, $P < 0.001$) and initiate a behavioral interaction (n = 60 of 73 nose-body and body contact combined, $P < 0.001$) with his mate during the breeding period than she was with him (binomial tests).

Parental behavior. The biparental investment hypothesis (below) predicts that monogamy is maintained when two parents are needed to rear young. Four categories of parental care, one direct and three indirect (Kleiman and Malcolm, 1981), are relevant to this hypothesis for IMV marmots.

1. Direct parental care: Only dams provided direct parental care to infants by feeding and caring for them in their natal burrow. I never saw an adult male spend more than about 30 s in a natal burrow and, indeed, males approaching a natal burrow were almost always rebuffed by their mates.

During juveniles' first 2 weeks aboveground, they were sometimes carried (n = 31 "carries," 1975–1976 data) to different parts of their colony. The dam always transported juveniles, never the sire. Juveniles did not learn to identify food from adults because young first fed on vegetation near the talus when adults were feeding well away from the talus. Finally, adult-juvenile social interactions were rare during this period. Dams tolerated juveniles who climbed on them or lay next to them, but neither dams nor sires actively guarded or maintained close proximity to their young (c.f. Barash, 1975).

2. Social interactions with young: I recorded five kinds of interactions (nose greeting, play fight, chase, mounting, and allogrooming), but I will examine only two of them here (nose greeting and play fight) because together they accounted for a clear majority (43.0% and 46.0%, respectively) of the 437 total interactions (chases are treated below). Most (94.7%) of the 437 interactions were intracolonial, involving marmots that lived in the same colonies. A "nose greeting" occurred when two animals made prolonged (> 3 s nose-to-nose or nose-to-mouth contact (Barash, 1973). A "play fight" occurred when two animals stood on their hind legs, forepaws on each other's chests, heads turned skyward, and pushed or sparred with each other (Barash, 1974a). Play fights (n = 201 interactions) appeared to be more physically vigorous than nose greetings (n = 186 interactions) and lasted several times longer (up to 17 min).

Ecological Basis of Monogamy in Alaskan Hoary Marmots

TABLE 11.2: Percentage of all nose greetings initiated by each class of
hoary marmot directed toward various recipients

	Recipient				
Initiator	Adult male	Adult female	2-year-old	Yearling	Juvenile
Adult male (35)[a]	—[b]	31.4	31.4	31.4	5.7
Adult female (23)	8.7	—	8.7	65.2	17.4
2-year-old (32)	18.8	34.4	46.9	—	—
Yearling (56)	3.4	25.0	—	71.4	—
Juvenile (40)	20.0	17.5	—	—	62.5

NOTE: Data are based on marked marmots in five colonies, 1974–1976.
[a] Number in parentheses are total intracolonial nose greetings initiated by a class.
[b] Dashes indicate that these dyads did not exist within a colony.

The percentages of nose greetings (Table 11.2) and play fights (Table 11.3) initiated and received by different age classes varied considerably. I calculated the rates of these two behaviors based on their frequency of occurrence, the number of residents living in a colony, and the number of hours I observed them. Adult males (n = 6, 0.019 behaviors/animal/observation hour) and adult females (n = 6, 0.014 behaviors/animal/observation hour) were about equally likely to initiate a nose greeting with their young (n = 14 2-year-olds, n = 10 yearlings, and n = 14 juveniles combined). On the other hand, adult males (0.012 behaviors/animal/observation hour) initiated play fights with their young at about twice the rate of adult females (0.005 behaviors/animal/observation hour). Note, however, that the clear majority of nose greetings and play fights involved same-aged siblings as the initiator and recipient (Tables 11.2 and 11.3, respectively). Barash (1974a) reported similar trends for *M. caligata* in Montana: Adult males were more "socially active" than adult females, and the most "socially active" marmots were young, especially yearlings, who interacted primarily among themselves.

3. Construction and protection of colony resources: The initial excavation of sleeping and hibernation burrows may have represented indirect parental investment, but I never observed these burrows being constructed. New refuge burrows (ca. 1–2 m long, single-entrance burrows in meadows where animals foraged) were dug (5.5 ± 0.2 new burrows/colony/year; n = 5 colonies, 1975–

259

TABLE 11.3: Percentage of all play fights initiated by each class of
hoary marmot directed toward various recipients

	Recipient				
Initiator	Adult male	Adult female	2-year-old	Yearling	Juvenile
Adult male (22)[a]	—[b]	22.7	9.1	68.2	0.0
Adult female (8)	12.5	—	25.0	62.5	0.0
2-year-old (52)	5.8	17.3	76.9	—	—
Yearling (87)	0.0	5.7	—	94.3	—
Juvenile (32)	12.5	6.3	—	—	81.3

NOTE: Data are based on marked marmots in five colonies, 1974–1976.

[a] Numbers in parentheses are total intracolonial play fights initiated by a class.

[b] Dashes indicate that these dyads did not exist within a colony.

1976), but there was no significant difference in the number of times I observed each age class digging in them ($P > 0.1$, χ^2).

Defense of colony boundaries could have been parental investment. I recorded a total of 42 intrusions (> 5 min spent in another colony's foraging area) by a marmot into the colony of its adjacent neighbor, 71.4% of which elicited a response from one of the resident adults (Table 11.4). If these responses represented parental investment, the low rate of intrusion (0.005 intrusions/colony/observation hour) indicates that adult responses were an infrequent investment. The relative infrequency of intrusions also prevents a statistical analysis of various factors (e.g., age or sex of the intruder and respondent) that might account for them and the responses they elicited. It is possible, of course, that the simple presence of two adults may have been responsible, in part, for the low intrusion rate.

4. Warning young: When an aerial or terrestrial predator was detected, IMV marmots emitted a single-note, high-pitched vocalization (Taulman's [1977] long call) that caused other marmots to search visually for the predator and often seek refuge (Noyes and Holmes, 1979). To determine if these "predator calls" were parental behavior, I noted the first marmot calling in response to live predators (42 first callers, 31 elicited by golden eagles [*Aquila chrysaetos*] and 11 by coyotes [*Canis latrans*]) or a model golden eagle flown over the study site (18 first callers). (I considered only the first marmot calling because most colony mem-

bers who detected the predator eventually began calling themselves.) I combined the results from live and model predators because marmots responded similarly to them (details in Noyes and Holmes, 1979). I compared the number of times members of each age class were the first to call (number of first callers / number of animals per age class present when the predator appeared; adults = 1.2, 2-year-olds = 1.1, yearlings = 1.0, juveniles = 0.8) and found no significant difference across age classes ($P > 0.1$, χ^2). However, when only adults and their juveniles were present (n = 28 instances), adults were first callers significantly more often than juveniles ($P < 0.01$, binomial test), with dams and sires calling about equally often ($P > 0.1$). Calling may thus represent parental care of juveniles.

Colony Resources

Polygyny depends on whether or not a female will form a pair bond with an already mated male. In some circumstances a female's decision is affected by resources held by males. Accordingly, I examined two ecological resources, food and hibernacula, that appeared to affect the mating system of IMV marmots. Four points indirectly indicated that food available in a colony was an important resource for females. First, females spent over 90% of their foraging time feeding within their colony's home range (the area encompassing 95% of all locations recorded during the collection of the 5-min census data in five colonies from 1974 to 1976). Furthermore, they concentrated their feeding in areas of greatest food abundance, even though these areas often had few refuge burrows and frequently

TABLE 11.4. Intrusions by hoary marmots into colonies of their immediate neighbors and responses to those intrusions

Intruder	Resident respondent	Frequency	Result of intrusion
Adult male	Adult male	5	Fight, intruder departs
Adult female	Adult female	{ 5	Chase, intruder departs
		3	Nose greeting, intruder departs
2-year-old	Adult male	{ 11	Chase, intruder departs
		2	Nose greeting, intruder remains
		4	No response, intruder remains
2-year-old	2-year-old	{ 8	Nose greeting, intruder remains
		4	Play fight, intruder remains

N = 42 total intrusions in five colonies, 1974–1976.

261

were far from the safety of their home talus. Thus there was a significant association ($r = 0.68, P < 0.01$) between the abundance of "preferred plants" (those composing 90% of marmots' diets by dry weight as determined by fecal analysis) and the use of foraging areas by females in their home range (Holmes, 1979). In addition, I augmented food on three 10 m by 10 m plots in each of two colonies by applying fertilizer (nitrogen) to them in 1975. Use of fertilized plots by females was 590% greater in 1976 than in 1975, while use of control plots (no fertilizer) did not change significantly between years (Holmes, 1979).

Second, females' foraging behavior changed as a function of their reproductive condition and the temporal availability of nutrients. Pregnant or lactating females foraged significantly farther from the talus ($P < 0.01, \bar{X} = 57.5 \pm 6.3\,\text{m}$, n = 5) than nonreproductive females ($\bar{X} = 44.9 \pm 4.7\,\text{m}$, n = 5, data collected in 1975 and 1976 for both kinds of females). Because vegetation standing crop (g/m^2) was significantly correlated with distance from the talus ($r = 0.95, P < 0.01$; Holmes, 1979), reproductive females availed themselves of more food per unit area by feeding farther from the talus. These females presumably had greater immediate need of nutrients than nonreproductive females owing to the energy demands of gestation and lactation. In regard to the temporal availability of food, nonreproductive females had a significantly greater ($P < 0.01$) mean foraging distance from the talus in years of delayed snowmelt when forage was available for a reduced period (1975; $\bar{X} = 59.9 \pm 11.1$ m) compared with years when snowmelt was not delayed (1974, 1976; $\bar{X} = 41.5 \pm 8.0$ m). (Delayed snowmelt was determined by noting that 70% or more of five colonies was covered by snow on 15 June compared with 30% or less coverage in years when melt was not delayed. Too few females reproduced in years of delayed snowmelt to make foraging distance calculations for them.) By ranging farther from the talus, nonreproductive females could presumably lessen the energy or time costs imposed on them by a temporal reduction in the availability of nutrients.

Third, when delayed snowmelt reduced the period when nutrients were available (by about 2 weeks), females' mean weight at entry into hibernation ($3.9 \pm 0.5\,\text{kg}$, n = 6) had not changed significantly ($P > 0.1$) from their mean weight at emergence from hibernation the previous spring (3.3 ± 0.5 kg, n = 6). In contrast, when the timing of snowmelt was normal and the foraging season longer, mean weight at entry into hibernation (4.9 ± 0.2 kg, n = 5) was significantly greater ($P < 0.05$) than at emergence (3.6 ± 0.3 kg, n = 6). Variation in adult body mass is primarily due to fat storage in the summer and may be important to help marmots survive hibernation (Armitage et al., 1976). Furthermore, parous females may also depend on energy stored from the previous summer to meet the early demands of reproduction before the first appearance of green vegetation (Andersen et al., 1976; Snyder et al., 1961).

Finally, a direct relation may exist between food abundance and female reproductive success in a high-altitude population of *M. flaviventris:* the number of offspring weaned by females was significantly associated with the estimated number they could wean based on food resources (Andersen et al., 1976). In addition, Johns and Armitage (1979) reported that these same females increased the size of their foraging areas in years of low food availability, as described above for female *M. caligata.*

Hibernacula appeared to be a second colony resource that was important to females. Hibernacula were not abundant in the valley. I systematically searched all 11 colonies for a single-opening, rock-free burrow entrance heading directly into the ground, features that characterized all identified hibernacula. I found only one in each colony. In addition, in 21 instances I observed all colony members emerge from hibernation in at least two consecutive years (some colonies observed three years). All members of a colony emerged from the same burrow entrance each year. These burrows were probably difficult to excavate because of the extremely rocky soil and the short frost-free period in the valley (Rieger, 1973).

Evidence from other *Marmota* suggests that a hibernaculum is an important colony resource. Thus, because overwinter mortality among juveniles averages about 50% (*M. flaviventris:* Armitage et al., 1976; *M. olympus:* Barash, 1973; *M. caligata:* Holmes, 1979), females having a high-quality hibernaculum (well insulated and dry) would be more likely to have young that reach reproductive age than females without such a hibernaculum. Furthermore, overwinter survival of juvenile *M. flaviventris* varies from 37% to 75% at different colonies in the same year (Armitage and Downhower, 1974), which suggests that variation in the quality of hibernacula may be in part responsible for variation in survival. Finally, Downhower and Armitage (1971) report a 7% survival rate among juveniles overwintering at satellite sites (compared with a 50% rate at colony sites) that "may be considered mini-habitats, with the most limited resource being burrow sites" (Svendsen, 1974:760).

Discussion

Theories about vertebrate mating systems have been developed largely for polygynous animals, especially birds and mammals (Emlen and Oring, 1977; Orians, 1969; Wittenberger, 1979). Monogamy seems to be considered a "default system'' that exists when ecological conditions preclude polygyny. In any discussion of the evolution of behavior, it is important to distinguish factors that operated in ancestral populations to favor a trait (e.g., monogamy) and those that currently operate to maintain it. The maintenance of monogamy can be explained by three general hypotheses. (Other schemes are available in Kleiman, 1977; Wilson, 1975; Wittenberger and Tilson, 1980.) In several cases, more than one hypothesis may help account for the mating system.

The Limited Access Hypothesis

Monogamy may occur when one sex (almost always males) has its access to potential mates limited by any of several factors. If population density is low and males and females are widely dispersed (Rathbun, 1979; Stirling, 1975), if sex ratios are skewed (Wiley, 1974), or if the breeding season is short and/or intrasexual competition intense (Johnsgard, 1975), then few opportunities may exist to form more than one pair bond.

Mate access for male hoary marmots was not limited by population density, a skewed sex ratio, or an extremely short breeding period. Colonies were numerous in the valley, and there were several more in the three valleys surrounding (< 1 km away) the study site. Similarly, I found no indication of a skewed adult sex ratio (1.1 males:1.0 females; 1974–1977 data). Finally, a male would have had little trouble locating a second mate (even if a 2-week mating period was ''short'') because colonies were in close proximity (Fig. 11.1).

The Biparental Investment Hypothesis

A monogamous mating system may be maintained when two parents are essential to rear young or when one parent cannot optimally divide its efforts between groups of young (Lack, 1968). Under this hypothesis, males invest in their offspring either directly or indirectly (Kleiman and Malcolm, 1981). Direct investment involves behavior that has immediately favorable consequences for young, such as feeding (Kleiman and Eisenberg, 1973; Moehlman, 1979), guarding (Rood, 1974; van Lawick, 1971), carrying (Chivers, 1974; Epple, 1975), or warming them (Dudley, 1974). Indirect investment includes behavior that has future (rather than immediate) benefits and that often occurs in the absence of young, sometimes before they are born. Examples include constructing and maintaining shelters (Wilsson, 1971), acquiring and defending resources (Ellefson, 1974; Tenaza, 1975), and assisting (e.g., feeding) a mate in ways that increase her ability to invest in young (Kleiman and Eisenberg, 1973). Under this hypothesis, it is important to distinguish cases in which a female would rear fewer young without a male's assistance from those in which she would rear no young without assistance (Wittenberger and Tilson, 1980). The latter occurs in birds, but it has not been reported in mammals, even though some males (e.g., various canids and primates) are substantially involved in rearing young (references in Wittenberger, 1979).

Because female marmots provided all direct parental care, it did not appear that two parents were essential to rear at least one offspring or even that a female would have reared fewer young without a male's *direct* assistance. Under the biparental investment hypothesis, a female's fitness is lowered only if the presence of a second female precludes (or reduces) a male's investment in his first mate or her offspring (Maynard Smith, 1977). If some behaviors by IMV males represented important *indirect* paternal investment (e.g., social interactions with young), this investment would probably not have been decreased if shared with another female or her young. However, although the available evidence does not support the biparental investment hypothesis, direct manipulation (e.g., removal of the resident male) would be required to confirm this.

The Resource Distribution Hypothesis

When males cannot control sufficient amounts of those resources most needed by females to reproduce (e.g., food, nest sites), monogamy may result (Emlen and Oring, 1977; Wittenberger and Tilson, 1980). Thus, monogamy occurs when the polygyny threshold is not surpassed (Orians, 1969; Verner, 1964). If, however, the threshold is approached or just surpassed, an already-paired female might attempt to prevent her partner from acquiring an additional mate because the second mate (and her young) might compete with the first for limited resources (Downhower and Armitage, 1971; Tenaza, 1976).

In their review of mating systems, Emlen and Oring (1977: 215) wrote, "The *environmental potential for polygamy* (their italics) depends on the degree to which multiple mates, or resources critical to gaining multiple mates, are economically defendable." Male marmots did not appear to defend or guard their mates, although they were likely to be closer to them during than after the breeding period (Fig. 11.2). Guarding would be inferred only if males regularly intruded into other colonies during the breeding period (Barash, 1981), and, as reported above, I almost never observed this. On the other hand, two environmental resources, food and hibernacula, did seem important determinants of females' fitness (see above). Thus I suggest that these two resources acted as the primary ecological factors affecting the environmental potential for polygyny.

If food abundance and hibernacula availability acted as suggested, male *M. caligata* could have been polygynous if (1) two (or more) females shared a single hibernaculum and the food associated with it, or (2) one male controlled two (or more) hibernacula, the surrounding food, and the females associated with each burrow. I believe, however, that the particular distribution of winter burrows and the quality or quantity of food associated with each burrow prevented either (1) or (2) and led to monogamy.

I hypothesize that IMV females did not share hibernacula because a single burrow did not have sufficient food associated with it to support more than one female and her young. (In all 11 colonies, hibernacula were within the boundaries of each colony's home range. Animals hibernated and foraged in the same area.) Net annual aboveground production of herbaceous vegetation in low Arctic meadows is relatively low: $60-150 \text{g}/\text{m}^2$ (Bliss et al., 1973). At my study site, the maximum standing crop of herbaceous vegetation was $117 \text{g}/\text{m}^2$. In addition, plants grew slowly in the valley: the biomass of herbaceous plants inside grazing exclosures (n = 8) did not increase significantly ($P > 0.1$) after one year's protection from foraging marmots (Holmes, 1979).

For a different perspective, I examined data from other marmot populations to see if females share winter burrows and, if so, the associated vegetation biomass (Table 11.5). In populations in which sharing occurs, vegetation biomass is 76–227% greater than at my study site, each of these populations is polygynous (see Table 11.7), and the foraging areas of females mated to the same male overlap at least 75% (Barash, 1973; Johns and Armitage, 1979), compared with 5% overlap in the IMV (Holmes, 1979). Given the positive association between total plant biomass and the biomass of plants preferred by marmots ($r = 0.68$; Holmes, 1979), I suggest that IMV females had relatively little food available to them and consequently did not share hibernacula.

In conjunction with the one female per hibernaculum hypothesis, I suggest that males were unable to economically control two hibernacula owing to the wide spatial separation of these burrows. The mean nearest-neighbor distance for a hibernaculum in the valley was 259 m (range $105-420$ m; Fig. 11.1), and frequent movement between them would presumably entail large costs. In fact, routine male traverses were considerably less than 259 m. For example, males' (n = 7) mean foraging distance from their home talus was 53.5 ± 4.1 m; the greatest distance I observed a male foraging away from his home talus was 275 m; finally, the longest excursion I observed by any (nondispersing) marmot was about 500 m. Furthermore, trips between hibernacula to associate with females during the breeding period would have increased the risk of predation because all potential escape burrows other than hibernacula were snow covered.

TABLE 11.5. Relation between shared use of a hibernaculum and vegetation biomass
in populations of marmots

Species	Shared[a] burrow	Standing[b] crop	Source
Marmota caligata	No	117 g/m²	Holmes, 1979
M. olympus	Yes	206 g/m²	Barash, 1973; Wood, 1973
M. flaviventris	Yes	207 g/m²	Johns & Armitage, 1979; Andersen et al., 1979
M. caligata	Yes	325 g/m²	Noyes & Holmes, 1979; Holmes, unpubl. data
M. flaviventris	Yes	383 g/m²	Kilgore & Armitage, 1978; Armitage, pers. comm.

[a] Two (or more) females typically overwinter in the same hibernaculum.

[b] Mean dry weight of live, aboveground herbaceous vegetation at the height of the growing season.

In summary, I suggest that the resource distribution hypothesis provides the best explanation for monogamy in IMV marmots. First, the density of vegetation (food), a resource crucial to female reproductive success, was low at my Alaskan study site compared with other study areas in which females share hibernacula (Table 11.5). This probably prevented two females from sharing a single hibernaculum and partitioning the forage around it, one of the two pathways that could have resulted in polygyny. This could be examined by applying fertilizer across the entire foraging area of a colony (in the experiment mentioned above, fertilizer was put on a few patches in two colonies) to determine if bigamy occurred after the food supply was augmented. Second, the wide dispersion of hibernacula, another crucial resource, probably prevented a male from economically controlling more than one of them, another strategy that would have led to polygyny. Evidence that two parents were needed to rear young (the biparental care hypothesis) was not strong, but this hypothesis may provide a limited explanation for monogamy given the possibility that indirect parental care by males was important to young (c.g., social interactions with young, defense of colony resources, calls warning of a predator).

Female:Male Breeding Ratios in Marmota

To examine whether the abundance and distribution of hibernacula and herbaceous vegetation (food) might affect mating systems in other *Marmota*, I examined the relation of these two resources to female:male breeding ratios across the genus. To the degree that forage is important to marmots, they will construct burrows where food is accessible and economically defendable. Other factors also affect burrow location (e.g., characteristics of the soil), but if placement depends in part on vegetation biomass, then both food and winter burrow availability should be related to breeding ratios within and between species of marmots. Thus, I predict that (1) as the mean nearest-neighbor distance between hibernacula increases, the female:male breeding ratio will decrease and that (2) as the mean density of vegetation biomass increases in a colony, the breeding ratio will also increase. (Breeding ratio refers to the mean number of adult females per male as measured over at least three years and includes all resident females even though they do not breed annually.) Of course, the effect on the breeding ratio of increases in one variable (e.g., interhibernacula distance) could be balanced by increases in the other variable (e.g., vegetation biomass).

Four factors may complicate tests (below) of these predictions. First, marmots feed selectively rather than taking plants in proportion to their occurrence (Andersen et al., 1976; Holmes, 1979; Wood, 1973). Thus, unless there is a positive correlation between total vegetation biomass and the biomass of those particular plants eaten most frequently by marmots (Hansen, 1975; Holmes, 1979), the biomass-breeding ratio relation may not exist. Furthermore, vegetation available early in the breeding season (rather than across the entire active season) may be most critical to females (Andersen et al., 1976). Second, if habitat suitable for marmots is concentrated in small, discontinuous patches (e.g., open subalpine meadows separated by rocky outcroppings) the calculation of mean nearest neighbor distances for hibernacula should be restricted to those burrows occupied by marmots interacting with some regularity. Third, social factors may complicate predictions. Not only do individual marmots vary in their behavioral profiles and competitive abilities (Svendsen and Armitage, 1973), but factors such as kinship might affect how females partition foraging areas

TABLE 11.6. Relation between mean distance to nearest neighbor hibernaculum and female:male breeding ratio in populations of various species of marmots

Species	Interburrow distance	Breeding ratio	Source
Marmota caligata	259 m	1.0:1	This study
M. caligata	145 m	1.7:1	Noyes & Holmes, 1979; Holmes, unpubl. data
M. olympus	<200 m	1.9:1	Barash, 1973, pers. comm.
M. flaviventris	<50 m	2.1:1	Armitage, pers. comm.
M. flaviventris	<30 m	3.3:1	Andersen, 1975; Johns & Armitage, 1979

(Armitage, this volume; Johns and Armitage, 1979). Finally, if significant variation exists in the quality of hibernacula (e.g., insulating properties), females might tolerate greater overlap in foraging areas to gain access to better winter burrows.

Despite the potential complications from these four effects, I considered my two predictions in light of the available data. Because investigators have collected more data on vegetation biomass than on interhibernacula distances, I could examine the biomass prediction colony by colony, in contrast to the burrow-distance prediction, which I examine population by population. I do not perform statistical analyses on the data because not all investigators used similar methods in data collection. As predicted, there is an inverse relation between the mean distances to the nearest-neighbor hibernaculum and the breeding ratios for the five marmot populations for which data have been collected (Table 11.6). Similarly, the prediction that the breeding ratio will increase as a colony's vegetation biomass increases is generally supported by the ten study groups for which data have been collected (Table 11.7). Not enough data are available to examine the remaining three (of six) North American species. Because *M. monax* densities increase dramatically where human crops are grown (Grizzell, 1955), caution must be used in choosing test populations for this species. No data are available for *M. vancouverensis* or *M. broweri.* However, *M. broweri,* an inhabitant of the high Arctic in Alaska's Brooks Range, may breed monogamously (Rausch and Rausch, 1971) and may provide an important test of predictions.

Downhower and Armitage (1971) first hypothesized that food was a major determinant of spatial relations and reproductive success among female yellow-bellied marmots. Barash (1974*b*) developed a general theory of social organization of *Marmota* based on the length of time food was available to animals during their active season (''environmental severity''; but see Armitage, 1977). Finally, Andersen et al. (1976) advised that the role of hibernacula warranted more attention as a factor in the evolution of marmot societies. My data on *M. caligata* in Alaska and those presented above for other populations and species support these ideas and suggest that food and winter burrows are related to breeding ratios across the genus.

Acknowledgments

For assistance in the field, I thank S. Dirks (1976) and D. Jacobi (1975). H. Wurlitzer allowed me to use his cabin and supplied coal to heat it! Personnel at the Institute of Arctic Biology (University of Alaska, Fairbanks) provided advice

TABLE 11.7. Relation between vegetation biomass (arranged in increasing order) and female:male breeding ratio in "colonies" of various species of marmots

Species	"Colony" and standing crop[a]	Female:male breeding ratio	Source
Marmota caligata	Wilderland 110 g/m²	1:1	Holmes, 1979, this study
M. caligata	Lorien 126 g/m²	1:1	Holmes, 1979, this study
M. caligata	Table Mountain 143 g/m²	1:1	Noyes & Holmes, 1979; Holmes, unpubl. data
M. olympus	Marigold 174 g/m²	2:1	Barash, 1973; Wood, 1973
M. olympus	Picnic 206 g/m²	2:1	Barash, 1973; Wood, 1973
M. flaviventris	North Pole Basin 207 g/m²	3.3:1	Andersen, 1975; Andersen et al., 1979; Johns & Armitage, 1979
M. flaviventris	Locality 1 247 g/m²	2:1	Kilgore & Armitage, 1978; Armitage, pers. comm.
M. caligata	Bagley Lake 325 g/m²	2:1	Noyes & Holmes, 1979; Holmes, unpubl. data
M. flaviventris	Locality 4 348 g/m²	1.9:1	Kilgore & Armitage, 1978; Armitage, pers. comm.
M. flaviventris	Locality 5 737 g/m²	2.6:1	Svendsen, 1974; Armitage, pers. comm.

[a] Mean dry weight of live, aboveground herbaceous vegetation at the height of the growing season.

and equipment, including R. Rausch, who initially directed me to the Independence Mine Valley. W. Mitchell and J. McKendrick of the Agricultural Experiment Station in Palmer, Alaska, identified several species of plants and discussed techniques for sampling vegetation. R. Alexander, K. Armitage, D. Barash, who was my graduate adviser, J. Hoogland, J. Lockard, G. Orians, and S. Woods commented on early drafts of this paper. I was given help with more recent versions by D. Andersen, L. Blumer, J. Downhower, G. Michener, J. Murie, and P. Sherman. D. Andersen and K. Armitage shared ideas and unpublished data, and D. Barash and G. Orians discussed marmots and mating systems, respectively, with me at length. My research was supported in part by funds from the National Science Foundation (Grant GB-43350 to D. Barash), the Society of Sigma Xi, the Graduate School Research Fund of the University of Washington, and other aid from the Department of Psychology of the University of Washington. Finally, my special thanks to G. Michener and J. Murie, who organized the Banff symposium on sciurid biology in September 1982, where this material was first presented.

Literature Cited

Altmann, J. 1974. Observational study of behavior: sampling methods. Behaviour, 49:227–265.

Andersen, D. C. 1975. Socio-ecology of *Marmota:* reproductive strategies of female yellow-bellied marmots (*M. flaviventris*). Unpubl. M.S. thesis, Univ. Kansas, Lawrence, 50 pp.

Andersen, D. C., K. B. Armitage, and R. S. Hoffmann. 1976. Socioecology of marmots: female reproductive strategies. Ecology, 57:552–560.

Andersen, D. C., R. S. Hoffmann, and K. B. Armitage. 1979. Aboveground productivity and floristic structure of a high subalpine herbaceous meadow. Arctic Alpine Res., 11:467–476.

Armitage, K. B. 1962. Social behaviour of a colony of the yellow-bellied marmot (*Marmota flaviventris*). Anim. Behav., 10:319–331.

———. 1977. Social variety in the yellow-bellied marmot: a population behavioural system. Anim. Behav., 25:585–593.

———. 1981. Sociality as a life-history tactic of ground squirrels. Oecologia, 48:36–49.

Armitage, K. B., and J. F. Downhower. 1974. Demography of yellow-bellied marmot populations. Ecology, 55:1233–1245.

Armitage, K. B., J. F. Downhower, and G. E. Svendsen. 1976. Seasonal changes in weights of marmots. Amer. Midland Nat., 96:36–51.

Barash, D. P. 1973. The social biology of the Olympic marmot. Anim. Behav. Monogr., 6:171–245.

———. 1974a. The social behaviour of the hoary marmot (*Marmota caligata*). Anim. Behav., 22:256–261.

———. 1974b. The evolution of marmot societies: a general theory. Science, 185:415–420.

———. 1975. Ecology of paternal behavior in the hoary marmot (*Marmota caligata*): an evolutionary interpretation. J. Mamm., 56:613–618.

———. 1981. Mate guarding and gallivanting by male hoary marmots (*Marmota caligata*). Behav. Ecol. Sociobiol., 9:187–193.

Blalock, H. M. 1972. Social statistics. McGraw-Hill, New York, 583 pp.

Bliss, L. C., G. M. Courtin, D. L. Pattie, R. R. Riewe, D. W. A. Whitfield, and P. Widden. 1973. Arctic tundra ecosystems. Ann. Rev. Ecol. Syst., 4:359–399.

271

Brown, J. L. 1975. The evolution of behavior. W. W. Norton, New York, 761 pp.

Chivers, D. J. 1974. The siamang in Malaya: a field study of a primate in a tropical rain forest. Contrib. Primatol., 4:1–335.

Dewsbury, D. A. 1981. An exercise in the prediction of monogamy in the field from laboratory data on 42 species of muroid rodents. Biologist, 63:138–162.

Downhower, J. F., and K. B. Armitage. 1971. The yellow-bellied marmot and the evolution of polygamy. Amer. Nat., 105:355–370.

———. 1981. Dispersal of yearling yellow-bellied marmots (*Marmota flaviventris*). Anim. Behav., 29:1064–1069.

Dudley, D. 1974. Contributions of paternal care to the growth and development of the young in *Peromyscus californicus*. Behav. Biol., 11:155–166.

Ellefson, J. O. 1974. A natural history of white-handed gibbons in the Malayan Peninsula. Gibbon and Siamang, 3:1–136.

Emlen, S. T., and L. W. Oring. 1977. Ecology, sexual selection and the evolution of mating systems. Science, 197:215–223.

Epple, G. 1975. Parental behavior in *Sanguinus fuscicollis* ssp. (Callithricidae). Folia Primatol., 24:221–238.

Foltz, D. W. 1981. Genetic evidence for long-term monogamy in a small rodent, *Peromyscus polionotus*. Amer. Nat., 117:665–675.

Grizzell, R. A. 1955. A study of the southern woodchuck, *Marmota monax monax*. Amer. Midland Nat., 53:257–293.

Hansen, R. M. 1975. Foods of the hoary marmot on Kenai Peninsula, Alaska. Amer. Midland Nat., 94:348–353.

Hock, R. J., and V. Cottini. 1966. Mammals of the Little Susitna Valley, Alaska. Amer. Midland Nat., 76:325–339.

Holmes, W. G. 1979. Social behavior and foraging strategies of hoary marmots (*Marmota caligata*) in Alaska. Unpubl. Ph.D. dissert., Univ. Washington, Seattle, 130 pp.

Johns, D. W., and K. B. Armitage. 1979. Behavioral ecology of alpine yellow-bellied marmots. Behav. Ecol. Sociobiol., 5:133–157.

Johnsgard, P. A. 1975. Waterfowl of North America. Univ. Indiana Press, Bloomington, 575 pp.

Kilgore, D. L., and K. B. Armitage. 1978. Energetics of yellow-bellied marmot populations. Ecology, 59:78–88.

Kleiman, D. G. 1977. Monogamy in mammals. Quart. Rev. Biol., 52:39–55.

Kleiman, D. G., and J. F. Eisenberg. 1973. Comparisons of canid and felid social systems from an evolutionary perspective. Anim. Behav., 21:637–659.

Kleiman, D. G., and J. R. Malcolm. 1981. The evolution of male parental investment in mammals. Pp. 347–387, *in* Parental care in mammals (D. Gubernick and P. Klopfer, eds.). Plenum Press, New York, 459 pp.

Lack, D. 1968. Ecological adaptations for breeding in birds. Methuen, London, 409 pp.

Maynard Smith, J. 1977. Parental investment: a prospective analysis. Anim. Behav., 25:1–9.

Moehlman, P. D. 1979. Jackal helpers and pup survival. Nature, 277:382–383.

Noyes, D. J., and W. G. Holmes. 1979. Behavioral responses of free-living hoary marmots to a model golden eagle. J. Mamm., 60:408–411.

Orians, G. H. 1969. On the evolution of mating systems in birds and mammals. Amer. Nat., 103:589–603.

Rathbun, G. B. 1979. The social structure and ecology of elephant shrews. Z. Tierpsychol. suppl., 20:1–77.

Rausch, R. L., and V. R. Rausch. 1971. The somatic chromosomes of some North American marmots (Sciuridae), with remarks on the relationship of *Marmota broweri*, Hall and Gilmore. Mammalia, 35:85–101.

Rieger, S. 1973. Temperature regimes and classification of some well-drained alpine soils in Alaska. Soil Sci. Soc. Amer. Proc., 37:806–807.

Rood, J. P. 1974. Banded mongoose males guard young. Nature, 248:176.

Siegel, S. 1956. Nonparametric statistics for the behavioral sciences. McGraw-Hill, New York, 312 pp.

Snyder, R. L., D. E. Davis, and J. J. Christian. 1961. Seasonal changes in the weights of woodchucks. J. Mamm., 42:297–312.

Stirling, I. 1975. Factors affecting the evolution of social behaviour in the Pinnipedia. Rapporte de Procès-Verbaux Réunions Conseil Internationale Exploration de Mer, 169:205–212.

Svendsen, G. E. 1974. Behavioral and environmental factors in the spatial distribution and population dynamics of a yellow-bellied marmot population. Ecology, 55:760–771.

Svendsen, G. E., and K. B. Armitage. 1973. Mirror-image stimulation applied to field behavioral studies. Ecology, 54:623–627.

Taulman, J. F. 1977. Vocalizations of the hoary marmot, *Marmota caligata*. J. Mamm., 58:681–683.

Tenaza, R. R. 1975. Territory and monogamy among Kloss' gibbons (*Hylobates klossii*) in Siberut Island, Indonesia. Folia Primatol., 24:60–80.

———. 1976. Songs, choruses and countersinging of Kloss' gibbons (*Hylobates klossii*) in Siberut Island, Indonesia. Z. Tierpsychol., 40:37–52.

Trivers, R. L. 1972. Parental investment and sexual selection. Pp. 139–179, *in* Sexual selection and the descent of man, 1871–1971 (B. Campbell, ed.). Aldine, Chicago, 378 pp.

van Lawick, H. 1971. Golden jackals. Pp. 105–149, *in* Innocent killers (H. and J. van Lawick-Goodall, eds.). Houghton Mifflin, Boston, 222 pp.

Verner, J. 1964. Evolution of polygamy in the long-billed marsh wren. Evolution, 18:252–261.

de Vos, A., and D. I. Gillespie. 1960. A study of woodchucks on an Ontario farm. Canadian Field-Nat., 74:130–145.

Wiley, R. H. 1974. Evolution of social organization and life-history patterns among grouse. Quart. Rev. Biol., 49:201–227.

Williams, G. C. 1966. Adaptation and natural selection. Princeton Univ. Press, Princeton, 307 pp.

Wilson, E. O. 1975. Sociobiology: the new synthesis. Belknap Press, Cambridge, Massachusetts, 697 pp.

Wilsson, L. 1971. Observations and experiments on the ethology of the European beaver (*Castor fiber* L.). Viltrevy, 8:115–266.

Wittenberger, J. F. 1979. The evolution of mating systems in birds and mammals. Pp. 271–349, *in* Handbook of behavioral neurobiology: social behavior and communication (P. Marler and J. Vandenbergh, eds.). Plenum Press, New York, 427 pp.

Wittenberger, J. F., and R. L. Tilson. 1980. The evolution of monogamy: hypotheses and evidence. Ann. Rev. Ecol. Syst., 11:197–232.

Wood, W. A. 1973. Habitat selection and energetics of the Olympic marmot. Unpubl. M.S. thesis, Western Washington Univ., Bellingham, 56 pp.

P. L. SCHWAGMEYER

University of Oklahoma

Chapter 12

Multiple Mating and Intersexual Selection in Thirteen-lined Ground Squirrels

Abstract. Multiple mating by females may affect several important features of a population, including genetic heterogeneity within and between families, degree of polygyny, and intensity of sexual selection. Seven possible advantages of multiple mating by females in polygynous and monogamous systems are reviewed. Preliminary data on multiple mating in *Spermophilus tridecemlineatus* are discussed in terms of these hypotheses, and in terms of their implications for the existence of female mating preferences in *S. tridecemlineatus*.

Introduction

Females in diverse taxa foster postcopulatory competition among males by accepting more than one mate during a single breeding cycle; in species with sperm storage, the same effect sometimes occurs when females mate with more than one male over a lifetime. Only in rare cases does multiple mating seem obviously advantageous to females: if the mating system is polyandrous, females probably increase the number of young produced by increasing the number of males providing parental care (Emlen and Oring, 1977). In polygynous or monogamous mating systems, by contrast, multiple mating does not affect female reproductive success in any clear-cut or simple fashion: the total amount of male investment received cannot be assumed to increase automatically with multiple mating, and several authors have commented that there is no conspicuous advantage to copulating with additional males once fertilization is assured (Bateman, 1948; Parker, 1974, 1979; see also Walker, 1980).

Among the North American ground-dwelling sciurids, multiple mating has been reported in *Cynomys ludovicianus* (Foltz and Hoogland, 1981; Hoogland, 1981, 1982), *Spermophilus beldingi* (Hanken and Sherman, 1981; Sherman, 1976) and *S. tridecemlineatus* (McCarley, 1966; Schwagmeyer and Brown, 1983). For unknown reasons these species differ in frequency of occurrence of multiple mating; the phenomenon, however, has potential impact on several aspects of social interaction. It has been implicated as an influence on the evolution of paternal care (Alexander, 1974; see also Maynard Smith, 1978; Trivers, 1972; Werren et al., 1980) and on physiological and behavioral reproductive strategies of males (Parker, 1970a, 1979, 1982; Stacey, 1982). If multiple mating results in mixed paternity, the evolution of social behavior among related individuals may be affected (Hamilton, 1964; Trivers, 1974). The particular aspects discussed below are (1) the relation between multiple mating and hypotheses regarding intersexual selection; (2) the ways females may benefit from multiple mating; and (3) possible effects of multiple mating on variability in male mating success.

Despite persistent challenges (see Ghiselin, 1974; Otte, 1979, for reviews), Darwin's theory of intersexual selection (1871) remains the most general explanation for the evolution of sexually dimorphic traits that have no apparent utility in intrasexual competition. Over the past 10 years, the image of female choice as a selective mechanism has expanded with the recognition that intrasexual competition among males merely shapes their potential for acquiring mates, while intersexual interactions ultimately determine male mating success. Recent evaluations of the potential power of intersexual selection indicate that the mate selection criteria of females, and opportunities for their expression, are likely to vary with the mating system. When males control material resources or offer paternal care, females are expected to choose mates on the basis of the quality, quantity, or assurance of receipt of those benefits (Borgia, 1979; Searcy, 1979; Trivers, 1972). Conversely, when males offer neither paternal care nor access to resources, females are predicted to choose mates according to genetic quality alone (Borgia, 1979; Searcy, 1979; Trivers, 1972; Williams, 1966; but see Maynard Smith, 1978; Thornhill, 1980; Williams, 1975). In other words, females in polygynous systems frequently are depicted now as highly discriminatory and very selective, and only systems in which males can effectively monopolize females have escaped speculation on how females *ought* to make their mating decisions.

The phenomenon of multiple mating implies that female mating preferences may be less precise or less prevalent than is commonly assumed. Females that mate multiply often seem to have the option of choosing among males yet do not restrict themselves to a single best partner. In some cases they do not even restrict themselves to what might seem a best type of partner, but instead copulate in succession with males that differ in phenotypic characters such as age, dominance, or courtship style (Farentinos, 1980; Jackson, 1981; Taub, 1980; Tutin, 1979). This seems contradictory to the assumption that they are mating preferentially, that is, only with conspecific males of a specific type. It may be argued, of course, that multiple mating is entirely irrelevant to sexual selection if females exercise discrimination when mating with the males that will sire their offspring: copulations at other times may be literally inconsequential because they are not effective in fertilizing ova. This is probably true in some cases. For example, multiple mating in hummingbirds (*Eulampis jugularis*) occurs outside the breeding season (Wolf, 1975), and although some female prairie dogs are reported to mate multiply, there is no electrophoretic evidence of mixed paternity (Foltz and Hoogland, 1981). Nevertheless, the taxonomic diversity of multiple paternity (e.g., fish: Borowsky and Kallman, 1976; Darling et al., 1980; insects: Cobbs, 1977; snakes: Gibson and Falls, 1975; rodents: Birdsall and Nash, 1973) testifies that female mating preferences frequently should be expressed during multiple matings if offspring genotype is of consequence to female reproductive success.

Seven proposed advantages to females of multiple mating, in particular those that seem most appropriate for polygynous or monogamous vertebrates, are summarized below. For each hypothesis I have projected the degree to which mating multiply, rather than singly, could affect the distribution of mating success among males within a population under various outcomes of sperm competition. These comments are based on an extension of a model formulated by Wade and Arnold (1980), in which variability in male mating success is compared across three sperm-precedence regimes. Second, I have also indicated whether the hypotheses rely on the assumptions that female choice is operative and that females prefer particular types of conspecific males. Male mating success is defined in terms of the number of females *successfully* inseminated by a male, so that matings ineffective because of sperm competition or sterility are excluded.

Proposed Functions of Multiple Mating

Assurance of fertilization. The most fundamental explanation for why a female mates with more than one male is that doing so ensures fertilization (Darling et al., 1980; Gibson and Jewell, 1982; Oglesby et al., 1981; Pollak et al., 1981; Taylor, 1967). In contrast to the traditional assumption that male sterility and/or sperm depletion are rare, recent studies indicate that sperm production is surprisingly limited in some species (see Dewsbury, 1982; Knakatsuru and Kramer, 1982) and sterility is common in others (Taylor, 1967). Lott (1981) suggested that repeated copulation with the *same male* may guard against sperm depletion in American bison (*Bison bison*). From the female's perspective, if mating repeatedly with the same male can compensate for a reduction in the number of sperm per ejaculate, there is no advantage to switching mates in order to assure fertilization. Reinseminating the same female may not be optimal for sperm-limited males, however, and it is possible that females accept second or third mates because the number of sperm "allocated" to them by their first partner was inadequate (see Dewsbury, 1982, in press). The tendency to mate with more than one male then could be considered an incidental result of females' remaining sexually receptive until fertilization is assured. The critical variable would be the amount of ejaculate received rather than the number of mates accepted. By contrast, females likely to encounter sterile males (defined as those that, regardless of the number of times they copulate, cannot fertilize ova) obviously *would* benefit from mating with more than one male instead of copulating repeatedly with a single individual. Given exposure to a sufficient number of alternative males, female preferences for certain types of males could be retained across successive matings. If so, mating multiply rather than singly should have minimal effects on the distribution of male mating success.

High costs of resistance. Females may copulate with several different males simply to avoid the loss of time and energy or the risk of injury necessary to resist or evade sexual approaches (Alcock et al., 1977; Gibson and Fall, 1975; Parker, 1970b). If all "courtship" in a population is of this sort (without opportunity for exertion of female choice), then multiple rather than single-male mating should have little effect on the distribution of male mating success regardless of the outcome of sperm competition. However, if females actively favor males employing alternative methods of acquiring copulations, then coerced rematings with randomly encountered males can reduce variability in male mating success when paternity is mixed.

Material benefits. In systems characterized by male control of food items, copulation sometimes occurs in the context of gaining access to those resources; thus females mate multiply in the course of feeding near different males. Multiple rather than single-male mating may be associated with benefits derived from a savings in the time and energy required to locate "free" alternative food (Alcock et al., 1977; Wolf, 1975). Mating preferences could remain operative in these systems if females choose to collect only from males of a particular type. If they are not selective in that sense and approach resource-holding males randomly, male mating success should be a function of territory ownership, territory quali-

278

TABLE 12.1. Proposed functions of multiple mating

Hypothesis	Preferred males	Nature of benefit
Assurance of fertilization	No preference assumed	Production of offspring
High costs of resistance	No preference assumed	Immediate avoidance of risk
Material benefits	Those with resources	Immediate access to resources
Material benefits / genetic quality	Those providing paternal investment and those of high genetic quality	Survivorship and genetic quality of offspring
Promotion of male tolerance / care of offspring	No preference assumed	Survivorship of offspring
Increases in hetero-geneity of progeny	No preference assumed	Genetic quality of offspring
Fertilization assurance / exertion of preference	No preference for initial mate; unspecified preference on subsequent matings	Production and quality of off-spring

NOTE: See text for references and Walker (1980) for hypotheses applicable to insect multiple mating.

ty, or possession of prey items. The distribution of male mating success should be determined in large part by the results of male/male competition for access to those resources. Unless there is reason to suspect that the successive mates of females would be of differing types, variability in male mating success should be relatively unaffected by the results of sperm competition.

Material benefits/genetic quality combination. In cases where at least some males within a population provide paternal investment, mating with one such male may allow a female to secure that investment, while an additional copula-tion with a genetically superior male may boost the quality of the progeny being reared (Borgia, 1979). If both matings are effective, females are selecting dual-ly—for paternal investment *and* for genetic quality. Assuming that their first priority would be for paternal care or material gain (Borgia, 1979; Searcy, 1979; Trivers, 1972), the addition of supplemental matings for the sake of genetic quality could favor male tendencies to provide investment if they are of mediocre genetic quality and to withhold investment if they are of high genetic quality.

Promotion of male tolerance or care of offspring. Under the premise that a male is more likely to care for the offspring of a female with which he has copulated (even when he is one of many partners), multiple mating has been viewed as a means by which females increase the *total amount* of male parenting available to their young (Blaffer Hrdy, 1981; Taub, 1980). In essence this argument resembles the explanation for why females in polyandrous species mate with a series of males—except that, in the situation to which it has been applied, only one of the female's sexual partners sires the single offspring produced. If females avoid exhibiting a preference for certain males during ovulation, as has been reported for Barbary macaques (*Macaca sylvanus*), their behavior will reduce variability in male mating success (Taub, 1980). Over the long run, however, single-male, nonpreferential mating could also lead to uniformity of male mating success. In other words, the effect on the distribution of male mating success is probably due more to the *lack* of female preference than to multiple mating per se.

Multiple mating has also been proposed to affect offspring survivorship by reducing male incentives to kill or injure young (Altmann et al., 1978; Blaffer Hrdy, 1981). Again, females of the species for which this has been proposed bear one young per breeding attempt, but it is hypothesized that infanticide is inhibited if several males have some probability of paternity.

Increases in heterogeneity of progeny. Recent attention to the evolution of sexual reproduction has yielded information regarding the environmental factors favoring genetic heterogeneity (Hamilton et al., 1981; Hartung, 1981; Maynard Smith, 1978; Williams, 1975). Several authors have noted that multiple mating that results in mixed paternity increases offspring heterogeneity relative to mating with a single partner; thus, environments promoting the evolution of sex could promote multiple mating as well (Oglesby et al., 1981, Pollak et al., 1981; Williams, 1975). If females seek several genetically diverse males to sire their offspring rather than selecting one mate of a particular type, their lack of preference and multiple mating should decrease variability in male mating success.

Fertilization assurance/exertion of preference combination. This hypothesis focuses on the possibility that the availability of males may be limited, so there is some risk that overparticular females will remain unmated. A receptive female might assure fertilization by copulating with the first male she encounters and, if additional mating opportunities arise, exercise discrimination then. In species with sperm displacement, progeny would be sired by the second, preferred male (Borowsky and Kallman, 1976; Jackson, 1981; Lloyd, 1979). Alternatively, if females somehow are not able to manipulate sperm from their mates so that the preferred type sires their offspring (see Lloyd, 1979; Walker, 1980), paternity is mixed, and if the initial matings are distributed fairly evenly among males, then multiple mating should decrease variability in male mating success relative to conditions where only a few preferred males sire offspring and increase variability in male mating success relative to conditions where the first male encountered sired offspring.

These proposed functions of multiple mating and their assumptions regarding female mating preferences are presented for comparison in Table 12.1. I also have categorized the hypotheses according to the nature of the proposed advantage; three of the possible functions, for example, involve enhancement of the genetic quality of offspring, whereas high costs of resistance postulates a much more immediate benefit.

This is a rather one-sided perspective on sexual behavior, of course: multiple mating can occur only if females are not effectively monopolized by a male. Male tendencies to monopolize may in turn be affected by the consequences of their alternative option of departure—that is, by the advantages to females of copulating with additional males.

Multiple Mating in Spermophilus tridecemlineatus

Multiple mating in the thirteen-lined ground squirrel was first reported by McCarley (1966) from observations in Texas. It has been observed subsequently in southeastern Michigan (Schwagmeyer and Brown, 1983) and central Oklahoma populations (Schwagmeyer, unpubl. data). The data discussed below were collected from 1977 to 1979 at the Michigan site; most are derived from observations conducted during more than 500 h of fieldwork in the premating and mating periods of 1978 and 1979. Descriptions of the study area and behavior sampling techniques are reported in Schwagmeyer and Brown (1983).

The mating system in the Michigan population conformed to that typically denoted (Alcock, 1980; Emlen and Oring, 1977) male dominance polygyny, in that males were not territorial and did not defend females for prolonged periods. However, because males actively searched for females, the mating system may be more appropriately considered a scramble competition (Alcock, 1980; Wells, 1977). Intrasexual conflict began soon after males emerged from hibernation, and the results of male/male contests (usually simply chases) were strongly related to the participants' weights. Although males covered large areas of the study site before and during the breeding season, the location of their aggressive interactions seemed to have little bearing on the outcome: reversals of dominance within particular dyads rarely occurred (Schwagmeyer and Brown, 1983).

The mating season in the population lasted an average of 12 days. Copulations occurred aboveground, and estrous females that retreated into burrows were seldom followed by males. Estimating the average duration of estrus is difficult because behavioral indicators of female sexual receptivity depend upon contacts by males. The maximum observed interval between matings for any single female was about 6 h; by contrast, some females were sexually active for less than 1 h. Because the changes in genital appearance that accompany estrus appeared rather suddenly (over approximately 2 h) and because of the difficulty in discriminating between "coy" behavior and a lack of sexual receptivity (Parker, 1974), estrus onset was defined as concurrent with the first copulation.

There are also problems in estimating male mating success in *S. tridecemlineatus*. As in other sciurid species with aboveground copulation, intromissions and ejaculations were not detectable in the field (e.g., *Marmota olympus:* Barash, 1973; *M. flaviventris:* Armitage, 1965). Consequently, mounts that successfully transfer sperm and those that fail cannot be distinguished by behavioral observation alone. Furthermore, because electrophoretic paternity analyses have not been performed on this species, the fates of sperm from various mates of a female are unknown. We do not know if there are mating order effects such that paternity is more likely for the first or last male to mate with a female or to what extent repeated copulation by the same male influences his chances of fathering offspring (see Dewsbury, 1982, in press; Dewsbury and Baumgardner, 1981; Oglesby et al., 1981, for pertinent data on other rodents). The estimates of male mating success discussed below basically represent opportunities for insemination: "copulation" was defined operationally as a mount that lasted at least 1 min (to exclude attempts that did not appear to involve genital contact), and a male's mating success was not inflated by copulating repeatedly with the same female. In 1978, male success was sampled from observation of 12 (50%) of the 24 resident females ($\bar{X}$ duration of observation per estrous female = 4.8 h; SD = 1.9); in 1979, eight (27%) of the population's 30 females were observed ($\bar{X}$ = 4.1 h per estrous female; SD = 1.9).

Frequency of multiple mating. In 1978, 50% of the sampled females (6/12) mated with more than one male (Schwagmeyer and Brown, 1983). This value is somewhat higher than those reported for *C. ludovicianus* in various years and combinations of years (2/22, 9%: Hoogland, 1981; 22/94, 23%: Hoogland, 1982) and somewhat lower than those reported for *S. beldingi* (67%: Sherman, 1976; 4/4, 100%, 12/15, 80%: Fig. 1; Hanken and Sherman, 1981). Although interspecific comparisons may be misleading because of investigator differences in operationally defining copulation, Hanken and Sherman's (1981) electrophoretic evidence that 78% of *S. beldingi* litters are multiply sired indicates that multiple mating probably was more common in their study population than for *S. tridecemlineatus* in some years.

282

TABLE 12.2. Preliminary evidence on the limitations of
female choice in *Spermophilus tridecemlineatus*

	1978	1979
Female mates with all males		
Single male	3	5
Multiple males	3	0
Female does not mate with all males		
Unsuccessful males		
limited by competitors	4	2
do not attempt to mount	2	1

Indeed, the 1979 data on the mating behavior of thirteen-lined ground squirrels revealed that multiple mating may not occur at all in some years and that its incidence may depend upon the population's operational sex ratio (OSR: ratio of fertilizable females to sexually active males at any given time [Emlen and Oring, 1977]). Male yearlings did not participate in breeding during that season; consequently the number of sexually active males fell from eight in 1978 to four in 1979, and the 1979 OSR became much less male biased than during preceding years. None of the eight females observed in 1979 mated with more than one male, and only three were approached by another male after their first copulation. In other words, the number of mates accepted by a female in that season seemed to be limited in most cases by the number of males encountered, and multiple mating appeared to be prohibited simply by a shortage of males (Schwagmeyer and Brown, 1983).

Analysis of data from the 1978 season suggests that the number of males encountered by an estrous female frequently serves as a determinant of, as well as a limit on, the number of mates she accepts (Table 12.2). Six (50%) of the females observed in 1978 copulated with all males that approached them while they were in estrus. That is, they either mated with one male and were not subsequently approached by alternative partners (n = 3), or they accepted any additional male(s) encountered after their first mating (n = 3). The remaining six females sampled in 1978 were approached by at least one male with whom they did not mate and thus could have been exerting a mating preference. The unsuccessful males in these cases, however, appeared to fail either because competitors were restricting access to the female or because they approached the female 3–5 h after her first copulation (when she may no longer have been sexually receptive) and did not attempt to mount her (Table 12.2). In short, the number of mates accepted by female thirteen-lined ground squirrels appears to be determined primarily by

283

the number of males that locate them while they are in estrus and are then capable of outmaneuvering potential competitors. In general, there is very little evidence that males achieving access to estrous females are subject to rejection.

Factors related to male mating success. Both the age and the size of male *S. tridecemlineatus* in the Michigan population were related to their mating success (Schwagmeyer and Brown, 1983). The 1978 cohort of sexually active males consisted of eight individuals that varied in age from 1 to 3 or more years and ranged in mean weight from 97 to 144 g. There were no significant differences in average weight of the three age classes, and both factors proved to be about equally strongly associated with estimated mating success. When mating success was scored as the number of females each male mated (i.e., without respect to the number of males each female copulated with), age and weight together accounted for 70% of the variance in 1978.

Because male weight was positively related to success in male/male conflict in 1978, it seems plausible to attribute the mating advantage of larger males to their intrasexual prowess. As is suggested by the results discussed above, sometimes males are deterred by competitors, and success in male/male contests showed a nonsignificant tendency to correlate positively with the number of mates males acquired ($r_s = 0.54$, n = 8, $0.05 < P < 0.10$; Schwagmeyer and Brown, 1983).

The source of the mating advantage for older males in 1978 is less obvious. Because age was not related to success in intrasexual conflict that year, it cannot be argued that older males obtained more copulations through superiority in male/male contests. The data presented in Fig. 12.1 reveal one unexpected feature of the performance of older males that bears on the association between age and mating success: older males were particularly successful in copulating with females *that had not mated in that season with other males* (male age and success with previously unmated females: $r_s = 0.85$, n = 8, $P < 0.01$). Conversely, matings of younger males tended to be with females that had already mated in that season (male age and success in mating with previously mated females: $r_s = -0.37$, n = 8, $P > 0.10$).

Two plausible ad hoc explanations for the correlation between age and success in mating with previously unmated females can be constructed. First, possibly females had a significant preference for older males, but only as they entered estrus (i.e., on their first copulations). In other words, intersexual selection could be invoked to account for the advantage of age, a trait that does not appear to be strongly associated with male dominance. Alternatively, older males simply may have been more efficient at locating estrous females. If so, their mating

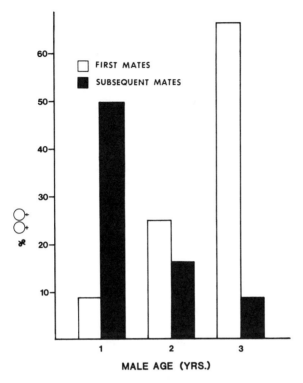

FIGURE 12.1. The percentage of females (n = 12) in 1978 that copulated with a 1-, 2-, or 3-year-old male as their first mate of that season (light bars), and the percentage of females that mated with males of those ages after having copulated previously with at least one other male (dark bars). Four yearling males, two 2-year-olds, and two males that were at least three years old were present during the mating season in 1978.

success could be attributed to intrasexual competition of a sort less conspicuous than aggressive interaction.

These explanations cannot be evaluated yet because of the difficulties in determining onset of estrus. For example, if a female encountered several younger males before copulating with an older one, the differential success could be construed as a preference, or it could be due to the coincidence of estrus onset and the arrival of the older male. Estrous females in Michigan did not appear to solicit either copulations or contact with males. Consequently, neither their receptivity nor their preferences could be monitored accurately through changes in tendencies to approach potential partners. While there is little evidence for the existence of female preferences after females have mated with at least one male, it would be

285

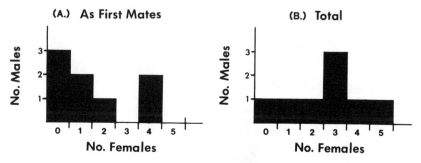

FIGURE 12.2. (A) Distribution of the success of males in 1978 in copulating with females that had not yet mated with other males. (B) Distribution of copulatory success of males in 1978, irrespective of the number of mates each female accepted.

unwise at this point to dismiss intersexual selection entirely as an influence on male mating success.

Impact of multiple mating on sexual selection. The number of copulations achieved by certain types of male *S. tridecemlineatus* appears to be influenced by female behavior, if not necessarily by female preference. In particular, males that lost in competition for first matings were salvaged from total failure through copulations with previously mated females; such gains simultaneously diminished the relative advantage of males highly successful in first matings (Fig. 12.2). In other words, the tendency of females to mate multiply reduces the variability among males in the number of females with which they copulate.

The significance of this effect depends both on the outcome of sperm competition and on whether the probability of sperm transfer per copulation changes with female mating history. If one assumes that only matings with previously unmated females are effective, then the additional copulations with younger males have no influence on the distribution of "genuine" mating success. On the other hand, if all copulations are equally potent and paternity is mixed, then the acceptance of additional partners does decrease the variance in male mating success and, in effect, decreases the intensity of sexual selection on males (Wade and Arnold, 1980).

Ironically, this reduction in the intensity of selection may occur when the OSR is sufficiently male biased to permit multiple mating. An exaggeration of male bias in OSR has been predicted to *increase* the intensity of sexual selection (Emlen and Oring, 1977). However, if the occurrence of multiple mating is related directly to the skew in OSR (as suggested by the between-season comparisons), then variability in male mating success may actually *decline* in years of increased skew in OSR. That is, multiple mating in the Michigan population may dampen the effects of OSR fluctuations on sexual selection.

Selective advantages of multiple mating in S. tridecemlineatus. Most female *S. tridecemlineatus* seem to accomplish in their first (or only) matings what might be considered "ideal" matches. Because males of this species provide neither parental care nor any material resources, thirteen-lined ground squirrel females should be well suited for mate selection according to male genetic quality alone (Borgia, 1979; Searcy, 1979; Trivers, 1972). Several authors have argued that females in this position should choose the oldest males available to them because age corresponds with survival ability (Halliday, 1978; Howard, 1978; Trivers, 1972). Thirteen-lined ground squirrel females achieve liaisons with older males, then risk diluting the presumed genetic benefit of those matings by copulating with other males they encounter.

Three of the proposed functions of multiple mating, material benefits, material benefits/genetic quality combination, and male tolerance or care of offspring, are unsuited to *S. tridecemlineatus* because they presuppose types of behavior not observed in this species (namely, male control of resources, paternal care, and/or infanticide). A fourth possible function, the fertilization assurance/preference combination, stipulates that females should be more choosy after their initial matings guarantee fertilization. The hypothesis can account for cases where females became more selective over successive matings, but it fails to explain situations in which females mate indiscriminately after fertilization has been assured.

The simple fertilization assurance advantage of multiple mating could account for the behavior in *S. tridecemlineatus*. The strongest support for this function consists of laboratory evidence that female moths (*Atteva punctella*) are most likely to accept additional mates when their initial matings have been infertile (Taylor, 1967). The incidence of multiple mating among thirteen-lined ground squirrel females seems to be determined primarily by male availability, yet it is hard to deny that remating when the opportunity arises would be beneficial if male sterility or sperm depletion is ever a problem. Some *S. tridecemlineatus* females do seem to have difficulty becoming pregnant: three of 20 females in the Michigan study returned to estrus 7–9 days after mating. Following the lead of Sakaluk and Cade (1980), Dewsbury and Baumgardner (1981), and others, we currently are collecting data that will allow us to compare conception rates and offspring production of singly and multiply mated females.

The progeny heterogeneity hypothesis suffers generally from a lack of empirical support (Walker, 1980). The hypothesis can be proved false for a given species if paternity could be proved to be single-male. Conversely, only long-term studies demonstrating that maternal fitness is a function of within-litter genetic diversity can verify it.

The remaining potential advantage of multiple mating, high costs of resistance, can be evaluated more easily. The strongest case for this function can be made for species in which females are unable to avoid contact with males, and (1) the time or energy required for sexual resistance can be considered a serious constraint on female reproductive output, or (2) there is evidence that resistance is dangerous. Thirteen-lined ground squirrels fail to meet these criteria in two ways. First, females seem to have a fairly effective and safe means of escaping male attention: they simply retreat into a burrow. Second, it is difficult to imagine that this species lives at such a frantic reproductive pace or on such a tight energy budget that sexual compliance on one day a year constitutes a biologically significant savings in time and energy.

Chiefly through default, the most likely advantages of multiple mating in *S. tridecemlineatus* are assurance of fertilization and genetic heterogeneity of offspring.

Conclusions and Summary

The incidence of multiple mating in the Michigan population of *S. tridecemlineatus* seems to be determined primarily by the availability of sexually active males: the number of mates per female frequently corresponds with the number of males encountered. Females appear to mate with more than one male whenever they have the opportunity to do so, that is, whenever more than one male achieves access to them while they are still in estrus. In this case, multiple mating *does* seem to be accompanied by a lack of female preference for certain types of conspecific males.

The tendency of thirteen-lined ground squirrel females to remain sexually receptive after mating once alters the distribution of copulations among males. In particular, it increases the number of copulations performed by younger males. If these are effective in fertilizing ova, they represent a significant contribution to the males' lifetime reproductive success: only about 50% of males that are sexually active as yearlings are known to survive to breed as 2-year-olds (5/11 yearling males, 1977 and 1978 combined). Alternatively, if only the first male to copulate with a female sires offspring, the results suggest that in years when older males are present, few yearling males profit from participation in breeding activity. Aboveground copulations of ground squirrels can be very conspicuous to human observers, so they may also be conspicuous to potential predators. Why female *S. tridecemlineatus* expose themselves to possible physical risk in order to mate with additional males is not clear (especially when their supplemental matings tend to be with males that could be considered less valuable genetically than their first mates). At this time the most plausible advantages of multiple mating in this system are: assurance of fertilization and increased genetic heterogeneity of offspring.

Although the behavioral observations fail to support the theoretical assumption that females mate selectively, several limitations on the data have been noted. The results of merely monitoring sexual behavior (even when it occurs aboveground) may be too crude to detect the operation of mating preferences. As discussed above, one possible, but undetectable, point at which female choice may be exerted is at estrus onset. Defining onset of estrus as concurrent with the first copulation automatically excludes any preferences for the initial partner. Likewise, the operational definition of copulation carries a second source of bias if copulation duration is the mechanism through which female preference, and ultimately the probability of fertilization, is effected.

Acknowledgments

I am grateful to D. Mock, D. Dewsbury, S. Dobson, W. Holmes, G. Michener, J. Murie, and B. Vestal for their suggestions and comments on the manuscript, and I thank C. Brown, C. Prosen, and D. Silverman for field assistance in 1978 and 1979. Funding was provided by an NIMH fellowship (F31 MHO7339) and the Sigma Xi Grant-in-Aid of Research program.

Literature Cited

Alcock, J. 1980. Natural selection and the mating systems of solitary bees. Amer. Sci., 68:146–153.

Alcock, J., G. C. Eickwort, and K. R. Eickwort. 1977. The reproductive behavior of *Anthidium maculosum* (Hymenoptera: Megachilidae) and the evolutionary significance of multiple copulations by females. Behav. Ecol. Sociobiol., 2:385–396.

Alexander, R. D. 1974. The evolution of social behavior. Ann. Rev. Ecol. Syst., 5:325–383.

Altmann, J., S. A. Altmann, and G. Hausfater. 1978. Primate infant's effects on mother's future reproduction. Science, 201:1028–1030.

Armitage, K. B. 1965. Vernal behaviour of the yellow-bellied marmot. Anim. Behav., 13:59–68.

Barash, D. P. 1973. The social biology of the Olympic marmot. Anim. Behav. Monogr., 6:171–249.

Bateman, A. J. 1948. Intrasexual selection in *Drosophila*. Heredity, 2:349–368.

Birdsall, D. A., and D. Nash. 1973. Occurrence of successful multiple insemination of females in natural populations of deer mice (*Peromyscus maniculatus*). Evolution, 27:106–110.

Blaffer Hrdy, S. 1981. The woman that never evolved. Harvard Univ. Press, Cambridge, 256 pp.

Borgia, G. 1979. Sexual selection and the evolution of mating systems. Pp. 19–80, *in* Sexual selection and reproductive competition in insects (M. Blum and N. Blum, eds.). Academic Press, New York, 463 pp.

Borowsky, R., and K. D. Kallman. 1976. Patterns of mating in natural populations of *Xiphophorus* (Pisces: Poeciliidae). I. *X. maculatus* from Belize and Mexico. Evolution, 30:693–706.

Cobbs, G. 1977. Multiple insemination and male sexual selection in natural populations of *Drosophila pseudoobscura*. Amer. Nat., 111:641–656.

Darling, J. D. S., M. L. Noble, and E. Shaw. 1980. Reproductive strategies in surfperches. I. Multiple insemination in natural populations of the shiner perch, *Cymatogaster aggregata*. Evolution, 34:271–277.

Darwin, C. 1871. The descent of man, and selection in relation to sex. J. Murray, London, 475 pp.

Dewsbury, D. A. 1982. Ejaculate cost and male choice. Amer. Nat., 119:601–610.

———. In press. Sperm competition in muroid rodents. *In* Sperm competition and the evolution of animal mating systems (R. L. Smith, ed.). Academic Press, New York.

Dewsbury, D. A., and D. J. Baumgardner. 1981. Studies of sperm competition in two species of muroid rodents. Behav. Ecol. Sociobiol., 9:121–133.

Emlen, S., and L. Oring. 1977. Ecology, sexual selection and the evolution of mating systems. Science, 198:215–233.

Farentinos, R. C. 1980. Sexual solicitation of subordinate males by female tassel-eared squirrels (*Sciurus aberti*). J. Mamm., 61:337–341.

Foltz, D. W., and J. L. Hoogland. 1981. Analysis of the mating system in the black-tailed prairie dog (*Cynomys ludovicianus*) by likelihood of paternity. J. Mamm., 62:706–712.

Ghiselin, J. T. 1974. The economy of nature and the evolution of sex. Univ. California Press, Berkeley, 346 pp.

Gibson, A. R., and J. B. Falls. 1975. Evidence for multiple insemination in the common garter snake, *Thamnophis sirtalis*. Canadian J. Zool., 53:1362–1368.

Gibson, R. M., and P. A. Jewell. 1982. Semen quality, female choice and multiple mating in domestic sheep: a test of Trivers' sexual competence hypothesis. Behaviour, 80:9–31.

Halliday, T. R. 1978. Sexual selection and mate choice. Pp. 180–213, *in* Behavioural ecology (J. R. Krebs and N. B. Davies, eds.). Sinauer Associates, Sunderland, Massachusetts, 494 pp.

Hamilton, W. D. 1964. The genetical evolution of social behavior, I and II. J. Theor. Biol., 7:1–52.

Hamilton, W. D., P. A. Henderson, and N. A. Moran. 1981. Fluctuation of environment and coevolved antagonist polymorphisms as factors in the maintenance of sex. Pp. 363–381, *in* Natural selection and social behavior (R. D. Alexander and D. W. Tinkle, eds.). Chiron Press, New York, 532 pp.

Hanken, J., and P. W. Sherman. 1981. Multiple paternity in Belding's ground squirrel litters. Science, 212:351–353.

Hartung, J. 1981. Genome parliaments and sex with the Red Queen. Pp. 382–402, *in* Natural selection and social behavior (R. D. Alexander and D. W. Tinkle, eds.). Chiron Press, New York, 532 pp.

Hoogland, J. L. 1981. Nepotism and cooperative breeding in the black-tailed prairie dog (Sciuridae: *Cynomys ludovicianus*). Pp. 283–310, *in* Natural selection and social behavior (R. Alexander and D. Tinkle, eds.). Chiron Press, New York, 532 pp.

———. 1981. Prairie dogs avoid extreme inbreeding. Science, 215:1639–1641.

Howard, R. D. 1978. The evolution of mating strategies in bullfrogs, *Rana catesbiana*. Evolution, 32:850–871.

Jackson, R. R. 1981. Relationship between reproductive security and intersexual selection in a jumping spider *Phidippus johnsoni* (Araneae: Salticidae). Evolution, 35:601–604.

Knakatsuru, K., and D. L. Kramer. 1982. Is sperm cheap? Limited male fertility and female choice in the lemon tetra (Pisces, Characidae). Science, 216:753–755.

Lloyd, J. E. 1979. Mating behavior and natural selection. Florida Entomol., 62:17–34.

Lott, D. F. 1981. Sexual behavior and intersexual strategies in American bison. Z. Tierpsychol., 56:97–114.

Maynard Smith, J. 1978. The evolution of sex. Cambridge Univ. Press, London, 222 pp.

McCarley, H. 1966. Annual cycle, population dynamics and adaptive behavior of *Citellus tridecemlineatus*. J. Mamm., 47:294–316.

Oglesby, J. M., D. L. Lanier, and D. A. Dewsbury. 1981. The role of prolonged copulatory behavior in facilitating reproductive success in male Syrian golden hamsters (*Mesocricetus auratus*) in a competitive mating situation. Behav. Ecol. Sociobiol., 8:47–54.

Otte, D. 1979. Historical development of sexual selection theory. Pp. 1–18, *in* Sexual selection and reproductive competition in insects (M. Blum and N. Blum, eds.). Academic Press, New York, 463 pp.

Parker, G. A. 1970a. Sperm competition and its evolutionary consequences in the insects. Biol. Rev., 45:525–567.

———. 1970b. The reproductive behaviour and the nature of sexual selection in *Scatophaga stercoraria* L. (Diptera: Scatophagidae). V. The female's behaviour at the oviposition site. Behaviour, 37:140–168.

———. 1974. Courtship persistence and female-guarding as male time investment strategies. Behaviour, 48:157–184.

———. 1979. Sexual selection and sexual conflict. Pp. 123–166, *in* Sexual selection and reproductive competition in insects (M. Blum and N. Blum, eds.). Academic Press, New York, 463 pp.

———. 1982. Why are there so many tiny sperm? Sperm competition and the maintenance of two sexes. J. Theor. Biol., 96:281–294.

Pollak, E. I., T. Thompson, A. L. Stabler, and D. Keener. 1981. Multiple matings in the blue gourami, *Trichogaster trichopterus* (Pisces, Belontiidae). Anim. Behav., 29: 55–63.

Sakaluk, S. K., and W. H. Cade. 1980. Female mating frequency and progeny production in singly and doubly mated house and field crickets. Canadian J. Zool., 58:404–411.

Schwagmeyer, P. L., and C. H. Brown. 1983. Factors affecting male-male competition in thirteen-lined ground squirrels. Behav. Ecol. Sociobiol., 13:1–6.

Searcy, W. A. 1979. Female choice of mates: a general model for birds and its application to red-winged blackbirds (*Agelaius phoeniceus*). Amer. Nat., 114:77–100.

Sherman, P. W. 1976. Natural selection among some group-living organisms. Unpubl. Ph.D. dissert., Univ. Michigan, Ann Arbor, 254 pp.

Stacey, P. B. 1982. Female promiscuity and male reproductive success in social birds and mammals. Amer. Nat., 120:51–64.

Taub, D. M. 1980. Female choice and mating strategies among wild Barbary macaques (*Macaca sylvanus* L.). Pp. 287–344, *in* The macaques: studies in ecology, behavior and evolution (D. Lindburg, ed.). Van Nostrand-Reinhold, New York, 384 pp.

Taylor, O. R. 1967. Relationship of multiple mating to fertility in *Atteva punctella* (Lepidoptera: Yponomeutidae). Ann. Entomol. Soc. Amer., 60:583–590.

Thornhill, R. 1980. Rape in *Panorpa* scorpion-flies and a general rape hypothesis. Anim. Behav., 28:52–59.

Trivers, R. L. 1972. Parental investment and sexual selection. Pp. 136–179, *in* Sexual selection and the descent of man, 1871–1971 (B. Campbell, ed.). Aldine, Chicago, 378 pp.

———. 1974. Parent-offspring conflict. Amer. Zool., 14:249–264.

Tutin, C. E. G. 1979. Mating patterns and reproductive strategies in a community of wild chimpanzees (*Pan troglodytes schweinfurthii*). Behav. Ecol. Sociobiol., 6:29–38.

Wade, M. J., and S. J. Arnold. 1980. The intensity of sexual selection in relation to male sexual behaviour, female choice, and sperm precedence. Anim. Behav., 28:446–461.

Walker, W. F. 1980. Sperm utilization strategies in nonsocial insects. Amer. Nat., 115:780–799.

Wells, K. D. 1977. The social behaviour of anuran amphibians. Anim. Behav., 25: 666–693.

Werren, J. H., M. R. Gross, and R. Shine. 1980. Paternity and the evolution of male parental care. J. Theor. Biol., 82:619–631.

Williams, G. 1966. Adaptation and natural selection. Princeton Univ. Press, Princeton, 307 pp.

———. 1975. Sex and evolution. Princeton Univ. Press, Princeton, 200 pp.

Wolf, L. L. 1975. "Prostitution" behavior in a tropical hummingbird. Condor, 77: 140–144.

5. Dispersal and Dispersion

KAY E. HOLEKAMP

University of California

Chapter 13

Dispersal in Ground-Dwelling Sciurids

Abstract. Breeding dispersal (movement of individuals that have reproduced) and natal dispersal (permanent emigration of young animals from their birthplaces) occur in many ground-dwelling sciurids. Breeding dispersal, the less common type, may involve both sexes or males only, whereas natal dispersal is always male biased. Males usually disperse from their natal areas during the active season before attaining reproductive maturity. Temporal patterns of natal dispersal often differ between males and females, as well as between conspecific males in consecutive years. The latter differences may be related to variations among years in weight gain.

Natal dispersal in males appears to be proximally caused by changes in amicable interactions with conspecifics and /or by ontogenetic changes in locomotion, exploration, and "fearfulness." Female dispersal may be proximally caused by aggressive competition for resources with female conspecifics. Ultimate causes for natal dispersal may include reduction of competition for mates or other necessary resources and avoidance of inbreeding. These hypotheses have not been formally tested; nevertheless ultimate, as well as proximal, causes of dispersal appear to differ between males and females.

Introduction

Neither the proximal nor the ultimate causes of dispersal have been elucidated for the sciurid rodents (Michener, 1983) or, in fact, for any other vertebrate species (Gaines and McClenaghan, 1980; Greenwood, 1980; Lidicker, 1975; Packer, 1979). Several problems have thwarted previous attempts to explain dispersal.

These include terminological confusion in the dispersal literature, inherent difficulties in field and laboratory testing of dispersal hypotheses, insufficient exploitation in hypothesis testing of sex differences in dispersal, and confusion by investigators of immediate ("proximal") and evolutionary ("ultimate") explanations for dispersal. However, relative to that of most other vertebrates, sciurid dispersal is a tractable subject for naturalistic study. Therefore observation of these animals may significantly facilitate investigation of dispersal in the future.

Ground-dwelling sciurids, particularly members of the genus *Spermophilus,* are excellent subjects for tests of dispersal hypotheses because they are abundant, diurnal, and easy to trap and mark. They habituate rapidly to the presence of observers, and large groups of them often occur in habitats where visibility for observers is relatively good (e.g., plains and shortgrass meadows). Furthermore, their large body size (relative to most other abundant rodents) and physical hardiness make ground-dwelling sciurids suitable subjects for field studies of evolutionary, socioecological, and physiological influences on dispersal.

I adopt Lidicker's (1975: 104) definition of dispersal: "any movement of individual organisms . . . in which they leave their home area, sometimes establishing a new home area. This does not include short-term exploratory movements, or changes in the boundaries of a home range such that the new home range includes at least part of the former." Thus Lidicker indicates that dispersal involves a *complete* and *permanent* shift in home range. Lidicker also implies that mortality may influence observed differences between immigration and emigration, and therefore that the terms "dispersal" and "disappearance" should not be used interchangeably (also compare Tables 13.3 and 13.4).

Greenwood (1980) divided dispersal phenomena into two classes: *breeding dispersal* and *natal dispersal*. He defined breeding dispersal as the movement between successive breeding sites of individuals that have reproduced, and natal dispersal as the permanent emigration of young animals from their birthplaces. These two types of dispersal usually occur in members of different age/sex classes and at different times of year. Thus, breeding and natal dispersal may be caused by different selection pressures, ecological variables, and/or physiological mechanisms. Although I shall attempt to summarize the information available about breeding dispersal in adult ground squirrels, the bulk of this chapter is concerned with natal dispersal.

TABLE 13.1. Summary of breeding dispersal in 10 species of ground-dwelling sciurids

Species	Social grade[a]	Months after mating during which dispersal occurs[b]	Main dispersing sex	Source
Spermophilus tridecemlineatus	1	0–1	M	McCarley (1966)
S. tereticaudus	2	0–1	M	Dunford (1977)
S. richardsonii	2	0–1	M	Michener & Michener (1977); Schmutz et al. (1979)
S. beldingi	2	1–2	M	Sherman (1977, 1980)
S. armatus	2	0–1	M	Balph & Stokes (1963)
S. beecheyi	2–3	2	M & F	Evans & Holdenreid (1943)
S. parryii	3	0–1 (2)[c]	M	McLean (1983)
S. columbianus	3	0–2	M & F	Boag & Murie (1981); Murie & Harris (this vol.)
Marmota flaviventris	4	3–4	M & F	Armitage (1974); Svendsen (1974)
Cynomys ludovicianus	5	4	M & F M	King (1955) Hoogland (1982)

[a] Social grades are from Michener (1983).

[b] Stated or implied in the text of reference cited.

[c] McLean (1983) observed a bimodal distribution of breeding dispersal in *S. parryii*: the first (narrower) peak occurred during and immediately after mating, and the second (broader) peak occurred later in the season.

Breeding Dispersal

Breeding dispersal is widespread among ground-dwelling sciurids, generally taking place within a few weeks of mating (Table 13.1), although it may also occur late during the lactation interval (*Spermophilus beecheyi:* Evans and Holdenreid, 1943), or following emergence of juveniles (*Cynomys ludovicianus:* King, 1955; *Marmota flaviventris:* Svendsen, 1974). Breeding dispersal is male biased in many species, particularly those in which males do not maintain exclusive access to one or more females during the breeding season (*S. armatus, S.*

299

beldingi, S. richardsonii, S. tereticaudus, S. tridecemlineatus). Among those species in which male/female association is relatively stable and enduring, breeding dispersal often involves adults of both sexes (*M. flaviventris, S. beecheyi, S. columbianus*). King (1955) found that males and females may disperse together in *C. ludovicianus,* but Hoogland (1982) described a marked male bias in breeding dispersal in this species. Male *S. parryii* apparently have exclusive access to estrous females, but McLean (1983) reported that adult males commonly disperse from their original breeding territories.

Smaller proportions of surviving sciurid males apparently engage in breeding dispersal than natal dispersal. For example, Sherman (1977, 1980) found that, whereas all surviving subadult male *S. beldingi* dispersed, only the most polygynous males were likely to disperse as adults. Males failing to mate were unlikely to disperse. Among those species that engage in both natal and breeding dispersal, mean distances of breeding dispersal tend to be the shorter (e.g., *S. beldingi:* Sherman, 1977, 1980; *S. columbianus:* Murie and Harris, this volume; Table 13.2).

Neither proximal nor ultimate mechanisms of breeding dispersal have been elucidated for any species. However, McLean (1983) hypothesized that the evolutionary reasons for breeding dispersal in male sciurids might be obtaining a superior territory, avoiding inbreeding, reducing competition for resources, or improving their chances to kill unrelated juveniles. McLean believed all these benefits, but particularly the first, might accrue to dispersing adult male *S. parryii.* Inbreeding avoidance was the hypothesis favored by Hoogland (1982, *C. ludovicianus*), Michener and Michener (1977, *S. richardsonii*), and Sherman (1980, *S. beldingi*), but systematic examination of this hypothesis awaits future investigators.

Natal Dispersal

Which individuals disperse? In all but the most asocial ground-dwelling sciurids, females exhibit philopatry to the natal site whereas males emigrate from it (Table 13.2). Both males and females apparently emigrate from the natal area in *S. lateralis, S. franklinii, S. townsendii,* and *M. monax.* However, for most species, males are reported to travel farther before settling than do females. Furthermore, in most studies (but see Pfeifer, 1980), immigration by nonadults was also male biased.

Most male ground-dwelling sciurids disappear from their natal areas before attaining sexual maturity (Tables 13.2, 13.3). There is much variation in the literature in the distance criteria used to indicate dispersal (Table 13.4), yet males are always much more likely to satisfy these criteria than are females. Although the sciurid literature now contains many summary statements emphasizing male dispersal and female philopatry, the data presented in Tables 13.3 and 13.4 indicate that dispersal is actually quite variable in this taxon. Male sciurids do not inevitably disperse, nor are females invariably philopatric.

How far do dispersers travel? The literature contains only a few estimates of mean dispersal distances for sciurid rodents (Table 13.2), undoubtedly because accurate information of this type is difficult to obtain. The longest known dispersal distances were 4.0 km for *M. flaviventris* (Svendsen, 1974), 6.7 km for *S. columbianus* (Boag and Murie, 1981), 9.6 km for *S. richardsonii* (Quanstrom, 1971), 1.4 km for *S. parryii* (McLean, 1982), and 1.3 km for *S. beldingi* (Holekamp, 1983). However, none of the species for which data are available exhibits mean dispersal distances in excess of 0.55 km (Table 13.2). Dispersal distances probably are influenced by topographic features and by resource availability, population density, and population composition in habitat surrounding the natal area. Dispersal distances may also be affected by distribution of female kin (see "Ultimate Causes of Dispersal" below). The effects of these variables may be elucidated by careful monitoring and comparison of mean and maximal dispersal distances in different populations of conspecifics.

When does dispersal occur? Natal dispersal in most ground-dwelling sciurids occurs during the first summer of life, usually between 1 month after initial emergence from the natal burrow and approximately 1 month before immergence into hibernation. Among those species in which the primary dispersal period occurs during the juvenile summer, a few individuals typically delay their departure until the spring of their yearling year. In some species exhibiting delayed maturation, natal dispersal does not usually occur until the second (*S. columbianus, M. flaviventris, C. ludovicianus*) or third summer (*M. olympus*).

Armitage (1981) noted that sciurid dispersal occurs during the active season before attainment of reproductive maturity. This pattern is most clearly shown by members of the genus *Marmota,* in which Barash (1973) observed a negative correlation between length of growing season and age of dispersal. That is, *M. monax* experience a long growing season, mature as yearlings or 2-year-olds, and disperse during their juvenile summer. *M. flaviventris* experience a shorter growing season, mature as 2- or 3-year-olds, and disperse as yearlings, and *M. olympus* experience a very short growing season, mature as 3-year-olds, and

TABLE 13.2. Summary of data describing natal dispersal and relevant life-history characteristics in 18 species of ground-dwelling sciurids

Species	Social grade[a]	Main dispersing sex	Main immigrant sex	Sex moving longest distance	Age of dispersal	Age of first reproduction	Diameter of home range of adult females[b]	Source
Spermophilus franklinii	1	M & F		M	J	Y	135 m	Iverson & Turner (1972); Jackson (1961); Murie (1973)
S. lateralis	1	M & F	M	M	J (8–16 WPE)	Y		Bronson (1977)
Marmota monax	1	M & F	M	M	J (4 + WPE)	Y (2)	237 m	Bronson (1963, 1964)
Spermophilus townsendii	1–2	M & F	M		J (4 + WPE)	Y		Alcorn (1940)
S. tridecemlineatus	1–2	M	M	M (292 m) F (308 m)	J (4–12 WPE) or Y (46 + WPE)	Y	222 m	McCarley (1966); Rongstad (1965); Wistrand (1974)
S. elegans	2	M	F	M (90 m) F (77 m)	J (5–6 WPE) or Y (48 + WPE, 2%)	Y		Clark (1970); Pfeifer (1980, 1982)
S. tereticaudus	2	M	M	M	J (5–7 WPE)	Y		Dunford (1977)
S. richardsonii	2	M	M	M (182 m) F (64 m)	J (4–10 WPE) or Y (50 + WPE)	Y	150 m	Michener (1979, 1981); Michener & Michener (1973, 1977); Schmutz et al. (1979); Yeaton (1972)
S. beldingi	2	M	M	M (224 m) F (38 m)	J (3–12 WPE) or Y (46–50 WPE, 10%)	Y (F) 2 (M)	160 m	Holekamp (1983); Sherman (1977); Turner (1972)
S. armatus	2	M	M	M	J	Y (F) 2 (M)	120 m	Amend (1970); Balph & Stokes (1963); Saunders (1970); Slade & Balph (1974)

Species	Grade[a]					Maturity	Distance[b]	References
Cynomys leucurus	2	M	M	M	J	Y (F) / Y or 2 (M)		Bakko & Brown (1967); Tileston & Lechleitner (1966)
Spermophilus beecheyi	2–3	M	M	M (179 M)[c] (296 m) / F (88 m)	J (4 + WPE)	Y	120 m	Dobson (1979, 1981); Evans & Holdenreid (1943); Fitch (1948); Owings et al. (1977)
S. parryii	3	M	M	M (555 m)	J (4 + WPE)	Y	142 m[d] / 47 m	Carl (1971); McLean (1983)
S. columbianus	3	M	M	M (395 m)[e] / F (45 m)	Y (50 + WPE)	2 (F) / 3 (M)	150 m	Boag & Murie (1981); Murie (pers. comm.); Murie & Harris (this vol.)
Cynomys gunnisoni	4	M	M	M	J (6 + WPE)	2 or Y	150 m	Fitzgerald & Lechleitner (1974); Longhurst (1944)
Marmota flaviventris	4	M	M	M	Y (48–52 WPE)	3 or 2 (F) / 3 (M)	160 m	Armitage & Downhower (1974); Downhower & Armitage (1981); Johns & Armitage (1979)
M. olympus	5	M	M	M	2	3		Barash (1973)
Cynomys ludovicianus	5	M	M	M	Y (48–56 WPE)	2 or Y (F) / 2 (M)	120 m	Hoogland (1982); King (1955)

NOTE: M = males; F = females; J = juveniles; Y = yearlings; WPE = weeks postemergence.

[a] Social grade classifications from Michener (1983).

[b] Estimates of home range diameters either stated or implied (calculated as the square root of the area of stated female home range). Where a range of home range diameters (or areas) was provided, the largest was selected. Where home ranges were presented pictorially, the length across their largest dimension was selected.

[c] Dobson (1979) reported 179 m for male *S. beecheyi*; Fitch (1948) reported 296 m.

[d] Carl (1971) reported 142 m for *S. parryii*; McLean (1983) reported 47 m.

[e] Median dispersal distances; all others are mean dispersal distances.

TABLE 13.3. Sex differences in disappearance (mortality plus emigration) in seven species of ground-dwelling sciurids. If not stated explicitly in the cited references, percentage disappeared was calculated as 100 minus percentage remaining in the natal area (or natal colony for *C. ludovicianus* and *M flaviventris*). PE = postemergence.

Species	Disappeared by	Years of study	% males in original cohort disappeared	% females in original cohort disappeared	Source
Cynomys ludovicianus	1 year PE	1975–1979	97	3	Hoogland (1982)
Marmota flaviventris	2–3 years PE	1962–1977	95	51	Schwartz & Armitage (1980)
Spermophilus elegans	6 weeks PE	1977	47	42	Pfeifer (1982)
		1978	78	24	
S. parryii	1 year PE	1978–1979	99	58	McLean (1982)
S. richardsonii	1 year PE	1969–1970	94	58	Michener &
		1970–1971	77	58	Michener (1977)
		1971–1972	91	77	
		1975–1976	71	37	Michener (1979)
		1976–1977	93	70	
		1977–1978	100	100	
		1976–1977	81	75	Schmutz et al. (1979)
		1977–1978	97	76	
S. tereticaudus	8 weeks PE	1972	61	20	Dunford (1977)
		1973	43	8	
S. armatus	1 year PE	1964–1967	52	34	Slade & Balph (1974)

disperse as 2-year-olds. Similarly, I observed that *S. beldingi,* living at an elevation of 2,246 m, where they experience a relatively long growing season, disperse at slightly younger ages than do squirrels living at 3,050 m (Holekamp, 1983). However, at both elevations, males mature as 2-year-olds, and dispersal occurs most commonly when they are 9–10 weeks of age. Fewer than 10% of the observed dispersers in either population emigrated as yearlings. Thus the intraspecific differences in dispersal age in *S. beldingi* were much more subtle than those Barash (1973) observed among marmot species.

Temporal patterns of natal dispersal often differ between male and female sciurids. Downhower and Armitage (1981) found that incidents of yearling male dispersal in *M. flaviventris* were evenly distributed throughout the summer, whereas distribution of dispersal dates for females was bimodal, flanking the median dates for appearance of young in their colonies. I found that female *S. beldingi* are significantly older when they disperse than are males (Holekamp, 1983). Pfeifer (1982) and Dunford (1977) reported differences in temporal patterns of disappearance between juvenile male and female *S. elegans* and *S. tereticaudus*, respectively. Dobson (1981) observed sex differences in temporal patterns of immigration by young *S. beecheyi*. By contrast, temporal patterns of disappearance did not differ between the sexes in either *S. columbianus* (Boag and Murie, 1981) or *S. tridecemlineatus* (McCarley, 1966). Downhower and Armitage (1981) and Pfeifer (1980) suggested that temporal differences in dispersal between males and females reflect underlying differences in the causes of the behavior (see ''Proximal Causes'' below).

In addition to sex differences in the temporal pattern of dispersal, intraspecific variations have been observed between years in seasonal occurrence of dispersal, and in the ages of dispersing individuals. With respect to *S. richardsonii*, Michener and Michener (1977: 367) suggested that ''the time of year at which dispersal occurs, and hence the age of dispersing animals, depends on factors such as the severity of the winter and spring, reproductive success, mortality, density, and dispersion of the population.'' These authors predicted that when the adult female population is small or the reproductive success of females is low, there will be no juvenile dispersal. In a later study, Michener (1979) observed no

TABLE 13.4. Sex differences in dispersal (emigration, indicated by successful relocation after disappearance from the natal area) in five species of ground-dwelling sciurids. PE = postemergence.

Species	Dispersed by	Spatial criterion	% surviving males dispersed	% surviving females dispersed	Source
Spermophilus beecheyi	12 weeks PE	>250 m	100	5	Dobson (1979)
	Juvenile				Evans and
	summer	> 300 m	36[a]	17[a]	Holdenreid (1943)
	40 weeks PE		93	12	Fitch (1948)
S. beldingi	50 weeks PE	> 80 m	100	8	Holekamp (1983)
S. columbianus	52 weeks PE	>100 m	83	13	Murie and Harris (this volume)
S. elegans	6 weeks PE	>5–12 m	65	35	Pfeifer (1982)
S. parryii	52 weeks PE	>200 m	15	0	McLean (1982)

[a] Indicates percentage of original cohort rather than percentage of surviving cohort members.

305

dispersal by juvenile males in 1975, whereas in other years approximately 27% of surviving males dispersed as juveniles. Michener proposed that unusually low population density in 1975 resulted in decreased dispersal. Although low population density probably attracted immigrants to the area (cf. Dobson, 1981), an alternative explanation for the absence of dispersal in 1975 might be the unusual tardiness of initial juvenile emergence from their natal burrows (Michener, 1979; Fig. 13.1). Juveniles emerged 2–3 weeks later in 1975 than in either 1976 or 1977. Perhaps late emergence precluded acquisition of the energy stores (or weight) necessary for successful dispersal.

Michener (1979), Dorrance (1974), and Schmutz (1977) suggested that juveniles usually must attain some minimum age before dispersing. The hypothesis that juveniles must attain some minimum weight, rather than some minimum age, is consistent with observations of variation in the temporal pattern of juvenile dispersal in *S. richardsonii* between years (Michener, 1979), natal dispersal in *S. beldingi* at different elevations (Holekamp, 1983), and natal dispersal in marmot species experiencing different growing seasons and maturing at different ages (Armitage, 1981; Barash, 1973). In a multivariate discriminant analysis, I found that sex and weight together proved to be the best predictors of dispersal status in juvenile *S. beldingi* (Holekamp, 1983). By delaying dispersal until it has attained sufficient size or stored sufficient energy, an animal may maximize its chances of surviving the move. Although the relation between weight and emigration has not yet been examined empirically, earlier investigators speculated that weight affects the probability (Balph and Stokes, 1963; Dunford, 1977; Pfeifer, 1980) or success (Andersen et al., 1976; Downhower and Armitage, 1981) of dispersal in ground-dwelling sciurids. More thorough analysis of the relation between weight and dispersal will probably be extremely fruitful.

Spatial configuration of dispersal. Although ontogenetic changes in movement by juveniles throughout the dam's home range have been documented for many ground-dwelling sciurids, the configuration of the dispersal event itself is unknown for most species. Quanstrom (1971) suggested that dispersal may occur suddenly in *S. richardsonii*, in a period of days or even hours. In one case a juvenile male was marked in the study area and was relocated 9.6 km away only 72 h later. Similarly, Boag and Murie (1981) described dispersal movements of more than 250 m in less than 2 days in *S. columbianus*. Slade and Balph (1974:998) reported for *S. armatus*, that "after leaving the natal burrow, juveniles wander about, seldom using the same burrow for more than a few days." In studies of *S. beecheyi*, (Evans and Holdenreid, 1943), *S. beldingi*, (Holekamp,

306

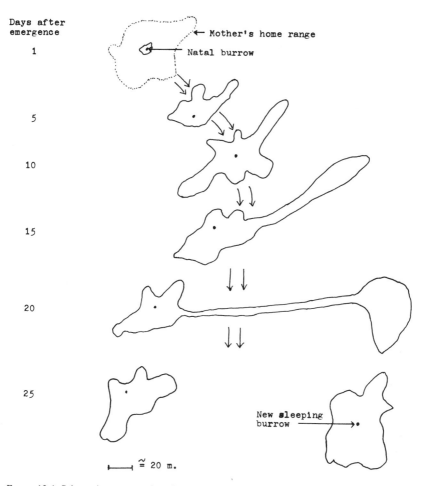

Figure 13.1. Schematic representation of the expansion and shift of home range that often character- ize natal dispersal in *S. beldingi* (Holekamp, 1983). The juvenile depicted disperses during its 7th week of age. When the juvenile first emerges (day 1 after emergence) the home range is restricted to the immediate vicinity of the natal burrow. However, the young animal soon begins to move around and explore its habitat, thereby expanding the home range into an amorphous shape, the boundaries of which are established by topographic features or by the presence of other animals. The juvenile starts to make longer exploratory excursions out of the natal area during its 3rd week aboveground (15–20 days after emergence). The animal may spend its days hundreds of meters from the natal burrow yet continue to return home to sleep. Eventually the animal ceases to return to the natal burrow at nightfall and thereby completes the shift in its home range to the immigration area.

1983), and *S. tereticaudus* (Dunford, 1977), dispersal was often found to be preceded by a series of exploratory excursions out of the natal area, sometimes covering hundreds of meters.

Combined use of trapping, diurnal and sunset observations, and radio telemetry (Holekamp, 1983) enabled me to observe dispersal in *S. beldingi* more effectively than was possible in most earlier studies. I frequently saw or trapped juvenile males long distances from their natal burrows in midday but found them back at their natal burrows at sunset. In some cases the dispersal move appeared to occur quite suddenly, with no previous exploratory journeys. However, the more typical situation involved exploratory trips on at least 2 or 3 days before dispersal actually took place. The shift in home range that accompanied dispersal in *S. beldingi* can therefore best be conceptualized by analogy to the fissioning of an amoeba (Fig. 13.1).

Proximal causes of dispersal. Dunford (1977) and Dobson (1979) tested the hypothesis that food shortage stimulates natal dispersal in *S. tereticaudus* and *S. beecheyi,* respectively. Both authors provisioned free-living populations with supplemental (and highly preferred) food but found that the probability of natal dispersal by males was not significantly changed by provisioning. I observed no relation in *S. beldingi* between natal dispersal and food consumption (percentage of time seen ingesting 27 plant types). Although *M. flaviventris* populations were estimated to use only 2–3% of the food energy available to them and were therefore not limited by its availability (Kilgore, 1972; Svendsen, 1974), virtually all male yearlings dispersed (Armitage and Downhower, 1974). Thus it appears that dispersal in male sciurids is not caused by food shortage. However, Dobson (1979) suggested that relative abundance of food in habitat peripheral to the natal area might attract female *S. beecheyi* and thus stimulate their dispersal.

Carl (1971) suggested that *S. parryii* might disperse in search of suitable hibernacula. However, Armitage and Downhower (1974) reported that, despite the existence of excess burrows at localities of colonies of *M. flaviventris,* 95% of all yearling males dispersed. King (1955) and Hoogland (1982) observed that natal dispersal occurred in black-tailed prairie dogs (*Cynomys ludovicianus*) even though parents often vacated their nest sites, leaving them to their young (King, 1955). I observed no apparent relation between nest-site availability and either dispersal or immigration in *S. beldingi* (Holekamp, 1983). Neither qualitative features of available burrows nor their role in the initiation of dispersal have been evaluated, but it seems unlikely that either quantitative or qualitative characteristics of burrow systems function as important proximal causes of dispersal.

Many investigators have suggested that conspecific aggression promotes natal dispersal in ground-dwelling sciurids. Sources of dispersal-promoting aggression suggested in past research include unspecified groups of conspecifics (Hohn, 1966; King, 1955; Steiner, 1972), male and female peers of dispersers (McCarley, 1966; Sheppard and Yoshida, 1971), the dam (or dam and siblings) (Carl, 1971; Michener, 1972; Pfeifer, 1982), and other adults, particularly adult males (Armitage, 1962, 1973, 1974; Armitage and Downhower, 1974; Downhower, 1968; Downhower and Armitage, 1981; Green, 1977; Pfeifer, 1982; Steiner, 1972). No experimental tests of aggression hypotheses have been performed to date. However, many observational and correlative data have been gathered in recent years, usually of one or more of the following types: wounding, spatial and temporal overlap of dispersers and potential aggressors, general levels of aggressive interaction in the entire population, and levels of aggressive interaction specifically involving dispersers. General levels of aggression were apparently not related to male dispersal in *M. monax* (Bronson, 1963, 1964), *M. flaviventris* (Downhower and Armitage, 1981), *S. richardsonii* (Yeaton, 1972), or *S. tereticaudus* (Dunford, 1977). Nor was wounding related to dispersal in *M. monax* (Bronson, 1964), *S. armatus* (Slade and Balph, 1974), *S. beldingi* (Holekamp, 1983), or *S. tereticaudus* (Dunford, 1977).

More direct observational tests of the hypothesis that the dam (or the dam and her other offspring) aggressively drives her sons out of the natal area have yielded negative results in *S. beldingi* (Holekamp, 1983), *S. richardsonii* (Michener, 1972; Michener and Michener, 1973; Michener and Sheppard, 1972; Yeaton, 1969), and *S. tereticaudus* (Dunford, 1977). Similarly, the hypothesis that adult aggression actively promotes dispersal by young male conspecifics was rejected in studies of *M. flaviventris* (Armitage, 1973, 1974; Armitage and Downhower, 1974; Downhower and Armitage, 1981), *S. beecheyi* (Dobson, 1979), and *S. beldingi* (Holekamp, 1983). Thus most available evidence from all ground-dwelling sciurids strongly supports the conclusion that male dispersers are not actively driven from their natal areas by conspecifics.

Two additional general conclusions pertinent to the role of aggression in sciurid dispersal should be drawn from the literature. First, though young males do not disperse in direct response to conspecific aggression, evidence is accumulating that aggression does stimulate natal dispersal in some young female sciurids (Downhower and Armitage, 1981; Holekamp, 1983; Pfeifer, 1980, 1982). In particular, dispersal by young females appears to be related to high levels of aggression directed against them by their mothers and sisters, perhaps in competition for resources in the natal area. Second, although high levels of aggression are not necessary for dispersal of young males, in some species adult aggression may hasten or otherwise facilitate their dispersal (*M. flaviventris:*

Armitage, 1973, 1974; Downhower and Armitage, 1981; *S. elegans:* Pfeifer, 1982).

Several investigators have proposed that the proximal cause of natal dispersal involves avoidance of conspecifics. Although rarely defined (but see Yeaton, 1972), "avoidance" usually takes one of two implicit meanings in the sciurid literature: absence or low frequency of social interactions, particularly absence of amicable interactions, and increase in distance between conspecifics, presumably to minimize the frequency of social encounters.

Results of studies invoking the first definition of avoidance (absence of social interaction) indicate that this mechanism may be important in initiating natal dispersal in *M. flaviventris* (Armitage, 1962, 1973, 1974; Armitage and Downhower, 1974; Downhower, 1968; Downhower and Armitage, 1981). Data gathered since 1962 show that natal dispersal is delayed when rates of amicable interaction are high between yearling males and adults. Although the exact nature of the relation between rates of amicable interaction and dispersal has not yet been identified, dispersal by young males possibly ensues from conspecifics' failure to respond to their social overtures. Michener and Sheppard (1972) observed this type of interaction between adult female *S. richardsonii* and their male offspring but found that dams engaged in relatively frequent amicable interactions with female offspring. Armitage and Johns (1982) observed similar trends in *M. flaviventris*. These intriguing results indicate that this hypothesis merits further attention.

Predictions of the hypothesis invoking the second definition of avoidance (increasing distance between conspecifics) vary with the size and composition of the conspecific group that dispersers are presumed to be avoiding: individuals might emigrate to avoid either family members or members of the larger deme in which the kin group resides. Thus the hypothesis predicts that dispersers should originate only from kin or demographic groups of particular sizes or compositions.

Litter size and gender composition apparently have little influence on dispersal by juvenile male *S. beldingi* (Holekamp, 1983) or *S. elegans* (Pfeifer, 1980). However, Dunford (1977) reported that male *S. tereticaudus* from large litters were more likely to disappear than males from small litters. Dunford (1977) also noted that the proportion of a dam's offspring that dispersed was not statistically significantly related to her age (yearling versus older adult). Sherman (1976) found that in *S. beldingi* a dam's disappearance had no apparent influence on the probability that her sons would hibernate in the natal area. By contrast, yearling male *S. richardsonii* (Michener and Michener, 1973) and *S. elegans* (S. L. R. Pfeifer, pers. comm.) whose mothers disappeared were more likely to remain near their natal burrows than were yearlings with living mothers. Systematic removal of mothers of litters of various sizes may permit analysis of the effects of the dam's absence on the probability of natal dispersal and on such potential mediators of dispersal as body weight.

Dispersal may occur as an avoidant response to some characteristic of the larger population in which the family unit resides. Michener and Michener (1977) found that both time of year and ages of juveniles appeared to influence dispersal more than did the presence of other animals in a population of *S. richardsonii*. Slade and Balph (1974) culled a population of *S. armatus* and compared movements of juveniles before and after population reduction. They concluded that the tendency of males to leave the natal burrow was not dependent on population density. Similarly, natal dispersal by males was found not to be density dependent in *S. beecheyi* (Dobson, 1979), *S. beldingi* (Holekamp, 1983), and *S. elegans* (Pfeifer, 1980). Thus male dispersal does not appear to be proximally caused by high population density or by any of several features of the dispersing animal's immediate family. However, Dobson (1979, 1981) proposed that low population density in surrounding habitat might stimulate dispersal by female sciurids from more crowded natal areas. Immigration patterns in *S. armatus* (Slade and Balph, 1974), *S. beecheyi* (Dobson, 1979, 1981), and *S. parryii* (Green, 1977) indeed suggest that females are attracted to areas inhabited by relatively few conspecifics.

My observations (Holekamp, 1983) support the hypothesis that dispersal in *S. beldingi* is proximally caused by ontogenetic change in the juvenile's behavioral interaction with its environment. Specifically, dispersal is temporally correlated with high levels of locomotor and exploratory activity and with relatively low response levels in simple tests of "fearfulness" (Turner, 1972; Holekamp, 1983). After being frightened into a burrow by simulation of a predator's approach (lateral tossing of a dark cushion near the animal), juvenile males reappeared more rapidly than did juvenile females at ages 4 – 10 weeks, (initial emergence from the natal burrow through the end of the main dispersal period). Thereafter, male latency to reappearance increased and no longer differed significantly from that observed in females. I suggest that the low level of "fearfulness" during weeks 4 – 10, in combination with high levels of locomotion and exploration, might produce the expansion and shift of home range that ultimately results in dispersal (Fig. 13.1). Dunford (1977) and Yeaton (1969) offered similar suggestions when they hypothesized that emigration is caused by an "innate tendency to disperse" in *S. tereticaudus* and *S. richardsonii* respectively. King (1955) observed similar trends in exploration and "fearfulness" in young *C. ludovi-*

cianus. The physiological processes that might mediate expression of these behaviors remain unknown, as does the relation between these locomotor, exploratory, and "emotional" measures and other variables proposed to influence dispersal such as aggression, avoidance, and body weight.

In summary, available data contradict predictions of hypotheses suggesting resource availability, direct aggression by conspecifics, or specific characteristics of kin or demographic groups as proximal mechanisms of dispersal by young male sciurids. However, suggestions exist that natal dispersal by females may be caused by aggressive interaction with female kin, high population density in the natal area relative to that in surrounding habitat, or both. Available data also support hypotheses suggesting low levels of amicable interaction with conspecifics and ontogenetic changes in "fearfulness," exploration, and locomotion as proximal causes of natal dispersal by male sciurids. These causal mechanisms need not be mutually exclusive. In fact, interaction of two or more variables may be necessary to initiate dispersal, and their relative contributions may depend on such additional parameters as severity of winter or resource availability.

What terminates dispersal movements? Dunford (1977) and Drabek (1970) agreed that conspecific aggression can significantly influence settlement by *S. tereticaudus* immigrants: dispersers are most likely to settle in areas where they are objects of the least conspecific aggression. Turner (1972) and Carl (1971) reported that young dispersers often settle in suboptimal habitat in *S. beldingi* and *S. parryii*, respectively. Immigrants may settle in inferior areas because conspecific aggression or density or both precludes settlement in prime habitat. However, most sciurid biologists have described dispersal by some individuals into their main study areas (Table 13.2), so immigrants do not invariably settle in suboptimal habitat. Results obtained by Dobson (1981), McLean (1983), and Slade and Balph (1974) suggest that settlement may depend on resource availability, territorial behavior by residents, and population density, but the roles of these variables have not been directly analyzed.

Ultimate causes of dispersal. Three hypotheses have been suggested as evolutionary, or "ultimate," explanations for dispersal in ground-dwelling sciurids. First, dispersal might reduce competition for environmental resources, such as food or nestsites. Second, dispersal might reduce probability of inbreeding or maximize probability of outcrossing. Third, dispersal might reduce competition for mates. I shall preface further discussion of these hypotheses with two general observations. First, the ultimate explanations for dispersal may differ both among species and between male and female conspecifics. Second, as Dobson

312

(1982) and others have pointed out, it is possible that multiple evolutionary forces have shaped each of the existing sciurid dispersal patterns.

The first hypothesis predicts that emigration and immigration should be directly dependent on population density relative to critical resources such as food or burrows (Dobson, 1979). Existing data are sparse, but they suggest that competition for environmental resources, particularly within the dam's territory, may stimulate natal dispersal by females but not by males (Dobson, 1979; Green, 1977; Pfeifer, 1980, 1982; Slade and Balph, 1974). These data imply that those female littermates that lose in competition for portions of the mother's territory may disperse (Pfeifer, 1982).

The outcrossing hypothesis has been suggested as an ultimate explanation for dispersal in sciurids by Dobson (1979), Holekamp (1983), Michener and Michener (1977), Pfeifer, (1982), Schwartz and Armitage (1980), and Sherman (1976, 1977, 1980). This hypothesis predicts that dispersal should occur before the age of first reproduction, and that likelihood of dispersal should vary with the probability of having kin as potential mates. Because dispersal is apparently dangerous (Schmutz et al., 1979), the outcrossing hypothesis implies that dispersers need only move as far as is necessary to reduce the probability of consanguineous mating. Two of these predictions have been verified in ground-dwelling sciurids: dispersal usually occurs before reproductive maturity (Armitage, 1981), and probability of male dispersal does not appear to vary significantly with population density or resource availability (Armitage, 1981; Armitage and Downhower, 1974; Boag and Murie, 1981; Dobson, 1979, 1981; Downhower and Armitage, 1981; Dunford, 1977; Fitch, 1948; Holekamp, 1983; King, 1955; Michener and Michener, 1977; Pfeifer, 1980; Rongstad, 1965; Slade and Balph, 1974). However, males of some species appear to disperse farther than necessary to avoid mating with philopatric female relatives (Table 13.2). Furthermore, inbreeding avoidance could be accomplished equally well if juvenile females dispersed and males remained sedentary (Dobson, 1982). Why then do males, rather than females, disperse?

Among sciurids, access to mates is rarely limited for females but often is for males (Dobson, 1982; Sherman, 1976, 1977). Improved access to females, the third ultimate hypothesis, may be accomplished by reducing male/male competition, maximizing the probability of selection by females as mates, or both. The former model predicts that dispersers should be poor competitors for females (subordinates or juveniles) and that the probability of their dispersal should increase with the ratio of successful competitors (adult males) to females. Although juvenile males constitute the main dispersing group in most sciurids, this is also predicted by the outcrossing hypothesis. Furthermore, Sherman

313

(1976, 1977) and I (Holekamp, 1983) observed an apparent equality between immigration and emigration by juvenile males in our study populations of *S. beldingi*. This equality suggests that males disperse from our study areas for reasons other than minimizing competition for mates. Sherman and I also observed that all subadult males dispersed in all years from our respective populations, despite variations in the adult sex ratio. Nevertheless, competition for mates may influence dispersal in this and other sciurid species.

Sciurid males may also improve their chances of being selected as mates by increasing proximity to females that find them attractive. Thus male dispersal patterns may be secondary consequences of female choice (Hoogland, 1982). Although this hypothesis has not been tested, Holmes and Sherman (1982) found that female sciurids can recognize nestmates, suggesting a mechanism for discrimination among potential mates. If females prefer to mate with unfamiliar males, their former nestmates might indeed be obliged to disperse. Yearling male *S. richardsonii* (Michener and Michener, 1973) and *S. elegans* (Pfeifer, pers. comm.) whose mothers had disappeared were less likely to disperse than were yearlings with living mothers. Thus male sciurids may fail to disperse when their close female kin have disappeared from the natal area.

Consequences of dispersal. Dispersal has important effects on the size, composition, genetic structure, longevity, spatial distribution, and social structure of vertebrate populations (Hamilton, 1972; Howard, 1949; Lidicker, 1975; MacArthur and Wilson, 1967; Taylor and Taylor, 1977). Of these effects, only two have been discussed in the sciurid literature. Schwartz and Armitage (1980) included dispersal among mechanisms operating to retard fixation of genetic variation in *M. flaviventris*. Thus, dispersal patterns in this species apparently result in outcrossing, regardless of whether they were naturally selected to do so.

Barash (1973), Armitage (1981), and Michener (1983) suggested that delayed dispersal might be one of the most important mechanisms promoting increased sociality in ground-dwelling sciurids. Michener (1983) also observed that the male bias in dispersal has significantly influenced the structure of sciurid societies: sons disperse, leaving female kin clusters in localities already proved successful by the survival and reproductive success of the mother. Thus, both the sex and the age of dispersers appear to have played critical roles in the evolution of sciurid social behavior.

Suggestions for Future Research

The most fundamental questions to be answered in any initial investigation of dispersal are as follows: Which individuals disperse? At what age or weight does dispersal occur? What is the configuration of the dispersal event in space and time? What environmental, behavioral, and physiological variables change in temporal association with dispersal? Do changes in any of these variables consistently predict dispersal? For example, Bekoff (1977) suggested that there might be regular behavioral precursors of dispersal in some species.

After departing from their original home ranges, where do dispersers go? What factors influence settlement? Most important, what are the fates of dispersers? Do they suffer inordinately high mortality? Documentation of survivorship among dispersers would permit initial estimation of the risks associated with dispersal. Furthermore, observation of the mating success of immigrants, as well as their success in competition for other necessary resources, would allow us to test hypotheses suggesting ultimate causes of dispersal.

Among the most fruitful of future research efforts will be intra- and interspecific comparative studies of dispersal. Why does dispersal appear to be inevitable for young males of some species but not others? Are the proximal and ultimate causes of dispersal the same for males and females? Studies of populations or species in which sufficient numbers of female dispersers could be followed over time would permit investigation of causes of female emigration. To date most samples of dispersing females have been too small to permit meaningful examination of possible causal variables.

The most significant contributions to our understanding of sciurid dispersal will probably be attempts to test predictions of hypotheses suggesting its proximal causes. Observational and experimental tests of hypotheses with mutually exclusive predictions will be particularly valuable. Such studies will not be easy, but the correlative approach used in past research has left us with a rather hazy picture of both proximal and ultimate causes of dispersal in ground-dwelling sciurids.

Acknowledgments

I would like to express my appreciation to the National Science Foundation, the American Association of University Women, Sigma Xi, and Phi Beta Kappa for financial support. I would also like to thank the following individuals for helpful comments on portions of this manuscript: Roy L. Caldwell, Stephen E. Glickman, Gail R. Michener, Jan O. Murie, Sharon L. R. Pfeifer, Paul W. Sherman, and an anonymous reviewer.

Literature Cited

Alcorn, J. R. 1940. Life history of the Piute ground squirrel. J. Mamm., 21:160–170.

Amend, S. R. 1970. On the population ecology of Uinta ground squirrels. Unpubl. M.S. thesis. Utah State Univ., Logan, 60 pp.

Andersen, D. C., K. B. Armitage, and R. S. Hoffmann. 1976. Socioecology of marmots: female reproductive strategies. Ecology, 57:552–560.

Armitage, K. B. 1962. Social behaviour of a colony of yellow-bellied marmots (*Marmota flaviventris*). Anim. Behav., 3:319–331.

———. 1973. Population changes and social behavior following colonization by the yellow-bellied marmot. J. Mamm., 54:842–845.

———. 1974. Male behaviour and territoriality in the yellow-bellied marmot. J. Zool. London, 172:233–265.

———. 1981. Sociality as a life-history tactic of ground squirrels. Oecologia, 48:36–49.

Armitage, K. B., and J. F. Downhower. 1974. Demography of yellow-bellied marmot populations. Ecology, 55:1233–1245.

Armitage, K. B., and D. W. Johns. 1982. Kinship, reproductive strategies and social dynamics of yellow-bellied marmots. Behav. Ecol. Sociobiol., 11:55–63.

Bakko, E. B., and L. N. Brown. 1967. Breeding biology of the white-tailed prairie dog, *Cynomys leucurus*, in Wyoming. J. Mamm., 48:100–112.

Balph, D. F., and A. W. Stokes. 1963. On the ethology of a population of Uinta ground squirrels. Amer. Midland Nat., 69:106–126.

Barash, D. P. 1973. The social biology of the Olympic marmot. Anim. Behav. Monogr., 6:173–245.

Bekoff, M. 1977. Mammalian dispersal and the ontogeny of individual behavioral phenotypes. Amer. Nat., 111:715–732.

Boag, D. A., and J. O. Murie. 1981. Population ecology of Columbian ground squirrels in southwestern Alberta. Canadian J. Zool., 59:2230–2240.

Bronson, F. H. 1963. Some correlates of interaction rate in natural populations of woodchucks. Ecology, 44:637–643.

———. 1964. Agonistic behaviour in woodchucks. Anim. Behav., 12:470–478.

Bronson, M. T. 1977. Altitudinal variation in the annual cycle and life history of the golden-mantled ground squirrel (*Spermophilus lateralis*). Unpubl. Ph.D. dissert., Univ. California, Berkeley, 134 pp.

Carl, E. A. 1971. Population control in Arctic ground squirrels. Ecology, 52:395–413.

Clark, T. W. 1970. Richardson's ground squirrel (*Spermophilus richardsonii*) in the Laramie basin, Wyoming. Great Basin Nat., 30:55–70.

Dobson, F. S. 1979. An experimental study of dispersal in the California ground squirrel. Ecology, 60:1103–1109.

———. 1981. An experimental examination of an artificial dispersal sink. J. Mamm., 62:74–81.

———. 1982. Competition for mates and predominant juvenile male dispersal in mammals. Anim. Behav., 30:1183–1192.

Dorrance, M. J. 1974. The annual cycle and population dynamics of Richardson's ground squirrel. Unpubl. Ph.D. dissert., Univ. Wisconsin, Madison, 150 pp.

Downhower, J. F. 1968. Factors affecting the dispersal of yearling yellow-bellied marmots (*Marmota flaviventris*). Unpubl. Ph.D. dissert., Univ. Kansas, Lawrence, 161 pp.

Downhower, J. F., and K. B. Armitage. 1981. Dispersal of yearling yellow-bellied marmots (*Marmota flaviventris*). Anim. Behav., 29:1064–1069.

Drabek, C. M. 1970. Ethoecology of the round-tailed ground squirrel, *Spermophilus tereticaudus*. Unpubl. Ph.D. dissert., Univ. Arizona, Tucson, 108 pp.

Dunford, C. 1977. Behavioral limitation of round-tailed ground squirrel density. Ecology, 58:1254–1268.

Evans, F. C., and R. Holdenreid. 1943. A population study of the Beechey ground squirrel in central California. J. Mamm., 24:231–260.

Fitch, H. S. 1948. Ecology of the California ground squirrel on grazing lands. Amer. Midland Nat., 39:513–596.

Fitzgerald, J. P., and R. R. Lechleitner. 1974. Observations on the biology of Gunnison's prairie dog in central Colorado. Amer. Midland Nat., 92:146–163.

Gaines, M. S., and L. R. McClenaghan. 1980. Dispersal in small mammals. Ann. Rev. Ecol. Syst., 11:163–196.

Green, J. E. 1977. Population regulation and annual cycles of activity and dispersal in the Arctic ground squirrel. Unpubl. M.S. thesis, Univ. British Columbia, Vancouver, 193 pp.

Greenwood, P. J. 1980. Mating systems, philopatry, and dispersal in birds and mammals. Anim. Behav., 28:1140–1162.

Hamilton, W. D. 1972. Altruism and related phenomena, mainly in the social insects. Ann. Rev. Ecol. Syst., 3:193–232.

Hilborn, R. 1975. Similarities of dispersal tendency among siblings in four species of voles (*Microtus*). Ecology, 56:1221–1225.

Hohn, B. M. 1966. Movements and activity patterns in a population of thirteen-lined ground squirrels, Itasca State Park, Minnesota. Unpubl. M.S. thesis, Univ. Minnesota, Minneapolis, 78 pp.

Holekamp, K. E. 1983. Proximal mechanisms of natal dispersal in Belding's ground squirrels (*Spermophilus beldingi*). Unpubl. Ph.D. dissert., Univ. California, Berkeley, 288 pp.

Holmes, W. G., and P. W. Sherman. 1982. The ontogeny of kin recognition in two species of ground squirrels. Amer. Zool., 22:491–517.

Hoogland, J. L. 1982. Prairie dogs avoid extreme inbreeding. Science, 215:1639–1641.

Howard, W. E. 1949. Dispersal, amount of inbreeding, and longevity in a population of prairie deermice on the George Reserve, Southern Michigan. Contrib. Lab. Vert. Zool. Univ. Michigan, no. 43, 42 pp.

Iverson, S. L., and B. N. Turner. 1972. Natural history of a Manitoba population of Franklin's ground squirrel. Canadian Field-Nat., 86:145–149.

Jackson, H. H. T. 1961. Mammals of Wisconsin. University of Wisconsin Press, Madison, 540 pp.

Johns, D. W., and K. B. Armitage. 1979. Behavioral ecology of yellow-bellied marmots. Behav. Ecol. Sociobiol., 5:133–157.

Kilgore, D. L. 1972. Energy dynamics of the yellow-bellied marmot (*Marmota flaviventris*): a hibernator. Unpubl. Ph.D. dissert., Univ. Kansas, Lawrence, 83 pp.

King, J. A. 1955. Social behavior, social organization, and population dynamics in a black-tailed prairiedog town in the Black Hills of South Dakota. Contrib. Lab. Vert. Biol., Univ. Michigan, 67:1–123.

Lidicker, W. Z. 1975. The role of dispersal in the demography of small mammals. Pp. 103–128, *in* Small mammals: their productivity and population dynamics (F. B. Golley, K. Petruscewicz, and C. Ryszkowski, eds.). Cambridge University Press, Cambridge, 451 pp.

Longhurst, W. 1944. Observations on the ecology of the Gunnison prairie dog in Colorado. J. Mamm., 25:24–36.

MacArthur, R. H., and Wilson, E. O. 1967. The theory of island biogeography. Princeton University Press, Princeton, 203 pp.

McCarley, H. 1966. Annual cycles, population dynamics and adaptive behavior of *Citellus tridecimlineatus*. J. Mamm., 47:294–316.

McLean, I. G. 1982. The association of female kin in the Arctic ground squirrel *Spermophilus parryii*. Behav. Ecol. Sociobiol., 10:91–99.

———. 1983. Parental behaviour and killing of young in Arctic ground squirrels. Anim. Behav., 31:32–44.

Michener, G. R. 1972. Social relationships between adult and young Richardson's ground squirrels *Spermophilus richardsonii richardsonii*. Unpubl. Ph.D. dissert., Univ. Saskatchewan, Regina, 256 pp.

———. 1979. Yearly variations in the population dynamics of Richardson's ground squirrels. Canadian Field-Nat., 93:363–370.

———. 1981. Ontogeny of spatial relationships and social behavior in juvenile Richardson's ground squirrels. Canadian J. Zool., 59:1666–1676.

———. 1983. Kin identification, matriarchies, and the evolution of sociality in grounddwelling sciurids. Pp. 528–572, *in* Recent advances in the study of mammalian behavior (J. F. Eisenberg and D. G. Kleiman, eds.). Spec. Publ., Amer. Soc. Mamm., 7:1–753.

Michener, G. R., and D. R. Michener. 1973. Spatial distribution of yearlings in a Richardson's ground squirrel population. Ecology, 54:1138–1142.

———. 1977. Population structure and dispersal in Richardson's ground squirrels. Ecology, 58:359–368.

Michener, G. R., and D. H. Sheppard. 1972. Social behavior between adult female Richardson's ground squirrels (*Spermophilus richardsonii*) and their own and alien young. Canadian J. Zool., 50:1343–1349.

Murie, J. O. 1973. Population characteristics and phenology of a Franklin ground squirrel

318

(*Spermophilus franklinii*) colony in Alberta, Canada. Amer. Midland Nat., 90: 334–340.

Murie, J. O., D. A. Boag, and V. K. Kivett. 1980. Litter size in Columbian ground squirrels (*Spermophilus columbianus*). J. Mamm., 61:237–244.

Owings, D. H., M. Borchert, and R. Virginia. 1977. The behaviour of California ground squirrels. Anim. Behav., 25:221–230.

Packer, C. 1979. Inter-troop transfer and inbreeding avoidance in *Papio anubis*. Anim. Behav., 27:1–36.

Pfeifer, S. L. R. 1980. Demographic and behavioral influences on juvenile Wyoming ground squirrel dispersal. Unpubl. Ph.D. dissert., Univ. Colorado, Boulder, 146 pp.

———. 1982. Disappearance and dispersal of *Spermophilus elegans* juveniles in relation to behavior. Behav. Ecol. Sociobiol., 10:237–243.

Quanstrom, W. R. 1971. Behaviour of Richardson's ground squirrel *Spermophilus richardsonii richardsonii*. Anim. Behav., 19:646–652.

Rongstad, O. J. 1965. A life history study of thirteen-lined ground squirrels in southern Wisconsin. J. Mamm., 46:76–87.

Saunders, D. A. 1970. The ontogeny of social behavior in Uinta ground squirrels. Unpubl. M.S. thesis, Utah State Univ., Logan, 42 pp.

Schmutz, S. M. 1977. Role of dispersal and mortality in the differential survival of male and female Richardson's ground squirrels. Unpubl. M.S. thesis, Univ. Alberta, Edmonton, 96 pp.

Schmutz, S. M., D. A. Boag, and J. K. Schmutz. 1979. Causes of the unequal sex ratio in populations of adult Richardson's ground squirrels. Canadian J. Zool., 57:1845–1859.

Schwartz, O. A., and K. B. Armitage. 1980. Genetic variation in social mammals: the marmot model. Science, 207:665–667.

Sheppard, D. H., and S. M. Yoshida. 1971. Social behavior in captive Richardson's ground squirrels. J. Mamm., 52:793–799.

Sherman, P. W. 1976. Natural selection among some group-living organisms. Unpubl. Ph.D. dissert., Univ. Michigan, Ann Arbor, 254 pp.

———. 1977. Nepotism and the evolution of alarm calls. Science, 197:1246–1253.

———. 1980. The limits of ground squirrel nepotism. Pp. 505–544, *in* Sociobiology: beyond nature/nurture? (G. W. Barlow and J. Silverberg, eds.). AAAS Selected Symposium no. 35. Westview Press, Boulder, Colorado, 627 pp.

Slade, N. A., and D. F. Balph. 1974. Population ecology of Uinta ground squirrels. Ecology, 55:989–1003.

Steiner, A. L. 1972. Mortality resulting from intraspecific fighting in some ground squirrel populations. J. Mamm., 53:601–603.

Svendsen, G. E. 1974. Behavioral and environmental factors in the spatial distribution and population dynamics of a yellow-bellied marmot population. Ecology, 55:760–771.

Taylor, L. R., and R. A. Taylor. 1977. Aggregation, migration, and population mechanics. Nature, 265:415–421.

Tileston, J. V., and R. R. Lechleitner. 1966. Some comparisons of the black-tailed and white-tailed prairie dogs in north-central Colorado. Amer. Midland Nat., 75:292–316.

Turner, L. W. 1972. Autecology of the Belding ground squirrel in Oregon. Unpubl. Ph.D. dissert., Univ. Arizona, Tucson, 149 pp.

Wistrand, H. 1974. Individual, social, and seasonal behavior of the thirteen-lined ground squirrel (*Spermophilus tridecemlineatus*). J. Mamm., 55:329–347.

Yeaton, R. I. 1969. Social behaviour, social organization, and daily activity patterns in the Richardson's ground squirrel, *Spermophilus richardsonii*. Unpubl. M.S. thesis, Univ. Saskatchewan, Regina, 106 pp.

———. 1972. Social behavior and social organization in Richardson's ground squirrel (*Spermophilus richardsonii*) in Saskatchewan. J. Mamm., 53:139–147.

IAN G. MCLEAN

University of British Columbia

Chapter 14

Spacing Behavior and Aggression in Female Ground Squirrels

Abstract. I review the factors that affect spacing behavior among female ground squirrels, summarize methods that have been used to describe spacing behavior, summarize the patterns of female spacing behavior that have been found among different species of ground squirrels, and make some suggestions for future work. Most data on spacing behavior of female ground squirrels are based on analyses of home range patterns and social interactions. Considerable variation occurs among the methods different researchers use to analyze their data, so it is difficult to make comparisons among all studies for which information is available. I describe these differences and suggest that comparative information would be more readily obtained if researchers attempted to use similar methods in their analyses. The most consistent pattern of spacing behavior among ground squirrels is that females are most likely to be aggressive, perhaps territorial, during pregnancy and lactation. Patterns among species are variable at other times in the annual cycle. Data have not been separated by sex in most studies of highly social forms such as *Marmota olympus, M. flaviventris,* and *Cynomys ludovicianus,* making interpretation of patterns of female behavior difficult. The information available at present is primarily descriptive, and I suggest that a more experimental approach would provide a better understanding of the patterns that have been identified.

Introduction

In the most detailed analysis of spacing behavior of female ground squirrels published to date, Michener (1979a:137) commented that the social behavior of female *Spermophilus richardsonii* could be considered a ''borderline case within the generally accepted definition of a territory as an area occupied more or less exclusively by an animal by means of repulsion of conspecifics through overt aggression or advertisement.'' This statement reflects the difficulty researchers have faced when attempting to categorize spacing behavior by female ground squirrels. There are numerous references to territorial behavior by females (Dunford, 1977; Festa-Bianchet and Boag, 1982; Hoogland, 1981; Michener, 1979a; Sherman, 1981b; Slade and Balph, 1974; Yeaton, 1972), but some authors use ''home range,'' ''dominance reversals,'' or ''reciprocal avoidance'' (Armitage, 1975; Michener, 1973; Owings et al., 1977), and others have found little evidence for any relation between female behavior and use of space (Barash, 1973a; Bronson, 1964; Wistrand, 1974). Researchers have faced difficulty in categorization in part because of lack of data or because investigations were directed primarily at other questions. There are at least three other reasons, however. First, individual females exhibit great behavioral variability in the field (this statement will be developed further), making the development of a concise quantitative description of spacing behavior very difficult. Second, behavior of ground squirrels shows variation over relatively short time intervals, so that detailed analysis of short periods may be required if meaningful patterns of spacing behavior are to be identified. Third, variables such as kinship, which must be considered in order to explain some of the observed variability in behavior, cannot be incorporated into the analysis unless the study is continued intensively for several years. The time frame in which some researchers have operated has not allowed them to gather this kind of information.

Here I use ''spacing behavior'' to refer to aspects of the behavior of ground squirrels that may be related, either directly or indirectly, to movements in and association with space. The relation between an animal and space is measured most directly by monitoring site dependence, but an understanding of patterns in use of space is facilitated by measurements of behavior, particularly agonistic behavior, and features such as wounding that may be related to agonism. Where I refer to ''territory'' I mean the sense used by the authors cited. Readers should consult the original literature for definitions. I use ''ground squirrel'' in the general sense, referring to members of the genera *Spermophilus, Marmota,* and *Cynomys*.

When it occurs, paternal care in ground squirrels appears to be restricted to protection afforded through territorial behavior (Armitage, 1974; Barash, 1975; McLean, 1983). Multiple paternity of litters may occur (Hanken and Sherman, 1981; Schwagmeyer, this volume), resulting in a low probability of paternity for any one male, and female behavior may ensure that paternity is confused even if multiple paternity does not occur (McLean, 1983). Infant ground squirrels are altricial, are sequestered underground in natal burrows, and usually emerge when 3–4 weeks old; thus females provide most direct parental care. There are no records of females sharing natal burrows before the young have emerged aboveground (although female *S. parryii* sometimes clump their young at about the time of emergence; McLean, 1982), suggesting that females do not cooperate to rear young. Females of many ground squirrel species are aggressive and except in some highly social species will attack both males and other females. In some species females are dominant over males after the spring mating period (review in Michener, 1983). There are undoubtedly costs to this aggression, indicated by wounds received and by time spent watching and interacting with other squirrels. Any benefits appear to be best measured in terms of protection of young (from infanticidal attacks by other females in *S. beldingi:* Sherman, 1981*a;* and possibly *S. columbianus:* A. D. Balfour, pers. comm.; or males in *S. parryii:* McLean, 1983) and ensuring access to essential resources. If aggression is more than defense of a litter, individual distance, or a home burrow, then defense of space is implicated.

In this review I ask what factors affect spacing behavior among females, summarize methods that have been used to describe spacing behavior, summarize the patterns of female spacing behavior that have been found among different species of ground squirrels, and make some suggestions for future research. To date, only one experiment has been performed (an investigation of infanticide; Sherman, 1976) that directly addresses the question of why female ground squirrels space themselves. I know of no experiments that, for example, have involved manipulation of food or the occurrence of predators in relation to female spacing behavior. Rather, experiments have been designed to investigate how behaviors vary in relation to genetic structure of the population (e.g., Davis, 1982*b;* Sherman, 1977; Vestal and McCarley, this volume). Information presented here was obtained by searching for patterns in data that measure any aspect of movements in space or agonistic behavior among females.

Factors That Affect Spacing Behavior among Female Ground Squirrels

Clustering of female kin occurs in many species of ground squirrel (reviews in Holmes and Sherman, 1982; Michener, 1983; Vestal and McCarley, this volume). Closely related females are more likely to interact amicably, more likely to have overlapping home ranges, more likely to share burrow systems, and more likely to assist each other during interactions with other squirrels than are more distant relatives (Davis, this volume; Holmes and Sherman, 1982;

Hoogland, 1981; McLean, 1982; Sherman, 1980, 1981*b*). Whether or not clusters of female kin occur in particular populations probably depends on a combination of life history, demography, and available resources, and we may expect considerable intraspecific and interspecific variability. For example, populations of *S. columbianus* in which yearlings breed (Festa-Bianchet, 1981) will be more likely to contain closely related breeding females than will populations in which yearlings do not breed (Michener, 1977; Murie et al., 1980; Murie and Harris, this volume). Future studies will have to determine the extent to which kinship affects the interactions and spatial relations among females before detailed analyses of spatial patterns are attempted.

Factors other than kinship affect interactions and spacing behavior between females. Familiarity can decrease the absolute numbers of aggressive interactions between individuals (e.g., Armitage, 1977), and in practice it may be difficult to distinguish familiarity from kinship during analysis of interaction data (Davis, 1982*a*). Older animals are more likely to be dominant (*M. flaviventris:* Armitage, 1975; *M. monax:* Bronson, 1964; *S. tereticaudus:* Dunford, 1977), particularly in the spring (*S. parryii:* McLean, unpubl. data), leading to avoidance behavior by subordinates and possibly to a decrease in absolute levels of interaction rates. Different behavioral "types" have been reported in ground squirrel populations (*M. flaviventris:* Svendsen, 1974; Svendsen and Armitage, 1973; *S. columbianus:* Balfour, 1979). In these studies, wild-caught animals were exposed to their reflections in a mirror, and most individuals were either aggressive, sociable, or avoiders (see Armitage, this volume). These differences appear to translate into predictable differences in behavior among individuals in the field. Although the underlying reasons remain obscure, recent work on infanticide and parental behavior in mice may provide a clue. Differences in adult behavior were found to correlate with differing hormonal environments in which individuals in large litters are reared in utero (vom Saal and Bronson, 1980). Similar experiments should be possible with ground squirrels and could lead to greater understanding of the mechanisms causing individual differences in behavior.

Behavior may vary with reproductive status. Females may breed only every second year (*M. flaviventris:* Johns and Armitage, 1979; *M. caligata:* Barash, 1980; Holmes, this volume), resulting in differences in activity patterns between reproductive and nonreproductive individuals. Female *S. beldingi* that lose young may disperse and kill the young of females in other areas in which the dispersers attempt to establish residence (Sherman, 1981*a*). Females that lose young may expand their home ranges, hence overlapping more with neighbors, and may enter hibernation earlier than those that breed successfully (*S. richard-*

sonii: Michener, 1978, 1979*b*, pers. comm.). These behaviors could affect relations among females the next spring, and they certainly affect the structure of the active population (and hence could affect measures of spacing behavior such as interaction rates) by changing density.

This list is not exhaustive and does not include a presumably diverse array of proximate factors (e.g., a recent interaction with a predator) that can affect aggression and spacing behavior among female ground squirrels. To compensate for the variability introduced by these many factors, studies of female spacing behavior will require information from large samples of females.

Data Used to Investigate Spacing and Aggressive Behavior by Female Ground Squirrels

Four main kinds of data have been obtained in studies related to use of space by rodents: (1) home range maps drawn from sites at which an individual was trapped, usually on a trapping grid; (2) home range maps drawn from sites at which individuals were observed, either directly or indirectly using equipment such as radio transmitters; (3) records of wounding, again taken from trapping records; (4) records of interactions. Scent marking is common in some species of ground squirrels and appears to be related to advertisement or defense of an area (Harris and Murie, 1982; Holekamp, this volume; Kivett et al., 1976), but most work has been done with males. Only one study has considered scent marking by females in relation to spacing behavior (Festa-Bianchet and Boag, 1982), so this behavior will not be dealt with here.

Home ranges drawn from trapping data. Most ground squirrels are easily trapped (*Cynomys sp.:* Hoogland, 1981; *S. townsendii:* Rickart, 1982; and *S. tridecemlineatus:* Vestal and McCarley, this volume, appear to be exceptions), and in some species virtually all individuals in a population can be captured when desired. Trapping does not seem to affect reproductive success of females as it does in mice (Boonstra, 1980). Ground squirrels are usually trapped to obtain demographic data, particularly information on dispersal, weight changes, reproductive condition, and wounding. Traps are usually set at burrows rather than in a grid pattern, biasing the drawing of home range maps from trapping sites toward burrow locations. For most species, data on movements in space are best obtained by direct observation.

Range maps. Maps of home ranges are usually drawn from plots of points obtained either through focal-animal sampling or through instantaneous sampling of all animals seen during a rapid scan (Altmann, 1974). Focal-animal sampling provides a great deal of information on each animal over a short time but ignores the effects of other animals on the focal animal. For example, if avoidance is an important feature of spacing behavior, as it is in *M. monax* (Bronson, 1964) and *M. flaviventris* (Armitage, 1975; Barash, 1973b), then movements of a focal individual are likely to depend on its dominance relations with other animals in the vicinity. Instantaneous sampling provides less detailed information for each individual during a short period but allows comparisons of the movements of different individuals at the same time. Points obtained from one "scan" approximate a still photograph of all animals in relation to each other (Dunford, 1977; Michener, 1979a).

Once a number of points have been obtained, researchers have used various techniques to draw range boundaries. These include drawing lines around outermost points (Armitage, 1975; Bronson, 1964; Dunford, 1977; Festa-Bianchet and Boag, 1982; McLean, 1982; Michener, 1979a; Owings et al., 1977); calculating a "confidence ellipse" enclosing all observations (Johns and Armitage, 1979); determining the number of small squares in which individuals did or did not occur (Dunford, 1977; Michener, 1972; Murie and Harris, 1978); or drawing lines directly onto maps in the field (Barash, 1973a; Sherman, 1980). Interpretation of spatial relations may be based on fewer than 100% of the available points (e.g., Michener, 1979a, emphasized 95% and 50% of points; McLean, 1982, and Festa-Bianchet and Boag, 1982, used various criteria for dropping outlying points). Only Dunford (1977) used two techniques in analyzing the same data, but he did not compare the answers that each approach would give to exactly the same questions.

Wounding. Wounding provides a useful index of aggressive interactions when animals cannot be observed directly. Wounds on rodents heal relatively rapidly (Rose and Heuston, 1978), so that even if animals are captured weekly, most wounds are likely to be counted only once.

Four factors make the use of wounding data of only moderate usefulness in studies of female-female behavior. First, in some species of ground squirrels wounding of females is rare. Second, wounds received from females cannot be distinguished from wounds received from males. Third, interactions between females may be less intense than interactions between males (Owings et al., 1977); thus females may be less likely to wound each other than to be wounded by males. Fourth, whether wounds are received will depend on the types of interactions occurring. For instance, interactions between male *S. parryii* undergo a qualitative change from intense fighting involving considerable wounding during the mating period (i.e., when copulations are occurring), to a more ritualized form of aggression related to territorial defense after mating (McLean, 1983). Few wounds are given or received during these territorial disputes because, although the animals interact agonistically, there is little physical contact between them. Qualitative changes in types of aggressive interactions have not been reported for females, but there is no reason to believe they will not be found in the future (some suggestions of this may be found in Dunford, 1977, but he did not develop that theme). Bronson (1964), working with *M. monax,* attempted to compare interaction and wounding rates, but his samples were too small to permit conclusions. Researchers comparing interaction and wounding rates should ensure that only those interactions likely to result in wounding are included in the data. This will be possible only if careful attention is given to the consequences of identifiable types of interactions by, for example, capturing animals for inspection immediately after an interaction is observed.

Interactions. Interactions between ground squirrels vary in length from less than 1 s to as long as 1 h. Longer interactions usually consist of identifiable units such as a chase, a fight, nose-to-nose contact, vocalizations, and so on. These units may overlap in time, and the sequence in which they occur is often difficult to record because events follow one another so rapidly. Most researchers have treated any interaction as a single datum and hence ignored any significance of length or complexity of interactions.

Interactions between adult ground squirrels have traditionally been divided into agonistic and nonagonistic types. Nonagonistic interactions are sometimes further divided into sexual and amicable. Holmes and Sherman (1982) and McLean (1982) identified a "neutral" or intermediate type of interaction (termed "identification" by McLean) that was neither agonistic nor amicable and could involve components attributable to either of these types. Interactions have also traditionally been classified subjectively by the observer. Usually certain features of the interaction such as a chase, fight, or nose-to-nose touching ("kiss") are used to determine classification. There appears to be fairly general agreement among ground-squirrel workers that subjective classification of interactions is both possible and acceptable. This has been disputed by Davis (1982a; this volume), who used transitional analysis to group behaviors objectively. Davis's interaction types appear to be fairly similar to those used by other researchers working with the same species (*S. richardsonii*), but more detailed work comparing the two techniques must be done before definite conclusions can be drawn.

Researchers are not consistent on whether interactions should be classified with respect to a specific behavior typical of the interaction, the initial response of one animal to another, or the outcome of the interaction. When classifying interactions, Sherman (1981*a*) used the first behavior seen, McLean (1982) used the outcome (essentially the last major behavior type seen), Hoogland (1981) and Yeaton (1972) classified any interaction containing amicable and agonistic components as agonistic, Michener (1980) used the behavior that was occurring at the moment the animal was seen during instantaneous (scan) sampling, Dunford (1977) and Armitage (1975) used major components of behavior (although in different ways), and Festa-Bianchet and Boag (1982) used only those interactions that contained a chase. Some authors did not provide enough information to allow me to determine how they may have classified any amibiguous interactions (e.g., Johns and Armitage, 1979).

Consider the following scenario: a squirrel (A) sees another squirrel (B) in A's home range. A charges B, running right into B and knocking B over. Both animals stand up, sniff each other (usually a nose-to-nose or naso-inguinal sniff), then move apart feeding. The part of this interaction in which A knocks B over is not essential but is included to ensure that the first part of the interaction is regarded as agonistic. Possible classifications of this interaction are agonistic (Hoogland, Sherman, Yeaton), nonagonistic (McLean), either of these depending on which portion of the interaction was occurring at the instant of sampling (Michener), neither of these and not included in the data (no chase, Festa-Bianchet and Boag), both types of interaction counted twice (Dunford), or classification unclear (Johns and Armitage). It is impossible to determine the extent to which this variation in classification has affected these authors' conclusions, and introducing an intermediate interaction type to cope with ambiguous interactions seems a poor solution. At the very least, researchers must attempt to be more consistent in classification if comparative data are to be obtained. More important, one must exercise caution when citing other published material.

A second major area of inconsistency is the calculation of interaction rates. The methods various researchers use for calculating these, and a detailed example using two basic methods, were presented by Michener (1980). In summary, numbers of interactions are usually presented as frequencies (number of interactions over some time interval; this does not incorporate an adjustment for the number of animals available to interact) or as rates (number of interactions per animal per unit time). Some examples: Barash (1973*b*) presented frequencies of interactions, hence implicitly assuming that the number of animals available to interact was the same for all data-gathering periods (Barash was careful to point out problems with this approach and drew conclusions only based on comparisons between colonies). To calculate rates, Sherman (1980) used the number of animals seen each day, McLean (1981) used the number of animals seen active during the 1-h period within which the interaction was recorded, and Dunford (1977) used the number of animals seen during a 9-min interval immediately preceding the 9-min interval during which interactions were counted. Michener (1980) made the point that, since an interaction involves two animals, the appropriate divisor is the number of pairs of animals available to interact, ideally determined during a short time period in which interactions are counted.

Patterns in Spacing and Aggressive Behavior
Among Female Ground Squirrels

Making direct comparisons among results in the studies cited above is difficult. Rather, my approach was to identify patterns described by any researcher who applied a particular calculation and categorization procedure to data through time.

Two different patterns in interaction rates are apparent in the genus *Spermophilus:* (1) Female aggressiveness is generally frequent until young first emerge (and are weaned), after which females tend to interact rarely, (*S. armatus:* Balph, this volume; *S. richardsonii:* Michener, 1979*a*, 1980; *S. tereticaudus:* Dunford, 1977; *S. columbianus:* Betts, 1976; *S. parryii:* McLean, 1981; *S. beecheyi:* Dobson, pers. comm.; possibly *S. tridecemlineatus:* Schwagmeyer, 1979). In some of these species there is a decline in interaction rates from mating (copulation) until young emerge. (2) There are two peaks in aggressiveness, one immediately after the females mate, the second during lactation (*S. beldingi:* Sherman, 1980; *S. columbianus:* Festa-Bianchet and Boag, 1982). Few data on trends in interaction rates among females are available for marmots or prairie dogs, usually because data have not been analyzed by sex. Armitage (1965) found that aggression in female *M. flaviventris* peaks at the end of lactation. In a later paper, Armitage (1975) found no relation between population density and aggression among females, although amicable behavior decreased as the number of females in a group increased. Hoogland (1981) found for female *C. ludovicianus* that the proportion of interactions with coterie members that were amicable changed from high (prebreeding) to low (late breeding/lactation) to high (postweaning), suggesting similarities to the first trend outlined above for *Spermophilus* (see Michener and Murie, 1983), but he did not separate the data by sex of animal in his publication (Hoogland, 1979), which considers aggression. King's (1955) description also fits this interpretation.

In most studies in which home ranges have been calculated, the degree of overlap of female home ranges changes through the season, and most females have exclusive use of a home burrow system (exclusive use implying territoriality). Overlap of home ranges is usually least, indicating that females are most territorial, during pregnancy and lactation (*S. tereticaudus:* Dunford, 1977; *S. richardsonii:* Michener, 1979*a;* Yeaton, 1972; *S. beldingi:* Sherman, 1981*a; S. columbianus:* Festa-Bianchet and Boag, 1982; *S. parryii:* McLean, 1982). Exceptions occur at both ends of Michener's (1983) scale of sociality. There is virtually complete overlap of home ranges of all individuals in the highly social *M. olympus* (Barash, 1973*a*) and *C. ludovicianus* (Hoogland, 1981), and high-altitude *M. flaviventris* populations may be similar (Barash, 1973*b*). At the other extreme, there appears to be little or no overlap or interaction between females in the asocial *S. tridecemlineatus* (McCarley, 1966; Wistrand, 1974), although more recent data suggest that interactions may be more amicable and overlap of home ranges may be greater between kin than between nonkin in this species and that some populations at least may be more social (Schwagmeyer, 1979; Vestal and McCarley, this volume). Bronson (1964) attributed exclusive use of parts of the home range by female *M. monax* to dominance rather than territoriality (the data were not analyzed by sex, but females were dominant over males). In a more recent study of this species, P. T. Meier (pers. comm.) found that females were subordinate to males; thus any conclusions for this species remain equivocal. In *S. parryii,* closely related females may clump their young at about the time of first emergence aboveground; hence females may lose exclusive use of a burrow system at this time (McLean, 1982).

Only Dunford (1977), Michener (1979*a*), and Festa-Bianchet and Boag (1982) plotted interactions between females, related these to the home ranges of the individuals involved, and related this combination to within-season variability in social behavior. The primary conclusion from each of these studies (on *S. tereticaudus, S. richardsonii,* and *S. columbianus,* respectively) was that females can be regarded as territorial during pregnancy and lactation. Female *S. richardsonii* also show site-dependent dominance within a core area (defined as the most clustered 50% of the locations at which an animal was seen) through most of the active season, whereas some clumping of core areas (defined by a series of criteria that allowed for inclusion of between 50% and 100% of the locations of an animal) of *S. tereticaudus* occurs outside pregnancy and lactation, particularly in early spring. Differences between these two species may be accounted for by the different ways in which Dunford (1977) and Michener (1979*a*) calculated core areas. Festa-Bianchet and Boag (1982) did not consider core areas. Both Dunford (1977) and Festa-Bianchet and Boag (1982) studied populations that were at unusually high density. At high densities animals are more likely to interact, hence providing large sample sizes allowing detailed analyses, home ranges may be small, and areas of overlap of home ranges may be more likely to appear as lines or boundaries on plots of points obtained from instantaneous sampling regimes. In such situations researchers may be more likely to conclude that animals are territorial than if they had been working with animals at lower densities.

Conclusions

Two features are clear from this review: there is considerable variation in spacing behavior among different species of ground squirrels, and, except in asocial and highly social species, spacing behavior of females varies through the season. Neither of these is surprising. More interesting is that females are most likely to be aggressive, perhaps territorial, during pregnancy and lactation. Territorial behavior presumably involves costs (e.g., from wounds received or time spent interacting), though as yet there have been no attempts to measure such costs. The only studies that offer some direct suggestion of the benefits females may derive from territorial behavior are those of Sherman (1976, 1981a) for *S. beldingi* and McLean (1983) for *S. parryii,* the only two species in which infanticide has been documented in more than an anecdotal way (Michener, 1982). However, the benefits that accrue are presumably measurable in terms of access to resources such as food or a breeding site. Even for *S. beldingi* and *S. parryii,* benefits other than protection of young from infanticide can presumably be obtained from spacing behavior.

Can data-gathering techniques be developed to permit better comparisons among species? Many of the studies described here used similar methods for gathering data, but different analyses were made. In many cases the decision to use a particular method appears to have been based on relatively arbitrary criteria; for example, Sherman's (1980) use of the number of animals seen during a particular day to calculate interaction rates versus McLean's (1981) use of the number of animals seen during a particular hour. Presumably both authors could have used the same calculation method if a decision had been made to do so before the data were gathered. I believe that for many members of the genus *Spermophilus* similar data-gathering and analytical procedures could be used, permitting more direct comparisons of the results. For asocial species, and for the highly social *Marmota* and *Cynomys,* this may be more difficult because of the sample sizes that can be obtained (individuals of asocial species rarely interact; usually only one marmot colony can be observed at one time, and numbers of observed interactions are low). Large sample sizes for home range data are readily obtained for most species and comparative results should be obtainable, even if several

331

analyses of the same data are required so that different questions can be addressed. Attention to the comments made in Michener (1980) for interaction rates, and Michener (1979a) and Murie and Harris (1978) for home range data, should make this exercise easier, but direct communication among researchers on ground squirrels is the best approach.

In this review I have described a wide variety of methods that have been used in studies of spacing behavior of female ground squirrels. This variation among researchers has severely hampered my efforts to identify patterns of behavior among species. However, despite this variability, considerable evidence suggests that female ground squirrels space themselves, and I suggest that they suffer some costs in doing so. Whether spacing is regarded as territorial behavior may depend as much on the definitions used by different researchers as on variability in female behavior. Clearly the conceptual framework within which particular researchers are operating must be clearly stated and must be acknowledged by other researchers citing published material.

Considerably more work is needed on the significance of spacing behavior for individual females. I suggest that as a beginning the following questions should be addressed: Are females spacing themselves during pregnancy and lactation to protect young, or are they defending resources such as food or home sites? Why are the patterns of spacing behavior among females of different species more variable outside than during pregnancy and lactation? Is there any relation between the spacing behavior of females and the dispersion of males in space once mating has been completed? The descriptive work summarized here provides the beginning of a baseline allowing more rigorous hypothesis-testing experiments designed to address questions such as these.

Acknowledgments

I am indebted to J. O. Murie for his encouragement and support in all the work I have done on ground squirrels, and to J. O. Murie and G. R. Michener for bringing me to the ground squirrel conference. Ideas presented in this review have benefited from discussions with L. S. Davis, J. L. Craig, D. Balfour, and J. N. M. Smith. I thank the numerous people who assisted during gathering of field data on Arctic ground squirrels, and I thank D. Zitten for computing assistance. A. Able assisted in preparation of the manuscript. J. O. Murie, G. E. Svendsen, J. N. M. Smith, and G. R. Michener offered many useful comments on the manuscript. Support for aspects of this work was provided by an NSERC grant to J. N. M. Smith; the Department of Zoology, University of British Columbia; the Department of Zoology, University of Auckland; the computing center of the Institute of Ecology, University of British Columbia; the Arctic Institute of North America; and the Boreal Institute for Northern Studies.

Literature Cited

Altmann, J. 1974. Observational study of behavior: sampling methods. Behaviour, 49:227–267.

Armitage, K. 1965. Vernal behaviour of the yellow-bellied marmot (*Marmota flaviventris*). Anim. Behav., 13:59–68.

———. 1974. Male behaviour and territoriality in the yellow-bellied marmot. J. Zool. London, 192:233–265.

———. 1975. Social behavior and population dynamics of marmots. Oikos, 26:341–354.

———. 1977. Social variety in the yellow-bellied marmot: a population-behavioural system. Anim. Behav., 25:585–593.

Balfour, A. D. 1979. Mirror-image stimulation as a behavioral profiling technique in Columbian ground squirrels. Unpubl. M.S. thesis, Univ. Alberta, Edmonton, 103 pp.

Barash, D. P. 1973a. The social biology of the Olympic marmot. Anim. Behav. Monogr., 6:173–245.

———. 1973b. Social variety in the yellow-bellied marmot (*Marmota flaviventris*). Anim. Behav., 21:579–584.

———. 1975. Ecology of paternal behavior in the hoary marmot (*Marmota caligata*): an evolutionary interpretation. J. Mamm., 56:613–618.

———. 1980. The influence of reproductive status on foraging by hoary marmots (*Marmota caligata*). Behav. Ecol. Sociobiol., 7:201–205.

Betts, B. J. 1976. Behaviour in a population of Columbian ground squirrels, *Spermophilus columbianus columbianus*. Anim. Behav., 24:652–680.

Boonstra, R. 1980. Infanticide in microtines: importance in natural populations. Oecologia, 46:262–265.

Bronson, F. H. 1964. Agonistic behaviour in woodchucks. Anim. Behav. 12:470–478.

Davis, L. S. 1982a. Sociality in Richardson's ground squirrels *Spermophilus richardsonii*. Unpubl. Ph.D. dissert., Univ. Alberta, Edmonton, 152 pp.

———. 1982b. Sibling recognition in Richardson's ground squirrels (*Spermophilus richardsonii*). Behav. Ecol. Sociobiol., 11:65–70.

Dunford, C. 1977. Social system of round-tailed ground squirrels. Anim. Behav., 25:885–906.

Festa-Bianchet, M. 1981. Reproduction in yearling female Columbian ground squirrels (*Spermophilus columbianus*). Canadian J. Zool., 59:1032–1035.

Festa-Bianchet, M., and D. A. Boag. 1982. Territoriality in adult female Columbian ground squirrels. Canadian J. Zool., 60:1060–1066.

Hanken, J., and P. W. Sherman. 1981. Multiple paternity in Belding ground squirrel litters. Science, 212:351–353.

Harris, M. A., and J. O. Murie. 1982. Response to oral gland scents from different males in Columbian ground squirrels. Anim. Behav., 30:140–148.

Holmes, W. G., and P. W. Sherman. 1982. The ontogeny of kin recognition in two species of ground squirrels. Amer. Zool., 22:491–517.

Hoogland, J. L. 1979. Aggression, ectoparasitism, and other possible costs of prairie dog (Sciuridae: *Cynomys* sp.) coloniality. Behaviour, 69:1–35.

———. 1981. Nepotism and cooperative breeding in the black-tailed prairie dog (Sciuridae: *Cynomys ludovicianus*). Pp. 283–310, *in* Natural selection and social behavior: recent research and new theory (R. D. Alexander and D. W. Tinkle, eds.). Chiron, New York, 532 pp.

Johns, D. W., and K. B. Armitage. 1979. Behavioral ecology of the alpine yellow-bellied marmot. Behav. Ecol. Sociobiol., 5:133–157.

King, J. A. 1955. Social behavior, social organization, and population dynamics in a black-tailed prairiedog town in the Black Hills of North Dakota. Contrib. Lab. Vert. Biol., Univ. Michigan, 67:1–123.

Kivett, V. K., J. O. Murie, and A. L. Steiner. 1976. A comparative study of scent-gland location and related behavior in some northwestern Nearctic ground squirrel species (Sciuridae): an evolutionary approach. Canadian J. Zool., 54:1294–1306.

McCarley, H. 1966. Annual cycle, population dynamics, and adaptive behaviour of *Citellus tridecemlineatus*. J. Mamm., 47:294–316.

McLean, I. G. 1981. Social ecology of the Arctic ground squirrel. Unpubl. Ph.D. dissert., Univ. Alberta, Edmonton, 149 pp.

———. 1982. The association of female kin in the Arctic ground squirrel. Behav. Ecol. Sociobiol., 10:91–99.

———. 1983. Paternal behaviour and intraspecific killing in the Arctic ground squirrel (*Spermophilus parryii*). Anim. Behav., 31:32–44.

Michener, D. R. 1972. Notes on home range and social behavior in adult Richardson's ground squirrels (*Spermophilus richardsonii*). Canadian Field-Nat., 86:77–79.

Michener, G. R. 1973. Field observations on the social relationships between adult female and juvenile Richardson's ground squirrels. Canadian J. Zool., 51:33–38.

———. 1977. Effect of climatic conditions on the annual activity and hibernation cycle of Richardson's ground squirrels and Columbian ground squirrels. Canadian J. Zool., 55:693–703.

———. 1978. Effect of age and parity on weight gain and entry into hibernation in Richardson's ground squirrel. Canadian J. Zool., 56:2573–2577.

———. 1979a. Spatial relationships and social organization of adult Richardson's ground squirrels. Canadian J. Zool., 57:125–139.

———. 1979b. The circannual cycle of Richardson's ground squirrels in southern Alberta. J. Mamm., 60:760–768.

———. 1980. The measurement and interpretation of interaction rates: an example with Richardson's ground squirrels. Biol. Behav., 5:371–384.

———. 1982. Infanticide in ground squirrels. Anim. Behav., 30:936–937.

———. 1983. Kin identification, matriarchies, and the evolution of sociality in ground-dwelling sciurids. Pp. 528–572, *in* Recent advances in the study of mammalian behavior (J. F. Eisenberg and D. G. Kleiman, eds.). Spec. Publ., Amer. Soc. Mamm. 7:1–753.

334

Michener, G. R., and J. O. Murie. 1983. Black-tailed prairie dog coteries: are they cooperatively breeding units? Amer. Nat., 121:266–274.

Murie, J. O., and M. A. Harris. 1978. Territoriality and dominance in male Columbian ground squirrels (*Spermophilus columbianus*). Canadian J. Zool., 56:2402–2412.

Murie, J. O., D. A. Boag, and V. K. Kivett. 1980. Litter size in Columbian ground squirrels (*Spermophilus columbianus*). J. Mamm., 61:237–244.

Owings, D. H., M. Borchert, and R. Virginia. 1977. The behavior of California ground squirrels. Anim. Behav., 25:221–230.

Rickart, E. A. 1982. Annual cycles of activity and body composition in *Spermophilus townsendii mollis*. Canadian J. Zool., 60:3298–3306.

Rose, R. K., and W. D. Heuston. 1978. Wound healing in meadow voles. J. Mamm., 59:186–188.

Schwagmeyer, P. L. 1979. The function of alarm calling behavior in *Spermophilus tridecemlineatus*, the thirteen-lined ground squirrel. Unpubl. Ph.D. dissert., Univ. Michigan, Ann Arbor, 82 pp.

Sherman, P. W. 1976. Natural selection among some group-living organisms. Unpubl. Ph.D. dissert., Univ. Michigan, Ann Arbor, 256 pp.

———. 1977. Nepotism and the evolution of alarm calls. Science, 197:1245–1253.

———. 1980. The limits of ground squirrel nepotism. Pp. 505–544, *in* Sociobiology: beyond nature/nurture? (G. W. Barlow and J. Silverberg, eds.). Westview Press, Boulder, Colorado, 627 pp.

———. 1981a. Reproductive competition and infanticide in Belding's ground squirrels and other organisms. Pp. 311–331, *in* Natural selection and social behavior: recent research and new theory (R. D. Alexander and D. W. Tinkle, eds.). Chiron Press, New York, 532 pp.

———. 1981b. Kinship, demography, and Belding's ground squirrel nepotism. Behav. Ecol. Sociobiol., 8:251–259.

Slade, N. A., and D. F. Balph. 1974. Population ecology of Uinta ground squirrels. Ecology, 55:989–1003.

Svendsen, G. E. 1974. Behavioral and environmental factors in the spatial distribution and population dynamics of a yellow-bellied marmot population. Ecology, 55:760–771.

Svendsen, G. E., and K. B. Armitage. 1973. Mirror-image stimulation applied to field behavioral studies. Ecology, 54:623–627.

vom Saal, F. S., and F. H. Bronson. 1980. Sexual characteristics of adult female mice are correlated with their blood testosterone levels during prenatal development. Science, 208:597–599.

Wistrand, H. 1974. Individual, social, and seasonal behavior of the thirteen-lined ground squirrel (*Spermophilus tridecemlineatus*). J. Mamm., 55:329–347.

Yeaton, R. I. 1972. Social behavior and social organization in Richardson's ground squirrel (*Spermophilus richardsonii*) in Saskatchewan. J. Mamm., 53:139–147.

DAVID F. BALPH

Utah State University

Chapter 15

Spatial and Social Behavior in a Population of Uinta Ground Squirrels: Interrelations with Climate and Annual Cycle

Abstract. This chapter relates the annual cycle and behavior of a population of Uinta ground squirrels (*Spermophilus armatus*) to the broad climatic and rangeland conditions of the Intermountain West. It is based on a review of published and unpublished studies on the population conducted primarily from 1964 to 1971 and develops inductively several hypotheses.

1. The decay of grass nutrient density promotes early emergence and sexual preparedness of adults and early birth and rapid development of young.

2. Changes in the value and defensibility of resources through space and time cause males to exhibit elements of both territorial and dominance/subordination social systems.

3. The territoriality of females serves several functions, including the maintenance of a "garden" of nutritious vegetation and the reduction of predation and disturbance to young.

4. Females abandon their young during the daytime after the young appear aboveground, perhaps because of difficulty with heat loads.

Essentially, the chapter proposes that the natural history of Uinta ground squirrels is a story of a small herbivore that is forced through selection and circumstance to make a series of physiological and behavioral adjustments. These adjustments enable the animal to cope with the exigencies of both harsh springs with little food and summers characterized by poor food, little moisture, and conditions promoting high heat loads.

Introduction

I first became interested in Uinta ground squirrels at Utah State University's Forestry Field Station in 1959. After documenting their activity for several years, I became impressed by two characteristics of the squirrels. First, their season of aboveground activity began very early in the spring and was very brief. Second, the squirrels appeared highly intolerant of one another for animals that lived so close together. Only after studying the squirrels for a number of years did I begin to see relations between the brevity of the season, degree of sociality, and certain environmental conditions. In this chapter I shall describe the annual cycle and the social and spatial organization of the population and discuss how the two might be related to general climatic conditions in the Intermountain West. The chapter is based primarily on a series of published and unpublished studies made from 1964 to 1971 that examined the relation between behavior and regulation of population density of the squirrels at the Station. The results of other investigations of the population and other populations in the vicinity are discussed as they relate to the subjects considered.

Methods

The study site was on about 9 ha of land at Utah State University's Forestry Field Station, 35 km northeast of Logan, Utah, at an elevation of 1,920 m. The center of the study area consisted of approximately 1 ha of lawn and roadways near the buildings of the Station. The rest of the site contained patches of meadowland, brush, and trees with heavy understory.

The procedures central to the primary study were designed to record the locations, activity, and status of every squirrel on the site from birth to its disappearance from the population. The work, which required the full-time effort of at least five people, began every spring with the appearance of the first squirrel and continued nearly every day until the squirrels disappeared in late summer. The site was gridded with numbered stakes at 12-m intervals to aid in recording the location of individuals. Seven intensive sampling areas (26 by 40 m) representing different habitats and supporting different numbers of squirrels were established within the area. A trapping program attempted to capture every animal at least once every 10 days to document such things as reproductive status and body weight and to ensure that the identifying marks dyed on each animal's fur were visible. A sighting program conducted at nonprescribed times during the day documented the identity, location, and activity of squirrels throughout the study area. A scanning program recorded the same information systematically for squirrels in six of the seven sampling areas. Information on social encounters was documented for 5 min immediately following each scan of a sampling area. An attempt was made to obtain a minimum of 20 scans for each 3-h time interval during the day for each 10-day interval through the season. Details of activity and encounters are not dealt with here; see Walker (1968) and Slade and Balph (1974) for procedural details.

The population density of squirrels on the 9-ha site at the Station averaged 220 adults and yearlings and 486 juveniles annually from 1964 to 1967. In 1968 the population was experimentally reduced by 60% in such a way as to maintain the existing age, sex, and dispersion pattern. The density was held relatively low in 1969 and 1970 by removing 40% of the juveniles as they appeared aboveground. The primary study ended in 1971 after spring emergence.

Results and Discussion

General description of environment and annual cycle. The climate at the Station is highly seasonal and typical of mountainous regions in the Intermountain West where Uinta ground squirrels are found (Durrant and Hansen, 1954). Winters at the Station are relatively cold (January, 1960, $\bar{X}$ maximum $-4°$ C, $\bar{X}$ minimum $-14°C$) and snowy, with snow accumulation usually peaking in February at $1-2$ m. Spring is marked by widely fluctuating temperatures and relatively wet weather. The snowpack melts during March and April, and the Station is usually clear of snow by May. Summer begins rather abruptly sometime during the first half of June. The weather becomes quite uniform with warm, cloudless days, cool nights (July, 1960, $\bar{X}$ maximum 27°C, $\bar{X}$ minimum 7°C), and very little rain. As a result the ground dries, plant moisture decreases (Sharif and West, 1968), and most of the vegetation matures in May and June. By August the growing season for much of the vegetation is over. The soil is hard, and the grasses and forbs are brown. The only patches of green that remain in the once lush area are aspens (*Populus tremuloides*), vegetation beside streams, and a few small areas of grass near the buildings of the Station that are sporadically irrigated from mid-June through July.

The squirrels have adapted to this environment with a short period of aboveground activity in spring and summer and a long period of aestivation-hibernation. The sequence of events in the annual cycle is as follows. The first squirrels appear aboveground approximately the first week of April through a melting snowpack of about 0.5 m. The adults and yearlings emerge over a 4- to 7-week period. The females breed within a few days of emergence and establish nesting burrows near where they emerged. After mating, the breeding males

338

retreat from areas occupied by females, gain body weight rapidly, and begin to immerge into aestivation-hibernation about mid-July. Females begin to give birth about the first of June after a gestation period of about 23 days. The young appear aboveground about 22 days after they are born, and females engage in little parental care after the young appear. Females, like males, gain weight rapidly and begin to immerge about mid-July. The last of the juveniles disappear about the first week in September. Individual squirrels are active for an average of only about 3 months per year.

Emergence from hibernation. The date on which the first squirrel emerged aboveground in spring varied from year to year. From 1962 to 1973, the earliest emergence date was 20 March 1970 and the latest was 16 April 1965 ($\bar{X}$ 3 April, SD 9 days). The population usually emerged in an overlapping sequence of age and sex groups, beginning with adult males followed by adult females, yearling females, and yearling males (Fig. 15.1). This sequence has been documented for other populations of Uinta ground squirrels (Knopf and Balph, 1977) as well as other species of squirrels (see Michener, this volume, for review). The date of first appearance, the date on which 50% of any specific age or sex group had emerged, the degree of emergence synchrony, and the time required for all squirrels to appear aboveground (Fig. 15.1) seemed to be related to spring weather conditions (Knopf and Balph, 1977). In the relatively cold spring of 1965, squirrels appeared later, more synchronously, and over a shorter time than in the relatively warm springs of 1966 and 1967 (Fig. 15.1). Periods of cold weather during emergence appeared to decrease the rate of squirrel emergence, but I did not observe squirrels returning to torpor or dying (see Morton and Sherman, 1978) during harsh spring weather.

One complicating factor in the emergence pattern of yearling males (and perhaps to a lesser extent that of yearling females) is that a stressful social environment for juveniles the preceding summer is associated with a delay in their spring emergence and an impairment in their ability to breed when they emerge (Slade and Balph, 1974). Body weight also may play some role in emergence. French (1982) found that heavier Belding's ground squirrels (*S. beldingi*) are more likely to emerge from torpor early and breed than lighter squirrels.

I believe the timing of spring emergence is probably under selective pressure promoting juvenile survival (female fitness). Nutrient density of the type of plants eaten by squirrels declines sharply through the spring and summer (Murray et al., 1978; Stoddart and Greaves, 1942). For example, the total nitrogen content of *Poa* (and six other genera of grasses) decreases by 50% by about mid-May (Murray et al., 1978). The squirrels are small, monogastric herbivores.

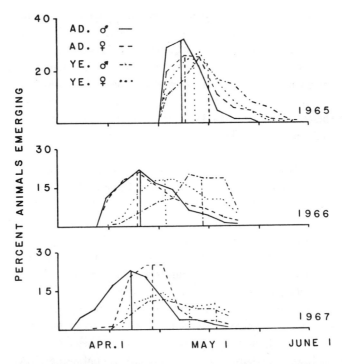

FIGURE 15.1. Times of emergence of age and sex classes of Uinta ground squirrels from hibernation. Data are presented as 3-day moving averages. Vertical lines indicate median dates of emergence for each cohort. Sample sizes for adult males, adult females, yearling males, and yearling females were 21, 50, 55, and 80 in 1965; 42, 67, 68, and 87 in 1966; 36, 55, 56, and 86 in 1967. Figure after Walker (1968). Median dates of emergence given here for yearling males and yearling females in 1967 are about 2 weeks later than the mean dates given in Knopf and Balph (1977) because the latter source excluded data from late-appearing animals that may not have been detected on their first day of activity.

The earlier they are born during the growing season, the better able they are to obtain quality vegetation for a longer period; and this is probably true even when the squirrels select the more nutritious plant parts. Logically, there should be selective pressure on females for early emergence and immediate breeding and on juveniles for rapid pre- and postnatal development. However, weather and food availability place constraints on early emergence (see Morton and Sherman, 1978). This constraint, coupled with selective pressure for early emergence, may explain the mechanism of emergence described by Knopf and Balph (1977)—a mechanism that ensures that the squirrels are prepared to emerge very early in the spring (endogenously controlled circannual rhythm) yet are able to remain underground temporarily should spring weather be harsh.

I believe the timing of emergence of breeding males is influenced by the emergence of females, a point developed by Michener (this volume) for Richardson's ground squirrels (*S. richardsonii*). Females breed within a few days of emergence. Each female that emerges before any particular male emerges is a potential copulation lost to that male. However, males too are constrained by weather and food availability in the spring. Thus breeding males emerge rather synchronously and precede females, though only by a very short time.

The pressure for early breeding presents a problem for males that does not exist for females. Males pass directly from a long aestivation-hibernation period into the energetically costly reproductive season. Breeding males lose body weight during the reproductive season whereas females gain weight (Knopf and Balph, 1977). The energy demands placed on them in early spring may partially explain why males are substantially heavier at emergence than females (Knopf and Balph, 1977). Similar sex differences in weight at emergence and in weight changes during the breeding season occur in Arctic ground squirrels (*S. parryii*) (McLean and Towns, 1981), Belding's ground squirrels (Morton and Sherman, 1978), and Richardson's ground squirrels (Michener, 1984).

The dispersion of squirrels at emergence was not uniform (Walker, 1968). Few squirrels had hibernacula in heavy brush, and those that did were immediately adjacent to more open habitats. Within that portion of the habitat occupied by squirrels, females were in more open, grassy areas than males. As a rough measure of this differential habitat use at the Station, 129 (30%) of 435 females and 38 (13%) of 278 males lived on the lawn before the population was reduced. This general pattern of dispersion continued throughout the active season. The tendency of Uinta ground squirrels (especially females) to select open habitat was evident in a population less influenced by human activity than at the Station. At Franklin Basin, 5 km from the Station and at about the same elevation, S. F. Millard (unpubl. obs.) found 24 males and 41 females on a plot covered by 59% grasses, 12% shrubs, and 50% aspen, as opposed to 10 males and 15 females on an adjacent plot of equal size covered by 41% grasses, 47% shrubs, and 12% aspen.

Male reproductive season. Adult males were physiologically prepared for reproduction at emergence; testicular weight, plasma androgen levels, and number of spermatozoa in the epididymis were at their seasonal maxima at spring emergence (Ellis and Balph, 1976; Ellis et al., 1983). Immediately thereafter these levels declined, reaching a low point in June. We also found that the testes showed marked regression owing to hypoplasia and maturation depletion of germinal elements at spring emergence. Physiological preparedness for breeding probably was achieved during homeothermic intervals associated with hibernation as described by Morrison and Galster (1975) for Arctic ground squirrels and observed in Uinta ground squirrels in the laboratory (L. Anderson, unpubl. obs.; J. Cranford, pers. comm.).

Adult males spent the first 1 – 2 days after emergence beside their burrows and were relatively inactive. Then they began scent marking, calling, and fighting among themselves. Marking consisted of moving about and periodically wiping the side of the head on the ground (described by Balph and Stokes, 1963). I examined a histological section of the face and found aprocrine glands, a condition found in some other species of ground squirrels (see Kivett et al., 1976). The call they used was a "chirp," a signal I could not distinguish sonographically from the "chirp" used by all squirrels throughout the season in threat and in response to avian predators (Balph and Balph, 1966; however, see Leger and Owings, 1978). Males repeatedly gave the call in response to the sight or sound of other males or with no apparent external stimulus. I often recorded more than 100 calls per 5-min period at the height of the breeding season. Males readily fought at this time; the probability of aggressive interactions at meeting was greater for them than for females (Table 15.1). The outcome of encounters was weakly but not significantly associated with location (Table 15.2). The probability of a male's being subordinate (defined as retreating at the approach or threat of another squirrel) tended to increase the farther he was from the center of his activity. However, males seemed to dominate in a core area (Table 15.2; see Brown, 1975:62) and home ranges overlapped, results somewhat similar to Michener's (1979) for Richardson's ground squirrels.

TABLE 15.1. Percentage of total encounters observed in 1965 and 1966 that were between adult males and between adult females compared with the probabilities of males meeting and of females meeting

	Dates after first squirrel emerged from hibernation									
Encounters	0–9	10–19	20–29	30–39	40–49	50–59	60–69	70–79	80–89	90–99
Male / male										
Encounters observed (%)	65	17	5	1	1	1	0	1	0	0
Probability of encounters (%)	11	5	3	2	1	1	0	0	1	0
Female / female										
Encounters observed (%)	23	25	20	11	8	7	8	5	2	1
Probability of encounters (%)	32	22	16	9	8	8	2	1	3	0

SOURCE: See Burns (1968) for details of calculations.

Although one could observe this activity of males at any time during the breeding season, individual males did not maintain this level of activity through the entire season. I repeatedly saw individual males localize their movement and become very active (marking, calling, fighting, and pursuing females) only to disappear, move elsewhere, or become relatively quiet a few days later. Never did I see a male establish itself in one area and dominate that area throughout the 2–3-week breeding season, even after the population was reduced.

I believe the function of marking, calling, and fighting was associated in some way with obtaining females, since the behavior was so closely associated with the breeding season. However, an explanation of how males attempted to obtain females is problematic. Two common systems of obtaining females are defense of individual territories with access to females within territories and dominance / subordination relationships among males with the dominant having access to nearby females (see Dobson, this volume). Which of the two systems males adopt is probably determined by the costs and benefits each affords under a particular set of circumstances (see Brown, 1964; Emlen and Oring, 1977; Balph and Balph, 1979). Males at the Station exhibited characteristics of both systems. Logically, one is likely to associate marking the ground and repeatedly calling with territorial advertisement. I did see individual males defend what I thought was a geographic position (a territory) for a short time. However, the outcome of encounters (Table 15.2) suggests that males in general were consistently not subordinate only in a core area and did not always defend a geographic position (see Michener, 1979, for discussion).

Perhaps the explanation of why male behavior had elements of both systems lies in the possible costs and benefits of male territoriality at the Station. A patch of ground free of snow where females gathered to feed appeared to be a valuable and defensible resource. The smaller the patch and the larger the number of females, the better the resource was to defend. However, the cost of defense probably was high. Males had just emerged from a 9-month hibernation, were losing body weight, and were competing with a relatively large number of other males. Moreover, as females bred, they began to space themselves and became intolerant of other squirrels, especially males. The value and defensibility of the patches also changed during the breeding season. The patches grew larger as the snow melted, and fewer females fed together as the breeding season progressed. I currently believe that changes in the defensibility of the resource through space and time were responsible for the system males used to obtain females.

Males bred females in burrows after briefly courting them (Balph and Stokes, 1963). Indirect evidence suggests that males bred more than one female (see Paul, 1977; Ruff, 1971). Possibly more than one male bred one female.

After the 2–3-week breeding season, adult males avoided open areas where pregnant females had territories and spent much of their time aboveground feeding (Walker, 1968). Essentially they became isolates that seldom fought (Table 15.1) or interacted at all with others. They were difficult to catch or even see.

The degree to which yearling males participated in reproduction varied. Before the population was reduced, they emerged after females were bred, and only 16% (n = 136) had scrotal testes (Slade and Balph, 1974). After the population was reduced most yearling males emerged with adults, many behaved sexually, and 61% (n = 51) had scrotal testes. The male social system was not a function of age per se as described by Murie and Harris (1978) for Columbian ground squirrels (*S. columbianus*).

Female reproductive season. Upon emergence, adult and yearling females moved 1–20 m to nearby areas where they could obtain food and spent much of their time feeding (Walker, 1968). Green grass was available in early spring on the south side of objects such as trees and buildings and on south-facing banks and hillsides. Females did not attempt to defend the food resource but rather maintained an individual distance of about 1 m (Paul, 1977). Their general lack of aggressiveness at this time was indicated by a lower percentage of total encounters than one would expect by chance (Table 15.1).

Most females bred at these food patches within 2–4 days of their emergence (see Paul, 1977, for discussion of evidence). Within 1–3 days of breeding, females began spacing themselves aggressively near where they had hibernated. The strong association between becoming pregnant and developing intolerance, an association seen in some other species of ground squirrels (e.g., *S. tereticaudus:* Dunford, 1977), suggests that female aggression is related to the endocrinological changes of pregnancy. The aggression and its outcome quickly became related to distance from the burrow (Table 15.2). Home ranges overlapped little (Ruff, 1971), and thus aggression was territorial in nature. The success of females in establishing territories where they hibernated depended upon when they emerged relative to when their female neighbors emerged. In 1965 and 1966 the percentages of emerging females that nested at their hibernation sites were 80% (n = 94), 72% (n = 93), and 63% (n = 60) for those that emerged in the first, second, and third 10-day periods respectively (Walker, 1968). Females that emerged early conceived early, became aggressive early, and easily drove later-appearing, nonaggressive squirrels (including their yearling daughters) from the vicinity of their burrows. When females emerged synchronously, as in 1965 (Fig. 15.1), equality existed in establishing territories. As a result, both adults and yearlings were present in larger numbers in the "preferred" lawn habitat

344

TABLE 15.2. Effect of distance from center of activity (males) or home burrow (females) on outcome of encounters with other squirrels during the reproductive season in 1966

Results of encounters (%)	Males					
	Distance from center of activity (m)					
	0–6	6–12	12–18	18–24	24–30	30–36
Dominant	62	77	90	63	47	33
Subordinate	0	0	0	21	21	22
Other[a]	38	23	10	16	32	45

Number of encounters $= 78; \chi^2 = 13.94 \, (0.10 < P < 0.20)$

Results of encounters (%)	Females				
	Distance from home burrow (m)				
	0–4	4–8	8–12	12–16	16–20
Dominant	79	77	59	24	44
Subordinate	4	7	21	21	33
Other[a]	18	17	20	37	22

Number of encounters $= 265; \chi^2 = 31.96 \, (P < 0.005)$

SOURCE: After Burns (1968).

[a] Classed as "stand-off" by Burns (1968).

(Walker, 1968). This phenomenon was best illustrated in a sampling area at the core of the population where four adult females nested in 1966 and where five adult and six yearling females nested in 1965.

After parturition, females began to make excursions of 50–200 m away from the areas they usually occupied. These excursions lasted from a few minutes to several hours. Although their aggressiveness did not decline, as indicated by the distance apart at which females initiated encounters (Paul, 1977), they spent more time away from the vicinity of their burrows as the lactation period progressed. After the young appeared aboveground, the females spent most of their time in relatively closed habitats away from their old territories, although they still returned to spend nights in their original burrows. At this time they were no longer territorial (Paul, 1977).

Cues as to how female territoriality functioned at the Station may lie in the nature and timing of the behavior. Territorial behavior by a female consisted of

345

defending a rather small area around a burrow from all other squirrels (except her own young of the year). It began with pregnancy, waned with parturition, and ceased when the young appeared aboveground. I suspect that the behavior was related directly or indirectly to juvenile survival in one of the following ways.

First, territoriality may ensure a nutritious food source during pregnancy and lactation. Cropped grass sends up new shoots. These shoots have greater nutrient density than older leaves, and herbivores select the newer leaves (reviewed by Arnold, 1964). A female squirrel that restricted her feeding to a small area would be rewarded in time by a dense crop of new shoots in that area. This "garden" near the burrow would be a valuable and defensible resource for a pregnant female (see Charnov et al., 1976).

Second, territoriality could function to protect the young from harm by intruding squirrels as suggested by Burns (1968) for squirrels at the Station and Sherman (1981) for Belding's ground squirrels. If so, the behavior functioned very well at the Station, since I documented only one case of infanticide there (see Michener, 1982; Sherman, 1982, for discussion of infanticide in ground squirrels). However, if territoriality functioned to protect the young, why did the behavior begin at conception rather than at parturition, and why did it end before the young could fend for themselves? A potential mechanism does exist for females to begin aggressiveness at parturition, since hormonal changes associated with the beginning of lactation trigger maternal care and aggressiveness in some mammals. One could argue that it is of advantage to begin defense 3 weeks early to have surrounding squirrels well conditioned not to intrude. However, single-trial (experience) place avoidance has been demonstrated in Uinta ground squirrels (Balph, 1968). If territoriality functioned to protect young, it seems inappropriate for females to decrease territorial behavior before the young are able to take care of themselves. However, the heart rates of females were higher in response to being in an unfamiliar area after territorial behavior ceased than when territories were being defended (Ruff, 1971). When females made excursions away from their old territories, they seemed to anticipate attack. This anticipation (conditioned through past experience) perhaps is what prevented squirrels from disturbing young. Nevertheless, as territoriality decreased and females spent more and more time away from their burrows and out of sight of their old territories, the opportunity to harm young was there for any conspecific (see Sherman, 1981, for discussion of the selective advantage of infanticide in Belding's ground squirrels).

A third possible function of territoriality is associated with preparations females make for the emergence of juveniles. A few days before the young appear aboveground, the mother makes a small hole to the surface from below, some distance from other entrances to her burrow (noted also by J. Cranford in Uinta ground squirrels at Alta, Utah; pers. comm.). Not once did I see a female use the hole until a few days after the young had appeared. Even the blades of grass that extended over the hole were left undisturbed. I believe the importance of such holes lies in the fact that when the young first appear aboveground, they are poorly developed physically, and mothers rarely are present to assist them in any way. One can easily catch juveniles by hand if they are displaced more than a couple of meters from their burrow entrances. Thus, for the first few days aboveground they appear to be very vulnerable to predation. A juvenile's chance for survival should be increased by an inconspicuous burrow entrance and an adequate food supply within easy reach. Conversely, juveniles may suffer if other squirrels (including the mother) use the entrance and thereby provide cues to potential predators, or if other squirrels eat grass around the burrow and thus force the young to move farther into the open to feed.

The question why females so readily abandoned their territories and young during the daytime after the litters emerged is an important and difficult one. The abandonment clearly occurred every year at the Station. It also occurred in a population at Tony Grove Lake, 8 km away in an area less influenced by human activity (G. E. Wright, unpubl. obs.). The females emerged in the morning, moved to brushy areas to spend the day, and returned to their original burrows in the evening. This suggests that the females were avoiding something in their original territories, seeking something in brushy areas, or attempting to leave resources for young (see King, 1955; Yeaton, 1972).

A study of the activity of squirrels at the Station relative to the thermal environment indicated that adult and yearling squirrels experienced increasing difficulty with heat loads as the season progressed and that they changed their activities as a result. During gestation, lactation, and the postlactation period, variations in ambient temperature accounted for 5%, 28%, and 47% of the variation in female activity aboveground (Morse, 1978). Females did not lose body heat when in the burrow during the day (Gessaman, 1980) as do some desert ground squirrels (Bartholomew and Hudson, 1961). Remaining in the burrow with the young might interfere with weaning and would decrease aboveground foraging time. No information is available on how ground squirrel species that occur in habitats that have no shade cope with heat load. The role of heat stress in abandonment of territories by female Uinta ground squirrels may be revealed by observing whether or not squirrels that live in grassy areas beneath aspen trees likewise abandon their territories.

Juvenile development. Juveniles began to appear aboveground about the last week of May, at an age of about 22 days (see Paul, 1977, for evidence), about 55 days after the first squirrel appeared in the spring. Each litter emerged over a 1–3-day period at the burrow entrance the mother had constructed a few days before the young appeared. Litter size averaged 5.4 (n = 114) and varied with female age and habitat but not density (Slade and Balph, 1974). The dispersion of both juvenile males and females at their appearance aboveground coincided with that of the mothers, that is, in the more open, grassy habitats.

During the first 2–3 days aboveground, juveniles remained within 1–2 m of their burrow entrances. At emergence, juveniles were relatively small ($\bar{X}$ = 60.3 g, SD = 5.4, n = 20) and poorly coordinated. Their activities included tentative movements away from and escape to burrow entrances, periods of remaining motionless, and occasional feeding on vegetation. Although siblings were in close contact, they seldom interacted socially. When they did, it was to make nose-to-mouth contact, the most common social behavior exhibited in the first few days aboveground (Saunders, 1970). I seldom saw mothers with their young when the young were aboveground. When a mother did move toward her young, it usually was to enter the burrow. On these occasions the mother and young readily approached each other and appeared to recognize each other. Juveniles readily followed their mothers into the burrow, presumably to nurse.

The initial movements of juveniles away from the immediate vicinity (0–1 m) of the burrow entrance typically consisted of rapid runs of a few meters, followed

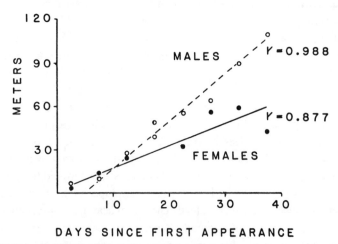

FIGURE 15.2. Average distance juvenile Uinta ground squirrels at the station were captured from their natal burrows in 1966 (after Walker, 1968).

either by a rapid run of a few more meters to a new feeding location or a hasty return to the burrow. In a detailed study of 16 juveniles in the Tony Grove Lake population, G. E. Wright (unpubl. obs.) found that these early movements were away from vision-obstructing vegetation (where it occurred) and toward open grass. These observations lead me to hypothesize that young squirrels rely for safety on the holes prepared by their mothers and on a clear view of their surroundings.

During the first 2–3 weeks aboveground, juveniles continued to use the natal burrow and remained together as sibling groups. Each day they increased the distance they ranged from the burrow. About 10 days after emergence, juvenile males at the Station and at Tony Grove Lake began moving farther from the natal burrow during the day than juvenile females (Fig. 15.2). These movements represent the beginning of sex differences in dispersal (Slade and Balph, 1974) that led to the sex difference in dispersion evident in the adult population.

About 2–3 weeks after the young appeared, they no longer returned to their natal burrows in the evening and no longer associated as sibling groups, much as described for thirteen-lined ground squirrels (McCarley, 1966) and Richardson's ground squirrels (Michener, 1981). Nearly all juveniles behaved as isolate wanderers until shortly before immergence, when they localized their aboveground activity near the burrow in which they would spend the fall and winter.

Several features of the social system of Uinta ground squirrels suggest that this species is among the less social ground-dwelling sciurids and would be classed as grade 2 in the social indexes developed by Armitage (1981) and Michener (1983). As with round-tailed squirrels and Richardson's ground squirrels (Dunford, 1977; Michener, 1979), males do not defend territories beyond the breeding season, adult females do not share living space although female kin may live in close proximity, sibling groups dissolve a few weeks after young come aboveground, and juveniles become independent of their mother and sibs before their first hibernation season. In summary, the Uinta ground squirrels at the Utah State University Forestry Field Station were isolates living as an aggregation.

Acknowledgments

I acknowledge the work of S. Amend, R. Burns, F. Knopf, C. Larlham, R. McQuivey, T. Morse, D. Olson, R. Paul, R. Ruff, A. Saunders, J. Sector, N. Slade, A. Stokes, and R. Walker on the squirrel population at the Station. I thank M. Balph, J. Byers, C. Dunford, G. Michener, and J. Murie for their helpful comments on the manuscript.

Literature Cited

Armitage, K. B. 1981. Sociality as a life-history tactic of ground squirrels. Oecologia, 48:36–49.

Arnold, G. W. 1964. Factors within plant associations affecting the behaviour and performance of grazing animals. Pp. 133–154, *in* Grazing in terrestrial and marine environments (D. J. Crisp, ed.). Blackwell, Oxford, 322 pp.

Balph, D. F. 1968. Behavioral responses of unconfined Uinta ground squirrels to trapping. J. Wildl. Mgmt., 32:778–794.

Balph, D. F., and M. H. Balph. 1979. Behavioral flexibility of pine siskins in mixed species foraging groups. Condor, 81:211–212.

Balph, D. F., and A. W. Stokes. 1963. On the ethology of a population of Uinta ground squirrels. Amer. Midland Nat., 69:106–126.

Balph, D. M., and D. F. Balph. 1966. Sound communication of Uinta ground squirrels. J. Mamm., 47:440–450.

Bartholomew, G. A., and J. W. Hudson. 1961. Desert ground squirrels. Sci. Amer., 205:107–166.

Brown, J. L. 1964. The evolution of diversity in avian territorial systems. Wilson Bull., 76:160–169.

———. 1975. The evolution of behavior. Norton, New York, 761 pp.

Burns, R. J. 1968. The role of agonistic behavior in regulation of density in Uinta ground squirrels (*Citellus armatus*). Unpubl. M.S. thesis, Utah State Univ., Logan, 57 pp.

Charnov, E. L., G. H. Orians, and K. Hyatt. 1976. The ecological implications of resource depression. *Amer. Nat.* 110:247–259.

Dunford, C. 1977. Social system of round-tailed ground squirrels. Anim. Behav., 25:885–906.

Durrant, S. D., and R. H. Hansen. 1954. Distribution patterns and phylogeny of some western ground squirrels. J. Syst. Zool., 3:82–85.

Ellis, L. C., and D. F. Balph. 1976. Age and seasonal differences in the synthesis and metabolism of testosterone by testicular tissue and pineal HIOMT activity of Uinta ground squirrels (*Spermophilus armatus*). Gen. Comp. Endocrinol., 28:42–51.

Ellis, L. C., R. A. Palmer, and D. F. Balph. 1983. The reproductive cycle of male Uinta ground squirrels: some anatomical and biochemical correlates. Comp. Biochem. Physiol., 74A:239–245.

Emlen, S. T., and L. W. Oring. 1977. Ecology, sexual selection, and the evolution of mating systems. Science, 197:205–223.

French, A. R. 1982. Intraspecific differences in the pattern of hibernation in the ground squirrel, *Spermophilus beldingi*. J. Comp. Physiol., 148B:83–91.

Gessaman, J. A. 1980. Heart rate and body temperature of the Uinta ground squirrel in the field. Comp. Biochem. Physiol. 66:707–710.

King, J. A. 1955. Social behavior, social organization, and population dynamics in a

350

black-tailed prairiedog town in the Black Hills of North Dakota. Contrib. Lab. Vert. Biol., Univ. Michigan, 67:1–123.

Kivett, V. K., J. O. Murie, and A. L. Steiner. 1976. A comparative study of scent-gland location and related behavior in some northwestern Nearctic ground squirrel species (Scuiridae): an evolutionary approach. Canadian J. Zool., 54:1294–1306.

Knopf, F. L., and D. F. Balph, 1977. Annual periodicity of Uinta ground squirrels. Southwestern Nat., 23:213–224.

Leger, D. W., and D. H. Owings. 1978. Responses to alarm calls by California ground squirrels: effects of call structure and maternal status. Behav. Ecol. Sociobiol. 3: 177–186.

McCarley, H. 1966. Annual cycle, population dynamics and adaptive behavior of *Citellus tridecemlineatus*. J. Mamm., 47:294–316.

McLean, I. G., and A. J. Towns. 1981. Differences in weight changes and the annual cycle of male and female Arctic ground squirrels. Arctic, 34:249–254.

Michener, G. R. 1979. Spatial relationships and social organization of adult Richardson's ground squirrels. Canadian J. Zool., 57:125–139.

———. 1981. Ontogeny of spatial relationships and social behavior in juvenile Richardson's ground squirrels. Canadian J. Zool., 59:1666–1676.

———. 1982. Infanticide in ground squirrels. Anim. Behav., 30:936–938.

———. 1983. Kin identification, matriarchies, and the evolution of sociality in ground-dwelling sciurids. Pp. 528–572, *in* Recent Advances in the study of mammalian behavior (J. F. Eisenberg and D. G. Kleiman, eds.). Spec. Publ., Amer. Soc. Mamm., 7:1–753.

———. 1984. Sexual differences in body weight patterns of Richardson's ground squirrels during the breeding season. J. Mamm. 65: 59–66.

Morrison, P., and W. Galster. 1975. Patterns of hibernation in the Arctic ground squirrel. Canadian J. Zool., 53:1345–1355.

Morse, T. E. 1978. A description and analysis of behavior patterns among Uinta ground squirrels. Unpubl. Ph.D. dissert., Utah State Univ., Logan, 197 pp.

Morton, M. L., and P. W. Sherman. 1978. Effects of a spring snowstorm on behavior, reproduction, and survival of Belding's ground squirrels. Canadian J. Zool., 56: 2578–2590.

Murie, J. O., and M. A. Harris. 1978. Territoriality and dominance in male Columbian ground squirrels (*Spermophilus columbianus*). Canadian J. Zool., 56:2402–2412.

Murray, R. B., H. F. Mayland, and P. J. Van Soest. 1978. Growth and nutritional value to cattle of grasses on cheatgrass range in southern Idaho. USDA Forest Service Research Paper INT-199.

Paul, R. T. 1977. Social behavior and social organization in an unconfined population of Uinta ground squirrels. Unpubl. M.S. thesis, Utah State Univ., Logan, 75 pp.

Ruff, R. L. 1971. Telemetered heart rates of free-living Uinta ground squirrels in response to social interactions. Unpubl. Ph.D. dissert., Utah State Univ., Logan, 125 pp.

Saunders, D. A. 1970. The ontogeny of social behavior of Uinta ground squirrels. Unpubl. M.S. thesis, Utah State Univ., Logan, 35 pp.

Sharif, C. M., and N. E. West. 1968. Forage moisture variations on mountain summer range. J. Range Mgmt., 21:228–235.

Sherman, P. W. 1981. Reproductive competition and infanticide in Belding's ground squirrels and other animals. Pp. 311–331, *in* Natural selection and social behavior: recent research and new theory (R. D. Alexander and D. W. Tinkle, eds.). Chiron Press, New York, 532 pp.

———. 1982. Infanticide in ground squirrels. Anim. Behav., 30:938–939.

Slade, N. A., and D. F. Balph. 1974. Population ecology of Uinta ground squirrels. Ecology, 55:989–1003.

Stoddart, L. A., and J. E. Greaves. 1942. The composition of summer range plants in Utah. Utah Agric. Exp. Sta. Bull., no. 305.

Walker, R. E. 1968. Local distribution in a population of Uinta ground squirrels. Unpubl. Ph.D. dissert., Utah State Univ., Logan, 71 pp.

Yeaton, R. I. 1972. Social behavior and social organization in Richardson's ground squirrels (*Spermophilus richardsonii*) in Saskatchewan. J. Mamm., 53:139–147.

JAN O. MURIE AND MARGARET A. HARRIS
University of Alberta

Chapter 16

The History of Individuals in a Population of Columbian Ground Squirrels: Source, Settlement, and Site Attachment

Abstract. Livetrapping and observation of Columbian ground squirrels over seven years in southern Alberta revealed that, as adults, males lived farther from their natal areas than females, a result of sex-differential dispersal as yearlings. Successful recruitment to the breeding population depended in part on availability of vacant space for males but not for females. As adults, both sexes showed strong site fidelity. Successful recruits of both sexes were resident, on average, for more than three years. This combination of site attachment and longevity resulted in a relatively high potential for inbreeding between fathers and daughters and an increased likelihood for familiarity, based on long-term association, to affect patterns of social relations among both males and females.

Introduction

Long-term studies of populations can provide information on individuals from birth to death, unlike shorter studies that produce data on a cross section of a population covering only a portion of each individual's lifetime. The latter are suitable for describing general characteristics of a population but do not permit assessment of the eventual effects — for example, on reproductive success — of variation among individuals. Furthermore, only with longitudinal studies can we document the effect of differing environmental and social factors on the same individual and learn the extent and significance of long-term spatial and behavioral association among individuals.

Most ground-dwelling sciurids are characterized by sex-differential dispersal; males tend to move away from the natal site before they attain reproductive

353

maturity, whereas females remain at their place of birth or move shorter distances from it (Armitage, 1981; Holekamp, this volume; Michener, 1983). That pattern appears to exist in Columbian ground squirrels (*Spermophilus columbianus*) also (Boag and Murie, 1981), but the range of movements has not been well documented. After dispersal, regardless of sex and distance moved since birth, individuals must establish themselves within the spatial framework of a local population in order to achieve reproductive success, a process that has as yet received little study. After squirrels settle and attain reproductive maturity, individual longevity and site attachment could have important implications for sociality. Among ground squirrels the effects of kinship on social and spatial interactions have recently received attention (e.g., McLean, 1982; Michener, 1981; Sherman, 1980, 1981). Effects of familiarity through long-term association have received less attention (but see Armitage, 1974, 1977; Sherman 1980), despite extensive evidence that in primates familiarity strongly influences social interactions and relations (e.g., Bernstein et al., 1974; Carpenter, 1974; Kaplan, 1978).

In this chapter we present data, based on individual histories, on the source, settlement, and site attachment of Columbian ground squirrels (*Spermophilus columbianus*). We describe movements of ground squirrels from their birthplace, examine several factors that may influence the successful recruitment of 2-year-old adults to the breeding population, and document the longevity of successful adults and their length of association with neighbors.

Methods

The 8-ha study area was the western portion of 72 ha of grassy slopes and meadows occupied by Columbian ground squirrels along the Sheep River (50°38'N, 114°38'W, 1,470 m elevation), 32 km west of Turner Valley, Alberta. Squirrels were trapped throughout each summer from 1973 to 1979 on most of the 72 ha (Boag and Murie, 1981). Squirrels on the 8-ha area were trapped more intensively from late April to early July, 1975 through 1982. All squirrels were individually marked with a numbered fingerling fish tag in each ear. Each squirrel was marked with a distinctive pattern of hair dye on its fur. At each capture squirrels were weighed and their reproductive status assessed (Murie and Harris, 1978, 1982). The location of captures (to within 5 m) was noted, using topographical features, and recorded as the coordinates of a grid marked on an enlarged aerial photograph (1:40,000) of the area.

We observed squirrels on two portions of the study area about 200 m apart (WSA, ca. 2.5 ha, and ESA, ca. 1.5 ha). Observations began in late April, when squirrels were emerging from hibernation, and ended by late June, when juveniles were emerging from natal burrows. WSA was observed regularly from 1976 through 1980 (only to late May in 1978 and 1980) on a total of 196 days for 620 h. Less regular observations were done in May of 1981 and 1982. ESA was observed regularly from 1976 through 1978 (only to late May in 1978) on 108 days for 283 h; irregular, ad lib. observations were done in 1979 through 1982. During regular observation, scan sampling of locations of all visible squirrels was performed every 5–15 min. Locations were recorded as within 10 by 10 m squares of a grid overlying maps of the areas. For all interactions, the type, location, participants, and outcome were recorded. During ad lib. observation, locations and interactions were sampled intermittently.

The distance between the locations of a squirrel from one year to the next was calculated in two ways. For all animals captured in two or more years in the 8-ha study area, the geometric center of capture locations (trapping center) was calculated for each year and plotted on graph paper, and distances between centers were measured and converted to meters. If captures of a squirrel were concentrated in one area early in the year and later in another area more than 100 m away, the earliest trapping center was used for interyear comparisons. Data were obtained for 76 males and 75 females of known age (first captured as juveniles or in early spring as yearlings), and for 34 males and 38 females of known minimum age (first captured as adults). Both males and females were captured an average of three times each year. Of the 223 squirrels captured, 34 males and 29 females resided on the observation areas for two or more years. Centers of activity (observational centers) for each animal each year were calculated by taking the means of x and y coordinates of the center of each 10 by 10 m grid square in which the squirrel was seen for each day of the period of observation. These centers of activity were based on an average of 112 points over 25 days of observation per squirrel per year. Distances between yearly centers of activity were plotted and measured (from center to center of grid squares) as above. Trapping centers were used to determine the distance from the natal area at each age for squirrels of known age. Both measures of locations were used to examine movements of all squirrels between years.

Centers of activity based on small numbers of captures are likely to be less accurate than those based on large numbers of sightings. However, by using trapping centers we were able to increase our sample size, include squirrels that were caught off the observation areas as juveniles in our analysis of distance from natal areas, and include data for some animals from 1973 to 1975 when only trapping was done. For squirrels on the observation areas we have measures of distance moved between years from both trapping and observational centers; in

103 of 125 cases (82%), distances were the same or greater for trapping compared with observation centers. On average, distances based on trapping were 15 m (for males) and 18 m (for females) farther than those based on observation.

Factors affecting successful settlement and recruitment to the breeding population were assessed for all animals occurring on the observation areas at age two (known or minimum age). All squirrels $\geq$ 2 years old were considered adults. Most females were already present, as yearlings, on the area in which they settled; most males immigrated as yearlings and were then present only during the latter half of the active season, after our trapping and observations ended for the year and when interactions between males are infrequent (Betts, 1973). Hence females are first exposed as yearlings to interactions with resident, territorial females (Festa-Bianchet, 1981), whereas males, after dispersal as yearlings, first encounter high levels of intrasexual aggression at age two.

Success in settling was evaluated somewhat differently for males and females. Females in this population breed for the first time at age two (Murie et al., 1980). We designated them successful settlers if they were known to lactate in at least one year of their tenure on the area. All but one of 39 successful females were resident as adults for 2 years or more; all seven unsuccessful females were resident as adults for only 1 year.

Most males show external evidence of reproductive maturity at 2 years of age (Murie and Harris, 1978) but do not appear to participate in breeding until they are 3 or 4 years old. Males were classed as successful if they eventually achieved territorial status. Only territorial males were seen to engage in types of behavior from which we inferred underground copulation (Murie and Harris, 1982). After 1978 in ESA, and in 1981 and 1982 in WSA, the criteria used to assess territorial status (see Murie and Harris, 1978) could not be applied rigorously because observations were not sufficient to delineate core areas. In those years attainment of territorial status was evaluated subjectively. We assumed that a male was territorial if he consistently chased other males from the area in which he was most frequently seen during ad lib. observations, or if we inferred underground copulation from his behavior with an estrous female. Seven of 43 males were evaluated in this manner. All 2-year-olds that were resident for one year and disappeared before becoming territorial were deemed unsuccessful. Although some could have become resident elsewhere on the 72-ha site, none was subsequently captured or seen.

In analyses, squirrels of known age (26 males and 40 females) and minimum age (17 males and six females) were combined. Most of the latter were probably 2 years old as only one male and no females of known age first appeared on the area when older than 2 years.

356

TABLE 16.1. Median distance from location as a juvenile to location at later ages (based on trapping centers) for Columbian ground squirrels. Sample size is shown in parentheses. Comparisons between males and females are by Mann-Whitney *U*-tests.

	Median distance (m) from natal site		
Age (years)	Males	Females	*P*
1	35 (47)	30 (63)	> 0.30
2	360 (36)	50 (59)	< 0.001
3	370 (37)	45 (35)	< 0.001
4	450 (19)	50 (27)	< 0.001
5	372.5 (10)	85 (13)	< 0.01
6	227.5 (4)	107.5 (6)	> 0.25

Nonparametric statistical tests (Siegel, 1956) are used for most analyses because variances of most samples compared were unequal, distributions often were not normal, and medians were usually deemed the most suitable measures of central tendency. Sample sizes for analyses vary because complete data were not available for all individuals.

Results

Source

As yearlings, males and females who were resident on the 8-ha area at that age or later remained in similar proximity to their natal sites. At age two, males were significantly more distant (Table 16.1). That difference persisted to the age of five; at age six, the difference was not significant although the trend was in the same direction. Overall, 53 of 61 females (87%), but only eight of 46 males (17%) were less than 100 m from their natal sites as adults (Fig. 16.1). The same pattern was evident for 2-year-old squirrels on the observation areas; 74% of the females, but only 17% of the males were born on the area. Thus, most adult females were native to their area, whereas most adult males were immigrants.

The slight increase in distance from the natal site for females at the ages of five and six (Table 16.1) suggests that they may move farther from the natal site as they grow older. However, an examination, year by year, of changes in distance from the natal site revealed that only as 2-year-olds did females reside farther from natal sites than in the previous year (n = 42, p = 0.0013, Wilcoxon

357

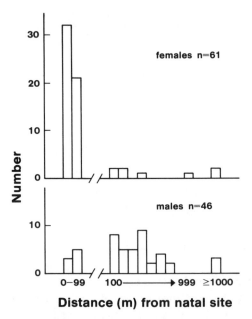

Distance (m) from natal site

FIGURE 16.1. Frequency histogram of the distance from the natal site at age two (or the first year thereafter if not captured at age two) for 46 male and 61 female Columbian ground squirrels.

matched pairs, signed-rank test). Alternatively, distance from the natal site might affect survival. For females on the observation areas, the correlation between distance from the natal site and length of residence as an adult was not significant ($r = 0.34, 0.10 > P > 0.05$, n = 23) but indicates a trend for greater survival farther from natal sites. A comparable correlation for males was not significant, and the trend was in the opposite direction ($r = -0.18, P > 0.10$, n = 18). Females known to be immigrants did not differ from nonimmigrants in likelihood of producing weaned juveniles or surviving yearlings during their tenure. Seven of 10 immigrants weaned juveniles versus 26 of 40 females born on the observation areas ($P = 1.00$, Fisher exact test), and four of six immigrants and 12 of 23 nonimmigrants that weaned juveniles had surviving yearlings ($P = 0.66$, Fisher exact test). Thus, immigrants did not show any strong reproductive advantage or disadvantage compared with females that were near their natal areas.

Settlement

Background information. From 1976 to 1982, 37 males and 31 females were resident as adults for one or more years on WSA, 21 males and 27 females on

ESA. Numbers of adults changed from year to year, as did age structure, turnover rates, and recruitment into the adult population. On both areas numbers declined over seven years (Fig. 16.2). The decline was precipitous in 1978 on ESA, but numbers increased somewhat in 1980 and later. The numbers of adult squirrels disappearing each year varied from 10% to 64% of those present the year before. On average, disappearance rate was similar on ESA and on WSA (33% and 38%, respectively) and was similar for males (35%) and females (34%). Numbers of 2-year-olds appearing on the areas followed a pattern similar to that of total numbers (Fig. 16.2). The numbers of 2-year-old squirrels of either sex or both together were not consistently correlated on either area with total numbers of adults in that or the previous year, nor with number of adults older than 2 years; trends were also not consistently positive or negative (Spearman's rho tests, r_s from -0.86 to $+0.94$). The only significant correlations were for males in WSA and reflect the trend seen in Fig. 16.2 for fewer 2-year-olds present as numbers declined. Thus there was no evidence for more recruitment when numbers were low.

The average age in years, obtained by combining all known and minimum age squirrels each year and calculating overall means for the seven years, was 3.8 (WSA) and 3.4 (ESA) for adult males and 3.7 (WSA) and 3.5 (ESA) for adult females. The greatest ages so far recorded are 10+ years for both sexes on WSA, 7+ years for both sexes on ESA. Of 44 females present on the observation area as yearlings during 1975 to 1982, 31 (70%) were eventually classed as successful.

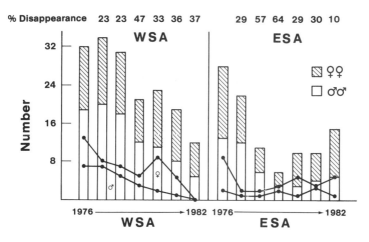

FIGURE 16.2. Number of adults (bars) and number of new 2-year-old squirrels (lines) present each year in observation areas, 1976 through 1982. Percentage of disappearance of adults from the previous year is shown above each bar.

359

Of 39 2-year-old females, 33 (85%) settled successfully, and 24 were known to have weaned young in at least one year. Of 34 2-year-olds (excluding five 2-year-olds present in 1982) 76% stayed on the area for more than one year. Among males, 56% of 39 2-year-olds were eventually successful, and 72% (including six unsuccessful males) remained for more than one year. The majority of males became territorial, that is, successful, at 3 (n = 11) or 4 (n = 9) years of age. One male was territorial at age two, another not until age five.

Effects on successful settlement: females. For most of the following analyses, the sample size for females not successful in settling is small (n ≤ 7). Although no comparisons showed significant differences between successful and unsuccessful females, probability values are given to indicate what effects deserve attention in future studies. Data on the nature and amount of interaction with other females were too few to analyze.

Proximity to the natal area was not a strong influence on a female's success. The median distance from the natal area at age two was somewhat less for successful than for unsuccessful females, but the difference was not significant (Table 16.2a).

Greater proximity to a neighboring female did not affect the chance of success, but at the age of 2 years successful females tended to be closer to another adult female than were unsuccessful females (Table 16.2b). Four of the successful females had mothers or sisters present, and in three cases a relative was the closest female neighbor. If only nonkin neighbors are used, the median distance to the nearest neighboring female is greater, 20 m, and the difference between successful and unsuccessful females is hence less (*P* = 0.14).

TABLE 16.2. Characteristics of dispersion in 2-year-old females examined for association with eventual successful settlement. Locations and distances in *b–e* were based on observational centers of activity; both observational and trapping centers were used in *a*. Median values or percentages are given. Sample sizes are in parentheses. *P* values for comparisons between successful and unsuccessful females are based on Mann-Whitney *U*-tests (MW) or Fisher exact tests (F).

	Successful	Unsuccessful	*P*
a. Distance from natal area (m)	45 (26)	70 (5)	0.13 (MW)
b. Distance to nearest adult female (m)	15 (21)	32 (6)	0.07 (MW)
c. Position within the study area (% central)	45% (22)	17% (6)	0.35 (F)
d. Vacant area (% filling vacancies or replacing)	70% (23)	83% (6)	0.65 (F)
e. Space available at age three (% with more space)	33% (27)	43% (7)	0.67 (F)

Location within each area was classified as peripheral (activity center was one of the outermost in the area occupied by squirrels) or central (activity centers of other squirrels lay between the activity center and unoccupied adjacent habitat). The slight tendency for successful females to be located centrally was not significant (Table 16.2c). Ten of 11 central females were successful, but so were many peripheral females (12 of 17).

The spatial milieu into which each 2-year-old female settled was evaluated by contrasting the presence and proximity of neighboring females in that year to the situation the year before. There were three possible means of settlement: (*a*) *replaced:* replacement of a female that had been within 30 m in the year before and had disappeared; (*b*) *filled vacancy:* occupation of a space in which no females were present the previous year, but had been in other years, that was greater than 30 m from the nearest female neighbor; and, (*c*) *insinuated:* settlement in an area in which females were within 30 m and had been there the previous year. We used 30 m in this analysis because females with activity centers farther apart shared little space and rarely interacted with each other. Most females at age two, both successful and unsuccessful, either filled vacancies or replaced other females (Table 16.2d). Having to insinuate into the population did not appear to decrease the likelihood of success.

We cannot directly assess effects of immigration or disappearance of female neighbors on settlement after our observations ceased (at or before the time of emergence of juveniles). Changes in dispersion of neighbors that may have occurred in mid to late summer were assessed by determining, for each 2-year-old female, whether more space was available the next year (i.e., one or more neighbors had disappeared or moved farther away), less space was available (other females settled nearby or neighbors moved closer), or the dispersion pattern remained unchanged. No effect of changes in dispersion was evident; successful females were no more likely to have more space available at age three than the unsuccessful females would have had they remained rather than disappeared (Table 16.2e).

The survival of the mother did not affect the probability of survival of either juvenile or yearling females. Of 66 juveniles 42% survived when the mother did, versus 28% of 25 juveniles when the mother did not ($P = 0.21$, χ^2 test for contingency); 73% of 15 yearlings survived when the mother did, compared with 74% of 19 when the mother did not ($P = 1.0$, Fisher exact test). Survival of females from age two to age three was similarly unaffected by survival of the mother (20% of five 2-year-olds survived when the mother did, 67% of 12 when the mother did not, $P = 0.13$, Fisher exact test), but the trend was for greater survival in the mother's absence.

TABLE 16.3. Characteristics of dispersion in males examined for association with eventual successful settlement. Locations and distances in *b–d* were based on observational centers of activity; both observational and trapping centers were used in *a*. Median values or percentages are given. Sample sizes are in parentheses. *P* values for comparisons between successful and unsuccessful males are based on Mann-Whitney *U*-tests (MW) or Fisher exact tests (F).

	Successful	Unsuccessful	*P*
a. Distance from natal area at age two (m)	435 (2)	568 (6)	0.82 (MW)
b. Distance to nearest territorial male (m)			
At age two	20 (8)	20 (16)	0.95 (MW)
Year before becoming territorial or disappearing	30 (14)	18 (16)	0.38 (MW)
First year as territorial or, if unsuccessful, males had survived in situ	30 (17)	18 (16)	0.03 (MW)
c. Position within study area (% central)			
At age two	35% (20)	53% (17)	0.33 (F)
At age three	20% (10)	57% (7)	0.16 (F)
d. Vacant area (% filling vacancy or replacing)	92% (25)	50% (16)	0.004 (F)

Effects on successful settlement: males. Although sample sizes were small, proximity to the natal area did not appear to influence likelihood of successful settlement by males (Table 16.3*a*).

At age two, the activity centers of males that were eventually successful and those that were unsuccessful did not differ in distance from the nearest territorial male (Table 16.3*b*). There was also no difference in the year before disappearing (for unsuccessful males) or becoming territorial (for successful males) (Table 16.3*b*). However, in their first year as territory-holders, successful males were farther from the nearest territorial neighbor than unsuccessful males would have been had they remained in the same place rather than disappearing (Table 16.3*b*). Thus, proximity to territorial neighbors may have influenced the success of males.

Unlike females, males that were eventually successful were more often peripheral at age two or three than unsuccessful males, but the differences were not significant (Table 16.3*c*).

In changing status from subordinate in one year to dominant and territorial the next, of 25 successful males 12 filled vacancies, 11 replaced territorial males that had disappeared, and two insinuated. Had the 16 unsuccessful males remained, seven could have filled vacancies the next year, one could have replaced another male, and eight would have had to insinuate (Table 16.3*d*). Thus, 74% of males able to replace or to fill vacancies were successful, whereas only 20% of males having to insinuate did so successfully. The same analysis for WSA yielded a

362

similar result (68% of 19 males able to replace or fill a vacancy were successful, 13% of eight insinuators were successful: $P = 0.013$, Fisher exact test). In ESA most males settled in vacant areas after the population decline in 1978 and 1979.

For the 25 successful males, 52% had more space available in the year they became territorial than in the preceding year; had unsuccessful males remained, only 25% would have had more space available ($P = 0.11$, Fisher exact test).

As subordinates of age two or three, successful and unsuccessful males did not differ in number of agonistic interactions with other males or the proportion in which they were chased (Table 16.4). At age three, unsuccessful males tended to engage in more agonistic interactions than those that later became successful; they tended to be chased in more interactions as well (Table 16.4). Although no strong effect of interactions with neighboring males is evident, we hesitate to conclude from this limited sample that agonistic behavior plays no role in the eventual success of males.

Site Attachment

Except between the ages of 1 and 2 years, when males moved much farther than females, movements between years based on trapping centers were similar for both sexes. As adults, males moved farther between years than females, significantly so at age intervals 2–3 and 4–5 years (Table 16.5), but movements of most males were within the range of movements by females of the same age. For the three intervals from ages two to five, movements between years did not differ with age for males (n = 12, Friedman's $\chi^2 = 5.57, P > 0.05$) or for females (n = 14, Friedman's $\chi^2 = 0.80, P > 0.50$).

More precise estimates of interyear movements were obtained for a smaller

TABLE 16.4. Median number of agonistic interactions with other males per 100 h observation and median percentage in which successful and unsuccessful males were chased when they were subordinates at ages two and three. Number of males in the sample is given in parentheses. *P* values are based on Mann–Whitney *U* tests.

	Successful	Unsuccessful	*P*
Median number of agonistic interactions			
At age two	7.7 (9)	7.4 (15)	0.14
At age three	8.3 (7)	43.6 (4)	0.16
Median percentage chased			
At age two	88% (10)	92% (13)	0.85
At age three	65% (7)	81% (4)	0.18

Dispersal and Dispersion

TABLE 16.5. Median distance (m) between geometric centers of trap locations from year to year for squirrels at different ages. *P* values for differences between sexes are based on Mann-Whitney *U*-tests.

	Male			Female			
Age (years)	N	Median	Range	N	Median	Range	*P*
0–1	47	35	(5–175)	63	30	(5–1,330)	0.32
1–2	42	387.5	(5–1,470)	60	40	(0–1,140)	<0.001
2–3	37	35	(0–200)	35	25	(5–90)	0.02
3–4	21	35	(5–145)	26	30	(5–140)	0.23
4–5	12	47.5	(15–180)	14	30	(5–70)	0.03
5–6	5	35	(5–65)	6	30	(5–110)	0.80

sample of squirrels using centers of activity based on observations. As adults, most males (46 of 62 cases) and females (41 of 48 cases) shifted their centers of activity within an observation area by less than 25 m from year to year, and never by more than 60 m. The sexes did not differ significantly at any age. In only nine cases (five male, four female) did squirrels move 40–60 m between years. The movements of the four females were probably overestimates. Their locations in the second year were based on observations made only in May (1978 and 1981), and all four females were trapped later in the summer closer to their locations of the previous year. The longer shifts made by males (three by subordinates, two by territorial males) could not be attributed to inadequate observational sampling. The proximity of one male to other squirrels in his new location could not be assessed, but the other four males tended to be closer to females in their new location than if they had not moved (overall mean distances to the three nearest females were 27 m versus 36 m and the average numbers of females within 40 m were 3.4 versus 2.6). The average distance to the nearest dominant male, on the other hand, was little different in the new location than in the old one (20 m versus 21 m). Three other males on WSA, the only adults known to move off the observation areas, moved to a location about 150 m away. In two cases the number of females appeared to be greater at the new than the previous location. In all three instances the males had fewer territorial male neighbors on WSA in the year they moved than in the previous year.

Thus, once established in an area, most squirrels showed strong site attachment as adults. Both males and females resided on the observation areas as adults an average of 3 years ($\bar{X}$ = 2.9 ± 1.66 SD for 53 females; $\bar{X}$ = 3.0 ± 1.70 SD for

54 males). Maximum residency as an adult was 9 years for both sexes. Successful females (n = 47) were present an average of 3.2 (±1.60 SD) years, successful males (n = 28, including six already territorial in 1976), an average of 3.7 (±1.30 SD) years (*P* = 0.11, Mann-Whitney *U*-test). Successful males were territorial for an average of 2.7 (±1.30 SD; range, 1–6) years.

To assess association of individuals over time we used information only from WSA, since numbers on ESA declined so drastically in 1978 and 1979. For each squirrel present as an adult on WSA for at least 3 years (the mean length of residency for both males and females), the number of adult neighbors during its tenure and their length of residency as neighbors while adult were calculated. For males, both male and female neighbors were considered to be those squirrels whose center of activity was within a 40 m radius of each male's center of activity. The area encompassed by a 40 m radius (about 0.50 ha) is similar to the average minimum home range size of 0.42 ha for males in this area (Murie and Harris, 1978). The same criterion was used for male neighbors of females. To determine a female's female neighbors, a radius of 30 m was used because that area (about 0.28 ha) more closely approximated the average home range size of females in the area (0.29 ha, unpublished data). The procedure was used for 18 males (mean residency 4.0 ± 0.91 years) and 13 females (mean residency 3.8 ± 1.21 years).

Males had similar numbers of male and female neighbors during their tenure, and were associated with them for a similar number of years (Table 16.6). Females had about the same number of male neighbors as males did, but fewer female neighbors; on average, they were associated with both for just under 2

TABLE 16.6. Mean number of neighbors and mean length of association as adults for squirrels that lived on an observation area (WSA) for three or more years

	Number of neighbors		Length of association (years)	
	Mean	Range	Mean	Range
Males (N = 18)				
Male neighbors	12	(4–20)	1.6	(1–4)
Female neighbors	11	(5–16)	1.9	(1–5)
Females (N = 13)				
Female neighbors	6[a]	(1–14)	1.8	(1–4)
Male neighbors	13	(4–24)	1.8	(1–4)

[a] Value different from all others in the column (*P* < 0.01, Mann-Whitney U-tests). No other values in either column differ significantly.

years (Table 16.6). All but two of the males were associated for 3 years or more with at least one male neighbor ($\bar{X}$ = 1.8 males), and all but one with at least one female neighbor ($\bar{X}$ = 2.5 females). Eleven of the 13 females had at least one female neighbor ($\bar{X}$ = 1.5 females), and 12 had at least one male neighbor ($\bar{X}$ = 3.2 males) for at least 3 years.

Values for length of association involving females are no doubt underestimated. Many females were born on the area near their location as an adult (see earlier), and residency as a juvenile or yearling was not counted in this analysis. In addition, all values for length of association may be underestimated because the criteria used to classify neighbors excluded some pairs of squirrels in some years who were known to have considerable overlap of home ranges and to interact with one another. In any case, the potential for developing familiarity over several years clearly exists.

Discussion

Source

Sexual differences in distance of dispersal before reproductive maturity is clearly evident in Columbian ground squirrels and follows the pattern that occurs in other species of ground squirrels (Holekamp, this volume). Nevertheless, some females do move as far as males and hence must establish themselves in a social milieu of strangers as do most males. Kin clusters of breeding females (Michener, 1981) occur in some populations of Columbian ground squirrels (W. J. King, pers. comm.; unpubl. data). If proximity of kin and beneficent relations between them confer some advantage to females, as Sherman (1980, 1981) implies for *S. beldingi,* those females moving away from their natal site could be at a disadvantage relative to those that remain nearby. Our data do not indicate that either survival or reproductive success was less for immigrants than for females living near their natal areas. However, even females born in the area rarely had close kin as neighbors, so our results cannot rule out an advantage to females in kin clusters.

Settlement

Approximately equal numbers of males and females were present on the study areas at age two (known or minimum age), and similar numbers survived on the area for more than one year. The greater success rate of females compared with that of males was due in part to females entering the reproductive population at an earlier age (2 years) than do most males (3–4 years). Only one 2-year-old male, who lacked older, territorial neighbors, was observed in a presumed precopulatory sequence of behavior with a female.

Successful settlement of females did not appear to be related to competition for space, perhaps because density of females was too low for any such effect to be observed. Both Betts (1973) and Festa-Bianchet (1981) reported much higher female densities elsewhere. The six unsuccessful females interacted with other females infrequently, partly because they were peripheral in location and relatively distant from neighboring females. Perhaps peripheral areas were less suitable for location of nest burrows, owing to suboptimal food supply or burrow conditions or to increased vulnerability to nest predators such as weasels.

For males, on the other hand, some effect of intrasexual competition for space was evident. Males that were eventually successful tended to be farther from adjacent territorial males, to be chased less, and to be in peripheral locations more frequently than unsuccessful males. Attainment of territorial status depended in part on disappearance or movement of neighboring territorial males. Nevertheless, proximity of neighbors or existence of "vacant" space did not always predict success; some males were successful insinuators.

Territorial males varied in such behavioral characteristics as the extent of movement during the breeding season, aggressiveness outside their territories, and vigor of territorial defense. Balfour (1979) classified three distinctive behavioral profiles of Columbian ground squirrels exposed to mirror-image stimulation (MIS). She found some correlation of MIS type with living situation and, for females, differences between MIS types and patterns of activity and interaction. Hence, success in recruitment might well vary according to behavioral characteristics of individuals, either of the sort related to MIS type (see Svendsen and Armitage, 1973) or others more difficult to measure. Behavioral characteristics of adjacent individuals, as well as their proximity, might also affect recruitment. Results of analyses of the effects of individual characteristics on recruitment and reproductive success of yellow-bellied marmots (Armitage, this volume) indicate the efficacy of that approach.

Site Attachment

Once settled as adults on the observation areas, both males and females usually remained in the same location. Some squirrels, primarily males, shifted their centers of activity between years by 40–150 m. Although the spatial contexts of these shifts were variable, most appeared to be more related to increasing proximity to females than to either increasing or decreasing proximity to males. The combination of longevity and site fidelity in these squirrels resulted in most successful recruits to the area living adjacent to several adult neighbors for at least 3 years. For both sexes these long-lasting associations were more often with members of the opposite sex.

Comparable information on longevity and site attachment is available for few other ground-dwelling sciurids. Female *Spermophilus beldingi* appear to live nearly as long as female *S. columbianus* and are similarly sedentary from year to year (Sherman, 1976). Males, however, neither live as long as male *S. columbianus* nor show strong site attachment as adults. In both *S. richardsonii* and *S. tereticaudus,* home ranges of individual females overlap extensively from one year to the next, but female longevity is probably less than for *S. columbianus* (Dunford, 1977*a,* 1977*b;* Michener and Michener, 1977; Michener, 1979). Both site attachment and longevity of males is less than for *S. columbianus,* a pattern that also appears to hold for *S. tridecemlineatus* (McCarley, 1966, 1970), *S. parryii* (McLean, 1981), and *Cynomys ludovicianus* (Hoogland, 1981). The general pattern of longevity and site attachment of adult male Columbian ground squirrels is perhaps most similar to that of *Marmota flaviventris* (Armitage, 1974, this volume; Armitage and Downhower, 1974), and perhaps other marmots (e.g., *M. olympus:* Barash, 1973). However, we have not been able to derive strictly comparable data on marmots from the literature.

For no species of sciurid have we found detailed information on length of association with neighbors, although Sherman (1980) mentions that 34 pairs of *S. beldingi* females were adjacent neighbors or within 50 m of each other in 2 or more (up to 4) years. Judging from data available and information on mortality rates, which tend to be somewhat higher in most other species of ground squirrels, adult male Columbian ground squirrels are more likely to have the same adult neighbors for several years than are males of other species; the difference from other species for adult females is probably less.

The relatively frequent long-term association of males and females suggests a higher probability of inbreeding than for many other ground-dwelling squirrels. Although sex-differential dispersal is an effective mechanism for preventing inbreeding of sibs (Hoogland, 1982), the longevity and site attachment of adult males could result in frequent opportunities for father/daughter matings. In ESA, low survival of juvenile females and high turnover in the adult population led to no instances of temporal coincidence of possible fathers with possible daughters at age two or more. Unfortunately, even indirect evidence of paternity like that used by Hoogland (1982) is lacking for most litters. We are able to infer potential for inbreeding only by determining if a territorial male that was adjacent to the mother in the year a female was born was also a neighbor of that female when she was sexually mature (age two). For 10 females born in WSA that survived to age two, none (n = 1), one (n = 7), or two (n = 2) territorial males that could have been their fathers were their neighbors at age two. In two cases, a possible father was also present when the female was age three, in one case when the female was age four. In eight of the 12 times when females could have bred with possible fathers, they weaned litters on five occasions, lactated but were not known to produce weaned young twice, and bred but were not known to lactate once. Of the remaining four cases, twice females did not lactate (in a year when late spring snow was associated with 40% of the females not lactating), and twice they disappeared before lactation could be assessed. Thus, circumstantial evidence does not suggest that females are less likely to come into estrus when a possible father is present. Also, the longer movements between years by territorial males were not associated with the presence of possible daughters. Four of the five territorial males that moved more than 40 m within or off the observation areas did not have possible daughters living nearby; one could have fathered two yearling females present in the area he left.

In yellow-bellied marmots, another species in which adult males apparently show site fidelity, the probability of father/daughter matings is relatively low, about six per 1,000 matings (Armitage, 1974). The probability of father/daughter matings for Columbian ground squirrels on WSA, calculated in the same way, is much higher, six per 100 matings (the probability of dominant males persisting for 3 years (0.44) times the probability of juvenile females' surviving to breeding age (0.25) times the probability of breeding at age two (0.58 = 0.06). However, that value should be lowered because, unlike yellow-bellied marmots, in which females in a colony usually have access to only one male, several males are available as potential mates for female *S. columbianus*. Taking that into account lowers the probability of father/daughter mating to five to 15 per 1,000 matings. However, such calculations based on gross percentages may be misleading. Of 2-year-olds whose mothers were known, 90% could have bred with males who could have been their fathers. Clearly paternity must be known to assess the actual occurrence of inbreeding and to determine whether behavioral mechanisms, such as those suggested for black-tailed prairie dogs (Hoogland, 1982), operate to minimize father/daughter mating.

The likelihood of having familiar neighbors over a period of years could have other implications for the social system of Columbian ground squirrels. Familiarity might affect the nature of social interactions. Most consideration of effects of familiarity on social and spatial relations are used as alternative explanations for apparent effects of kinship. In some cases kinship and proximity (familiarity) are linked so closely that discriminating their effects is difficult (Hoogland,

369

1981), although Sherman (1980) suggested that favoritism based on familiarity was unlikely in female *S. beldingi*.

In principle, familiarity with neighbors could benefit territorial individuals if more stable boundaries develop, if dominance relations are well established and mutually recognized, and if neighbors that have a territory are less likely to attempt to displace a resident than are strangers. In all cases, time and energy spent in territorial defense could be less than if neighbors were not familiar and their behavior was less predictable by a resident. These ideas were suggested in broad terms by Fisher (1954) for ''neighborhoods'' of territorial birds and were generalized by Wilson (1975) as the ''dear enemy'' phenomenon. Wilson (1975) suggested that the adaptive significance of the ''dear enemy'' phenomenon is problematic, although he cited several lines of suggestive evidence. Recently Jaeger (1981) experimentally demonstrated the employment of ''dear enemy'' recognition, via olfactory cues, in red-backed salamanders (*Plethodon cinereus*). He also provided evidence that the decreased likelihood of escalated aggression with neighbors was adaptive, since the cost of losing an escalated contest could be high.

Columbian ground squirrels, both males and females, are able to discriminate scent from neighboring and strange males (Harris and Murie, 1982). Squirrels also sometimes appear to discriminate between strangers and neighbors or to recognize certain individuals from a distance, presumably by visual means. In some cases males interact more frequently and intensely with a new neighboring territorial male than with a neighbor who was also present the year before; the rate and intensity of interactions between territorial neighbors declines somewhat from their first to their second year as neighbors (Murie and Harris, 1978). Thus, for males, greater familiarity through association as neighbors may be beneficial in reducing possible costs of aggression. Armitage (1977) reported similar results for yellow-bellied marmots. Agonistic behavior declined and amicable behavior sometimes increased in colonies consisting mainly of adults who had been resident the previous year; the presence of immigrants was associated with more agonistic and less amicable behavior. Assessing effects of familiarity based on length of association will not be easy because other factors, which also vary over time, may mask any but the most obvious effects.

The presence of established neighbors may also be advantageous in buffering an individual from interactions with less familiar, distant neighbors, a phenomenon akin to Getty's (1981) model of competitive collusion between potential (or in this case actual) competitors to preempt the establishment of further competitors. For example, when only one of five territorial males from the previous year survived on ESA in 1978, the remaining male engaged in far more agonistic interactions during the breeding season with males living beyond the borders of the observation area than in the previous year (0.91 / h of observation in 1978 versus 0.11 / h in 1977). Even his total rate of agonistic interaction in 1978 (1.5 / h) was slightly greater than in 1977 (1.2 / h) when he had three territorial neighbors.

Length of association with group members has been recognized as a factor affecting social relations and their development in primates (Kaplan, 1978; Marler, 1976). In relatively sedentary and long-lived sciurids, such as marmots, prairie dogs, and some ground squirrels, the potential for similar effects clearly exists. Just as it is inappropriate to ignore the possible significance of kinship when predicting and interpreting patterns of social relationships (Alexander, 1975; Sherman, 1980), it is inappropriate not to consider effects of familiarity in long-lived and relatively sedentary animals.

Acknowledgments

We thank E. Duncan, J. Duncan, V. Loewen, I. McLean, A. Towns, and H. Yanishewski for assistance in the field, and D. A. Boag for providing access to the facilities of the R. B. Miller Biological Station. G. R. Michener and an anonymous reviewer provided useful comments on an earlier draft of the manuscript. Financial support came from the National Science and Engineering Council of Canada (Grant A5865 to J. O. Murie) and the Department of Zoology, University of Alberta.

Literature Cited

Alexander, R. E. 1975. The search for a general theory of behavior. Behav. Sci., 20: 77–100.

Armitage, K. B. 1974. Male behaviour and territoriality in the yellow-bellied marmot. J. Zool. London, 172:233–265.

———. 1977. Social variety in the yellow-bellied marmot: a population-behavioural system. Anim. Behav., 25:585–593.

———. 1981. Sociality as a life-history tactic of ground squirrels. Oecologia, 48:36–49.

Armitage, K. B., and J. F. Downhower. 1974. Demography of yellow-bellied marmot populations. Ecology, 55:1233–1245.

Balfour, A. D. 1979. Mirror-image stimulation as a behavioral profiling technique in Columbian ground squirrels. Unpubl. M. S. thesis, Univ. Alberta, Edmonton, 103 pp.

Barash, D. P. 1973. The social biology of the Olympic marmot. Anim. Behav. Monogr., 6:173–245.

Bernstein, I. S., T. P. Gordon, and R. M. Rose. 1974. Factors influencing the expression of aggression during introductions to rhesus monkey groups. Pp. 211–240, *in* Primate aggression, territoriality, and xenophobia (R. L. Holloway, ed.). Academic Press, New York, 513 pp.

Betts, B. J. 1973. The adaptiveness of the social organization of a population of Columbian ground squirrels (*Spermophilus columbianus*). Unpubl. Ph.D. dissert., Univ. Montana, Missoula, 235 pp.

Boag, D. A., and J. O. Murie. 1981. Population ecology of Columbian ground squirrels in southwestern Alberta. Canadian J. Zool., 59:2230–2240.

Carpenter, C. R. 1974. Aggressive behavioral systems. Pp. 459–496, *in* Primate aggression, territoriality, and xenophobia (R. L. Holloway, ed.). Academic Press, New York, 513 pp.

Dunford, C. 1977a. Social system of round-tailed ground squirrels. Anim. Behav., 25:885–906.

———. 1977b. Behavioral limitation of round-tailed ground squirrel density. Ecology, 58:1254–1268.

Festa-Bianchet, M. 1981. Reproduction in yearling female Columbian ground squirrels (*Spermophilus columbianus*). Canadian J. Zool., 59:1032–1035.

Fisher, J. 1954. Evolution and bird sociality. Pp. 71–83, *in* Evolution as a process (J. Huxley, A. C. Hardy, and E.B. Ford, eds.). Allen and Unwin, London, 416 pp.

Getty, T. 1981. Competitive collusion: the preemption of competition during the sequential establishment of territories. Amer. Nat., 118:426–431.

Harris, M. A., and J. O. Murie. 1982. Responses to oral gland scents from different males in Columbian ground squirrels. Anim. Behav., 30:140–148.

Hoogland, J. L. 1981. Nepotism and cooperative breeding in the black-tailed prairie dog (Sciuridae: *Cynomys ludovicianus*). Pp. 283–310, *in* Natural selection and social behavior: recent research and new theory (R. D. Alexander and D. W. Tinkle, eds.). Chiron Press, New York, 532 pp.

———. 1982. Prairie dogs avoid extreme inbreeding. Science, 215:1639–1641.

Jaeger, R. G. 1981. Dear enemy recognition and the costs of aggression between salamanders. Amer. Nat., 117:962–974.

Kaplan, J. R. 1978. Fight interference and altruism in rhesus monkeys. Amer. J. Phys. Anthropol. 49:241–249.

Marler, P. 1976. On animal aggression—the roles of strangeness and familiarity. Amer. Psychol. 31:239–246.

McCarley, H. 1966. Annual cycle, population dynamics and adaptive behavior of *Citellus tridecemlineatus*. J. Mamm., 47:294–316.

———. 1970. Differential reproduction in *Spermophilus tridecemlineatus*. Southwestern Nat., 14:293–296.

McLean, I. G. 1981. Social ecology of the Arctic ground squirrel, *Spermophilus parryii*. Unpubl. Ph.D. dissert., Univ. Alberta, Edmonton, 149 pp.

———. 1982. The association of female kin in the Arctic ground squirrel *Spermophilus parryii*. Behav. Ecol. Sociobiol., 10:91–99.

Michener, G. R. 1979. Spatial relationships and social organization of adult Richardson's ground squirrels. Canadian J. Zool., 57:125–139.

———. 1981. Ontogeny of spatial relationships and social behavior in juvenile Richardson's ground squirrels. Canadian J. Zool., 59:1666–1676.

———. 1983. Kin identification, matriarchies, and the evolution of sociality in ground-dwelling sciurids. Pp. 528–572, *in* Recent advances in the study of mammalian behavior (J. F. Eisenberg and D. G. Kleiman, eds.). Spec. Publ., Amer. Soc. Mamm., 7:1–753.

Michener, G. R., and D. R. Michener. 1977. Population structure and dispersal in Richardson's ground squirrels. Ecology, 58:359–368.

Murie, J. O., and M. A. Harris. 1978. Territoriality and dominance in male Columbian ground squirrels (*Spermophilus columbianus*). Canadian J. Zool., 56:2402–2412.

———. 1982. Annual variation of spring emergence and breeding in Columbian ground squirrels (*Spermophilus columbianus*). J. Mamm. 63:431–439.

Murie, J. O., D. A. Boag, and V. K. Kivett. 1980. Litter size in Columbian ground squirrels (*Spermophilus columbianus*). J. Mamm., 61:237–244.

Sherman, P. W. 1976. Natural selection among some group-living organisms. Unpubl. Ph.D. dissert., Univ. Michigan, Ann Arbor, 254 pp.

———. 1980. The limits of ground squirrel nepotism. Pp. 505–554, *in* Sociobiology: beyond nature/nurture? (G. W. Barlow and J. Silverberg, eds.). Westview Press, Boulder, Colorado, 627 pp.

———. 1981. Reproductive competition and infanticide in Belding's ground squirrels and other organisms. Pp. 311–331, *in* Natural selection and social behavior: recent research and new theory. (R. D. Alexander and D. W. Tinkle, eds.). Chiron Press, New York, 532 pp.

Siegel, S. 1956. Nonparametric statistics for the behavioral sciences. McGraw-Hill, New York, 312 pp.

Svendsen, G. E., and K. B. Armitage. 1973. An application of mirror-image stimulation to field behavioral studies. Ecology, 54:623–627.

Wilson, E. O. 1975. Sociobiology: the new synthesis. Harvard University Press, Cambridge, 697 pp.

6. Kinship and Sociality

KENNETH B. ARMITAGE

University of Kansas

Chapter 17

Recruitment in Yellow-bellied Marmot Populations: Kinship, Philopatry, and Individual Variability

Abstract. Recruitment of females forms matrilines, most of which become extinct and are replaced by immigrants. Mother/daughter or sister/sister kin groups share space. Philopatry characterizes matrilines but is not essential for their persistence. Matrilineal bifurcation is associated with the partitioning of a single space into two or more spaces, each of which is shared by individuals who are related by 0.5. Although the number of residents may not change, the total space used increases when matrilines bifurcate. Recruiters differ from nonrecruiters primarily in the number of female yearlings produced. Social females recruit a greater proportion of their yearling daughters than do asocial animals. Male turnover and the presence of unrelated adult females do not significantly affect recruitment, whereas an immigrant adult female nearly always prevents recruitment. Recruitment of yearlings is more likely if they are philopatric; yearlings that wander widely disperse from their natal home ranges. Immigration generally is associated with occupying an empty area. There is no evidence of sex ratio adjustment by successful recruiters.

Introduction

A central problem of population biology is Why does no population increase without limit? Four schools of population regulation are the biotic, climatic, comprehensive, and self-regulation (Krebs, 1978*a*; Lidicker, 1978). The self-regulation school focuses on how members of a species may affect the dispersal, recruitment, and mortality of conspecifics. Central to the self-regulation school is the hypothesis that social interactions influence population dynamics by affecting spacing patterns (Krebs, 1978*b;* Wynne-Edwards, 1962). Spacing is postulated to lead to dispersal, which may be the key to population regulation (Gaines and McClenaghan, 1980; Krebs et al., 1973; Lidicker, 1975). However, dispersal is density-independent (Gaines and McClenaghan, 1980), and much dispersal may be a function of mating strategies (Armitage 1981; Greenwood, 1980).

Dispersal as a mating strategy suggests that population dynamics may be a consequence of the reproductive strategies of individuals rather than a process of population regulation per se. Fairbairn (1978), for example, suggested that benefits at the population level were probably by-products of selection for dispersal at the level of the individual. Individual survival is an exercise in probability (White, 1978). The significant relation between body size and reproductive effort among ground squirrels suggests that reproductive effort is maximal to increase the probability of producing surviving offspring (Armitage, 1981). If selection has maximized reproductive effort, then social mechanisms may evolve to produce a competitive edge. For example, an animal may attempt to exclude other individuals from resources, or kin groups could act cooperatively. If resources are abundant, whether patchy or widely dispersed, an animal increases its direct fitness (Brown, 1980) by sharing resources with its descendants and may increase its indirect fitness by sharing resources with collateral kin. However, sharing resources with collateral kin should be limited because greater return can be expected from investing in offspring rather than in other kin (Rubenstein and Wrangham, 1980).

This individual selection model requires that individuals be variable; individual variability is central to the hypothesis of self-regulation (Bekoff, 1977; Krebs, 1978*b;* Lømnicki, 1978). Although it is unclear whether individual variability has high heritability (Krebs, 1978*b,* 1978*c*) or is developmental (Bekoff, 1977; vom Saal, 1981), the important issue, as emphasized by White (1978), is to determine who survives. Determining the mechanisms that dictate survivorship is also important.

Although dispersal is central to any analysis of individual fitness, the fate of dispersers is rarely known (Gaines and McClenaghan, 1980). Therefore an alternative is to study the process of recruitment. I use recruitment to indicate the retention of individuals in their natal population. By contrast, immigration is the addition to a population of animals that were born elsewhere. The obvious advantage of studying recruitment rather than dispersal is that recruitment can be observed and measured, known individuals can be followed, and the conditions under which recruitment occurs can be analyzed for significant relations with demography, philopatry, and social dynamics.

Certain predictions about recruitment may be derived from the individual selection model and the different reproductive strategies of males and females. Because natal dispersal in mammals is predominantly by males (Greenwood, 1980), recruitment should establish matrilines, that is, groups of closely related females — for example, mother/daughters or sisters. Thus I define a matriline as consisting of all female descendants of a female who remain in their natal population to the end of their second summer of life. Because a greater return can be expected from investing in offspring rather than in the offspring of daughters or sisters, matrilines should bifurcate into potentially competing groups. For example, sisters or halfsisters, who are in a matriline that includes their mother, should initiate their own matrilines. This bifurcation should be characterized by spatial separation of the bifurcating matrilines. These predictions are tested for the yellow-bellied marmot (*Marmota flaviventris*).

Methods

Since 1962, demographic and behavioral data were obtained for six populations of marmots living in the East River Valley near Gothic, Colorado, at an elevation of 2,900 m. Marmots had a clumped distribution that conformed closely to the mosaic of meadow and forest vegetation (Svendsen, 1974). The characteristics of River-Bench, Picnic, North Picnic, and Marmot Meadow localities where marmots were intensively studied were described previously (Armitage, 1974; Svendsen, 1974). Each year all animals in the study sites were trapped, permanently labeled with numbered self-piercing metal ear tags, and marked in distinctive patterns with fur dye for visual identification. Because females with litters usually occupied a burrow distant from any other reproductive female, infants could be assigned to a specific mother. The few instances in which maternity could not be determined will be described later. Sex was recorded for each animal. Age was known for all animals first trapped as young. Age also could be determined for all animals first trapped as yearlings (animals 1 year old) or 2-year olds on the basis of body weight (Armitage et al., 1976). All marmots first trapped with body weights larger than those of 2-year-olds were assumed to be at least 3 years old.

Each summer marmots were observed for several hundred hours. Observations were concentrated in the morning and afternoon when marmots are most active (Armitage, 1962). Each population was censused regularly at intervals

Kinship and Sociality

varying from 5 to 20 min depending on the number of animals and the time required to locate each animal. The location of each animal was recorded as a pair of grid coordinates from a photographic map of each locality. All grid coordinates for each animal were used to plot a perspective block diagram of space use (Sampson, 1975). The individual behavioral profile was determined for 29 adults by mirror-image stimulation (Svendsen, 1974; Svendsen and Armitage, 1973). This profile was used as a measure of individual variability. Statistical analysis included multiple discriminant analysis (Cooley and Lohnes, 1971), chi-square, and ANOVA (Sokal and Rohlf, 1969). Hypotheses for chi-square testing were generated following the procedures described by Slade (1976).

Results

Patterns of Recruitment

Although River-Bench previously was treated as two localities (Armitage 1973, 1974), the exchange of animals between the two suggests that it contained one population. The Bench portion of this site was terminated in 1969 when the remaining animals were removed. One male, son of female 6, was recruited in 1970 at age five (Fig. 17.1). Although he probably fathered the young born that year, the matriline died out. Several matrilines were established in 1962, but all died out by 1973 (Fig. 17.1). The line of female 119 persisted for 10 years, possibly because individuals shifted between the River and Bench sites (Fig. 17.1). A matriline established by female 42 (Armitage, 1973) split into three groups. One group remained at Bench, female 42 returned to River in 1968 and evicted the residents, and female 728 lived as a peripheral animal for a year before moving into River in 1970 when female 42 did not return. Extinct matrilines were replaced by immigrants. Two of these immigrants were first trapped as yearlings. However, to date no immigrant has successfully established a matriline that persisted beyond one generation.

The mosaic of vegetation and rocky outcrops at North Picnic (Armitage, 1974) provides numerous burrow sites where residents may be spatially separated. Many of these sites are peripheral to the main area of meadow, and marmots occupying these sites were designated peripheral animals. The population was maintained almost entirely by immigrants (Fig. 17.2). No matriline has produced a granddaughter.

Closely related female kin groups were introduced twice into North Picnic. In 1969 the introduction coincided with the immigration of highly aggressive female 755. The introduced females disappeared within 3 days. In 1974 two

380

Recruitment in Yellow-bellied Marmot Populations

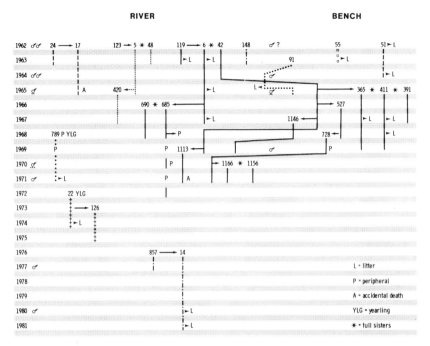

FIGURE 17.1. Patterns of residency, recruitment, and immigration at River-Bench. Each animal is identified by ear-tag number in the year of birth or immigration. Vertical lines show years of residency. Matrilines are represented by vertical lines of the same pattern. Recruits to a matriline are indicated by a short horizontal arrow in the year of birth. Litters from which there was no recruitment are indicated by an arrowhead pointing to L. Resident males are indicated by the male symbol in the first year of residency. The column of male symbols on the right represents males who were resident at Bench and separates Bench residents from River residents. Male symbols that have the same underline indicate that the same individual defended both River and Bench. The resident male of 1970 was born to female 6 in 1965.

females and their weaned young were introduced. Their introduction coincided with the immigration of aggressive female 324, who caused the introduced females to move to peripheral locations. Neither of the introduced females returned in 1975; only one of their young established residency (peripherally), and she failed to reproduce.

A second harem (see Downhower and Armitage 1971 for definition of harem) was established in 1970 when female 1047 immigrated into the locality to a burrow site that was in the territory of a second male and distant from the main burrow area. Although this female and her daughter 1076 collectively produced five litters, the matriline did not persist past 1975.

The failure of matrilines to persist at North Picnic is associated with the res-

381

NORTH PICNIC

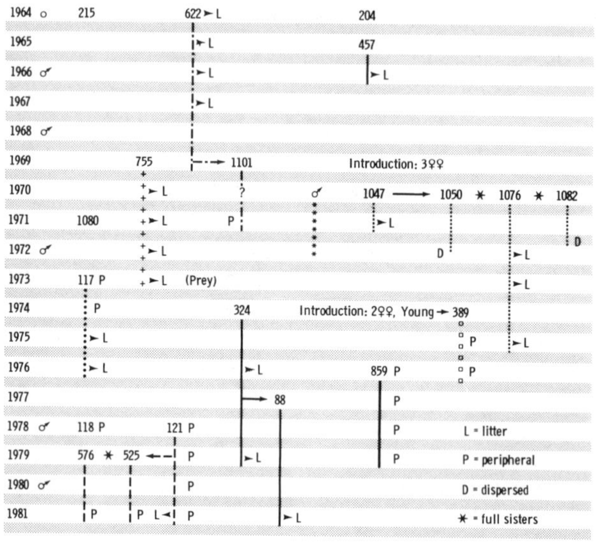

FIGURE 17.2. Patterns of residency, recruitment, and immigration at North Picnic. Numbers and symbols as in Fig. 17.1.

idency or immigration of highly aggressive animals. In 1982, aggressive females 121 and 88 were removed. Within a few days, peripheral females 576 and 525 moved into the main meadow area.

Usually only one adult female occupied Marmot Meadow. She lived at the major burrow site on the north side of an extensive meadow. In some years a second female occupied a secondary burrow site on the south side (Armitage, 1974). Matrilines died out after a few years (Fig. 17.3).

Because resident adult females at this locality generally acted aggressively, it was postulated that aggressiveness, coupled with chance events acting on a small population, prevented matrilines from persisting. For example, female 646 was shot by a tourist in 1967, and 1145 apparently died before she could reproduce. Therefore eight female young were introduced into this locality in 1971. By 1974 only one female remained, but this female established a matriline that persisted into 1982. Interestingly, three females occupying the main burrow area had litters in 1980 that lived in such close proximity that maternity could not be established. The entire group lived together as one social unit. In 1981 the same situation was repeated; in addition, four yearling females lived in the same burrow throughout the summer.

382

A second matriline was established at the secondary burrow site by female 110, who appeared in 1976. However, this line was virtually eliminated in 1981 when a badger dug into the burrow and destroyed female 458 and two litters of seven young. This incident illustrates further how a rare event impinging on a small population can cause extinction of a matriline. This instance of badger predation is the only one known at this locality in 21 years.

Recruitment at Picnic locality contrasts markedly with that at other sites. By 1980 all resident females were descended from female 67, who was a resident when the study began in 1962 (Fig. 17.4). Of eight immigrant females who became resident, only 880 established a matriline that persisted for any length of time, primarily because her daughter 843 lived to be 11 years old.

No immigrant entered Lower Picnic after 1967. By contrast, Upper Picnic was populated by successive immigrants. Some of the residents at Upper Picnic moved there from Lower Picnic. For example, immigrant 880 and her 2-year-old daughters moved there in 1970 when the resident females of the previous year

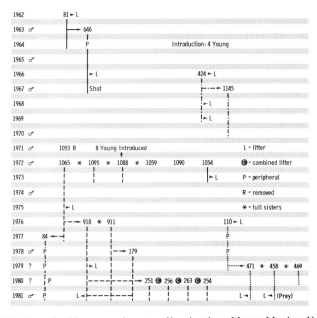

FIGURE 17.3. Patterns of residency, recruitment, and immigration at Marmot Meadow. Numbers and symbols as in Fig. 17.1. A horizontal arrow that crosses two or more vertical lines indicates that young were of uncertain maternity because adult females shared the same burrow system and young emerged as a single social group (1980).

383

failed to return. Likewise, females 167 and 174 moved to Upper Picnic as 2-year-olds when females 843 and 1082 failed to return (Fig. 17.4).

A few animals resided at Middle Picnic, an area between and slightly south of Lower and Upper (Armitage, 1974). In 1966 and 1967, a male living at Middle Picnic established a third harem. No recruit came from this harem.

In 1976 and 1978, litters occurred in a common burrow system, so maternity could not be determined. As in the instances at Marmot Meadow, the young of the litters mingled and the adult females and young formed one social group.

One male, born to 834 at Upper Picnic, became resident in 1975. Although he fathered several litters, none of his descendants persisted.

The major matriline repeatedly split into independent matrilines. For example, the descendants of female 785 formed a matriline distinct from that of females 301 and 349. These animals behaved amicably with animals within the matriline but behaved agonistically with females of the other matriline (Armitage

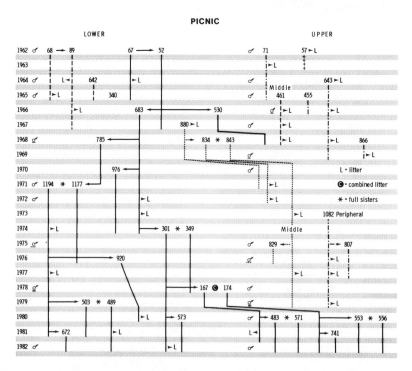

FIGURE 17.4. Patterns of residency, recruitment, and immigration at Picnic. The resident male at Lower Picnic in 1975 was born to female 834 at Upper Picnic in 1971. Note the combined litters in 1976 and 1978. Numbers and symbols as in Fig. 17.1.

and Johns, 1982). As in the other populations, most matrilines eventually became extinct, including the two established by immigrants.

Population Structure and Recruitment

Natal dispersal in yellow-bellied marmots occurs primarily in yearlings (Armitage and Downhower, 1974). Therefore recruitment is defined to have occurred if one or more female yearlings from the same litter remain in their natal locality throughout their second summer of life. In most instances, recruitment was verified by capture of the marmot as a 2-year-old. Of 135 female marmots who emerged as yearlings in their natal locality, 72 were recruited. Recruitment occurred 48 times; two or more yearlings from the same litter were recruited 18 times. In the data analysis, the recruitment of two or more yearlings from the same litter is treated as a single recruitment event.

The formation of matrilines and the higher than expected rates of amicable behavior between mothers and daughters (Armitage and Johns, 1982) suggest that mothers may actively recruit daughters. Therefore, the first question asked is, Is recruitment likely when the mother is present? The answer is affirmative; recruitment was twice as likely to occur as nonrecruitment (Table 17.1, $\chi^2 = 7.5$, $P < 0.01$). The mother's reproductive status did not significantly affect recruitment (Table 17.1, $\chi^2 = 1.7$, $P > 0.1$). However, given that recruitment occurs, neither the mother's presence or absence nor her reproductive status significantly affected recruitment (Table 17.1).

Recruitment could fail because another adult female's behavior causes the yearling female to disperse or become more susceptible to predation. However, recruitment occurred significantly more often than no recruitment when an adult female other than the mother was present (Table 17.1, $\chi^2 = 11.6$, $P < 0.001$). Recruitment also was more likely to occur when the other female was reproductive ($\chi^2 = 8.0$, $P < 0.005$). However, given that recruitment may occur, neither the presence or absence of another adult female nor her reproductive status significantly affected recruitment (Table 17.1). One possible explanation for why the presence of another adult female has no significant effect on recruitment is that some of these females could be closely related to the mother. Closely related adult females might accept potential recruits, thereby increasing their inclusive fitness (Hamilton, 1964). For this analysis, close kin were aunts, sisters, or daughters. There was no significant relation between degree of kinship between mothers and other females and whether recruitment occurred (Table 17.1).

If an immigrant adult female was newly resident in the same summer that

TABLE 17.1. Number of times recruitment occurred or failed in relation to the mother's presence and reproductive status and to the presence, reproductive status, or kinship of adult females other than the mother. Recruitment was considered to occur once each time one or more female yearlings from the same litter remained in their natal locality throughout their second summer of life.

	Recruitment occurred	Recruitment failed	χ^2	P
Mother				
Present	40	19 ⎫		
Absent	8	8 ⎭	1.7	>0.1
Reproductive	18	11 ⎫		
Nonreproductive	22	8 ⎭	0.86	>0.1
Other female				
Present	35	16 ⎫		
Absent	9	4 ⎭	0.002	>0.1
Reproductive	24	8 ⎫		
Non-reproductive	10	9 ⎭	2.68	≅0.1
Nonkin	20	10 ⎫		
Close kin	15	6 ⎭	0.13	>0.1

potential yearling recruits occurred (n = 9), recruitment was significantly unlikely ($\chi^2 = 5.4, P < 0.025$). The only instance of recruitment and immigration in the same year occurred when the immigrant occupied a peripheral area at North Picnic (Fig. 17.2, ♀ 121, 1978).

Newly resident males establish dominance over females; females often react by fleeing (Armitage, 1974). Fleeing may lead to dispersal by yearling females (Armitage and Johns, 1982). Of the 27 possible instances of recruitment coinciding with male turnover, half led to recruitment. Thus, the presence of a new male had no significant effect on recruitment ($\chi^2 = 0.04, P > 0.5$). Similarly, when the resident adult male from the previous year returned, recruitment did not differ significantly from no recruitment ($\chi^2 = 1.3, P > 0.1$).

Characteristics of Recruiters

Ninety-nine adult female yellow-bellied marmots were resident in the study localities; 40 females successfully recruited one or more of their female offspring. The failure of more than half of the females to recruit direct descendants suggests that there may be demographic or behavioral differences between the two classes of female marmots. Recruiters were resident for a longer time and produced more litters, more young, more female young, and more female yearlings than nonrecruiters (Table 17.2). However, there was no significant difference in mean litter size ($F = 1.7, 0.25 > P > 0.1$), nor did recruiters produce a higher proportion of female young than nonrecruiters (Table 17.2).

The demographic characteristics (Table 17.2) are likely highly correlated. For example, a female who is resident for a longer time would probably produce more litters. On average, more litters should produce more young, more female young, and eventually more female yearlings. Therefore, the demographic data were submitted to stepwise discriminant analysis using the BMDP program (Dixon, 1981).

Three variables entered the model: number of female yearlings, number of female young, and number of litters. The number of female yearlings was by far the most important variable. The model correctly classified 89.6% of the 77 females used in this analysis. Three of 44 nonrecruiters were misclassified as recruiters, and five of 33 recruiters were misclassified as nonrecruiters. Four of the five recruiters misclassified as nonrecruiters were females of short residency who produced only one litter, and one was a yearling female who was recruited into the natal population. The fifth female produced only two female yearlings from two litters, but both were recruited. Each of the three misclassified nonrecruiters produced two or more female yearlings from two or more litters, but none was recruited.

Individual Variability

Much of the variation in demographic parameters of recruiters and nonrecruiters, and the misclassification of some animals, could result from individual behavioral differences (Svendsen and Armitage, 1973). These differences are expressed

TABLE 17.2. Some demographic characteristics ($\bar{X} \pm SE$) of recruiters (n = 40) and nonrecruiters (n = 59). N for litter size: recruiters, 91; nonrecruiters, 42.

	Recruiters	Nonrecruiters
Number per female		
Years of residency	4.4 ± 0.32	2.6 ± 0.16
Litters	2.3 ± 0.20	0.7 ± 0.23
Total young	9.8 ± 0.87	2.8 ± 0.56
Female young	4.9 ± 0.45	1.4 ± 0.30
Female yearlings	2.9 ± 0.23	0.3 ± 0.10
Mean litter size	4.3 ± 0.15	3.9 ± 0.26
Mean sex ratio (♀♀/litter)	0.52 ± 0.03	0.46 ± 0.05

demographically; for example, aggressive females produced more young than social or avoider females, but social females produced more young in polygamous situations (Svendsen, 1974).

Twenty-nine adult females were classified as either social or asocial based on their behaviors during mirror-image stimulation (MIS). Social animals were those that made nose contact and pawed and nuzzled the image, usually fed, explored the MIS arena, and generally carried the tail up or wagged the tail during interaction with the image. Asocial animals did not make contact with the image, rarely fed or explored, frequently remained in the rear of the arena, often chirped or stared at the image, and often oriented away from the image. The asocial category probably included both the avoider and aggressive categories of Svendsen (1974).

The demographic characteristics of these two groups were similar except that social animals produced slightly more offspring and recruited about twice as many yearlings as the asocial animals (Table 17.3). The high standard errors indicate that most of the demographic differences were not significant. There was no significant difference in litter size (F = 0.51, $P \cong 0.5$). The mean sex ratios were virtually identical (Table 17.3).

The demographic data were submitted to stepwise discriminant analysis. One variable, number of recruits, entered the model. The model correctly classified 83.3% of the social animals and 56.3% of the asocial marmots. The two social animals classified as asocial failed to recruit; female 1050 never reproduced, and female 920 produced one litter with one daughter who was not recovered as a yearling.

The seven asocial animals misclassified as social were successful recruiters. Three resided at Picnic. Each one (349, 1177, 843) was recruited with a sister

TABLE 17.3. Some demographic characteristics ($\bar{X}$ ± SE) of adult female marmots classified as social (n = 13) or asocial (n = 16). N for litter size: social, 27; asocial, 26.

	Social	Asocial
Number per female		
Years of residency	4.6 ± 0.71	4.3 ± 0.48
Litters	2.3 ± 0.38	1.6 ± 0.33
Total young	7.9 ± 1.6	6.8 ± 1.4
Female young	3.7 ± 0.84	3.2 ± 0.89
Female yearlings	2.3 ± 0.44	1.8 ± 0.57
Female recruits	1.5 ± 0.34	0.7 ± 0.23
Mean litter size	3.8 ± 0.34	4.1 ± 0.30
Mean sex ratio (♀ ♀ / litter)	0.45 ± 0.06	0.43 ± 0.06

(Fig. 17.4). Females 349 and 1177 produced joint litters with their sisters, and each failed to return the year after reproduction (Fig. 17.4). Thus their recruits were shared with their sisters, and it was the sisters who were present when recruitment actually occurred. Female 843 lived most of her adult years alone at Middle Picnic, where one yearling remained with her for one year. Females 622 and 324 were highly aggressive animals living at North Picnic. Although each produced several yearling females, only one daughter of each was recruited (Fig. 17.2). Female 1101 was born in the last year of her mother's life and was present only as a peripheral animal. Female 88 was born in the fourth year of her mother's residency (Fig. 17.2). She was highly aggressive; perhaps this aggressiveness enabled her to become a recruit. Females 110 and 911 lived at Marmot Meadow (Fig. 17.3). The three recruits of female 110 became residents after their mother's death. In effect, they populated a vacated site. Although female 911 was classified as asocial, her MIS profile placed her close to the social group. Her recruitment pattern is more nearly like that of the social animals, and she seems to be the only female misclassified as social whose recruitment pattern was not associated with special circumstances.

Patterns of Space Use

One possible explanation for the lack of significant effects on recruitment by nonmothers (Table 17.2) is that space may be shared by close relatives and that other animals are excluded from this space. Thus juveniles and yearlings would be protected from agonistic behavior that might otherwise be directed toward them by unrelated or distantly related animals. The possible importance of patterns of space use is supported by the observation that female yearlings that are eventual recruits have home ranges that overlap considerably with those of female adults, whereas those that disperse do not (Armitage, 1975). In this chapter I will focus on the relation between kinship and use of space.

Only a sampling of the nearly 300 perspective block diagrams generated from the field data can be presented. Because the dynamics of matriline formation, bifurcation, and extinction are best demonstrated at Picnic locality, selected space-use patterns from Picnic are presented to illustrate six major points associated with recruitment. Picnic locality consists of a meadow on a steep slope with a talus area of 0.85 ha containing about 78 burrows (Armitage, 1974; Svendsen, 1974). The upper side of the talus is bordered by a line of aspen. Lower Picnic includes the line of aspen and all the area below it (the first 18 grids on the vertical axis of the perspective block diagrams). All the area beyond grid 25 on the horizontal axis is meadow. Above the aspen an exposure of rocks on a steep slope

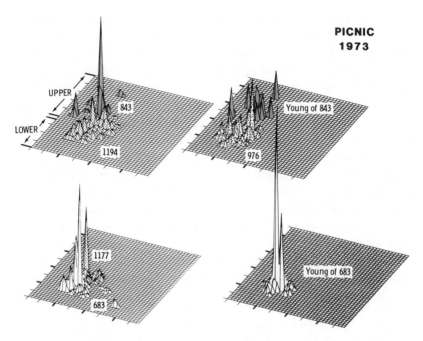

Figure 17.5. Perspective block diagram of space use at Picnic (8.7 ha) in 1973. The height of the peaks for each animal represents the frequency of occurrences. Each animal is identified by one ear-tag number. Closely related animals, such as mother and young or sister pairs, are indicated by the same pattern of shading. The grid lines on the horizontal axis (bottom and top of each diagram) that runs along the bottom and top of the mountain slope are 5 m apart. The grid lines on the vertical axis (left and right sides in the diagram), which runs up the mountain slope, are 9 m apart. Every fifth grid line is marked along the left (vertical) and bottom (horizontal) axes to facilitate comparison of space-use patterns. Every tenth grid line is accentuated. The talus area of Lower Picnic lies between grid lines 7 and 15 on the vertical axis and between lines 12 and 24 on the horizontal axis. All the remaining area of Lower Picnic is meadow with a few scattered clumps of trees. North is toward the bottom of the figure; east is to the left and west to the right.

forms the main burrow area of Upper Picnic. Above the burrow area is a gently sloping meadow studded with large boulders. Animals at Upper Picnic usually foraged from the burrow area up-slope or across-slope (line 20 and higher on the vertical axis of the perspective block diagrams).

Philopatry. I define philopatry as the use by descendants of the same space as their immediate ancestors. Philopatry is best exemplified by the similarity of space use of juveniles and their mothers. Not only was the overall area used by juveniles nearly identical to that of their mothers, but the frequency of use of space within the home range was similar (Fig. 17.5, ♀ 683 and her young; ♀ 843 and her young; Fig. 17.6, ♀ 1177, ♀ 1194, and their combined litter). Yearling females may be philopatric. In 1976 the space-use patterns of yearlings 829 and 807 were similar to those of their mothers, 843 and 1082, respectively (Fig. 17.6). Similarly, the space-use patterns of 489 and 503 were more like that of their mother 1194 than that of their older maternal half-sister 920 or their distant kin 301 (Fig. 17.7). This comparison is best demonstrated by the similarities in the major peaks representing high frequency of space use; the position of the peaks of 489, 503, and 1194 are virtually identical; the peak of 920 is displaced to the right, and that of 301 is displaced upward and to the left (Fig. 17.7).

Yearling excursions. Although space-use patterns of yearlings were philopatric, they frequently traveled into space used by nonkin or by distantly related kin or spent some time in areas little frequented by their mothers. The latter situation is exemplified by yearlings 503 and 489, who frequently were active in areas to the west of the main activity of their mother, 1194 (Fig. 17.7). This pattern of space use overlapped low use areas of their half-sister 920, but none of the space they used overlapped that of their distant kin 167, 174, and 301.

Although yearling 167 was observed most frequently in her mother's home

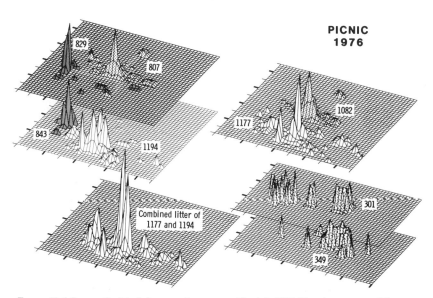

FIGURE 17.6. Perspective block diagram of space use at Picnic in 1976. Note that two sets of diagrams are overlapped to facilitate comparison and reduce the size of the figure. The horizontal base line of the overlapped diagram is accentuated to indicate separation of the two diagrams. The lower left corner is the common reference point for all diagrams.

area, she ranged into Upper Picnic or into areas of Lower Picnic inhabited by distant kin (Fig. 17.8). Such excursions were rare or nonexistent for the five resident adult females. Female 167 did not establish any area of prime use as evidenced by the lack of any major peak in her perspective block diagram. Her sister, 174, also wandered widely and was seen so rarely within the colony area that data were insufficient for analysis. Yearling 829 also ranged into Lower Picnic where unrelated animals lived (Fig. 17.6). These yearlings either did not return the next year or changed locations within the locality. By contrast, yearling 807 was completely philopatric, shared space with her mother, 1082, and returned to the same area the next year (Fig. 17.6).

In 1980, female 495 wandered widely and did not establish any area of primary use (Fig. 17.7). Her mother, 1082, failed to return from the previous year (Fig. 17.4). The space used by 1082 the previous year (Fig. 17.8) was occupied by adult females 167 and 174 (Fig. 17.7). Thus 495 was unable to occupy the space she had used as a juvenile. None of the residents was related to 495; she and a sister (not shown) dispersed by early summer.

The mother (981) of 1194 and 1177 was not present during their yearling year. However, these yearlings did not venture into adjoining home ranges but were

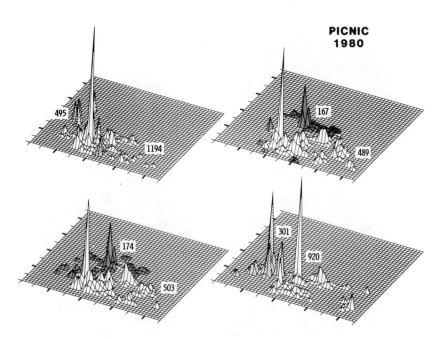

FIGURE 17.7. Perspective block diagram of space use at Picnic in 1980.

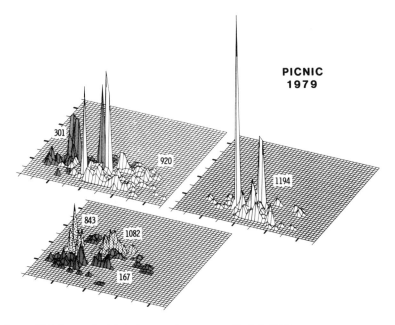

FIGURE 17.8. Perspective block diagram of space use at Picnic in 1979.

active as part of the kin group occupying Lower Picnic (Fig. 17.9). In contrast to 495, 1177 and 1194 were philopatric in their yearling year and were recruited into the population (Fig. 17.4).

Immigration. Successful immigration generally was associated with occupying an empty area or displacing a resident. The latter was rare, but it occurred when 4-year-old female 1082 immigrated into Upper Picnic in 1974. Female 843, who had ranged through much of that area (Fig. 17.9) moved to the east (Fig. 17.6). The space-use patterns of these two unrelated females remained separate during their subsequent residency (Fig. 17.8).

Twice females moved from Lower Picnic to Upper Picnic. Each time the residents of the previous year had not returned. In 1970 females 880, 843, and 834 formed a kin group unrelated to the kin group on Lower Picnic (Fig. 17.4). There was no overlap between the two kin groups in their space use (Fig. 17.9). By contrast, females 167 and 174 frequently returned to Lower Picnic but only into the area occupied by their mother, 301 (Fig. 17.7). In each case the immigrants usurped space that might otherwise have been used by potential female yearling recruits. This takeover of space probably accounts for the lack of recruitment when a new immigrant is present.

**PICNIC
1972**

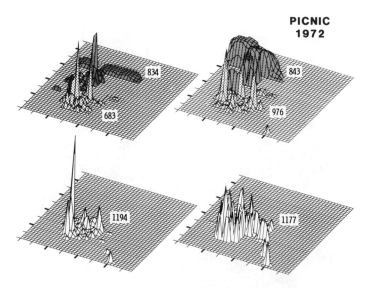

FIGURE 17.9. Perspective block diagram of space use at Picnic in 1972. The kin group on Upper Picnic consists of sisters 834 and 843. On Lower Picnic, the kin group consists of 683, her daughter 976, and her granddaughters 1177 and 1194, who are half-nieces of 976.

Matrilines share space. In 1972 sisters 834 and 843 occupied Upper Picnic, and a kin group consisting of mother, daughter, and granddaughters, who were half-nieces of the daughter, occupied Lower Picnic (Fig. 17.4). The members of each kin group shared space with each other but not with members of the other kin group (Fig. 17.9). Although the members of each kin group had nearly 100% overlap in their home range areas, each individual had its own characteristic pattern of areas of high frequency of use (Fig. 17.9). This pattern of each individual developing its own area of high frequency of use was characteristic of matrilines occupying the same general area; for example, females 683, 976, 1177, and 1194 in 1973 (Fig. 17.5). However, sometimes two sisters used space almost identically; for example, females 489 and 503 in 1980 (Fig. 17.7). Such similarity in both the areal extent and frequency of use of areas within the home ranges occurred only between sisters (excluding the philopatry of mother and juveniles), although mother/daughter patterns were often similar (e.g., ♀ 1194 and her 3-year-old daughter, 920; Fig. 17.8).

Over time, individuals in a matriline were replaced. Of the animals resident at Lower Picnic in 1973, one remained in 1979 (Fig. 17.4). In 1979 the residents were active in the meadows to the west of the talus, where they rarely went in 1973 (compare use of area beyond horizontal grid 25, Figs. 17.5, 17.8). This increase in the use of space at Lower Picnic occurred with no change in the density of residents and was evident by 1976, when a somewhat different cast of characters was present (Fig. 17.6). A possible explanation for the increased use of space by this matriline is given below.

Matrilines may continue without philopatry. Although the matriline on Lower Picnic demonstrates a strong association with philopatry, such an association is not essential for a matriline to continue. Females 843 and 834 continued a matriline at Upper Picnic (Fig. 17.9) that began at Lower Picnic with immigrant 880 (Fig. 17.4). Similarly, females 167 and 174 moved to Upper Picnic in 1980, where they continued a matriline initiated by female 301. Although they made incursions into their mother's space during this first year at Upper Picnic (Fig. 17.7), these incursions ceased in the following years.

Matrilines may continue when emigrants successfully establish residency in a new area. Female 1082, by immigrating into Upper Picnic (Fig. 17.4), continued a matriline begun by female 1047 at North Picnic (Fig. 17.2). The movement of females 42 and 728 from Bench to River (Fig. 17.1) also continued matrilines. The movement of female 42 is an example of breeding dispersal (Greenwood, 1980). Neither the frequency nor the causes of breeding dispersal are known, but it may continue matrilines in habitats distant from their origin.

Bifurcation of matrilines. The bifurcation of matrilines is associated with the partitioning of a single matrilineal space into two or more spaces, each of which is shared by individuals who are related by 0.5. This subdivision of matrilineal space occurred gradually over several years.

The members of the matriline occupying Lower Picnic in 1973 shared the space (Fig. 17.4) and had an average relatedness of 0.29. This group consisted of a female, her daughter, and her two granddaughters who were half-nieces of the daughter. By 1976 the average relatedness of the four residents was 0.25. Although the decrease in average relatedness was slight, the residents formed two groups consisting of two sisters each. Amicable behavior among the four females was significantly less than expected (Armitage and Johns, 1982), and the younger females 301 and 349 wandered widely and concentrated their activities in areas little frequented by females 1177 and 1194 (Fig. 17.6).

By 1979 average relatedness of the five residents had increased to 0.34, but they again formed two kin groups, female 1194 and her daughter 920, and female 301 and her daughters 167 and 174 (Fig. 17.4). The average relatedness within each kin group was 0.5, but relatedness was only 0.0625 between members of the different kin groups. The two kin groups clearly partitioned the available space, and this partitioning was associated with increased activity in the western part of Lower Picnic (Fig. 17.8). The original, closely associated kin group of 1973 (Fig. 17.5) had bifurcated into two matrilines by 1979 (Figs. 17.4, 17.8), and this division into two matrilines was clearly evident in 1980 (Fig. 17.7). Only female 301 remained in one of the matrilines (but her line continued by the emigration of her daughters to Upper Picnic), whereas the other matriline added two members. The addition of two females, daughters of 1194, reduced the average relatedness of the members of the matriline from 0.5 in 1979 to 0.4. Interestingly, the area of high frequency of use by female 920 differed markedly from the high frequency use areas of the other members of the group (Fig. 17.7). This difference suggests a potential bifurcation of the matriline, but female 920 did not return in 1981, and two matrilines continued on Lower Picnic through 1982.

Discussion

Recruitment in yellow-bellied marmot populations is consistent with the model that population dynamics is a consequence of the reproductive strategies of individuals. Recruitment and dispersal of female marmots are not density-dependent (Armitage, 1975; Armitage and Downhower, 1974; Downhower and Armitage, 1981). Population fluctuation seems to be related to whether individuals are successful recruiters rather than to numbers per se. This is not to say that density does not affect recruitment, but density is intricately interwoven with mating strategy and individual variability. For example, virtually all male marmots disperse from their natal areas; this dispersal is best understood as a result of mating strategy rather than as a response to density (Armitage and Johns, 1982; Greenwood, 1980). Breeding dispersal, however, may be related to density. The movement of female 42 from Bench to River (Fig. 17.1) occurred when population density at Bench reached its highest level (Armitage, 1973). Similarly, female 1082 emigrated from North Picnic when the density was high.

The predictions about recruitment were substantiated. Recruitment establishes matrilines of closely related individuals, matrilines divide into competing kin groups, and these groups partition the available space. Members of a matriline share space that may be passed from mother to daughter. Thus philopatry is an essential feature of recruitment and the formation of matrilines, but matrilines may persist when individuals emigrate to a new area. Philopatry is especially evident in the close similarity between the space-use patterns of mothers and their young. This space sharing and the subsequent inheritance of the space by descendants is a form of behavioral reproductive investment. Because juveniles and recruits share space with their mothers or other close relatives, they are buffered from social interactions of other adult females who occupy different space. This interpretation is supported by the high rates of amicable behavior among close kin and burrowmates and high rates of agonistic behavior among distantly related animals and nonburrowmates (Armitage and Johns, 1982). Spatial separation between kin groups (Figs. 17.6–17.8) probably accounts for the lack of significant effects of other females on recruitment (Table 17.1). The lack of recruitment when an immigrant is present may also be explained largely on patterns of space use. Most immigrants became resident in the mother's absence. The potential recruit was not spatially separated from unrelated adults and was unable to achieve residency.

The formation of kin groups or matrilines may be common in polygynous rodents. *Microtus pennsylvanicus* populations are organized into mother/young units during the breeding season (Madison, 1980), and *M. montanus* may form extended maternal families (Jannett, 1978). Kin groups occur in many ground squirrels (reviewed by Armitage, 1981; Michener, 1983). Matrilines are a social mechanism for increasing reproductive success, that is, for increasing direct fitness (Brown, 1980). Within matrilines, sisters may share resources. The formation of collateral kin groups is a component of indirect fitness (or the inclusive fitness of Hamilton, 1964). In these cases each animal increases its indirect fitness by sharing resources with closely related kin. The alternative is for those resources to be used by nonrelatives or distant relatives.

Not surprisingly, male turnover did not affect recruitment. The predominance of male dispersal in polygynous mammals has often been explained as a mechanism for avoiding inbreeding (reviewed by Greenwood, 1980). A male can assure himself of a population of unrelated females with whom to breed by accepting all adult and yearling females that are present in his first year of residency. To avoid inbreeding, a resident male should inhibit recruitment of yearling daughters because he might breed with them in subsequent years. Fifteen males were resident when 32 yearling daughters were present. Significantly more were recruited (23) than not ($\chi^2 = 6.1$, $0.025 > P > 0.01$). Six males resided with 10 2-year-old daughters; nine females did not breed ($\chi^2 = 6.4$, $P < 0.025$). Four of these females bred the first year a new male was present. By contrast, when their fathers were not present, the number (19) of 2-year-olds breeding was not significantly different from the number (26) not breeding ($\chi^2 = 1.1$, $P > 0.1$). These results suggest that males do not affect recruitment of females but do not experience extreme inbreeding. Because I have no evidence that adult males emigrate to avoid inbreeding, inbreeding avoidance probably occurs because a 2-year-old female does not come into estrus if her father is present (Hoogland, 1982).

A few females may produce most of the recruits. At Picnic, all residents in

1982 were descended from one female (Fig. 17.4). Of a population of 27 adult *Spermophilus tridecemlineatus*, 24 were derived from only four of 20 females resident four years earlier (McCarley, 1970). The average annual production of young was about 33% greater in the four successful reproducers than in the 16 unsuccessful reproducers. Chance may play a role as more female descendants may result from female-biased litters (Michener, 1980).

If more females may be recruited from female-biased litters, the question arises whether yellow-bellied marmots adaptively vary the sex ratio of their progeny (Clutton-Brock, 1982). This question focuses on whether reproductive success varies more widely among males and females when parental investment influences the success of offspring (Trivers and Willard, 1973). The reproductive success of individuals in the wild is related to mating strategy. In polygynous species such as yellow-bellied marmots, in which males predominate in dispersal, reproductive success is difficult to measure. Because for all practical purposes only female yellow-bellied marmots are recruited into their natal populations, sex-ratio manipulation by the best recruiters should favor females. If one examines small samples, evidence can be found to support this prediction. For example, two adult females produced all-female litters and recruited all their daughters. However, another recruiter produced only 27% female offspring, and seven of nine young of female 14 were males even though River was underpopulated (Fig. 17.1). When large sample sizes were considered, there was no evidence for sex-ratio manipulation (Table 17.2).

This relationship was explored further by comparing the eight best recruiters with the poor recruiters. The best recruiters recruited three or more daughters during their residency and produced 30 of the 72 recruits. The 20 poor recruiters produced one recruit each. The best recruiters produced more young ($\bar{X} = 14.1$ versus 8.6), more female young ($\bar{X} = 6.5$ versus 4.4), and more yearling daughters ($\bar{X} = 4.6$ versus 2.5). There was no difference in the proportion of female offspring (best: 0.46, poor: 0.52). The most striking difference was that the best recruiters recruited 81% and the poor recruiters recruited only 41% of their yearling daughters. This analysis supports the result of the stepwise discriminant analysis that producing yearling daughters is the critical factor determining successful recruitment. The analysis also indicates that some females simply are good recruiters. The behavioral profiles of seven of the best recruiters were known; five were classified as social. Thus individual variability in behavior is more important in determining recruitment than sex bias in litters.

One reason that sex-ratio bias does not occur in marmots is that dispersal may be a successful reproductive strategy. For males, dispersal is the only strategy, and any female who produces sons has some expectation of reproductive success. For example, female 683 (Fig. 17.4), who recruited all of her yearling daughters, produced a son who became resident at Cliff, where he was the putative father of four young. A son of female 424, who recruited only one daughter while resident at Marmot Meadow (Fig. 17.3), became resident at North Picnic, where he was the putative father of nine young. Females also disperse and successfully reproduce. For example, female 1082 moved from North Picnic to Picnic. A number of immigrant females produced litters (Figs. 17.1–17.4). The number of immigrants plus the large number of transient marmots trapped at our study sites (Armitage and Downhower, 1974) indicate considerable movement. Many of these animals become satellites (Svendsen, 1974). Possibly, reproductive success among some of these animals is as high as that of some recruiters. As a consequence, there may be no net gain for producing sex-biased litters over the long term, and annual breeders, such as marmots, may be unable to manipulate the sex ratio profitably in the short term. More fitness may accrue from successful recruitment than from sex manipulation.

If marmots are maximizing their direct fitness, why is there so much variation in recruitment? Population density does not account for this variation; some females failed to recruit daughters even when populations were low (e.g., River, after 1971, Fig. 17.1; North Picnic, Fig. 17.2; Marmot Meadow, Fig. 17.3). The characteristics of the potential recruits doubtless are a factor, and their role will be the subject of a future paper. A possible dispersal strategy to balance a recruitment strategy seems inadequate to explain the variability. Possibly selection has favored phenotypic plasticity. There are many social (Armitage, 1977) and ecological environments (Svendsen, 1974), and they are not constant but change in space and time. The variability among yellow-bellied marmots enables this species to live as isolated individuals, as monogamous pairs, in harems (Downhower and Armitage, 1971), or in large colonies consisting of several contiguous harems (Johns and Armitage, 1979). In the same geographic area, they occur in grass/forb or sagebrush/grass/forb meadows, along riverbanks, under cabins, in a small talus patch in an aspen woodland, and even in trees (Garrott and Jenni, 1978). Some of the variability, especially behavioral, expressed in marmots may result from intrauterine influences during development (vom Saal, 1981) or may be a consequence of postnatal developmental experiences (Bekoff, 1977). Heterozygosity may increase fitness (Lidicker, 1981; Smith et al., 1975). Both developmental and heterotic models imply that the production of superior phenotypes will be associated with inferior phenotypes. Thus phenotypic plasticity as an adaptive strategy and/or the mechanisms involved in producing superior

399

phenotypes will continually be associated with the production of individuals whose fitness is relatively low and who do not contribute to subsequent generations. Our attempts to describe and explain individual fitness may be confounded by the presence of these evolutionarily expendable animals. An adaptive system that produces phenotypes of differing fitnesses makes understandable the high rate of extinction of most matrilines and the high level of individual variability. Social biology and population dynamics theories are in a state of flux. We are well advised ''to concentrate on basic issues that bear on a variety of theoretical postures'' (Arnold, 1981). The formation of matrilines, the sharing of space by close relatives, and the differences between recruiters and nonrecruiters suggest that kinship and individual variability are central to these issues.

Acknowledgments

This research was supported by National Science Foundation grants G16354, GB1980, GB6123, GB8526, GB32494, BMS74-21193, DEB78-07327, and DEB81-21231. Field facilities were provided by the Rocky Mountain Biological Laboratory. My deepest appreciation goes to Keith Armitage, Jerry F. Downhower, Barbara A. Frase, Robert Fleet, Dennis Johns, Delbert L. Kilgore, Jr., Orlando A. Schwartz, Gerald E. Svendsen, Milton Topping, and Gary Worthen for their assistance in the field and with data analysis and for the intellectual stimulation they provided over the 21 years of this study. Daniel Leger, Gail Michener, and Jan Murie provided helpful comments on an earlier version of this manuscript.

Literature Cited

Armitage, K. B. 1962. Social behaviour of a colony of the yellow-bellied marmot (*Marmota flaviventris*). Anim. Behav., 10:319–331.
———. 1973. Population changes and social behavior following colonization by the yellow-bellied marmot. J. Mamm., 54:842–854.
———. 1974. Male behaviour and territoriality in the yellow-bellied marmot. J. Zool. London, 172:233–265.
———. 1975. Social behavior and population dynamics of marmots. Oikos, 26:341–354.
———. 1977. Social variety in the yellow-bellied marmot: a population-behavioural system. Anim. Behav., 25:585–593.
———. 1981. Sociality as a life-history tactic of ground squirrels. Oecologia, 48:36–49.
Armitage, K. B., and J. F. Downhower. 1974. Demography of yellow-bellied marmot populations. Ecology, 55:1233–1245.
Armitage, K. B., and D. W. Johns. 1982. Kinship, reproductive strategies and social dynamics of yellow-bellied marmots. Behav. Ecol. Sociobiol., 11:55–63.

Armitage, K. B., J. F. Downhower, and G. E. Svendsen. 1976. Seasonal changes in weights of marmots. Amer. Midland Nat., 96:36–51.

Arnold, S. J. 1981. Sociobiology evolving. Evolution, 35:824–825.

Bekoff, M. 1977. Mammalian dispersal and the ontogeny of individual behavioral phenotypes. Amer. Nat., 111:715–732.

Brown, J. L. 1980. Fitness in complex avian social systems. Pp. 115–128, *in* Evolution of social behavior: hypotheses and empirical tests (H. Markl, ed.). Verlag Chemie, Deerfield Beach, Florida, 253 pp.

Clutton-Brock, T. H. 1982. Sons and daughters. Nature, 298:11–13.

Cooley, W. W., and P. R. Lohnes. 1971. Multivariate data analysis. John Wiley, New York, 364 pp.

Dixon, W. J., ed. 1981. BMDP statistical software. University of California Press, Berkeley, 725 pp.

Downhower, J. F., and K. B. Armitage. 1971. The yellow-bellied marmot and the evolution of polygamy. Amer. Nat., 105:355–370.

———. 1981. Dispersal of yearling yellow-bellied marmots (*Marmota flaviventris*). Anim. Behav., 29:1064–1069.

Fairbairn, D. J. 1978. Dispersal of deermice, *Peromyscus maniculatus:* proximal causes and effects on fitness. Oecologia, 32:171–193.

Gaines, M. S., and L. R. McClenaghan, Jr. 1980. Dispersal in small mammals. Ann. Rev. Ecol. Syst., 11:163–196.

Garrott, R. G., and D. A. Jenni. 1978. Arboreal behavior of yellow-bellied marmots. J. Mamm., 59:433–434.

Greenwood, P. J. 1980. Mating systems, philopatry and dispersal in birds and mammals. Anim. Behav., 28:1140–1162.

Hamilton, W. D. 1964. The genetical theory of social behaviour. I, II. J. Theor. Biol., 7:1–52.

Hoogland, J. L. 1982. Prairie dogs avoid extreme inbreeding. Science, 215:1639–1641.

Jannett, F. J., Jr. 1978. The density-dependent formation of extended maternal families of the montane vole, *Microtus montanus manus*. Behav. Ecol. Sociobiol., 3:245–263.

Johns, D., and K. B. Armitage. 1979. Behavioral ecology of alpine yellow-bellied marmots. Behav. Ecol. Sociobiol., 5:133–157.

Krebs, C. J. 1978a. Ecology: the experimental analysis of distribution and abundance. 2nd ed. Harper and Row, New York, 678 pp.

———. 1978b. A review of the Chitty hypothesis of population regulation. Canadian J. Zool., 56:2463–2480.

———. 1978c. Aggression, dispersal, and cyclic changes in populations of small rodents. Pp. 59–60, *in* Aggression, dominance, and individual spacing (L. Krames, P. Pliner, and T. Alloway, eds.). Plenum, New York, 183 pp.

Krebs, C. J., M. S. Gaines, B. L. Keller, J. H. Myers, and R. H. Tamarin. 1973. Population cycles in small rodents. Science, 179:35–41.

Lidicker, W. Z., Jr. 1975. The role of dispersal in the demography of small mammals. Pp. 103–128, *in* Small mammals: their productivity and population dynamics (F. B. Golley, K. Petrusewicz, and L. Ryszkowski, eds.). Cambridge Univ. Press, London, 451 pp.

————. 1978. Regulation of numbers in small mammal populations—historical reflections and a synthesis. Pymatuning Symp. Ecol., 5:122–141.

————. 1981. Organization and chaos in population structure: some thoughts on future directions for mammalian population genetics. Pp. 309–320, *in* Mammalian population genetics (M. H. Smith and J. Joule, eds.). Univ. Georgia Press, Athens, 380 pp.

Lømnicki, A. 1978. Individual differences between animals and the natural regulation of their numbers. J. Anim. Ecol., 47:461–475.

Madison, D. M. 1980. Space use and social structure in meadow voles, *Microtus pennsylvanicus*. Behav. Ecol. Sociobiol., 7:65–71.

McCarley, H. 1970. Differential reproduction in *Spermophilus tridecemlineatus*. Southwestern Nat., 14:293–296.

Michener, G. R. 1980. Differential reproduction among female Richardson's ground squirrels and its relation to sex ratio. Behav. Ecol. Sociobiol., 7:173–178.

————. 1983. Kin identification, matriarchies, and the evolution of sociality in ground-dwelling sciurids. Pp. 528–572, *in* Recent advances in the study of mammalian behavior (J. F. Eisenberg and D. G. Kleiman, eds.). Spec. Publ., Amer. Soc. Mamm., 7:1–753.

Rubenstein, D. I., and R. W. Wrangham. 1980. Why is altruism towards kin so rare? Z. Tierpsychol., 54:381–387.

Sampson, R. J. 1975. Surface II graphics system. Kansas Geological Survey, Lawrence, Kansas, 240 pp.

Slade, N. A. 1976. Analysis of social structure from multiple capture data. J. Mamm., 57:790–795.

Smith, M. H., C. T. Garten, Jr., and P. R. Ramsey. 1975. Genic heterozygosity and population dynamics in small mammals. Pp. 85-102, *in* Isozymes IV: genetics and evolution (C. R. Markert, ed.). Academic Press, New York, 956 pp.

Sokal, R. R., and F. J. Rohlf. 1969. Biometry. W. H. Freeman, San Francisco, California, 776 pp.

Svendsen, G. E. 1974. Behavioral and environmental factors in the spatial distribution and population dynamics of a yellow-bellied marmot population. Ecology, 55:760–771.

Svendsen, G. E., and K. B. Armitage. 1973. An application of mirror-image stimulation to field behavioral studies. Ecology, 54:623–627.

Trivers, R. L., and D. E. Willard. 1973. Natural selection of parental ability to vary the sex ratio of offspring. Science, 191:90–91.

vom Saal, F. S. 1981. Variation in phenotype due to random intrauterine positioning of male and female fetuses in rodents. J. Reprod. Fert., 62:633–650.

White, T. C. R. 1978. The importance of a relative shortage of food in animal ecology. Oecologia, 33:71–86.

Wynne-Edwards, V. C. 1962. Animal dispersion in relation to social behaviour. Oliver and Boyd, Edinburgh, 653 pp.

BEDFORD M. VESTAL AND HOWARD McCARLEY

University of Oklahoma and Austin College

Chapter 18

Spatial and Social Relations of Kin in Thirteen-lined and Other Ground Squirrels

Abstract. Dispersion patterns can influence the pattern of social behavior within populations. The spatial overlap between the home ranges of thirteen-lined ground squirrel (*Spermophilus tridecemlineatus*) kin and nonkin was examined in two populations. Home ranges of adult female relatives (dam/daughter and sisters) overlapped more than did those of nonkin, dam/son, or brother/sister pairs. Adult littermate sibling home ranges overlapped more than those of nonlittermate siblings. Female kin live near each other in several other species of ground squirrels. Factors that influence spatial grouping of female kin in thirteen-lined ground squirrels and other species of ground squirrels may include adult fidelity to home range; a sexual difference in dispersal; differential reproduction among females; patchiness and structure of the habitat; population density; and the degree of temporal overlap of squirrels of different degrees of kinship. Spatial groupings of kin could lead to the evolution of nepotistic interactions. Those species exhibiting the most types and greatest frequencies of nepotistic interactions generally live in dense populations, where kin may be in close proximity and have opportunities for interactions. Increased contact among kin may lead to inbreeding, but little is known about the degree of inbreeding in ground squirrels. *S. tridecemlineatus* lives in sparse populations, and individuals appear to interact infrequently. A variety of information on the social behavior and organization of thirteen-lined ground squirrels is needed to compare this relatively asocial species with its more sociable congeners.

Introduction

Kinship within a ground squirrel aggregation, although not an evolutionary cause of sociality, may enhance the advantages of group living (Hoogland and Sherman, 1976; Sherman, 1980a). Interactions between kin can take the form of nepotism, which is unreciprocated assistance or favoritism directed more toward close kin than toward distant kin or nonkin (Sherman, 1980a, 1980b). Nepotism could increase inclusive fitness, but for nepotism to occur relatives must be spatially and temporally distributed so they can interact. Further, individuals must be able to discriminate kin from nonkin.

Our discussion concentrates on dispersion of relatives and social behavior in thirteen-lined ground squirrels (*Spermophilus tridecemlineatus*) and compares this species with other ground squirrels of the genus *Spermophilus*. *S. tridecemlineatus* has the widest geographic distribution of any ground squirrel species, ranging from Texas to the Canadian prairie provinces and from Ohio westward into Utah (Hall, 1981). In spite of its wide distribution, less is known about its social behavior than about that of several other less widely distributed species.

Rigorous descriptions of spatial distributions are difficult to obtain because an individual's use of space varies from day to day and over seasons (Getty, 1981). Individual ground squirrels have a burrow or burrows forming the focus of their activities. Individuals space themselves and their burrows relative to conspecifics and environmental factors (Murray and Vestal, 1979; Waser and Wiley, 1980). We deal mainly with the relation between spacing and the probability that interaction will occur among individuals, particularly kin. Only broad generalizations are considered because the detailed observations needed for precise descriptions are not available.

Little information is available on spatial relations of relatives in thirteen-lined ground squirrels. The clustering of initial trap captures of two groups of juveniles near their apparent dams was used to infer that they may live in family groups (Evans, 1951; Michener, 1983). However, since the capture dates were near the time of emergence from the natal burrow (Schwagmeyer, 1979), there had probably been little opportunity for young to disperse from their natal sites. Hohn (1966) noted that home range locations of yearling females were similar to the locations they occupied as juveniles before hibernation and that juvenile females settled near their natal areas. Silverman (1981) reported home range overlap among female relatives, but females shared nearly equal proportions of their home ranges with nonrelatives and relatives.

Other evidence indicates that thirteen-lined ground squirrel females are more likely than males to settle near their dams. Rongstad (1965) and McCarley (1966) reported juvenile males dispersing farther than females, but there was consider-able variation and overlap among dispersal distances of the sexes. Schwagmeyer (1979) found juvenile male dispersal /mortality to be so high that in one year none remained on the natal area as yearlings. Later, on the same study site, Silverman (1981) reported higher male than female mortality among juveniles but no sex difference in dispersal distance.

Methods

The data we present were collected by two sets of investigators using different methods (McCarley, 1966; Schwagmeyer, 1979, 1980). These data were origi-nally collected for other purposes, but they are the best available data sets for studying spatial overlap among kin of thirteen-lined ground squirrels. Descrip-tions of study sites and methods of data collection were presented in detail by McCarley (1966) for the Texas population and by Schwagmeyer (1979, 1980) for the Michigan population. In both studies, genetic relations were determined by capturing the undispersed litters with their dams or from a burrow that only their dam had used extensively. Any cases of questionable relations were not used.

The Texas population was on 29 ha of the Woodlawn Country Club Golf Course, 9.7 km north of Sherman, Texas. Population size varied from 24 to 34 adults per year. The fairways and tee areas were regularly mowed, and adjacent "roughs" had taller vegetation. The squirrels were captured by noosing or trap-ping, toe-clipped for permanent identification, and marked with fur dye for visual identification. Adults were individually dye marked, but juveniles had only a litter mark. From June 1963 through July 1968 squirrels were captured and marked primarily on the one day each week when the course was closed to the public, but observations were made on other days. Sightings and captures (loca-tions) of individuals were recorded onto gridded plots of the study site within 30.5 m quadrats. The area was not gridded, but adequate natural landmarks allowed accurate location. For analysis, only the quadrat number was used for location. Yearly home ranges of each squirrel were delineated by lines connect-ing the outermost corner of each quadrat in which the squirrel was observed. The lifetime home range encompassed each individual's yearly ranges.

There were 29 dam/daughter pairs and 14 dam/son pairs. To measure the overlap of the home ranges of dams and their offspring, the offspring's home range plot was overlaid on the plot of the dam's home range and the number of the offspring's locations that fell within the dam's home range or in quadrats adjacent to it was counted. The proportions of the offspring's locations in quadrats that were within and adjacent to the dam's range were calculated for the following conditions: (1) dam's lifetime home range versus offspring's location in its year of birth when a juvenile, (2) dam's lifetime home range versus offspring's location during the years the offspring was an adult, (3) dam's lifetime home range versus offspring's location during the years the offspring was an adult but the dam was not present, and (4) the dam's home range versus offspring's location for those years when both were alive and present on the study site as adults. Measures 3 and 4 are subsets of measure 2.

The measures of dam/offspring overlap must be compared with random overlap measures. To generate a comparison measure, dams were randomly paired with unrelated offspring. The only constraints to a strictly random pairing were that each dam was compared with the same number of male and female nonkin as in the comparison of relatives, and the members of the pair had to overlap in time on the study site by at least one year. The plots of the nonkin (random) group were then measured for overlap in the same way as those of the kin had been.

A number of siblings (offspring of the same dam) were also present on the study site. They were divided into either littermates (LM) or nonlittermates (NLM). Twelve female/female pairs (eight LM, four NLM), 15 male/female pairs (six LM, nine NLM), and five male/male pairs (two LM and three NLM) were available. The plots were overlaid as in the dam/offspring comparisons, but slightly different measures were recorded. We recorded the overlap of one member of the pair (a) with the second member (b). We then reversed the plots and recorded the overlap of b on a. The proportion of locations of an individual in quadrats within and adjacent to its sibling's range were calculated for the following conditions: (1) sibling's lifetime home range versus individual's location in its year of birth when a juvenile; (2) sibling's lifetime home range versus individual's location while an adult; (3) sibling's lifetime home range versus individual's location during the years the individual was an adult but the sibling was not present; and (4) sibling's home range versus individual's home range for those years when both were alive and present as adults. Measures 3 and 4 are subsets of measure 2.

Comparison groups of nonkin were randomly generated (as in the dam/offspring comparisons) for both female/female and the male/female groups; the male/male group was too small for this. Each individual was present in as many pairs as it was in the kin group, and the pairs overlapped by at least one year. In the case of one male/female pair the latter constraint could not be met.

The overlap measures of dam/offspring and sibling pairs were summed over pairs within each group and compared by means of the *G*-test of independence (Sokal and Rohlf, 1981). If *P* was less than 0.05 the differences were considered significant.

The Michigan data are from work by Schwagmeyer (1979, 1980), who trapped and observed squirrels during the summers of 1976–1978. The distance data reported here were collected during the summer of 1978 when genetic relations were known. The study site was a 5.2 ha section of the University of Michigan's Matthaei Botanical Garden in Ann Arbor, Michigan. Most of the area was regularly mowed to a height of 5 cm. A variety of ornamental trees and shrubs provided landmarks for mapping squirrel locations. The ground squirrels were trapped and toe-clipped for permanent identification and dye marked for visual identification. Population size ranged from 12 to 33 adults over the three years of the study. Home range data were collected during two periods of the 1978 season; during pregnancy and lactation (spring range, 9 May to 23 June) and 3–5 weeks after emergence of litters from natal burrows (summer range, 31 July to 15 August). Home range data were collected for individuals during 1 h of morning and 1 h of afternoon activity on different days, with locations recorded at 10-min intervals. The locations of observations were recorded onto a plot of the study site and

TABLE 18.1. Percentage of offspring locations that were within or adjacent to the dam's home range in a Texas population of thirteen-lined ground squirrels. Nonkin data are derived from randomly pairing unrelated dams and offspring from the daughter/dam and son/dam groups and calculating the percentage of overlap as was done for relatives. Numbers of offspring locations observed in parentheses.

	Overlap (%)			
	Daughter/dam	Nonkin	Son/dam	Nonkin
Overlap with dam's lifetime home range when				
Juvenile	92% (50)	* 22% (50)	96% (25)	* 36% (25)
Adult	76% (138)	* 21% (138)	50% (48)	* 27% (48)
Adult; dam absent	82% (82)	* 26% (84)	50% (24)	27% (37)
Overlap with dam's home range in years				
both present	48% (56)	* 9% (54)	42% (24)	18% (11)
Total number of offspring locations observed	188		73	
Total pairs	29		14	
Number of dams	20		10	

* *P* < 0.05, *G*-test comparison of kin and nonkin groups.

a line drawn connecting the outermost points of each individual's observations to delineate a home range. Only data from adults were analyzed.

We measured to the nearest meter the shortest distance between the edges of the plotted home ranges of two individuals (minima) and the greatest distance between any points on the edges of the home ranges of the same two squirrels (maxima). Minima indicate how close relatives get to each other, and maxima indicate how far apart they may be (Schwagmeyer, 1979). Minima and maxima were measured for the spring home ranges of eight dam/daughter pairs (five dams and eight daughters), summer ranges of four dam/daughter pairs (three dams and four daughters), and spring ranges of three sister pairs (six individuals). In the Michigan population there were no males of known parentage to examine.

A comparison group of nonkin was generated by randomly pairing nonrelatives within each of these three groups, with each animal being represented as often as in the kin groups. Minima and maxima were measured for each unrelated pair. The maxima and minima of kin and nonkin were then compared with two-way analyses of variance (individual by relatedness; Sokal and Rohlf, 1981). The results presented are those for relatedness. No individual effects were significant.

Results

In the Texas population daughters overlapped their dam's home ranges significantly more than did nonkin, both as juveniles and as adults (Table 18.1). Females tended to remain in the area of their birth whether their dam was present or absent.

Son/dam overlap patterns differed somewhat from daughter/dam patterns (Table 18.1). Although sons overlapped their dams' lifetime home ranges more than did nonkin males when juvenile and when adult, as adults, sons were not different from nonkin when the data were divided into years when their dams were either present or absent.

Dispersion of Michigan females was similar to that in the Texas population (Table 18.2). Home ranges of dams and their adult daughters were closer on measures of both minimum and maximum distance during both spring and summer than were nonkin pairs.

Pairs of sisters in the Texas population, both littermate and nonlittermate, had greater overlap of lifetime home ranges than did nonkin as juveniles and adults (Table 18.3). As adults, littermate's home ranges overlapped more than did those of either nonlittermate siblings or nonkin in years when both individuals were alive.

TABLE 18.2. Mean ± SE minimum distance (minima) and maximum distance (maxima) (in meters) between home range boundaries of kin and nonkin in a thirteen-lined ground squirrel population in Michigan. Numbers of pairs in parentheses.

	Kin	Nonkin	*P*
Dam/daughter, spring (8)			
Minima	8.0	35.3	< 0.05
	±5.5	±6.8	
Maxima	73.4	115.6	<0.05
	±10.9	±9.9	
Dam/daughter, summer (4)			
Minima	12.4	70.4	<0.05
	±8.3	±13.4	
Maxima	80.4	131.7	<0.05
	±10.4	±15.4	
Sisters, spring (3)[a]			
Minima	17.0	72.9	
	±9.4	±26.5	
Maxima	92.4	139.1	
	±26.9	48.9	

[a] The number of sister pairs in spring was too small to permit statistical significance.

Juvenile brother/sister pairs' home ranges (both littermate and nonlittermate) overlapped more than those of nonkin (Table 18.3). Only littermate adults overlapped more than nonkin on the lifetime home range measure. Littermates overlapped more than nonlittermates both as juveniles and as adults.

The five pairs of brothers were related to each other in such a way that we could not form a group of nonrelatives for comparison. We compared home range overlap of brother pairs to the home range overlap of the male/female nonkin group and to sister littermate and brother/sister littermate pairs. Only as juveniles did brothers have greater overlap than nonkin. Home ranges of sisters and brother/sister pairs overlapped more than brother pairs as juveniles and as adults.

In summary, the home ranges of thirteen-lined ground squirrel females overlap the home ranges of their dams when both are alive. Daughters remain in or near the dam's lifetime home range after she dies. Males are much less likely to do this, although some stay in the general vicinity of their dam's lifetime home range. Since females remain near their mother's home range, littermate sisters should live near each other as adults, and they do. Nonlittermate sisters' home ranges overlap less than those of littermates. When both are alive, brothers are

410

less likely to share space than are brother/sister pairs or littermate sisters, but the picture is unclear because of the small number of brothers available for study. Brother/sister littermates overlap more than nonlittermates and more than nonrelatives. Thus there is opportunity both for nepotism among female relatives and for inbreeding.

Discussion

Dispersion in other species of Spermophilus. The general picture of spatial relations of kin among ground squirrels includes a consistent pattern of females and their daughters, dams, and sisters living in burrows near each other or having

TABLE 18.3. Percentage of locations that were within or adjacent to a sibling's home range in a Texas population of thirteen-lined ground squirrels. Nonkin data are derived from randomly pairing unrelated individuals from the female/female or male/female groups. Numbers of locations observed in parentheses.

	Overlap (%) with sib's lifetime home range when			Overlap (%) with sib's home range		
	Juvenile	Adult	Adult, sib absent	in years both present	Total pairs	Locations observed
Female/female littermate sib	100 (16)[a]	67 (21)[a]	0 (2)	53 (19)[a,b]	8	37
Female/female nonlittermate sib	76 (21)[a]	40 (45)[a]	47 (15)	20 (30)	4	66
Female/female nonkin	3 (37)	20 (66)	24 (29)	5 (37)	12	103
Male/female littermate sib	96 (27)[a,b]	67 (69) [a,b]	67 (3)	56 (66)[b]	6	96
Male/female nonlittermate sib	61 (54)[a]	44 (100)	35 (17)	30 (83)	9	154
Male/female nonkin	21 (80)	38 (188)	33 (75)	42 (113)	15	268
Male/male sib	58 (33)[a,d]	38 (48)[d]	38 (13)	29 (35)[c]	5	81

[a] $P < 0.05$, G-test, comparison of kin and nonkin.

[b] $P < 0.05$, G-test, comparison of littermate and nonlittermate groups.

[c] Male/male sib less than male/female littermate sib, $P < 0.05$, G-test.

[d] Male/male sib less than male/female and female/female littermate sibs, $P < 0.05$, G-test.

overlapping home ranges, making close adult female relatives available for behavioral interactions. Especially clear data for this pattern are available for Arctic (*S. parryii:* Carl, 1971; McLean, 1982), Belding's (*S. beldingi:* Sherman, 1980a, 1981), Richardson's (*S. richardsonii:* Michener, 1979a, 1980, 1981; Michener and Michener, 1973, 1977; Yeaton, 1972), and round-tailed (*S. tereticaudus:* Dunford, 1977a, 1977b, 1977c) ground squirrels. The data are less clear for other species, but indications of female relatives living near each other have been reported or inferred in Columbian (*S. columbianus:* Boag and Murie, 1981; Festa-Bianchet, 1981), Franklin's (*S. franklinii:* Haggerty, 1968), Uinta (*S. armatus:* Slade and Balph, 1974), Wyoming (*S. elegans:* Pfeifer, 1982a), and California (*S. beecheyii:* Dobson, 1979; Evans and Holdenreid, 1943; Fitch, 1948; Owings and Borchert, 1975) ground squirrels. The dispersion pattern of males is complicated by lack of data, owing in part to high mortality and dispersal of subadults leading to low numbers of males of known history within populations. In every species for which data are available, subadult males are more likely to disperse or die than females, and males also disperse farther than subadult females (see Holekamp, this volume). Thus males typically do not live near their kin. However, adult sons occasionally remain in or near their natal home range under some conditions, such as when litters are small (*S. tereticaudus:* Dunford, 1977a) or if the dam dies before the normal time of dispersal (*S. richardsonii:* Michener and Michener, 1973), allowing potential interaction with female relatives.

Factors promoting spatial kin group formation. Several behavioral and demographic factors promote the formation of spatial kin groups of females and influence potential interactions among relatives of both sexes. In those species where the location of females is known for two or more years, they tend to remain in the same area. Adult males typically exhibit year-to-year site fidelity in thirteen-lined (Hohn, 1966; McCarley, 1966; Rongstad, 1965), California (Evans and Holdenreid, 1943), and round-tailed ground squirrels (Drabek, 1970). Adult males sometimes remain but may change home areas in Arctic (McLean, 1982), Columbian (Boag and Murie, 1981), Uinta (Balph and Stokes, 1963), and round-tailed ground squirrels (Dunford, 1977a). Adult male Richardson's ground squirrels are probably sedentary, but there is high population turnover from year to year (Michener and Michener, 1977). Adult male Belding's ground squirrels tend to move between years (Sherman, 1980a).

Reduced- or short-distance dispersal of subadult females promotes the location of female kin near each other (Greenwood, 1980). Male ground squirrels, particularly subadults, disappear more often than females, through either death or dispersal (e.g., Schmutz et al., 1979).

Density may also influence the probability of kin interactions. In dense populations more squirrels are available for interaction, and home or activity ranges are likely to be small, so that neighboring kin are nearby for interactions. Large population size also promotes higher interaction rates, allowing observers to document kin differential interactions if they occur. Another, usually unstated, factor is that the high interaction rates within dense populations are much more likely to attract observers to study them than are the infrequent interaction rates of sparse populations.

One group of species, consisting of *S. beldingi, S. richardsonii, S. armatus,* and some populations of *S. tereticaudus* and *S. columbianus,* lives in dense populations of 20 or more adults/ha (Dunford, 1977c; Festa-Bianchet, 1981; Michener, 1979a, 1979b; Sherman and Morton, 1979; Slade and Balph, 1974). A somewhat intermediate group of *S. beecheyii, S. parryii, S. townsendii, S. elegans,* and most reported populations of *S. columbianus* ranges from about five to 20 adults/ha (Boag and Murie, 1981; Fitch, 1948; Johnson and Smith, 1978; McLean, 1982; Pfeifer, 1980). A third group, *S. tridecemlineatus* and *S. franklinii* (and the *S. tereticaudus* studied by Drabek, 1970), has sparse populations of fewer than five adults/ha (Haggerty, 1968; McCarley, 1966; Murie, 1973; Wistrand, 1974). Franklin's and thirteen-lined ground squirrels are consistently found in the lowest densities, and it is probably no coincidence that they are considered among the most unsociable of the ground squirrels (Howell, 1938; Michener, 1983). Thirteen-lined ground squirrels interact infrequently relative to other species (Schwagmeyer, 1979; Wistrand, 1974).

High densities, with more squirrels nearby for interaction, may be related to the evolution of complex social interactions in ground squirrels (e.g., *S. beldingii, S. parryii, S. tereticaudus*). Alternatively, the high density and relatively frequent interactions in dense populations may attract observers and allow the compilation of enough interaction data to allow us to discern complex social phenomena.

Differential reproduction by females potentially contributes to development of female kin clusters in *Spermophilus.* McCarley (1970) found that 89% of his population of thirteen-lined ground squirrels in 1967 were directly descended from only 20% (four) of the adult females present in 1963. Those females leaving young averaged larger litters and lived longer. Michener (1980) found that only two of 10 Richardson's ground squirrel females in 1975 had live descendants in 1978, and the successful dams had female-biased litters. In Wyoming ground squirrels burrow-site quality appears to be important for reproductive success. Females that nest in some types of burrow sites leave more descendants than those nesting in other types (Pfeifer, 1982*b*). Since young females live near their dams, groups of descendants of the successful females could develop. While the female groups could include both close and distant relatives, nepotistic interactions have been reported only among dams, their daughters, and littermate sisters (McLean, 1982; Sherman, 1981). Sherman (1981) hypothesized that, because distant relatives are unlikely to be temporally available for interactions, nepotism among them is unlikely to evolve.

The structure of a species' habitat, whether patchy or continuous, open or complex, may influence density, spatial distribution, and behavioral interactions (Esser, 1971; Waser and Wiley, 1980; Wilson, 1972). Ground squirrels often live in habitat patches (e.g., Festa-Bianchet, 1981; McCarley, 1966; Murie, 1973; Murie and Harris, 1978). Resource availability within the patches may be higher in some areas, leading to variable densities with high potential for behavioral interactions in areas of high density. Physical structure of the environment may influence density by affecting visually oriented agonistic interactions that space individuals. Differences have been reported in population density, territory size, or distinctness of territorial boundaries between populations living in broken terrain or dense cover and those living in more open areas (Melchior, 1965; Murie and Harris, 1978). Differential food availability between areas was not measured but could influence the differences listed above.

For kin groups to form and interact, individuals must cooccur in time as well as in space. Adults are aboveground before juveniles and enter hibernation earlier, leaving only a part of the active season for juveniles to form relations with adults (Michener, 1983; this volume). Mortality is typically high among ground squirrels, making it more common for closely related females (dam, daughter, sister) to cooccur than more distant relatives (Sherman, 1981).

Implications of spacing patterns among kin. The spatial distributions reviewed above influence the opportunities for nepotistic interactions in ground squirrel populations. In most species close female kin are often in close spatiotemporal proximity. There is increasing evidence that favoritism of kin (in the sense of cooperation, reduced aggression, etc.) is related to this proximity (Sherman, 1980*a*).

Nepotism requires discrimination of kin from nonrelatives. Simple spatial availability would not be sufficient, since neighbors may be either close relatives or nonkin (e.g., McLean, 1982; Michener, 1981; Sherman, 1981). Kin recognition has been reported in *S. parryii* and *S. beldingi* (Holmes and Sherman, 1982) and in *S. richardsonii* (Davis, 1982), and it may be present in all or most other species when they have been tested properly. It is uncertain how kin recognition develops and is mediated. Recognition is probably based in part on familiarity (Bekoff, 1981; Holmes and Sherman, 1982), but genetically shared characteristics may also be involved (Davis, 1982).

Several types of nepotistic behavior have been described for ground squirrels, including alarm calling in response to predators, cooperative defense of the nest burrow area against conspecifics, cooperative defense against predators, sharing of a burrow or hibernaculum, reduced aggression or more amicable behavior among relatives, allogrooming, clumping of litters into a single group, and sharing an area (Table 18.4).

The mere availability of relatives may be necessary, but not sufficient, for the evolution of nepotistic behavior. Although thirteen-lined ground squirrel females have adult relatives living within range of their alarm calls, they tend to call only when their own undispersed litters are present (McCarley, 1966; Schwagmeyer, 1979, 1980; Schwagmeyer and Brown, 1981). In contrast, *S. beldingi* and *S. tereticaudus* appear to direct calls to adult relatives in that they call at times of the year when only adults are aboveground (Dunford, 1977*b*; Schwagmeyer, 1979; Sherman, 1977).

The species exhibiting the greatest variety of types of nepotism are Belding's, round-tailed, and Arctic ground squirrels. They are also the ones (along with Richardson's ground squirrels) with the highest population densities; they have been the subjects of most detailed long-term behavioral studies and are the species on which data have been collected with sociobiological hypotheses in mind.

Inbreeding may potentially occur in ground squirrel populations when males settle near their female relatives. We do not have good information on how often this occurs, but the relative rarity of the event, coupled with high male mortality, may make inbreeding unlikely (Michener and Michener, 1977). We have so little information on paternity in general among ground squirrels (Hanken and Sherman, 1981; Michener, 1983) that we do not know how often inbreeding occurs or whether there are potential mechanisms for avoiding it, as in black-tailed prairie dogs (Hoogland, 1982). The probability of multiple paternity of litters complicates the problem (Hanken and Sherman, 1981).

Future work on S. tridecemlineatus. Although *S. tridecemlineatus* has a wide geographic range and is commonly found in association with humans, only one set of studies tests hypotheses about its social behavior (Schwagmeyer, 1979,

TABLE 18.4. Types of potentially nepotistic behavior (giving aid or exhibiting favoritism toward kin) in *Spermophilus*

Behavior	S. parryii	S. beldingi	S. tereticaudus	S. beecheyii	S. richardsonii	S. armatus	S. columbianus	S. franklinii	S. tridecemlineatus
Alarm call	Carl, 1971	Sherman, 1980a[a]	Dunford, 1977b[b]	Owings et al., 1977	K. Fagerstone, pers. comm.	Balph and Stokes, 1963	Betts, 1976		Schwagmeyer, 1980[a]
Cooperative defense of area against predators	McLean, 1982	Sherman, 1980a	Drabek, 1970	Owings and Coss, 1977, pers. comm.					
Burrow or hibernaculum sharing	McLean, 1982	Sherman, 1976	Dunford, 1977a	Evans and Holdenreid, 1943[b]				Sowls, 1948[b]; Gray, 1972	
Reduced aggression	McLean, 1982	Sherman, 1980a	Dunford, 1977a		Yeaton, 1972; Michener, 1981				
Allogrooming	McLean, 1982	Sherman, 1980a							
Clumping young	McLean, 1982	Sherman, 1980a							
Sharing home range or living nearer kin	McLean, 1982	Sherman, 1980a	Dunford, 1977a		Michener, 1981	Slade and Balph, 1974	Festa-Bianchet, 1981	Haggerty, 1968	This study

[a] Documented as being directed to close relatives.

[b] Genetic relations not known.

416

1980; Schwagmeyer and Brown, 1981), and only two provide substantial data on its social system and behavior in natural populations (McCarley, 1966; Wistrand, 1974). Thirteen-lined ground squirrels are one of the smallest species of ground squirrels (Armitage, 1981). They live in sparse populations, interact infrequently, and are generally considered asocial (Howell, 1938; Schwagmeyer, 1979; Wistrand, 1974). Although female relatives live near enough to each other to engage in nepotistic interactions, no nepotism has been reported between adults. Why? One problem to decide is where to study them, and another is what to study.

Currently thirteen-lined ground squirrel populations are commonly found in parks and cemeteries (Murray and Vestal, 1979), golf courses (McCarley, 1966), lawns and botanical gardens (Rongstad, 1965; Schwagmeyer, 1979), and closely grazed pastures (pers. obs.). In such areas, which are all typically mowed and/or managed by humans, the squirrels are reasonably observable. However, such habitats are often disparaged as "unnatural" because of management practices, human disturbance, relative lack of predators, and lack of "natural" food. Part of the problem, of course, is to define what is "natural." Certainly mowed and managed habitats are not the ancestral habitat of ground squirrels. Population densities may be somewhat higher in managed habitats than in unmanaged ones, but they are still far lower than in other species of *Spermophilus*. Some of the most detailed information we have on social behavior of other species is from dense populations in managed habitat (Dunford, 1977*a*, 1977*b*, 1977*c;* Slade and Balph, 1974). Visibility within managed habitats allows one to collect enough data within a reasonable time to test hypotheses. High density and consequent high interaction rates allow analysis of social patterns. Studies in both managed and unmanaged habitats are valuable and needed, but investigators must keep in mind the limitations on conclusions imposed by the situation under study.

What is the "natural" (or more appropriately "ancestral") habitat of thirteen-lined ground squirrels? Early reports refer to prairie (Howell, 1938), but prairie types vary in grass height and density and in topographic relief. Some prairie was undoubtedly heavily grazed by bison herds and also influenced by fire. Thirteen-lined ground squirrels are found in grazed pastures in Oklahoma and Texas, where grass may reach 30 cm height with open patches of short, heavily grazed grass (pers. obs.). They are sometimes found in association with black-tailed prairie dog towns where the vegetation is extremely short and sparse (pers. obs.). Thirteen-lined ground squirrels have been trapped in areas of tall, dense grass (60–75 cm tall) as well as on recently burned and shortgrass areas in Nebraska (Vacanti, 1981; J. Krupa, pers. comm.). Other investigators have found squirrels in low densities in grazed or sparse short- and tallgrass prairie, but not in ungrazed tallgrass areas (Grant et al., 1977, 1982).

We probably will never know what the "natural" or ancestral habitat was, since the prairie habitat in this country was highly modified by agriculture before extensive study by biologists. After human modification of its habitat in the nineteenth century, *S. tridecemlineatus* moved into the shortgrass, managed niche, where there are undoubtedly different selective pressures on its social organization than in the ancestral habitat. Thus we are in a position to observe the squirrels' behavior as they adapt to what will be their primary habitat for some time to come.

Ideally, future work will include studies in both managed and unmanaged (or relatively unmanaged) habitats. In the unmowed areas work will be limited primarily to trapping and radio-telemetry. Unfortunately, it is difficult to trap individuals repeatedly or to trap populations completely (Evans, 1951, pers. obs.). Thus, identifying all members of a population will be a problem. Radio-telemetry appears to offer possibilities for obtaining data on dispersion patterns, dispersal, and activity and movement patterns.

In managed habitats the prospects for fruitful studies are brighter but probably not so much as in the more sociable species that live at high densities. Long-term studies are needed that examine in detail the spatial relations and social interactions of kin and nonkin. We also need better information on male dispersal, paternity patterns, and the social role of males in the populations. Detailed information on the social and spatial relations of the relatively asocial thirteen-lined ground squirrels will contribute to our understanding of the evolution of ground squirrel sociality.

In summary, the social system of thirteen-lined ground squirrels appears to involve spatial overlap of the areas used by related adult females and some overlap between brothers and sisters. Based on the meager information available, the spatially overlapping individuals do not interact to any great degree. Armitage (1981) and Michener (1983) recently reviewed sociality in ground-dwelling sciurids and developed two different scales of social categories or grades. *S. tridecemlineatus* appears to fall into the grade 2 assigned by Armitage (1981), that of species that aggregate in favorable habitat though all members of the colony live individually. However, this category in his classification also includes such species as Belding's and round-tailed ground squirrels, which exhibit more types of nepotistic behavior than do thirteen-lined ground squirrels. Michener (1983) questioned whether *S. tridecemlineatus* would fall into her grade 1 (asocial, with individuals having home ranges distinct from dam and littermates) or grade 2 (single-family female kin clusters, with sons dispersing and dams and their adult daughters sharing the ancestral home ranges and being sociable with each other). Based on our information on spatial overlap, we would assign thirteen-lined ground squirrels to Michener's (1983) grade 2. However, we need more information about behavioral interactions among female kin and about the roles of males to determine how similar the social organization of *S. tridecemlineatus* is to that of other species in this social grade.

Acknowledgments

We thank Patricia L. Schwagmeyer for providing the data on the Michigan squirrel home ranges and for critically reading an earlier version of the manuscript. Gail Michener, Jan Murie, and an anonymous referee also contributed to improvement of the manuscript.

Literature Cited

Armitage, K. B. 1981. Sociality as a life-history tactic of ground squirrels. Oecologia, 48:36–49.

Balph, D. R., and A. W. Stokes. 1963. On the ethology of a population of Uinta ground squirrels. Amer. Midland Nat., 69:106–126.

Bekoff, M. 1981. Mammalian sibling interactions: genes, facilitative environments, and the coefficient of familiarity. Pp. 307–345, *in* Parental care in mammals (D. J. Gubernick and P. H. Klopfer, eds.). Plenum, New York, 459 pp.

Betts, B. J. 1976. Behaviour in a population of Columbian ground squirrels, *Spermophilus columbianus columbianus*. Anim. Behav., 24:652–680.

Boag, D. A., and J. O. Murie. 1981. Population ecology of Columbian ground squirrels in southwestern Alberta. Canadian J. Zool., 59:2230–2240.

Carl, E. 1971. Population control in Arctic ground squirrels. Ecology, 52:396–413.

Davis, L. S. 1982. Sibling recognition in Richardson's ground squirrels *Spermophilus richardsonii*. Behav. Ecol. Sociobiol., 11:65–70.

Dobson, F. 1979. An experimental study of dispersal in the California ground squirrel. Ecology, 60.1103–1109.

Drabek, C. 1970. Ethoecology of the round-tailed ground squirrel, *Spermophilus tereticaudus*. Unpubl. Ph.D. dissert., Univ. Arizona, Tucson, 108 pp.

Dunford, C. 1977*a*. Behavioral limitation of round-tailed ground squirrel density. Ecology, 58:1254–1268.

———. 1977*b*. Kin selection for ground squirrel alarm calls. Amer. Nat., 111:782–785.

———. 1977*c*. Social system of round-tailed ground squirrels. Anim. Behav., 25: 885–906.

Esser, A. H. 1971. Behavior and environment: the use of space by animals and man. Plenum, New York, 411 pp.

Kinship and Sociality

Evans, F. 1951. Notes on a population of the striped ground squirrel (*Citellus tridecemlineatus*) in an abandoned field in southeastern Michigan. J. Mamm., 32:437–449.
Evans, F., and R. Holdenreid. 1943. A population study of the Beechey ground squirrel in central California. J. Mamm., 24:231–260.
Festa-Bianchet, M. 1981. Reproduction in yearling female Columbian ground squirrels (*Spermophilus columbianus*). Canadian J. Zool., 59:1032–1035.
Fitch, H. S. 1948. Ecology of the California ground squirrel on grazing lands. Amer. Midland Nat., 39:513–596.
Getty, T. 1981. Structure and dynamics of chipmunk home range. J. Mamm., 62:726–737.
Grant, W. E., N. R. French, and D. M. Swift. 1977. Response of a small mammal community to water and nitrogen treatments in a shortgrass prairie ecosystem. J. Mamm., 58:637–652.
Grant, W. E., E. C. Birney, N. R. French, and D. M. Swift. 1982. Structure and productivity of grassland small mammal communities related to grazing-induced changes in vegetative cover. J. Mamm., 63:248–260.
Gray, W. C. 1972. Social behavior and population dynamics of the Franklin ground squirrel, *Citellus franklinii* (Sabine). Unpubl. M.S. thesis, Illinois State Univ., Normal, 49 pp.
Greenwood, P. J. 1980. Mating systems, philopatry and dispersal in birds and mammals. Anim. Behav., 28:1140–1162.
Haggerty, S. M. 1968. The ecology of the Franklin's ground squirrel (*Citellus franklinii*) at Itasca State Park, Minnesota. Unpubl. M.S. thesis, Univ. Minnesota, Minneapolis, 98 pp.
Hall, E. R. 1981. The mammals of North America. Vol. 1. Second ed. John Wiley, New York, 1–600 + 90 pp.
Hanken, J., and P. W. Sherman. 1981. Multiple paternity in Belding's ground squirrel litters. Science, 212:351–353.
Hohn, B. M. 1966. Movements and activity patterns in a population of thirteen-lined ground squirrels, Itasca State Park, Minnesota. Unpubl. M.S. thesis, Univ. Minnesota, Minneapolis, 74 pp.
Holmes, W. G., and P. W. Sherman. 1982. The ontogeny of kin recognition in two species of ground squirrels. Amer. Zool., 22:491–517.
Hoogland, J. L. 1982. Prairie dogs avoid extreme inbreeding. Science, 215:1639–1641.
Hoogland, J. L., and P. W. Sherman. 1976. Advantages and disadvantages of bank swallow (*Riparia riparia*) coloniality. Ecol. Monogr. 46:33–58.
Howell, A. 1938. Revision of the North American ground squirrels, with a classification of the North American Sciuridae. U.S. Dept. Agric. Bur. Biol. Surv., N. Amer. Fauna, 56:1–256.
Johnson, D. R., and G. W. Smith. 1978. Ecology of Townsend ground squirrels in the birds of prey study area. Snake river birds of prey research project contract 52500-CT5-

420

1002 final report, U.S. Dep. Int., Bur. Land Mgmt., Boise, Idaho. (As cited in Boag and Murie, 1981.)

McCarley, W. H. 1966. Annual cycle, population dynamics and adaptive behavior of *Citellus tridecemlineatus*. J. Mamm., 47:294–316.

———. 1970. Differential reproduction in *Spermophilus tridecemlineatus*. Southwestern Nat., 14:293–296.

McLean, I. G. 1982. The association of female kin in the Arctic ground squirrel *Spermophilus parryii*. Behav. Ecol. Sociobiol., 10:91–99.

Melchior, H. 1965. Ecological cut-off as a possible determinant of Arctic ground squirrel population densities. Bull. Ecol. Soc. Amer., 46:194 (abstr.).

Michener, G. R. 1979a. Spatial relationships and social organization of adult Richardson's ground squirrels. Canadian J. Zool., 57:125–139.

———. 1979b. Yearly variations in the population dynamics of Richardson's ground squirrels. Canadian Field-Nat., 93:363–370.

———. 1980. Differential reproduction among female Richardson's ground squirrels and its relation to sex ratio. Behav. Ecol. Sociobiol., 7:173–178.

———. 1981. Ontogeny of spatial relationships and social behavior in juvenile Richardson's ground squirrels. Canadian J. Zool., 59:1666–1676.

———. 1983. Kin identification, matriarchies, and the evolution of sociality in ground-dwelling sciurids. Pp. 528–572, *in* Recent advances in the study of mammalian behavior (J. F. Eisenberg and D. G. Kleiman, eds.). Spec. Publ., Amer. Soc. Mamm., 7:1–753.

Michener, G. R., and D. R. Michener. 1973. Spatial distribution of yearlings in a Richardson's ground squirrel population. Ecology, 54:1138–1142.

———. 1977. Population structure and dispersal in Richardson's ground squirrels. Ecology, 58:359–368.

Murie, J. O. 1973. Population characteristics and phenology of a Franklin ground squirrel (*Spermophilus franklinii*) colony in Alberta, Canada. Amer. Midland Nat., 90:334–340.

Murie, J. O., and M. A. Harris. 1978. Territoriality and dominance in male Columbian ground squirrels (*Spermophilus columbianus*). Canadian J. Zool., 56:2402–2412.

Murray, G., and B. M. Vestal. 1979. Effects of environmental structure on the burrow distribution of thirteen-lined ground squirrels, *Spermophilus tridecemlineatus* (Sciuridae). Southwestern Nat., 24:79–86.

Owings, D. H., and M. Borchert. 1975. Correlates of burrow location in Beechey ground squirrels. Great Basin Nat., 35:402–404.

Owings, D. H., and R. Coss. 1977. Snake mobbing by California ground squirrels: adaptive variation and ontogeny. Behaviour, 62:50–69.

Owings, D. H., M. Borchert, and R. Virginia. 1977. The behavior of California ground squirrels. Anim. Behav., 25:221–230.

Pfeifer, S. R. 1980. Demographic and behavioral influences on juvenile Wyoming ground squirrel dispersal. Unpubl. Ph.D. dissert., Univ. Colorado, Boulder, 146 pp.

―――. 1982*a*. Disappearance and dispersal of *Spermophilus elegans* juveniles in relation to behavior. Behav. Ecol. Sociobiol., 10:237–243.

―――. 1982*b*. Variability in reproductive output and success of *Spermophilus elegans* ground squirrels. J. Mamm., 63:284–289.

Rongstad, O. 1965. A life history study of thirteen-lined ground squirrels in southern Wisconsin. J. Mamm., 46:76–87.

Schmutz, S. M., D. A. Boag, and J. K. Schmutz. 1979. Causes of the unequal sex ratio in populations of adult Richardson's ground squirrels. Canadian J. Zool., 57:1845–1859.

Schwagmeyer, P. L. 1979. The function of alarm calling in *Spermophilus tridecemlineatus*, the thirteen-lined ground squirrel. Unpubl. Ph.D. dissert. Univ. Michigan, Ann Arbor, 82 pp.

―――. 1980. Alarm calling behavior of thirteen-lined ground squirrels, *Spermophilus tridecemlineatus*. Behav. Ecol. Sociobiol., 7:195–200.

Schwagmeyer, P. L., and C. H. Brown. 1981. Conspecific reaction to playback of thirteen-lined ground squirrel vocalizations. Z. Tierpsychol., 56:25–32.

Sherman, P. W. 1976. Natural selection among some group-living organisms. Unpubl. Ph.D. dissert., Univ. Michigan, Ann Arbor, 254 pp.

―――. 1977. Nepotism and the evolution of alarm calls. Science, 197: 1246–1253.

―――. 1980*a*. The limits of ground squirrel nepotism. Pp. 505–544, *in* Sociobiology: beyond nature/nurture? (G. Barlow and J. Silverberg, eds.). Westview Press, Boulder, Colorado, 627 pp.

―――. 1980*b*. The meaning of nepotism. Amer. Nat., 116:604–606.

―――. 1981. Kinship, demography, and Belding's ground squirrel nepotism. Behav. Ecol. Sociobiol., 8:251–259.

Sherman, P. W., and M. L. Morton. 1979. Four months of the ground squirrel. Nat. Hist., 88:50–57.

Silverman, D. L. 1981. The behavioral ecology of the thirteen-lined squirrel (*Spermophilus tridecemlineatus*). Unpubl. M.S. thesis, Univ. Michigan, Ann Arbor, 45 pp.

Slade, N., and D. Balph. 1974. Population ecology of Uinta ground squirrels. Ecology, 55:989–1003.

Sokal, R. R., and F. J. Rohlf. 1981. Biometry. Second ed. W. H. Freeman, San Francisco, 859 pp.

Sowls, L. K. 1948. The Franklin ground squirrel, *Citellus franklinii* (Sabine), and its relationship to nesting ducks. J. Mamm., 29:113–137.

Vacanti, P. L. 1981. Effects of controlled burning on small mammal populations of a restored tallgrass prairie. Unpubl. M.S. thesis, Univ. Nebraska, Omaha, 72 pp.

Waser, P., and R. H. Wiley. 1980. Mechanisms and evolution of spacing in animals. Pp. 159–223, *in* Handbook of behavioral neurobiology, vol. 3 (P. Marler and J. G. Vandenbergh, eds.). Plenum, New York, 411 pp.

Wilson, C. 1972. Spatial factors and the behavior of nonhuman primates. Folia Primatol., 18:256–275.

Wistrand, H. 1974. Individual, social and seasonal behavior of the thirteen-lined ground squirrel (*Spermophilus tridecemlineatus*). J. Mamm., 55:329–347.

Yeaton, R. 1972. Social behavior and social organization in Richardson's ground squirrel (*Spermophilus richardsonii*) in Saskatchewan. J. Mamm., 53:139–147.

LLOYD S. DAVIS

University of Alberta

Chapter 19

Behavioral Interactions
of Richardson's Ground Squirrels:
Asymmetries Based on Kinship

Abstract. The temporal sequence of behaviors in 1,774 interactions between Richardson's ground squirrels (*Spermophilus richardsonii*) in the wild was recorded during 454 h of observation over a three-year period. A catalog of 15 mutually exclusive behaviors was described. Factor analysis produced four groupings of the behaviors that together accounted for 93.4% of the total variance in the frequency of occurrence of the 15 behaviors. These factor groupings were interpreted post hoc as "chase-flee," "appeasement situation," "fighting," and "identification" behaviors. The intraindividual sequence of behaviors was significantly different in interactions of uterine kin and squirrels that were not uterine kin. "Appeasement situation" and "identification" behaviors were more prominent in interactions of uterine kin, which led to fewer "chase-flee" behaviors than occurred in interactions of other squirrels. As a consequence, interactions of uterine kin most often resulted in no displacement of the participants from the vicinity of the interaction, whereas one participant was usually displaced in interactions of those that were not uterine kin. This asymmetry based upon kinship in the outcome of interactions occurred in all age and sex classes. Thus the results are consistent with the occurrence of nepotism in Richardson's ground squirrels that is mediated by kin selection.

Introduction

Sociality is the association of conspecifics in time and space that is maintained by communication among them. The North American ground-dwelling sciurids

(Rodentia: Marmotini) are composed of just over 30 species (Hafner, this volume) that vary in their degree of sociality from essentially solitary species (Bronson, 1964) to those that live in groups sharing the same space and exhibiting mainly cohesive behaviors between all group members (Hoogland, 1981). Recent reviews (Armitage, 1981; Michener, 1983) have proposed that "kin selection" (Hamilton, 1963, 1964; Maynard Smith, 1964) is the primary mechanism that influenced the evolution and maintenance of sociality in the ground-dwelling sciurids. That is, sociality has been selected for in circumstances where animals may increase their "inclusive fitness" (Hamilton, 1963, 1964) by favorably influencing the survival or reproductive success of related conspecifics. One predictable outcome of sociality resulting from kin selection is that behavioral interactions will differ between kin and nonkin, since individuals should treat conspecifics according to whether or not they are related.

The aim of this study was to examine the behavioral interactions of Richardson's ground squirrels (*Spermophilus richardsonii*) in the wild for evidence that the level of relatedness of participants affects the nature of their interactions.

Ground squirrels can distinguish close relatives from distant relatives or non-relatives (Davis, 1982*a;* Holmes and Sherman, 1982), and preferential treatment of close kin has been documented in wild populations of several ground-dwelling sciurids (e.g., Dunford, 1977*a;* Hoogland, 1981; McLean, 1982; Sherman, 1980, 1981). Closely related *S. richardsonii* have been reported to behave more "amicably" than less closely related conspecifics in both field (Michener, 1973, 1981; Yeaton, 1972) and laboratory (Michener, 1974; Michener and Sheppard, 1972; Sheppard and Yoshida, 1971). However, the precise nature and effect of such differences in the interactions of kin and nonkin cannot be accurately quantified from these and other studies of the ground-dwelling sciurids (Armitage, 1974; Holmes and Sherman, 1982; McLean, 1981), because authors classified interactions as "agonistic," "amicable," or "neutral" based upon subjective interpretations of the motivational states leading to behaviors.

Problems of interpretation arise with such a subjective approach because:

1. Behaviors must be classified, and hence have their motivational states interpreted, a priori. For example, "alert" behavior (Armitage, 1974, 1977; Johns and Armitage, 1979) and "avoidance" behavior (Holmes and Sherman, 1982; Johns and Armitage, 1979; Michener, 1973) were called "agonistic"; but is an animal that is watching another or moving away from another really behaving agonistically?

2. Interactions are classified as a whole, when often they comprise elements of more than one category and represent paths to resolving the opposing tendencies

425

of aggressiveness and submissiveness. Yeaton (1972) acknowledged, but did not solve, this problem by scoring an interaction as "agonistic" if it contained "any agonistic component at all" within its sequence of behaviors.

3. Differences in definitions of "agonistic" and "amicable" among individual researchers make comparing their data difficult. Are any differences in their data representative of actual differences between the populations under study, or are the differences, in part or whole, the result of inconsistencies among the observers' observational criteria? For example, interactions between adult female *S. richardsonii* have been variously reported as being mainly amicable between related females while almost entirely agonistic between unrelated females (Michener, 1981), as mainly agonistic between female kin but less so than for nonkin (Yeaton, 1972), and as involving equal amounts of agonism in interactions of related and unrelated females (Wehrell, 1973).

4. Subjective classification does not take into account differences in the quality and intensity of interactions. For instance, an inclusive category such as "agonistic" can obscure subtle differences in the degrees of agonism (Kurland, 1977).

I analyzed all observed interactions in a field study of Richardson's ground squirrels without categorizing interactions according to a priori classifications. I attempted to record objectively the sequence of behaviors occurring in interactions, to measure and quantify any differences apparent in the interactions of closely related *S. richardsonii* compared with those of less closely related conspecifics, and to discern the effects of such differences, if any, on the outcome of interactions and the maintenance of sociality in this species.

Methods

Study Area and Subjects

Interactions of Richardson's ground squirrels were observed during 1979 and 1980 at my Highwood River study area (Davis, 1982b), 6 km northwest of Longview, Alberta, Canada (50°34'N, 114°18'W; elevation 1,235 m), and during 1981 at my Roi Lakes study area, 12 km northwest of Stony Plain, Alberta (53°35'N, 114°05'W; elevation 730 m). Both study sites were 1.3 ha in area, divided into a grid of 10 by 10 m squares, and were sometimes grazed by cattle. Maximum densities of adult squirrels on the areas averaged 27/ha (range = 23–31), and the maximum densities of juveniles averaged 66/ha (range = 44–93).

All squirrels on the study areas were marked so that they were individually identifiable, by using numbered metal ear tags with colored plastic disks or strips attached to one tag, and by painting letters or numbers on their pelage with "blue black" human hair dye. Age class (juvenile/adult) and sex were known for all squirrels, and often matrilineal kinship relations were also known. The latter were determined by livetrapping litters when they emerged from their natal burrow at weaning.

Definition of Kin and Nonkin Groups

In this study it was not possible to establish paternal kinship relationships, since copulations in Richardson's ground squirrels are rarely observed (Davis, 1982*c*) and individual females may be mated by more than one male, as occurs in *S. beldingi* (Hanken and Sherman, 1981). Hence, for the purposes of comparing a closely related group with a more distantly related group in this study, the relatedness of participants in interactions was classed according to matrilineal kinship:

Uterine kin (UK): Participants *known* to be either mother and offspring or littermate siblings. In effect, these were squirrels that had shared a natal burrow.

Not uterine kin (NUK): These were squirrels known *not* to have shared a natal burrow. That is, they were not mother and offspring or littermate siblings.

Unknown: Interactions in which the relatedness between the participants was unknown in terms of the criterion above.

Although NUK could include some related pairings (e.g., father-offspring, non-littermate siblings), on the average, squirrels in this group will be much less closely related than those in the UK group. Comparisons between UK and NUK are used, therefore, to investigate any differential effect of kinship in interactions. The test is a conservative one, since including some closely related pairings in the NUK group would tend to diminish any differences that might exist.

Of the 1,774 interactions observed, 271 involved UK, 890 involved NUK, and 613 involved squirrels of unknown relationship.

Observations

Squirrels were observed from an elevated tower or chair using 10 by 50 binoculars. Observation periods usually lasted from 2 to 4 h and were conducted between 0700 and 1900 h, with most occurring in the morning (0700–1100) or late afternoon (1500–1800). Sampling of interactions was conducted for 454 h of observation.

Interactions were recorded using sequential sampling (Slater, 1978). An ethogram of 15 readily recognizable, mutually exclusive, and virtually all-inclusive

427

behaviors was initially described (Table 19.1). All behaviors were described in strictly physical, operational terms, without any attempt to imply a motivational state or allocate them to a functional grouping. Anogenital sniffing and allo-grooming occurred at such extremely low frequencies that the ethogram was regarded as complete without them (Fagen and Goldman, 1977), since their inclusion would have undermined the robustness of the contingency table analyses by introducing too many cells with small expected values (Colgan and Smith, 1978). The temporal sequence of behaviors occurring in each interaction was written in a shorthand code and later transcribed for computer analysis. Whenever possible, the identities of the initiator and responder, the starting location (defined as the location of the responder when the interaction was initiated), and the end location (the location of the responder when the interaction terminated) were also recorded.

An interaction was initiated when one animal either ran, walked, or orientated itself directly toward another animal, which responded with at least one of the 15 behaviors recognized in the ethogram (Table 19.1). All interactions were defined to have ended when one animal fled or orientated its body away from the other participant and the latter ceased to perform any of the behaviors recognized in the ethogram.

Analyses

Factor analysis. The frequencies of occurrence of 15 behaviors in 1,774 interactions were arranged in a matrix (1,774 by 15), and R-type factor analysis (Aspey, 1977; Harris, 1975) was used to determine underlying associations between the behaviors by reducing the data to a set of uncorrelated factors. Factor analysis was carried out using the SPSS program "Factor" (Nie et al., 1975). Only factors with eigenvalues (measures of the variance accounted for by each factor) greater than 1.0 were rotated using Kaiser's normal varimax method.

Factor loadings indicate the degree to which behaviors were associated with each factor, and in this study positive factor loadings greater than 0.35 were considered to be evidence of association of a behavior with a factor. According to Comrey (1973), values below 0.35 indicate very poor association. For the sake of grouping the behaviors, any behavior that failed to load at more than +0.35 onto any factor was included with the factor onto which it loaded most highly. Factors were considered interpretable only if they accounted for at least 10% of the total variance in the original data.

Although criticized as being unsound for many practical situations (Chatfield

TABLE 19.1. Ethogram of behaviors of Richardson's ground squirrels used in social interactions. Names given by other authors to equivalent behaviors in ground squirrels are also noted.

Behavior	Description	Equivalent
Chase	Pursue opponent by running after it	Chase[a, b, d, g]
Flee	Rapidly run from opponent	Flee[a]
Run toward	Rapidly approach opponent	Running approach[b]
Move toward	Approach opponent by walking toward it	Walking approach[b]
Move away	Withdraw by orienting body away from opponent without leaving vicinity of interaction	
Side	Arch back while turned sideways, presenting flank to opponent; piloerection of hairs on back and tail, mouth often held open	Arching[e], back arched[b], flank to flank[g], lateral approach[d]
Rise	Raise anterior of body so front paws are lifted from the ground; animal faces its opponent, one paw often extended toward opponent, mouth usually open	Warding[e]
Box	Stand upon hindlegs facing opponent with forepaws extended; animal strikes at opponent with adductions of forelegs; mouth usually open	Sparring[e], Stand-up fight[b]
Foreward	Crouch facing opponent; some piloerection, mouth usually open; sometimes single forepaw may be extended toward opponent	Threat[e]
Lunge	Leap at opponent, forequarters first; sometimes accompanied by biting	Attack[e], lunge[a,b]
Stand over	Stand upon hindlegs, resting forepaws on opponent; posture frequently held for several seconds	
Supine	Lie upon back, legs raised upward and head and neck tilted forward	Full submission[c]
Roll fight	Tumble over with opponent, striking at it with adductions of legs	Fight[e,g], rolling fight[b]
Naso-oral	Extend neck toward opponent and tilt head slightly to one side; mouth open, contact made with naso-oral area	Greeting[f], Kissing[a], Nasal-nasal[g], nose-nose[b,e], nose-to-cheek[d]
No reaction	Although in contact with or beside (<0.25 m) opponent, animal shows no reaction in response to opponent's behavior	

[a] Betts 1976; [b] Dunford 1977a; [c] Michener and Sheppard 1972; [d] Owings et al., 1977; [e] Sheppard and Yoshida 1971; [f] Steiner 1975; [g] Watton and Keenleyside 1974.

and Collins, 1980), factor analysis remains a useful tool for seeking, as here, an underlying structure in a set of observed behaviors (Aspey, 1977; Chatfield and Collins, 1980; Harris, 1975).

Transitional analysis. Transitional analysis (Colgan and Smith, 1978; Fagen and Mankovich, 1980; Fagen and Young, 1978) was conducted on the two-act transitions between behaviors occurring in the 1,774 observed interactions, to determine the relations between behaviors and to aid the interpretation of the factor groups attained using the method above.

The frequencies with which behaviors followed one another within an individual were organized into a contingency table of two-act transitions (Appendix 19.1). There were 5,420 transitions, which exceeded the minimum desirable sample size of $10R^2$ ($= 2,250$, where R is repertoire size) recommended by Fagen and Young (1978). Expected values for each two-act transition, if the occurrence of a behavior was independent of the nature of the preceding behavior, were calculated in the same manner as for cells in a chi-square test for independence. Sequences of behaviors were coded according to the alternating method of Steinberg (1977), so that if an animal continued to perform a particular behavior in response to a change in behavior of its opponent, the animal was deemed to have repeated that behavior. Hence, within an individual's sequence of behaviors, any behavior could be followed by itself, so that cells falling along the main diagonal of the contingency table had nonzero expected values.

Those transitions that occurred significantly more often than expected by chance were determined following the method of Ainley (1974). The magnitudes of the positive standardized residuals (observed − expected/square root of expected) were used to identify the most important transitions. The standardized residuals were regarded as approximate standard normal variates. However, when using a relatively large behavioral catalog, the observed frequencies of some cells will differ significantly from chance expectation at the 0.05 level through random sampling error. Therefore I adjusted the probability level at which a behavioral transition was considered to occur at a frequency significantly wayward from chance expectation by dividing the 0.05 probability level by the repertoire size ($0.05/15 = 0.003$) (Aspey, pers. comm.). Transitions were considered significant, then, if the magnitude of the standardized residual was $+3.0$ or greater ($P < 0.003$, since $+2.96$ gives $P = 0.003$). Analysis was conducted using the BMDP program "P4F" (Brown, 1981).

Multidimensional contingency table analysis. The frequencies that behaviors of each factor grouping followed each other within the same individual during the

1,161 interactions of UK (271) and NUK (890) were arranged in a three-dimensional contingency table, with relatedness (i.e., UK or NUK) as the third dimension. The null hypothesis that the sequence of behaviors (formed by the two variables preceding [P] and following [F]) in interactions of Richardson's ground squirrels was independent of the relatedness (R) of the participants was tested by fitting a hierarchical set of log-linear models to the data. Fits of all models were gauged by comparing estimated expected cell frequencies with the observed cell frequencies using a chi-square statistic (Colgan and Smith, 1978). All computations were made with the BMDP program "P4F" (Brown, 1981).

Results

The varimax rotated factor matrix of the frequency of occurrence of 15 behaviors in 1,774 interactions of Richardson's ground squirrels produced four factors that together accounted for 93.4% of the total variance (Table 19.2). Twelve be-

TABLE 19.2. Varimax rotated factor matrix based on the frequency of occurrence of 15 behaviors during 1,774 interactions of Richardson's ground squirrels

	Factors			
Behavior	F1	F2	F3	F4
Chase	0.84			
Flee	0.95			
Run toward	0.61			
Lunge	0.31			
Stand over		0.78		
Supine		0.80		
Move away			0.41	
Side			0.53	
Rise			0.49	
Box			0.40	
Forward			0.16	
Roll fight			0.25	
Move toward				0.58
Naso-oral				0.53
No reaction				0.39
% Total variance	40.9	26.7	15.8	10.0
% Cumulative variance	40.9	67.6	83.4	93.4

haviors had positive factor loadings on one of the four factors that exceeded 0.35. No behavior loaded at higher than 0.35 on more than one factor.

From transitional analysis of these interactions, a flow diagram was produced of the significant transitions between and within the behaviors of each factor group (Fig. 19.1). Several relations are apparent. Factor 1 behaviors were linked in a pattern of "run to" – "chase" – "lunge" – "flee" – "run to."[1] that is consistent with a pattern that resulted from reversals of dominance, as seen in reverse chases over territorial boundaries. Factor 2 behaviors were preceded by a behavior involving physical contact ("boxing"), and they led to passive withdrawal ("move away") or no further response on the part of a "standing over" animal. This suggests that factor 2 behaviors represent an appeasement situation, with "stand over" the dominant posture and "supine" the submissive posture. Factor 3 behaviors, apart from "rise" and "roll fight" tended to be followed by "moving away," and none was significantly likely to lead to "fleeing." Factor 3 behaviors were often repeated or followed by other factor 3 behaviors, consistent with observations that they usually elicited similar responses from opponents and often occurred together in sequences within an interaction. The "side" posture preceded other factor 3 behaviors and, because it could be followed by withdrawal without leading to those behaviors involving physical combat ("box" and "roll fight"), "side" could reasonably be interpreted as a threat behavior. "Naso-oral" contacts (factor 4) were associated with passive approach and were followed by either passive withdrawal or no further response.

Hence, the factor groupings are interpreted, post hoc, as follows:

Factor 1: "Chase-flee" behaviors. These often occurred in interactions in which dominance was determined at or soon after the outset, being dependent largely upon the location of the participants. Such behaviors were common in disputes across territorial boundaries, intrusions by nonneighboring conspecifics, and interactions between unrelated adult females and juveniles (Davis, 1982*b*).

Factor 2: "Appeasement situation" behaviors. These generally caused cessation of the interaction and often stemmed from the following group of behaviors.

Factor 3: "Fighting" behaviors. These behaviors frequently occurred in interactions where dominance was not immediately obvious and might be determined in the course of the interaction. They are similar to the behaviors used to assess social rank in other species of rodents (Davis, 1979). Although only two of the behaviors in this category involved physical contact, I use "fighting" in the

---

1. This is not necessarily the sequence of behaviors as they occur in any given interaction, since it is derived from two-act transition probabilities only.

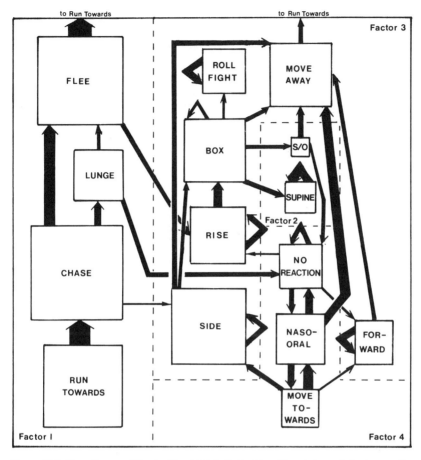

FIGURE 19.1. Flow diagram of the significant intraindividual transitions between behaviors used in 1,774 interactions of Richardson's ground squirrels. The area of the squares is proportional to the frequency of the behavior, and the width of the arrows showing the direction of significant transitions is proportional to the magnitude of the standardized residual. Dashed lines enclose factor groupings. S/O = stand over.

sense that this set of six behaviors was associated with ''contests'' from which dominance could be determined.

Factor 4: ''Identification'' behaviors. Naso-oral contacts, which were often preceded by passive approach and resulted in no further interaction, have been interpreted as most likely having an identification function (Steiner, 1975).

Asymmetries based upon kinship. The fit of all log-linear models to the three-dimensional contingency table of preceding (P) by following (F) behavior by

433

TABLE 19.3. Three-dimensional contingency table of preceding (P) by following (F) behaviors exhibited by an individual during interactions of Richardson's ground squirrels, as a consequence of the relatedness of the participants (whether they are uterine kin or not)

Following (F)	Preceding (P)				
	"Chase-flee"	"Appeasement situation"	"Fighting"	"Identification"	Total
Uterine kin					
"Chase-flee"	41	3	57	9	110
"Appeasement situation"	8	10	19	9	46
"Fighting"	109	20	166	98	393
"Identification"	55	5	48	157	265
Total	213	38	290	273	814
Not uterine kin					
"Chase-flee"	1,030	8	328	51	1,417
"Appeasement situation"	11	6	22	4	43
"Fighting"	435	14	535	156	1,140
"Identification"	31	4	29	43	107
Total	1,507	32	914	254	2,707

relatedness (R) (Table 19.3) is given in Table 19.4. Since all submodels of the saturated model (i.e., the complete model, which has a perfect fit as it incorporates the effects of all variables at all levels) have significant chi-square values, not one of the submodels adequately explains the data. This means that there are extremely complex interactions incorporating first-, second-, and third-order effects between the variables (P, F, and R) in the agonistic interactions of Richardson's ground squirrels.

The particular model of the null hypothesis being tested, that P and F are independent of R (i.e., R, PF) has a highly significant chi-square value ($\chi^2 = 821.58$, d.f. $= 15$, $P \ll 0.001$), indicating that the sequence of behaviors in interactions of Richardson's ground squirrels is *not* independent of the relatedness of the participants. The likelihood ratio statistic can be further partitioned into components to evaluate the conditional significance of individual terms in the models. Thus the significance of the interaction effect between preceding behavior and relatedness (PR) is examined by taking the difference in the chi-square statistic for models FR, PF and PF, PR, FR ($\chi^2 = 84.54$, d.f., $= 3$, $P < 0.001$). Similarly, the significance of the FR term ($\chi^2 = 420.61$, d.f., $= 3$, $P \ll 0.001$) and R term ($\chi^2 = 1068.08$, d.f., $= 1$, $P \ll 0.001$) are evaluated. Hence, relatedness has a highly significant effect in terms of the sequence of behaviors exhibited during interactions. Richardson's ground squirrels act differently both in how they behave initially and in how they continue to respond, depending upon whether they are closely related (UK) or not (NUK) to the other participant in an interaction.

The differences in interactions between UK and NUK had marked effects on the outcome of interactions. Whereas 81.2% (723/890) of interactions between NUK resulted in the displacement of one of the participants (i.e., one fled, usually chased by the other), only 31.7% (86/271) of interactions between UK ended in displacement of one of the participants (Fig. 19.2). This difference was highly significant ($\chi^2 = 240.96$, d.f. $= 1, P \ll 0.001$) and was independent of the age or sex of the participants (Fig. 19.3). Territorial disputes between neighboring

TABLE 19.4. Hierarchical set of all models of the variables preceding behavior (P), following behavior (F), and relatedness (R), and their fit to the data in Table 19.3 using the likelihood ratio chi-square

Model	d.f.	χ^2
P	28	5055.52
F	28	4884.31
R	30	6134.55
P, F	25	2737.19
F, R	27	3816.23
R, P	27	3987.44
P, F, R	24	1669.11
PF	16	1889.66
PR	24	3623.08
FR	24	3115.80
P, FR	21	968.68
F, PR	21	1304.75
R, PF	15	821.58
PF, PR	12	457.22
PR, FR	18	604.32
FR, PF	12	121.15
PF, PR, FR	9	36.61

NOTE: All chi-square values are highly significant ($P < 0.0001$).

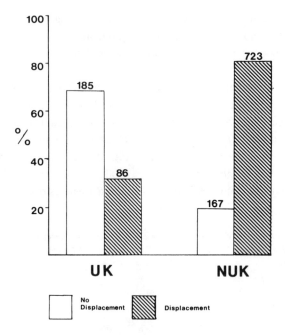

FIGURE 19.2. Percentage of interactions between uterine kin (UK) and squirrels that were not uterine kin (NUK) that resulted in displacement or no displacement of the participants. Numbers above the bars indicate the number of interactions involved.

ground squirrels often involve reverse chases, where individuals alternatively displace each other across a territorial boundary (e.g., Murie and Harris, 1978), and these accounted for 13.2% (117/890) of all interactions between NUK, whereas they made up only 0.4% (1/271) of interactions between UK ($\chi^2 = 37.14$, d.f., $= 1, P << 0.001$).

The differences in outcomes of interactions cannot be attributed to less agonism or "fighting" behavior between UK and NUK, since "fighting" behaviors (factor 3) were as likely to occur in interactions between UK as those between NUK (Table 19.5). However, "appeasement situation" behaviors (factor 2) and "identification" behaviors (factor 4) were more common in interactions of UK than of NUK. Naso-oral contacts, which are perhaps used to reinforce the bond between two squirrels, and appeasement postures ("supine") served to minimize the consequences of agonism between uterine kin. By contrast, the paucity of such behaviors in interactions involving those that were not uterine kin, meant that the conflict was often escalated, resulting in a greater preponderance of "chase-flee" behaviors (factor 1).

Discussion

My analyses suggest that interactions between uterine kin differ from those not involving uterine kin and hence usually between less closely related conspecifics. Differences were due to a greater proclivity for behaviors interpreted, in light of the analyses, as appeasement and identification behaviors to occur in interactions of uterine kin, resulting in less chasing and fleeing behavior and ultimately in less likelihood of displacement of the participants. The outcome of these behavioral asymmetries based upon kinship was the same regardless of age class or sex.

The ultimate effect of the differential treatment accorded close kin compared with less closely related conspecifics is that uterine kin tolerate more spatial overlap and greater proximity with each other than do those that are not uterine kin (Davis, 1982*b;* Michener, 1979, 1981). Such space-sharing behavior can be viewed as nepotistic, and advantages may accrue from a sharing of resources

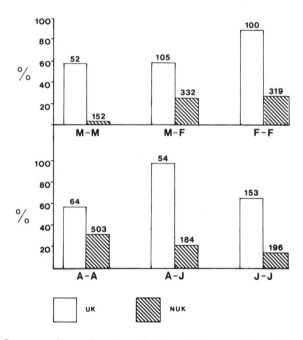

FIGURE 19.3. Percentage of interactions that resulted in no displacement of the participants in interactions between uterine kin (UK) and between squirrels that were not uterine kin (NUK) grouped by sex class (top) and age class (bottom). M = male, F = female, A = adult, J = juvenile. Sample sizes are given atop the bars and sum to slightly fewer than 1,161, since in a few interactions, age or sex class was not known for both participants.

TABLE 19.5. Absolute frequencies (f) and relative frequencies (Rel. f) of behaviors occurring in interactions between uterine kin (271 interactions) and squirrels that were not uterine kin (890 interactions) according to each factor grouping

Factor	Uterine kin		Not uterine kin	
	f	Rel. f	f	Rel. f
"Chase-flee"	351	25.9	2,697	58.4[a]
"Appeasement situation"	57	4.2	71	1.5[a]
"Fighting"	479	35.3	1,473	31.9 n.s.[b]
"Identification"	470	34.6	376	8.1[a]

[a] $P < 0.001$, d.f. = 1, chi-square test.

[b] = nonsignificant, chi-square test.

(e.g., food and burrows) within the overlap area. However, the advantages of sharing a boundary or overlap area with a close relative may simply lie in reducing the costs of agonistic interactions. Not only can conflict result in wounding (Davis, 1982c; McLean, 1981), it is also energetically expensive. Heart rates of free-living Uinta ground squirrels (*S. armatus*) frequently exceed 400 beats/min during combat, compared with a basal level of 284 beats/min, and this increase in energy output occurs irrespective of whether the animal initiates the encounter or is the responder (Ruff, 1971). Uterine kin were less often involved in energetically expensive territorial disputes. Behavioral mechanisms that reduced the amount of chasing and fleeing between uterine kin would also reduce the physiological costs for both participants, and this may ultimately lead to greater reproductive success (Davis, 1982b).

Hence, behavioral asymmetries observed in this study cannot be regarded as altruistic, since both participants in an interaction between close kin probably benefit from a deescalation in the level of agonism that reduced the likelihood of chasing and fleeing.

Differences in outcome of interactions depending upon the relatedness of participants are apparent from two other studies of ground squirrels. Uterine-kin females and nonlittermate sisters of Belding's ground squirrel (*S. beldingi*) seldom chase each other from territories, whereas more distantly related conspecifics chase each other significantly more often (Sherman, 1981). Adult female round-tailed ground squirrels (*S. tereticaudus*) are less likely to displace kin than nonkin, and among juveniles chases occur less frequently between sibs than between nonsibs (Dunford, 1977a). For many species of ground-dwelling sciurids, "chase-flee" behaviors may be less prevalent in interactions of uterine kin than in those that are not uterine kin, which may be a cause or an effect of greater home range overlap between uterine kin (Davis, 1982b; McLean, 1982; Michener, 1983).

The tendency for naso-oral contacts ("identification" behaviors) to occur most frequently between close kin has also been observed in other studies. In Arctic ground squirrels (*S. parryii*) (McLean, 1982) and in *S. tereticaudus* during the early part of the active season (Dunford, 1977a), closely related adult females engage in more naso-oral contacts than do other females. Naso-oral contacts were also found to be more common between adult female *S. richardsonii* and their own offspring than between adult females and juveniles from other litters (Michener, 1973).

In agreement with this field study, laboratory arena tests showed that pairs of Richardson's ground squirrel siblings did not differ significantly from nonsibling pairs in the relative proportion of "fighting" behaviors they exhibited (Davis, 1982a). By contrast, Michener and Sheppard (1972) recorded much less "agonistic" behavior between related pairs of *S. richardsonii* in arena tests. Their result may have been influenced by the association in close confinement of related pairs before and up to the time of testing, since such familiarity will reduce the level of agonism even between unrelated pairs (Holmes and Sherman, 1982). In the field, uterine kin of *S. beldingi* fight less per "encounter" (coming within 0.5 m of each other) than do those that are not uterine kin (Sherman, 1981), and the same may hold for *S. richardsonii*, since in this study only interactions were considered, and, possibly, "encounters" that do not result in interactions are more likely to occur among uterine kin.

Thus, behavioral asymmetries based upon kinship, similar to those found in this study, occur in other species of ground-dwelling sciurids as well. Asymmetries based upon kinship also occur in the propensity of some ground-dwelling sciurids to give alarm calls (Dunford, 1977b; Davis, 1982b; Schwagmeyer, 1980; Sherman, 1977) and in their use of burrows (Dunford, 1977a; M. A. Harris and J. O. Murie, pers. comm.; Johns and Armitage, 1979; McLean, 1982). The existence of such kin effects implicates kin selection as the mechanism responsible for their maintenance.

My results are consistent with the occurrence of favoritism of relatives (nepotism) in Richardson's ground squirrels. Inasmuch as differential treatment of kin occurs in a manner that appears to be adaptive, this suggests kin selection influences, at least in part, the maintenance of sociality in *S. richardsonii*.

When employing multivariate techniques of analysis in behavioral studies such as this one, it is imperative not to lose sight of the animal for the numbers.

The results of any analysis must be interpretable in a manner that explains the behavior of the actual animal, not the change in a given variable. Judicious application of multivariate techniques to the study of animal behavior, together with an objective approach to data gathering, can result in an understanding of behavioral patterns that would otherwise be too complex to interpret accurately. The results presented here add to those of previous studies that have reported behavioral asymmetries based upon kinship in Richardson's ground squirrels (Michener, 1973, 1981; Yeaton, 1972) by identifying those behaviors responsible for this difference, quantifying their relative levels of occurrence, and demonstrating how they affect the outcome of interactions. Taken together, these studies suggest that sociality in Richardson's ground squirrels is characterized by the prominent role of familial bonds (Davis, 1982*b*).

Acknowledgments

I especially thank J. O. Murie for advice and encouragement and F. T. McCaffrey for devoted assistance. Mr. and Mrs. J. Bews of the Y-Cross Ranch, and the owners of the Roi Lakes Ranch through Dr. J. Stelfox, kindly provided me with access to their land. For discussion of the analyses employed in this chapter I am grateful to W. P. Aspey, P. W. Colgan, and V. J. de Ghett. I also thank A. R. Blaustein, D. A. Boag, C. Dunford, L. M. Fedigan, M. A. Harris, D. W. Leger, G. R. Michener, and A. N. Spencer for their input. This research was funded by a NSERC grant (A5865) to J. O. Murie and a Canadian Commonwealth Scholarship to me.

Literature Cited

Ainley, D. G. 1974. The comfort behavior of Adelie and other penguins. Behaviour, 50:16–51.

Armitage, K. B. 1974. Male behaviour and territoriality in the yellow-bellied marmot. J. Zool. London, 172:233–265.

———. 1977. Social variety in the yellow-bellied marmot: a population-behavioural system. Anim. Behav., 25:585–593.

———. 1981. Sociality as a life-history tactic of ground squirrels. Oecologia, 48:36–49.

Aspey, W. P. 1977. Wolf spider sociobiology. 1. Agonistic display and dominance-subordinance relations in adult male *Schizocosa crassipes*. Behaviour, 62:103–141.

Betts, B. J. 1976. Behaviour in a population of Columbian ground squirrels, *Spermophilus columbianus columbianus*. Anim. Behav., 24:652–680.

Bronson, F. H. 1964. Agonistic behaviour in woodchucks. Anim. Behav., 12:470–478.

Brown, M. B. 1981. Two-way and multi-way frequency tables—measures of association and the log-linear model (complete and incomplete tables). Pp. 143–208, *in* BMDP statistical software (W. J. Dixon, ed.). Univ. California Press, Berkeley, 725 pp.

Chatfield, C., and A. J. Collins. 1980. Introduction to multivariate analysis. Chapman and Hall, London, 246 pp.

Colgan, P. W., and J. T. Smith. 1978. Multidimensional contingency table analysis. Pp. 145–174, *in* Quantitative ethology (P. W. Colgan, ed.). John Wiley, New York, 364 pp.

Comrey, A. L. 1973. A first course in factor analysis. Academic Press, New York, 316 pp.

Davis, L. S. 1979. Social rank behaviour in a captive colony of Polynesian rats (*Rattus exulans*). New Zealand J. Zool., 6:371–380.

———. 1982*a*. Sibling recognition in Richardson's ground squirrels *Spermophilus richardsonii*. Behav. Ecol. Sociobiol., 11:65–70.

———. 1982*b*. Sociality in Richardson's ground squirrels *Spermophilus richardsonii*. Unpubl. Ph.D. dissert., Univ. Alberta, Edmonton, 152 pp.

———. 1982*c*. Copulatory behaviour of Richardson's ground squirrels (*Spermophilus richardsonii*) in the wild. Canadian J. Zool., 60:2953–2955.

Dunford, C. 1977*a*. Social system of round-tailed ground squirrels. Anim. Behav., 25:885–906.

———. 1977*b*. Kin selection for ground squirrel alarm calls. Amer. Nat., 111:782–785.

Fagen, R. M., and R. N. Goldman. 1977. Behavioural catalogue analysis methods. Anim. Behav., 25:261–274.

Fagen, R. M., and N. J. Mankovich. 1980. Two-act transitions, partitioned contingency tables, and the "significant" cells problem. Anim. Behav., 28:1017–1023.

Fagen, R. M., and D. Y. Young. 1978. Temporal patterns of behaviour: durations, intervals, latencies and sequences. Pp. 79–114, *in* Quantitative ethology (P. W. Colgan, ed.). John Wiley, New York, 364 pp.

Hamilton, W. D. 1963. The evolution of altruistic behavior. Amer. Nat., 97:354–356.

———. 1964. The genetical evolution of social behaviour. I, II. J. Theor. Biol., 7:1–52.

Hanken, J., and P. W. Sherman. 1981. Multiple paternity in Belding's ground squirrel litters. Science, 212:351–353.

Harris, R. J. 1975. A primer of multivariate statistics. Academic Press, New York, 332 pp.

Holmes, W. G., and P. W. Sherman. 1982. The ontogeny of kin recognition in two species of ground squirrels. Amer. Zool., 22:491–517.

Hoogland, J. L. 1981. Nepotism and cooperative breeding in the black-tailed prairie dog (Sciuridae: *Cynomys ludovicianus*). Pp. 283–310, *in* Natural selection and social behavior: recent research and new theory (R. D. Alexander and D. W. Tinkle, eds.). Chiron Press, New York, 532 pp.

Johns, D. W., and K. B. Armitage. 1979. Behavioral ecology of alpine yellow-bellied marmots. Behav. Ecol. Sociobiol., 5:133–157.

Kurland, J. A. 1977. Kin selection in the Japanese monkey. Contrib. Primatol., vol. 12. Karger, Basel, 145 pp.

Maynard Smith, J. 1964. Group selection and kin selection. Nature, 201:1145–1147.

McLean, I. G. 1981. Social ecology of the Arctic ground squirrel, *Spermophilus parryii*. Unpubl. Ph.D. dissert., Univ. Alberta, Edmonton, 149 pp.

———. 1982. The association of female kin in the Arctic ground squirrel *Spermophilus parryii*. Behav. Ecol. Sociobiol., 10:91–99.

Michener, G. R. 1973. Field observations on the social relationships between adult female and juvenile Richardson's ground squirrels. Canadian J. Zool., 55:693–703.

———. 1974. Development of adult-young identification in Richardson's ground squirrel. Devel. Psychobiol., 7:375–384.

———. 1979. Spatial relationships and social organization of adult Richardson's ground squirrels. Canadian J. Zool., 57:125–139.

———. 1981. Ontogeny of spatial relationships and social behaviour in juvenile Richardson's ground squirrels. Canadian J. Zool., 59:1666–1676.

———. 1983. Kin identification, matriarchies, and the evolution of sociality in ground-dwelling sciurids. Pp. 528–572, *in* Advances in the study of mammalian behavior (J. F. Eisenberg and D. G. Kleiman, eds.). Spec. Publ., Amer. Soc. Mamm., 7:1–753.

Michener, G. R., and D. H. Sheppard. 1972. Social behavior between adult female Richardson's ground squirrels (*Spermophilus richardsonii*) and their own and alien young. Canadian J. Zool., 50:1343–1349.

Murie, J. O., and M. A. Harris. 1978. Territoriality and dominance in male Columbian ground squirrels (*Spermophilus columbianus*). Canadian J. Zool., 56:2402–2412.

Nie, N. H., C. H. Hull, J. G. Jenkins, K. Steinbrenner, and D. H. Bent. 1975. SPSS: statistical package for the social sciences, second ed. McGraw-Hill, New York, 675 pp.

Owings, D. H., M. Borchert, and R. Virginia. 1977. The behaviour of California ground squirrels. Anim. Behav., 25:221–230.

Ruff, R. L. 1971. Telemetered heart rates of free-living Uinta ground squirrels in response to social interactions. Unpubl. Ph.D. dissert., Utah State Univ., Logan, 124 pp.

Schwagmeyer, P. L. 1980. Alarm calling behavior of the thirteen-lined ground squirrel, *Spermophilus tridecemlineatus*. Behav. Ecol. Sociobiol., 7:195–200.

Sheppard, D. H., and S. M. Yoshida. 1971. Social behavior in captive Richardson's ground squirrels. J. Mamm., 52:793–799.

Sherman, P. W. 1977. Nepotism and the evolution of alarm calls. Science, 197:1246–1253.

———. 1980. The limits of ground squirrel nepotism. Pp. 505–544, *in* Sociobiology: beyond nature/nurture (G. W. Barlow and J. Silverberg, eds.). Westview Press, Colorado, 627 pp.

———. 1981. Kinship, demography, and Belding's ground squirrel nepotism. Behav. Ecol. Sociobiol., 8:251–259.

Slater, P. J. B. 1978. Data collection. Pp. 7–24, *in* Quantitative ethology (P. W. Colgan, ed.). John Wiley, New York, 364 pp.

Steinberg, J. B. 1977. Information theory as an ethological tool. Pp. 47–74, *in* Quantitative methods in the study of animal behavior (B. A. Hazlett, ed.). Academic Press, New York, 222 pp.

Steiner, A. L. 1975. "Greeting" behavior in some Sciuridae, from an ontogenetic, evolutionary, and socio-behavioral perspective. Nat. Canadien, 102:737–751.

Watton, D. G., and M. H. A. Keenleyside. 1974. Social behaviour of the Arctic ground squirrel, *Spermophilus undulatus*. Behaviour, 50:77–99.

Wehrell, S. 1973. Social organization and social status in relation to aspects of activity in Richardson's ground squirrel, *Spermophilus richardsonii*. Unpubl. M.S. thesis, Univ. Alberta, Edmonton, 126 pp.

Yeaton, R. I. 1972. Social behavior and social organization in Richardson's ground squirrel *(Spermophilus richardsonii)* in Saskatchewan. J. Mamm., 53:139–147.

APPENDIX 19.1. Frequencies of observed intraindividual behavioral transitions during 1,774 interactions of Richardson's ground squirrels. Behaviors are: chase (A), flee (B), run toward (C), move toward (D), move away (E), side (F), rise (G), box (H), forward (I), lunge (J), stand over (K), supine (L), roll fight (M), naso-oral (N), and no reaction (O). Preceding behaviors are across the top of the table, and following behaviors are down the left-hand margin.

Preceding

Following	A	B	C	D	E	F	G	H	I	J	K	L	M	N	O	Total
A	78	28	704	13	3	109	11	36	16	20	3	4	38	5	11	1,079
B	276	95	20	8	10	37	61	48	40	53	1	17	43	7	42	758
C	1	310	26	0	18	4	4	1	2	0	0	3	1	0	8	378
D	0	0	3	6	2	6	1	1	5	1	0	1	0	15	0	41
E	25	1	30	29	5	143	40	88	57	39	30	15	35	96	16	649
F	106	81	84	72	17	114	9	32	10	30	1	2	12	2	19	591
G	20	73	21	20	6	20	46	23	9	4	0	5	14	6	23	290
H	35	34	25	7	2	84	99	53	24	18	1	1	10	8	10	411
I	22	40	31	21	4	8	2	7	40	8	2	2	1	0	18	206
J	99	9	47	8	7	42	11	5	18	2	0	0	0	0	4	252
K	5	0	1	0	1	8	2	15	0	2	2	1	5	1	1	44
L	1	10	2	4	1	4	11	29	1	2	0	21	8	2	10	106
M	33	34	11	4	4	15	10	24	4	15	0	0	31	0	1	186
N	2	1	58	86	0	12	40	2	13	0	1	3	0	23	41	282
O	19	10	12	8	6	4	4	4	1	17	6	1	1	31	23	147
Total	722	726	1,075	286	86	610	351	368	240	211	47	76	199	196	227	5,420

7. Retrospective

JOHN A. KING

Michigan State University

Chapter 20

Historical Ventilations
on a
Prairie Dog Town

Abstract. A history of scientific progress applied primarily to prairie dog burrows provides a yardstick for the current state of research on the sociality of ground squirrels. The description of burrows proceeds to an interpretation of their function, which is influenced by contemporary cultural and scientific biases. The biases are retained when correlations are made between sociality and morphological, physiological, or ecological variables. The final analytic stage is achieved with experimental manipulation of the critical variable. The variable most likely to influence the sociality of ground squirrels is here postulated to be the burrow system, which is a valuable resource worth maintaining, protecting, and inheriting.

Introduction

Conferences like this one on the sociality of ground-dwelling squirrels reveal the current state of our science. They illuminate our strengths and weaknesses; they expose the gaps in our knowledge; they magnify our advances, they uncover our fads and conventions. Readers of this volume can profit from this survey in the seclusion of their own studies, evaluating where we stand and where to proceed further. They will note that much of ground squirrel research is still in the descriptive stage, albeit sometimes aided by experimental procedures like those used in describing physiological processes or tracking the movements of animals with radio transmitters. A few studies have compared populations or species, often attempting to discover a correlation between variables. Multivariate analysis in a couple of reports has furthered the process of isolating critical variables. The

447

ultimate analytical procedure, reported in a few studies, is to manipulate the variables experimentally. Formal synthetic models of ground squirrel sociality await further isolation of the critical variables that influence it.

A perennial controversy among biologists is whether we should study animals or specific problems. Some biologists adhere to the view that each species or small taxon provides so many problems that they can best be solved by recognizing the numerous variables influencing each. Other biologists believe that science is essentially problem solving and that the species used in testing hypotheses is secondary. This conference on the sociality of ground squirrels combines the best of both approaches. The participants are sufficiently concerned with the entire biology of ground squirrels to appreciate some of the assumptions that underlie their hypotheses. They are also ready to propose alternative interpretations of the results presented by their colleagues because they know (and like?) ground squirrels.

If we tolerate abundant diversity and a modicum of chance in our logical systems, then we can expect to find both, as well as strong cultural biases, in the history of any scientific endeavor. Functional interpretations of behavior are particularly prone to scientific fads and conventions. I will suggest how the functional interpretation of the earth mounds surrounding the entrances of prairie dog burrows may have changed historically. I will then proceed underground to speculate about the relation of burrows to sociality. After formulating a hypothesis, I will outline a series of procedures that often repeat the history of scientific advances. From initial descriptions, I will move on to inter- and intraspecific comparisons and finally to experimental manipulations of burrow systems. I offer this historical exercise in problem solving as a means of identifying the stage of progress represented by the papers presented at this conference. I conclude with a request for a technology that will let us observe the behavior of the squirrel underground.

Burrow Architecture: Description

An average prairie dog burrow is about 13 m long and 13 cm in diameter, which means that 0.17 m^3 of soil are excavated in constructing it (Sheets et al., 1971). Most burrowing mammals simply throw the soil out around the burrow entrance, often making a fan-shaped dump. The quantity of soil from a prairie dog burrow is too great for a fan, so it is deposited in all directions in a domelike mound with the hole in the center. Sometimes these mounds are huge, more than 1.8 m in diameter and 0.6–0.9 m high. Most burrows have two entrances. The second entrance is often steeper than the first, and it lacks subsoil, as if it had been opened from beneath. However, it does have topsoil scraped up from the surface surrounding the entrance and shaped into a relatively steep-sided, craterlike mound. Topsoil is often scraped for 3 – 4.5 m from the entrance, creating a depression in the surrounding surface.

The mass of subsoil in the dome-shaped mound is not readily disturbed by prairie dogs or by wallowing bison and cattle. In contrast, the crater-shaped mound, with its sharp edges and steep sides, is easily knocked down by bison or worn down by the prairie dogs' scrambling up and over it and down the hole in its center. After several weeks of frequent use it disintegrates into just another pile of dirt. Then comes rain. The hard-packed or dusty soil becomes a soft, pliable mud that can easily be scraped from the surface and stacked into a neat, sharp-edged form. Prairie dogs industriously pursue this task after a rain by digging, scraping, pushing, piling, and packing the topsoil into a crater again. They arch their backs and pound the soil into place with the points of their noses, leaving their nose prints in the soil as it bakes and hardens in the sun.

The interior of the burrow is no less elaborate than the exterior entrances. Nest chambers, cul-de-sacs, branches, soil-plugged passageways, and midden heaps have all been seen and described (Sheets et al., 1971). However, no one has published a description of the construction of a burrow from start to finish. Possibly an entire coterie territory is interconnected by a labyrinth whose passages are opened and closed from time to time. This remarkable feat of connecting underground passages could be made easier by following horizontal strata of soils, eliminating the necessity of joining tunnels on three dimensions.

Burrows are relatively permanent structures, though they may undergo considerable modification at the entrance and belowground. Some burrows probably have endured for centuries, and we know they pass from one generation to the next. Burrows are to ground squirrels what trees are to tree squirrels: a tangible fabric supporting the fragile life of their inhabitants. They may enable us to understand the evolution of ground-squirrel sociality.

Burrow Functions: Interpretation

Although one's culture may influence what one perceives and describes, cultural influences are particularly active in interpretations of one's observations. For example, the function of the mounds surrounding the entrances of prairie dog burrows has been interpreted in many ways. At one time the mounds were considered sentinel posts for individuals that warned the other town inhabitants of approaching danger. This early interpretation parallels the needs of early mountain men traversing hostile territory in western North America. The proposal that

449

the mounds functioned as dikes to prevent the torrential rains of the prairie summers from flooding the burrows could easily have been derived from the experience of settlers attempting to keep storms out of their own fragile homes. Now, in an age when it is popular to expect precision in the shaping of behavior by natural selection, mounds are believed to ventilate the subterranean tunnels (Krebs and Davies, 1981; Vogel et al., 1973). The carefully molded crater mound is said to circulate air through the tunnels as the wind produces a Bernoulli effect at the entrance.

Other functions for these conspicuous domes and craters of earth can be provided by a vivid imagination. The mounds could serve as orienting landmarks to allow a prairie dog foraging with its head down to locate its burrow rapidly on a featureless horizon when a predator appears. The mounds could also provide a protective collar for a prairie dog attempting to gain an elevated perspective of the flat terrain surrounding its burrow. Since a prairie dog's eyes are close to the top of its head, it can still see when most of its body is hidden in the burrow.

Although the possible selective advantages of mound construction have not been exhausted by this brief survey, let us now examine nonadaptive alternatives as Gould and Lewontin (1979) did when they discussed the spandrels at the San Marco cathedral. Beautiful paintings often adorn the spandrels, which are an otherwise boring but necessary accompaniment of the vaulted cathedral roof. Perhaps the mounds are spandrels to a prairie dog's subterranean cathedral. After all, one inevitable product of digging a hole is a pile of dirt. Therefore, if a mound is missing, as occurs when burrows are opened to the surface from below, the prairie dog builds one. Prairie dogs work on their mounds with diligence comparable to that of the Renaissance painters of spandrels.

I have used burrow mounds to illustrate how our interpretation of their function is a historical process that depends upon contemporary cultural and scientific conventions. Interpretations of the functions of various types of social behavior, like nepotism, infanticide, and cooperative breeding, could also illustrate this adherence to current scientific conventions or fashions, but burrows and their mounds are tangible, and they have been the object of speculation for a long time. Conventional interpretations are essential to scientific progress because they solidify the advances made to that point. The next advance requires a break from the traditional and the perception of totally different relations.

Burrows and Sociality: Escape from Tradition

There are no traditional views on the evolution of sociality in ground squirrels, though emphasis is usually placed on some ecological, physiological, or morphological constraints (Armitage, 1981; Hoogland, 1981; Michener, 1983).

I will diverge even from these constraints to propose a behavioral constraint that serves to illustrate the historical progression of scientific analysis. We usually think that ground-squirrel sociality is somehow influenced by the squirrels' annual periodicity, by their ability to hibernate or aestivate, or by their body size or rate of sexual maturation. A radical departure from these conventions might be to reverse our perspective. That is, perhaps behavior or some behavioral artifact influences periodicity, hibernation, and growth. In this exploratory spirit, I propose that the sociality of ground squirrels is proportional to the value of their burrows. I will examine this proposition by proceeding with the scientific progression that has taken us through description, cultural interpretations, and breaking away from conventions to the formulation of a hypothesis and the correlational and manipulative steps that follow.

Prairie dogs must have burrows to achieve longevity, reproduce successfully, and maintain their social organization; they expend considerable energy to construct and maintain them. Most of a prairie dog's life is spent inside its burrows or on the mounds at their entrances. This investment in time and energy pays off by protecting the animals from rain, heat, cold, and predation. Without the burrows, black-tailed prairie dogs could not inhabit the open prairie and feed upon the productive, nutritious prairie vegetation. The value of the burrows makes them worth defending and sharing.

Three selective factors are often considered responsible for the initiation of group living: protection from predation, collection of food, and localization of a resource, such as breeding or resting sites (Alexander, 1974). The fundamental feature of this often-cited triad is that something of value is being maintained, protected, and manipulated. The thing of value may be an individual's life or the lives of its mates or offspring. The resource may also be food, a feeding ground, a roost, a nest, or a burrow. The value of the resource is ultimately determined by its contribution to fitness, but it can also be measured in terms of the time or energy invested in maintaining it, in terms of its contribution in reducing risks of predation or competition, or in terms more closely associated with fitness, like its effects on viability and fertility.

The value of burrows to ground-dwelling squirrels is indicated by the effort spent in digging them, by the protection they provide from predators and weather, and by the extent to which they are defended. Although elaborate burrow systems can develop without sociality, I propose that complex social systems depend upon elaborate burrow systems or some other tangible environmental feature like a territory, granary (Koenig, 1981), or rock outcrop (Svendsen, 1974). Permanent, complicated burrow systems are worth protecting, and it may take several individuals to do so. Furthermore, the burrows are worth passing on to the descendants, which can then begin their reproductive life with the advantages of these homes. Once the inheritance of a territory or burrow system becomes critical for fitness, social complexities arise regarding who receives the inheritance. In ground squirrels, daughters benefit most, and a matrilocal social system develops around the valuable burrows (Michener, 1983). The matrilocal system provides an evolutionary means for positive feedback through kin selection (Sherman, 1977). The inclusive fitness of mothers and daughters contributes to the evolution of cooperative, mutualistic, and altruistic behavior.

Species and Burrows: Comparative Correlations

The idea that the evolution of social systems depends upon the value of some environmental feature like a burrow system needs further examination and refinement before a suitable hypothesis can be formulated. One of the first steps after the descriptive material is at hand is to reduce the accumulation of data to its significant constituents.

Criteria for assigning ranks to the burrows of each species of ground squirrel require that we reduce all the possible measures to a neat cluster. The criteria may come from a physical property of the burrows, like their permanence, location (Pfeifer, 1982), or number, the average volume of earth removed relative to body size, the number of subterranean connections, the size and shape of the passageways or amount and placement of excavated earth, or the proximity of other burrows. Alternatively, rather than using a physical property, ranks may be assigned on the basis of the burrows' use. The number of burrows per capita, the proportion of days used in relation to the total number of active days, the number of individuals using each burrow, and the frequency with which each burrow is visited are a few possible measurements of use.

A finer resolution of the relation between burrow and social system than that achieved by comparing species of ground-dwelling squirrels can be found by investigating this relation within a species. Variations in both systems probably occur throughout the range of widely distributed species like prairie dogs. Unfortunately, we lack suitable comparisons of either burrow or social systems throughout the range of any species. We must have comparable studies of geographically different populations before we can evaluate the relevance of environmental variables to social organization. Geographical as well as local variations in burrow systems should accompany different soil profiles, which may constrain the elaboration of burrows.

A number of burrow characteristics could be examined, but one that may be closely associated with sociality is the number of subterranean connections. Smoke-blowing devices could be used to measure such connections. After investigation in different geographic areas, we may find differences in the mean number of burrow connections among different populations.

Sociality will be more difficult to measure. The family structure Michener (1983) suggested for ranking social organization between species cannot discern differences within a species. Again, in the absence of a formal analysis of social characteristics we will arbitrarily select one feature, exclusiveness, for the sake of this discussion. Closed social groups tend to be more rigid, more hierarchical, and more permanent, and more individuals are involved in excluding others than in open social groups (King, 1954). Coteries that accept outsiders or that split and combine are considered to be less well organized than coteries with permanent memberships. Social instability seems to accompany simple burrow systems in new sections of a prairie dog town or in newly established towns (Z. T. Halpin, pers. comm.; King, 1955). The scale of exclusiveness could involve the number of nonmembers allowed in the coterie territory over a given period. If various geographical samples of burrow rankings correlate with social rankings, we are prepared to abandon correlation and invest our efforts in experimentation.

Experimental Burrows: The Final Analysis

The final analytical stage in the progress of science is experimental. Syntheses proceed beyond analyses, but only after sufficient analysis can provide some insight into what variables can be systematically combined. The experimental stage also goes through a progression of defining variables, learning how to manipulate and control them, and properly formulating the question or hypothesis. Usually the first question is simply whether an independent variable has an effect on a dependent variable: Do burrow connections have any effect on sociality? The next question deals with the direction of the effect: Do burrow connections enhance sociality among prairie dogs? This is the hypothesis explored here, although we might venture one step further and make a quantitative prediction: The number of burrow connections will be directly proportional to the degree of sociality.

Experimental manipulations are probably more easily accomplished with burrows than with sociality, although problems exist for both. The hypothesis is that black-tailed prairie dog groups inhabiting burrows with subterranean connections are more exclusive (intolerant of nonmembers) than those lacking connections. A field test of this hypothesis is possible. But when I think of all the uncontrolled variables in the field, I turn to a more controlled situation, such as field enclosures, either with artificial burrows or with the ground partitioned to prevent subterranean connections in one enclosure but not the other. Exclusiveness could be measured by introducing strangers into each enclosure. If the hypothesis endures this challenge, then another test or a refinement of this one, such as altering the number of burrow connections, would be necessary.

In our experiment on burrows and sociality, we can control such variables as age, sex, population density, space, and kinship while we manipulate burrow connections and measure exclusiveness. This control enables us to observe variables that may be obscured in the field by uncontrolled factors unless the conditions are just right for the effect of the variable to become noticeable. For example, burrow connections may become significant to social structure primarily after the young have emerged from their natal burrows. Once the connections are made, they may have a lasting effect upon sociality, even after they are plugged up again. The laboratory study exaggerates the effect to perceptible levels. After the variable has been isolated in the laboratory, its robustness can be tested by examining it in the field, where it is bombarded by natural factors.

Burrows and Technology

This discussion of burrows and the sociality of ground squirrels has omitted a significant part of squirrels' behavior: their life underground. Our observations are immediately terminated when the animals enter the burrow. We can only conjecture what may occur below by observing behavior on the surface.

The first recorded underground view (Merriam, 1901) was obtained by Osgood when he hired a couple of ditch diggers to excavate a 4.5-m deep burrow. A tractor with a backhoe helped Sheets and his co-workers (1971) dig up 18 burrows. These burrow dissections provide some clues to belowground activity. Nest chambers, side passages, dung heaps, food stores, plugged passages, skeletons, and other behavioral artifacts contribute to our interpretations. Technical devices have been employed, such as the smoke generators Vogel et al. (1973) used to test underground ventilation between burrow entrances. Artificial burrows, like those Walt Disney used to obtain some excellent film footage, or burrows dug next to transparent materials have only rarely been used scientifically, to study rabbit warrens in Australia (Mykytowycz, 1968), rat burrows (Lore and Flannelly, 1977), and the social behavior of naked mole rats, *Heterocephalus* (Jarvis, 1981; Jarvis and Sale, 1971).

Modern technology has bypassed our need to pierce the subterranean barrier so as to see, hear, or feel what is going on below. Perhaps some instrument used for related observations could be adapted to our purpose. Fiber optics or a tunnel-traveling television camera may provide a partial view of underground life. A microphone in the nest chamber could transmit the squeals of young being born or indicate when the mother has joined them or reveal if infanticide is occurring. A recording device fixed in a single place, such as the nest chamber, would be simpler than a moving monitor. Temperature recorders could indicate the presence of a warm body. Air-flow meters could further our knowledge of subterranean ventilation, gaseous exchanges, and perhaps the movement of animals pushing air before them. Other types of transducers might be inserted into burrows to record pressure, physical stress, humidity, and motion, assuming that prairie dogs will tolerate these foreign instruments in their burrows and not bury or gnaw them or abandon the burrows. The cost / benefit ratio must be calculated, but our lack of knowledge on underground activity prevents any valid assessment of the benefits.

Many technical problems could be avoided if squirrels would use artificial burrows. Nest boxes for birds and mice have provided investigators with many insights into the family life of these animals. Any method that would enable us to probe underground is certain to reveal something of significance about some species of burrowing animal, even if the underground life of ground squirrels is relatively uneventful. My confidence in the importance of underground behavior emboldens me to predict that the next major advance in our study of ground squirrel sociality will depend upon a technique to investigate the underground squirrel.

Literature Cited

Alexander, R. D. 1974. The evolution of social behavior. Ann. Rev. Ecol. Syst., 5:325–383.

Armitage, K. B. 1981. Sociality as a life-history tactic of ground squirrels. Oecologia, 48:36–49.

Gould, S. J., and R. C. Lewontin. 1979. The spandrels of San Marco and the Panglossian paradigm: a critique of the adaptationist programme. Proc. Roy. Soc. London, Ser. B, 205:581–598.

Hoogland, J. L. 1981. The evolution of coloniality in white-tailed and black-tailed prairie dogs (Sciuridae: *Cynomys leucurus* and *C. ludovicianus*). Ecology, 62:252–272.

———. 1982. Prairie dogs avoid extreme inbreeding. Science, 215:1639–1641.

Jarvis, J. U. M. 1981. Eusociality in a mammal: cooperative breeding in naked mole-rat colonies. Science, 212:571–573.

Jarvis, J. U. M., and J. B. Sale. 1971. Burrowing and burrow patterns of East African mole-rats, *Tachyoryctes, Heliophobius,* and *Heterocephalus.* J. Zool., 163:451–479.

Retrospective

King, J. A. 1954. Closed social groups among domestic dogs. Proc. Amer. Philos. Soc., 98:327–336.

―――. 1955. Social behavior, social organization, and population dynamics in a black-tailed prairiedog town in the Black Hills of South Dakota, Contrib. Lab. Vert. Biol., Univ. Michigan, 67:1–123.

Koenig, W. D. 1981. Reproductive success, group size, and the evolution of cooperative breeding in the acorn woodpecker. Amer. Nat., 117:421–443.

Krebs, J. R., and N. B. Davies. 1981. An introduction to behavioural ecology. Sinauer Associates, Sunderland, Massachusetts, 494 pp.

Lore, R., and K. Flannelly. 1977. Rat societies. Sci. Amer., 236:106–116.

Merriam, C. H. 1901. The prairie dog of the Great Plains. Yearb. Agric., 257–270.

Michener, G. R. 1983. Kin identification, matriarchies, and the evolution of sociality in ground-dwelling sciurids. Pp. 528–572, *in* Recent advances in the study of mammalian behavior (J. F. Eisenberg and D. G. Kleiman, eds.). Spec. Publ., Amer. Soc. Mamm., 7:1–753.

Mykytowycz, R. 1968. Territorial marking by rabbits. Sci. Amer., 218:116–126.

Pfeifer, S. R. 1982. Variability in reproductive output and success of *Spermophilus elegans* ground squirrels. J. Mamm., 63:284–289.

Sheets, R. G., R. L. Linder, and R. B. Dahlgren. 1971. Burrow systems of prairie dogs in South Dakota. J. Mamm., 52:451–453.

Sherman, P. W. 1977. Nepotism and the evolution of alarm calls. Science, 197:1246–1253.

Svendsen, G. E. 1974. Behavioral and environmental factors in the spatial distribution and population dynamics of a yellow-bellied marmot population. Ecology, 55:760–771.

Vogel, S., C. P. Ellington, and D. L. Kilgore. 1973. Wind-induced ventilation of the burrows of the prairie-dog, *Cynomys ludovicianus*. J. Comp. Physiol., 85:1–14.

Index

This index is primarily a guide to subject areas covered in the text. Sciurid genera and species that are treated in some detail are also listed (by scientific name only), and major topics for each are indicated. Taxa mentioned briefly are not included.

457

Index